7th Workshop on Online Abuse and Harms (WOAH 2023)

Toronto, Canada
13 July 2023

ISBN: 978-1-7138-8239-8

Printed from e-media with permission by:

Curran Associates, Inc.
57 Morehouse Lane
Red Hook, NY 12571

Some format issues inherent in the e-media version may also appear in this print version.

Association for Computational Linguistics
209 N. Eighth Street
Stroudsburg, Pennsylvania 18360

Phone: 1-570-476-8006
Fax: 1-570-476-0860

acl@aclweb.org

Additional copies of this publication are available from:

Curran Associates, Inc.
57 Morehouse Lane
Red Hook, NY 12571 USA
Phone: 845-758-0400
Fax: 845-758-2633
Email: curran@proceedings.com
Web: www.proceedings.com

ACL 2023

The 7th Workshop on Online Abuse and Harms (WOAH)

Proceedings of the Workshop

July 13, 2023

Order copies of this and other ACL proceedings from:

Association for Computational Linguistics (ACL)
209 N. Eighth Street
Stroudsburg, PA 18360
USA
Tel: +1-570-476-8006
Fax: +1-570-476-0860
acl@aclweb.org

Introduction

Digital technologies have brought many benefits for society, transforming how people connect, communicate and interact with each other. However, they have also enabled abusive and harmful content such as hate speech and harassment to reach large audiences, and for their negative effects to be amplified. The sheer amount of content shared online means that abuse and harm can only be tackled at scale with the help of computational tools. However, detecting and moderating online abuse and harms is a difficult task, with many technical, social, legal and ethical challenges. The Workshop on Online Harms and Abuse (WOAH) is the leading workshop dedicated to research addressing these challenges.

WOAH invites paper submissions from a wide range of fields, including natural language processing, machine learning, computational social sciences, law, politics, psychology, sociology and cultural studies. We explicitly encourage interdisciplinary submissions, technical as well as non-technical submissions, and submissions that focus on under-resourced languages. We also invite non-archival submissions for in progress work and reports from civil society to facilitate a meeting space between academic researchers and civil society.

This year marks the seventh edition of WOAH, which will be co-located with ACL 2023 in Toronto, Canada. The special theme for this year's edition is "subjectivity and disagreement in abusive language data". Hate speech and other forms of abuse are highly subjective, in that there are diverse valid beliefs about what is or is not hateful or abusive. Different beliefs are informed by different social, cultural and legal norms. Through annotation, these beliefs are encoded in labelled datasets, which are then used to train and evaluate detection models. Therefore, subjectivity and disagreement are an essential aspect of research into online abuse and hate. By choosing this theme, we want to encourage submissions that examine, address or make use of this inherent subjectivity.

We received 55 submissions, of which 25 were accepted for presentation at the workshop. These papers will be presented at an in-person, where possible, poster session on the day of the workshop. Authors who are unable to attend in person will be able to give a virtual lightning talk describing their work. The workshop day will also include keynote talks from: Dirk Hovy, Milagros Miceli, Maarten Sap, Su Lin Blodgett, Vinodkumar Prabhakaran and Lauren Klein. Finally, we will close the day by inviting the keynote speakers to participate in a panel on the topic of subjectivity and disagreement.

We thank all our participants and reviewers for their work, and our sponsors for their support. We hope you enjoy this year's WOAH and the research published in these proceedings.

Paul, Yi-Ling, Debora, Aida, and Zeerak

Sponsors

WOAH is grateful for support from the following sponsors:

Diamond Tier

OpenAI

Gold Tier

JIGSAW

Google

amazon

Organizing Committee

Workshop Organiser

Yi-Ling Chung, The Alan Turing Institute
Aida Mostafazadeh Davani, Google Research
Debora Nozza, Bocconi University
Paul Röttger, University of Oxford
Zeerak Talat, Independent Researcher

Program Committee

Emergency Reviewers

Gavin Abercrombie, Heriot Watt University
Greta Damo, Bocconi University
Lorenzo Lupo, Bocconi University

Program Committee

Syed Sarfaraz Akhtar, Apple Inc
Jisun An, Luddy School of Informatics, Computing, and Engineering, Indiana University Bloomington
Murali Raghu Babu Balusu, Georgia Institute of Technology
Francesco Barbieri, Snap Inc.
Valerio Basile, University of Turin
Thales Bertaglia, Maastricht University
Helena Bonaldi, Fondazione Bruno Kessler
Noah Broestl, University of Oxford, Google Research
Agostina Calabrese, The University of Edinburgh
Pedro Calais, UFMG, Brazil
Tommaso Caselli, Rijksuniversiteit Groningen
Amanda Cercas Curry, Bocconi University
Amit Das, Auburn University
Ona De Gibert, University of Helsinki
Daryna Dementieva, Technical University of Munich
Lucas Dixon, Google Research
Nemanja Djuric, Aurora Innovation
Hugo Jair Escalante, INAOE
Elisabetta Fersini, University of Milano-Bicocca
Björn Gambäck, Norwegian University of Science and Technology
Aitor García Pablos, Vicomtech
Sara Garza, FIME-UANL
Shlok Gilda, University of Florida
Lee Gillam, University of Surrey
Tonei Glavinic, Dangerous Speech Project
Darina Gold, Fraunhofer IIS
Marco Guerini, Fondazione Bruno Kessler
Udo Hahn, Friedrich-Schiller-Universitaet Jena
Christopher Homan, Rochester Institute of Technology
Muhammad Okky Ibrohim, University of Turin
Abhinav Jain, amazon.com
Mladen Karan, Queen Mary University
Mohammad Aflah Khan, IIIT Delhi
Ian Kivlichan, Jigsaw, Google
Vasiliki Kougia, University of Vienna
Haewoon Kwak, Indiana University Bloomington
Sandra Kübler, Indiana University
Andrew Lee, University of Michigan
Els Lefever, LT3, Ghent University

Chuan-jie Lin, National Taiwan Ocean University
Nikola Ljubešić, Jožef Stefan Institute
Davide Locatelli, Technical University of Catalonia
Holly Lopez, Indiana University
Adrian Pastor Lopez Monroy, Mathematics Research Center CIMAT
Elizabeth Losh, William and Mary
Hongyin Luo, MIT
Sarah Masud, LCS2, IIITD
Puneet Mathur, University of Maryland College Park
Diana Maynard, University of Sheffield
Do June Min, University of Michigan
Manuel Montes, INAOE
Hamdy Mubarak, Qatar Computing Research Institute
Smruthi Mukund, Amazon
Preslav Nakov, Mohamed bin Zayed University of Artificial Intelligence
Isar Nejadgholi, National Research Council Canada
Brahmani Nutakki, Saarland University
Ali Omrani, University of Southern California
Matthias Orlikowski, Bielefeld University
Viviana Patti, University of Turin, Dipartimento di Informatica
Naiara Perez, Vicomtech
Matúš Pikuliak, Kempelen Institute of Intelligent Technologies
Flor Miriam Plaza-del-arco, Bocconi University
Michal Ptaszynski, Kitami Institute of Technology
Georg Rehm, DFKI
Bjorn Ross, University of Edinburgh
Molly Sauter, McGill University
Tyler Schnoebelen, Decoded AI
Alexandra Schofield, Harvey Mudd College
Indira Sen, GESIS
Caroline Sinders, Convocation Design + Research
Jeffrey Sorensen, Google Jigsaw
Gerasimos Spanakis, Maastricht University
Arjun Subramonian, University of California, Los Angeles
Afrin Sultana, University of Chittagong
Maite Taboada, Simon Fraser University
Radiathun Tasnia, University of Chittagong
James Thorne, KAIST AI
Zuoyu Tian, Indiana University
Dimitrios Tsarapatsanis, University of York
Avijit Vajpayee, Amazon
Francielle Vargas, University of São Paulo
Ruyuan Wan, University of Notre Dame
Jing Xu, Facebook AI
Qiangeng Yang, University of Florida
Seunghyun Yoon, Adobe Research
Aleš Završnik, Institute of criminology at the Faculty of Law Ljubljana
Torsten Zesch, Computational Linguistics, FernUniversität in Hagen
Yi Zheng, University of Edinburgh

Table of Contents

Program

Thursday, July 13, 2023

09:00 - 09:15 *Opening Remarks*

09:15 - 09:45 *Invited Talk 1 - Dirk Hovy*

09:45 - 10:15 *Invited Talk 2 - Milagros Miceli*

10:15 - 11:45 *In-Person Poster Session*

Identity Construction in a Misogynist Incels Forum
Michael Yoder, Chloe Perry, David Brown, Kathleen Carley and Meredith Pruden

DeTexD: A Benchmark Dataset for Delicate Text Detection
Artem Chernodub, Serhii Yavnyi, Oleksii Sliusarenko, Jade Razzaghi, Yichen Mo and Knar Hovakimyan

Respectful or Toxic? Using Zero-Shot Learning with Language Models to Detect Hate Speech
Flor Miriam Plaza-del-arco, Debora Nozza and Dirk Hovy

Benchmarking Offensive and Abusive Language in Dutch Tweets
Tommaso Caselli and Hylke Van Der Veen

Cross-Platform and Cross-Domain Abusive Language Detection with Supervised Contrastive Learning
Md Tawkat Islam Khondaker, Muhammad Abdul-mageed and Laks Lakshmanan, V.s.

Aporophobia: An Overlooked Type of Toxic Language Targeting the Poor
Svetlana Kiritchenko, Georgina Curto Rex, Isar Nejadgholi and Kathleen C. Fraser

Concept-Based Explanations to Test for False Causal Relationships Learned by Abusive Language Classifiers
Isar Nejadgholi, Svetlana Kiritchenko, Kathleen C. Fraser and Esma Balkir

Conversation Derailment Forecasting with Graph Convolutional Networks
Enas Altarawneh, Ameeta Agrawal, Michael Jenkin and Manos Papagelis

Resources for Automated Identification of Online Gender-Based Violence: A Systematic Review
Gavin Abercrombie, Aiqi Jiang, Poppy Gerrard-abbott, Ioannis Konstas and Verena Rieser

Disentangling Disagreements on Offensiveness: A Cross-Cultural Study
Aida Mostafazadeh Davani, Mark Diaz, Dylan Baker and Vinodkumar Prabhakaran

Evaluating the Effectiveness of Natural Language Inference for Hate Speech Detection in Languages with Limited Labeled Data
Janis Goldzycher, Moritz Preisig, Chantal Amrhein and Gerold Schneider

Factoring Hate Speech: A New Annotation Framework to Study Hate Speech in Social Media
Gal Ron, Effi Levi, Odelia Oshri and Shaul Shenhav

Harmful Language Datasets: An Assessment of Robustness
Katerina Korre, John Pavlopoulos, Jeffrey Sorensen, Léo Laugier, Ion Androutsopoulos, Lucas Dixon and Alberto Barrón-cedeño

Robust Hate Speech Detection in Social Media: A Cross-Dataset Empirical Evaluation
Dimosthenis Antypas and Jose Camacho-Collados

[Findings] Responsibility Perspective Transfer for Italian Femicide News
Gosse Minnema, Huiyuan Lai, Benedetta Muscato and Malvina Nissim

[Findings] Scientific Fact-Checking: A Survey of Resources and Approaches
Juraj Vladika and Florian Matthes

[Findings] A New Task and Dataset on Detecting Attacks on Human Rights Defenders
Shihao Ran, Di Lu, Aoife Cahill, Joel Tetreault and Alejandro Jaimes

[Findings] ClaimDiff: Comparing and Contrasting Claims on Contentious Issues
Miyoung Ko, Ingyu Seong, Hwaran Lee, Joonsuk Park, Minsuk Chang and Minjoon Seo

[Findings] Which Examples Should be Multiply Annotated? Active Learning When Annotators May Disagree
Connor T Baumler, Anna Sotnikova and Hal Daumé III

Thursday, July 13, 2023 (continued)

[Findings] Playing the Part of the Sharp Bully: Generating Adversarial Examples for Implicit Hate Speech Detection
Nicolas Benjamin Ocampo, Elena Cabrio and Serena Villata

[Findings] Disagreement Matters: Preserving Label Diversity by Jointly Modeling Item and Annotator Label Distributions with DisCo
Tharindu Cyril Weerasooriya, Alexander Ororbia, Raj B Bhensadadia, Ashiqur KhudaBukhsh and Christopher Homan

[Findings] It's not Sexually Suggestive; It's Educative | Separating Sex Education from Suggestive Content on TikTok videos
Enfa Rose George and Mihai Surdeanu

[Findings] Debiasing should be Good and Bad
Robert A. Morabito, Jad Kabbara and Ali Emami

[Findings] The State of Profanity Obfuscation in Natural Language Processing Scientific Publications
Debora Nozza and Dirk Hovy

[Findings] COBRA Frames: Contextual Reasoning about Effects and Harms of Offensive Statements
Xuhui Zhou, Hao Zhu, Akhila Yerukola, Thomas Davidson, Jena D. Hwang, Swabha Swayamdipta and Maarten Sap

[Findings] Stereotypes and Smut: The (Mis)representation of Non-cisgender Identities by Text-to-Image Models
Eddie L. Ungless, Bjorn Ross and Anne Lauscher

11:45 - 12:15 *Invited Talk 3 - Maarten Sap*

12:15 - 13:30 *Lunch Break*

13:30 - 14:00 *Invited Talk 4 - Su Lin Blodgett*

14:00 - 14:30 *Best Paper Talks (General & Theme)*

14:30 - 15:00 *Lightning Talks for Remote Attendants*

Towards Safer Communities: Detecting Aggression and Offensive Language in Code-Mixed Tweets to Combat Cyberbullying
Nazia Nafis, Diptesh Kanojia, Naveen Saini and Rudra Murthy

Thursday, July 13, 2023 (continued)

Towards Weakly-Supervised Hate Speech Classification Across Datasets
Yiping Jin, Leo Wanner, Vishakha Kadam and Alexander Shvets

Distance from Unimodality: Assessing Polarized Opinions in Abusive Language Detection
John Pavlopoulos and Aristidis Likas

Relationality and Offensive Speech: A Research Agenda
Razvan Amironesei and Mark Diaz

Auditing YouTube Content Moderation in Low Resource Language Settings
Hellina Hailu Nigatu and Inioluwa Raji

ExtremeBB: A Database for Large-Scale Research into Online Hate, Harassment, the Manosphere and Extremism
Anh V. Vu, Lydia Wilson, Yi Ting Chua, Ilia Shumailov and Ross Anderson

Problematic Webpage Identification: A Trilogy of Hatespeech, Search Engines and GPT
Ojasvin Sood and Sandipan Dandapat

Female Astronaut: Because sandwiches won't make themselves up there": Towards Multimodal misogyny detection in memes
Smriti Singh, Amritha Haridasan and Raymond Mooney

HOMO-MEX: A Mexican Spanish Annotated Corpus for LGBT+phobia Detection on Twitter
Juan Vásquez, Scott Andersen, Gemma Bel-enguix, Helena Gómez-adorno and Sergio-luis Ojeda-trueba

Toward Disambiguating the Definitions of Abusive, Offensive, Toxic, and Uncivil Comments
Pia Pachinger, Julia Neidhardt, Allan Hanbury and Anna Planitzer

A Cross-Lingual Study of Homotransphobia on Twitter
Davide Locatelli, Greta Damo and Debora Nozza

15:00 - 15:30 *Invited Talk 5 - Vinodkumar Prabhakaran*

Thursday, July 13, 2023 (continued)

15:30 - 15:45 *Coffee Break*

15:45 - 16:15 *Invited Talk 6 - Lauren Klein*

16:15 - 17:15 *Panel Discussion*

17:15 - 17:25 *Closing Remarks*

Identity Construction in a Misogynist Incels Forum

Michael Miller Yoder,[1] Chloe Perry,[2] David West Brown,[3]
Kathleen M. Carley,[1] Meredith Pruden[4]
[1]Software and Societal Systems Dept., Carnegie Mellon University, Pittsburgh, PA, USA
[2]Dept. of American Culture, University of Michigan, Ann Arbor, MI, USA
[3]Dept. of English, Carnegie Mellon University, Pittsburgh, PA, USA
[4]School of Communication and Media, Kennesaw State University, Kennesaw, GA, USA
yoder@cs.cmu.edu, chloeper@umich.edu, dwb2@andrew.cmu.edu,
carley@cs.cmu.edu, mpruden@kennesaw.edu

Abstract

Online communities of involuntary celibates (incels) are a prominent source of misogynist hate speech. In this paper, we use quantitative text and network analysis approaches to examine how identity groups are discussed on incels.is, the largest black-pilled incels forum. We find that this community produces a wide range of novel identity terms and, while terms for women are most common, mentions of other minoritized identities are increasing. An analysis of the associations made with identity groups suggests an essentialist ideology where physical appearance, as well as gender and racial hierarchies, determine human value. We discuss implications for research into automated misogynist hate speech detection.

1 Introduction

Warning: this paper contains content that is disturbing, offensive, and/or hateful.

Online communities of those calling themselves "involuntary celibates," (incels) are known for online misogynist hate speech and offline violence targeting women, including incidents of mass violence in Isla Vista, California, in 2014 and Toronto, Canada, in 2018, among others. Though some work in natural language processing (NLP) has focused on features of misogynist language in general (Anzovino et al., 2018; Samghabadi et al., 2020; Guest et al., 2021), online incel communities are known for significant lexical innovation (Farrell et al., 2020; Gothard, 2021). Training with data from incel forums would enable misogynist hate speech classifiers to identify the neologisms and novel ideological features of this dangerous form of online misogyny (Jaki et al., 2019).

In this paper, we provide hate speech researchers with a quantitative overview of trends and particularities of language in one of the largest misogynist incel communities, incels.is, which launched in 2017 following the r/incels ban from Reddit. We focus this analysis on mentions of identities, which are key to automatically identifying hate speech (Uyheng and Carley, 2021) and a window into the ideologies of social movements (Benford and Snow, 2000). We ground this analysis in theoretical approaches that focus on how identities are *constructed* in interaction (Bucholtz and Hall, 2005; Burr and Dick, 2017) and investigate the following research questions:

RQ1. How frequently are different identities, including novel terms for identities, mentioned in incels.is discourse?

RQ2. How do identity mentions in incels.is discourse change over time?

RQ3. How are identity mentions used differently by central incels.is users?

RQ4. What textual associations are made with identity groups on incels.is?

To address these research questions, we first measure the distribution of identity term mentions using a large generic list of identity terms combined with community-specific identity terms surfaced from a word embedding-based approach. We confirm the most frequent identity mentions in this data are for women, with almost one-fourth of these being derogatory community-specific neologisms, such as "femoids." Mentions of gender are much higher than in a comparative white supremacist dataset, a similar commonly-used source of unlabeled hate speech (Simons and Skillicorn, 2020; Alatawi et al., 2021). We find increasing mentions of other minoritized identities, such as Black, LGBTQ+ and Jewish people on incels.is, suggesting a consolidation with broader far-right discourses. Users who are central to the network proportionally mention more of these other marginalized identities. From a quantitative analysis of the immediate contexts in which identity term mentions appear, a

The 7th Workshop on Online Abuse and Harms (WOAH), pages 1–13
July 13, 2023

pervasive hatred of women is clear, as well as reinforcement of stereotypes about other marginalized groups. The incel identity itself is often discussed with themes of victimhood and boundary-keeping for "true" versus "fake" incels.

Throughout our analysis, we find evidence of an essentialist, black-pilled ideological framework where physical appearance determines the value of individuals and groups. While rigid racial and gender hierarchies are not new (e.g., eugenics) and are often circulated in far-right discourse (Miller-Idriss, 2022), this incel community attaches many novel measurements to appearance related to these hierarchies, re-entrenching and extending them. We argue that to detect such a particular form of extremism, hate speech researchers must heed both the jargon and deeper ideologies of this movement.

2 Incels and Male Supremacism

Online misogynist incel communities are situated within a set of anti-feminist groups often termed the "manosphere." These groups include Men's Rights Activists, Pick Up Artists (PUAs), Men Going Their Own Way (MGTOW). Such groups are often associated with a "red pill" ideology, a *Matrix* film reference to seeing the hidden truth behind the world, in this far-right context a view that feminism has brainwashed and subordinated men (Ging, 2019). In addition, incels often refer to a "black pill," the idea that they are genetically predetermined to be incels and cannot improve their situation through work or self-improvement (Pruden, 2021). This leaves many black-pilled incels feeling that their only options are to cope, commit suicide, or commit mass violence (expressed in the common phrase, "cope, rope or go ER [Elliot Rodger, an incel mass shooter])." Among groups in the manosphere, incels are most associated with violent and high-profile events that demonstrate "extreme misogyny" (Ging, 2019).

Ribeiro et al. (2021) find that incel communities are both more extreme and more popular than older, more moderate male supremacist movements, while LaViolette and Hogan (2019) find more extreme manosphere movements contain essentialist, deterministic ideologies of identity, which we also find in incels.is. We find evidence of this reductionist and biologically essentialist worldview in associations with identities in incels.is.

Qualitative research on male supremacist extremism frequently examines Men's Rights Activists (Berger, 2018) and more moderate groups that are less niche and without the emergent vocabulary common in incel spaces. We find this tendency extends to the data sources in automated hate speech research and argue for the importance of attending to the particularly dangerous discourse of black-pilled incels such as those on incels.is.

Quantitative and computational studies of the manosphere often focus on the unique misogynist language use of these communities. Gothard (2021) and Jaki et al. (2019) surface incel jargon by comparing word frequencies in incel Reddit posts with subreddits and Wikipedia articles outside of the incel movement, while Farrell et al. (2020) find frequent incel terms not present in English dictionaries and expand their lexicon with a word embedding space. Such word frequency analysis, as well as hand-crafted lexicons, are often used to measure and study misogyny in the manosphere (Heritage et al., 2019; Farrell et al., 2019; Jaki et al., 2019). Pruden (2021) and Perry and DeDeo (2021) use topic modeling to characterize narratives and map out user trajectories on incels.is and r/theRedPill, respectively. Jaki et al. (2019) use word frequency analysis to study identity construction on a similar forum, incels.me, though their 6-month dataset only enables limited time-series analysis. In contrast, our work focuses on the use and contexts of generic and community-specific identity terms beyond a sole focus on misogyny, as well as how identity term use changes over time.

2.1 Automated misogyny detection

In early work on automated misogyny detection, Hewitt et al. (2016) and Waseem and Hovy (2016) developed small Twitter datasets annotated for sexism. Anzovino et al. (2018) proposed a keyword-based annotated dataset and taxonomy for misogyny detection on Twitter, with later shared NLP tasks (Fersini et al., 2018b,a; Basile et al., 2019; Bhattacharya et al., 2020). Data for these tasks came from Twitter posts and YouTube comments based on keywords, profile information, and YouTube video topics. Such data sources may capture mainstream misogyny but miss the unique linguistic characteristics of the incel movement.

Other annotated hate speech datasets have included data from manosphere subreddits, such as r/MensRights, r/MGTOW, r/incels, and r/TheRedPill, along with many other sources of online hate speech (Qian et al., 2019; Sap et al.,

2020; Mollas et al., 2020). Guest et al. (2021) propose a Reddit dataset annotated for misogyny by trained annotators, who would be more likely to understand community-specific jargon than crowdworkers with limited training. Though they include a variety of manosphere-related subreddits, absent from this dataset are banned black-pilled incel subreddits such as r/braincels, r/shortcels, and r/incels, the precursor of the more extreme incels.is.

3 Data

Our dataset contains 6,248,234 English-language public comments posted between the forum's creation in November 2017 and scraping in April 2021.[1] It includes forum and thread names, as well as the date of posting, user names and the comment's full text. However, it does not contain images, which is a limitation.

White supremacist dataset We compare identity mentions on incels.is to another common source of unlabeled hate speech: white supremacist texts. From a large, multi-domain, English-language white supremacist dataset (Yoder et al., 2023), we select posts from online forums in a similar time frame as the incels data, 2015-2019 (the latest year available in the white supremacist dataset). This subset includes 3,410,623 posts from Stormfront, Iron March, and 4chan /pol/ in threads with fascist and white supremacist topics or posted by users choosing white supremacist, Nazi, Confederate or fascist flags.

4 Methods

We take a quantitative approach to studying discursive identity construction (Bucholtz and Hall, 2005; Gee, 2011), borrowing a focus on in-group and out-group identity presentation from social identity theory (Tajfel, 1974; Seering et al., 2018). Specifically, we examine the use of identity terms and the immediate contexts in which they appear. A few mentions of an identity group may not represent attitudes of participants, but associations repeatedly made over the course of a 6 million-post corpus are more likely to capture widely shared beliefs (Stubbs, 2001).

[1]This dataset, without any private or identifying information, will be made available to vetted researchers upon publication of the main paper associated with it.

4.1 Measuring the use of identity terms

We first find identity terms using a generic lexicon combined from multiple sources: the extensive list of English identity terms from the NetMapper software (Joseph et al., 2016; Carley et al., 2018), as well as identity terms frequently found in hate speech (Yoder et al., 2022) and terms for LGBTQ+ and neurodiverse identities found online (Yoder et al., 2020; Yoder, 2021). This combined lexicon totals 19,050 unique identity terms. Ignoring case, 7,244 were present in the incels.is dataset.

Grouping identity terms We aggregate identity terms referring to similar groups (such as *LGBTQ+ people*) and then further group those identities into broader demographic categories (such as *gender/sexuality*). To form these groupings, we adapt identity terms group labels used in hate speech research from Uyheng and Carley (2020) and Yoder et al. (2022).[2] Intersectional identity terms are counted for all groups indicated by the term, e.g., "white women" was counted for both "white" and "women."

Identity lexicon expansion To capture the neologisms that incel communities are known for (Jaki et al., 2019; Gothard, 2021), we expand our generic identity lexicon to nearest neighbors in word embedding space, a common approach (Demszky et al., 2019; Simons and Skillicorn, 2020; Lai et al., 2021). We trained a 300-dimension word2vec model (Mikolov et al., 2013) over our data and manually examined terms appearing at least 1,000 times among the top 30 nearest neighbors by cosine distances to a) the 30 most frequent generic identity terms or b) the mean of identity term embeddings in an identity group. This resulted in 84 new terms, the most frequent of which are in Table 1.

Varieties of "incels" It is common in incel discourse to refer to different types of incels with terms including a "cel" suffix (Gothard, 2021). For example, "tallcels" refers to tall incels and the racist terms "currycels" and "ricecels" refer to South Asian and East Asian incels, respectively. Excluding usernames, over 1500 unique words used in our incels.is dataset contained the string "cel," many of which referred to varieties of incels. We examined the 100 most frequent words containing "cel"

[2]Non-proprietary portions of identity term lexicons (including groupings and categorizations) and code for analyses in this paper are available at https://github.com/michaelmilleryoder/incels_identities.

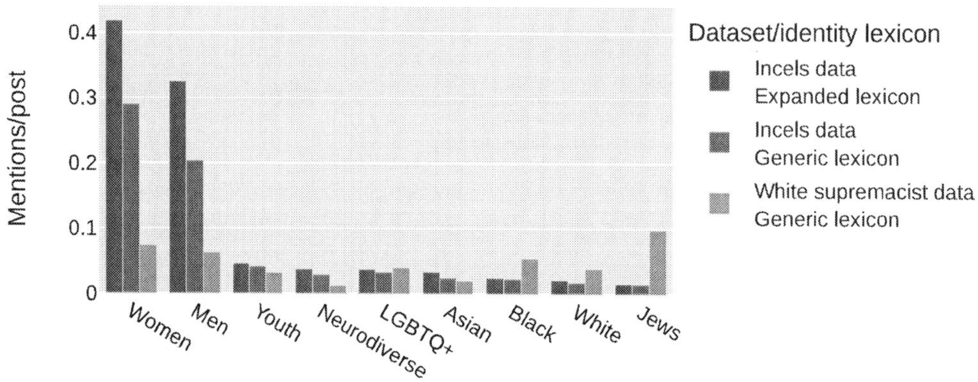

Figure 1: Identity group mention frequencies.

Community-specific identity terms
foids, chads, manlets, stacies, boyo, femoids, ethnics, chadlites, roasties, holes, betabux, landwhales, waifus, jbs, chicks, noodlewhores, soyboy, br0, aspie, betas, thots, traps, beckies, m8, boi
"Cel" variants
truecels, fakecels, volcels, greycels, escortcelling, gymcelling, ricecels, mentalcels, currycels, fatcels, femcels, whitecels, framecels, youngcels, oldcels, blackcels, ethnicels, brocels, itcels, incelistan, nearcels, tallcels, shortcels, locationcels, bluecels

Table 1: Most frequent 25 novel identity and "cel" terms found in the incels.is dataset. Plural and singular mentions are combined, as are "-ing" terms with their roots.

and grouped words that referred to incel variants, except those referring to "fake" incels, within the incels identity group for further analysis.

Central forum users We also analyze how forum leaders (prototypical incels) use identity terms. To find such leaders based on network structure, we construct a undirected graph where nodes are users and edges are weighted by the number of shared threads (out of 154,049 threads) between them. This graph contains 6819 users and 3,889,054 links. We operationalize central users as the top 5% ranked by eigenvector centrality, which measures if users share threads with other highly-connected users. These central users had a roughly similar number of posts as the rest of the users combined.

4.2 Associations with identity terms

Beyond the occurrence of identity term mentions, we analyze associations made with identities in their immediate contexts. Specifically, we extract *actions* taken by or to these groups, as well as *attributes* associated with them, a simple approach to analyzing the presentation of entities in discourse (Bamman et al., 2013, 2014; Yoder, 2021). For actions, we extract verbs where an identity term is the subject or object from a dependency parse. Attributes are adjectives and appositives whose head word is an identity term.

We surface the actions and attributes most distinctively associated with each identity group with PMI^3 (Daille, 1994; Role and Nadif, 2011), a variant of pointwise mutual information that lowers the ranking of low-frequency terms.

5 Results

5.1 Distribution of identity mentions (RQ1)

Prevalence of the most popular identity group mentions in our incels.is dataset is seen in Figure 1. Expanding the generic identity list with context-specific identity terms dramatically increases the detection of mentions of all identity groups, especially women, men, and neurodiverse people[3]. Adding these context-specific identity terms increases the total number of mentions identified from 6.46 million to 8.91 million–a jump of 37.8%–

[3]Many incels self-identify on the autism spectrum.

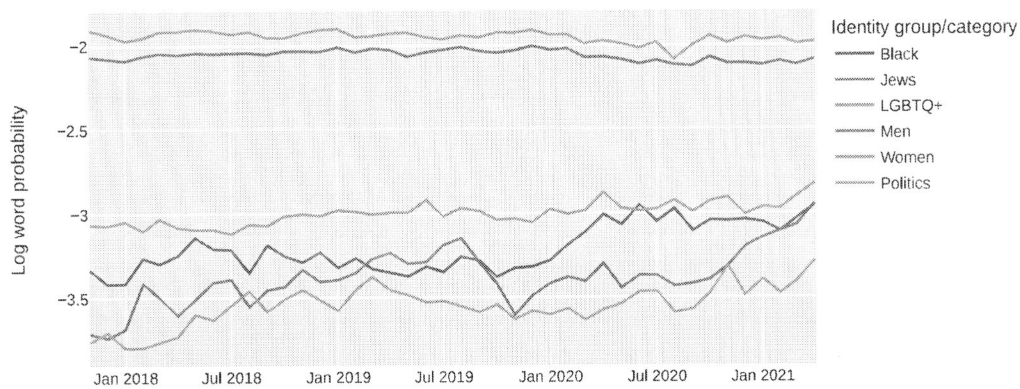

Figure 2: Selected identity group and category mentions over time in the incels.is dataset. Mentions of other identity groups remain steady.

demonstrating how common identity term innovations are in this community.

Also visible in Figure 1 is a comparison of identity group mention frequency with another common source of hate speech, white supremacist data. Mentions of women and men are much more frequent in the incel data than the white supremacist data, surpassing 0.4 mentions/post for women. Mentions of racial identities and Jewish people are more commonly found in the white supremacist data. This confirms that discourse from incel communities can be a useful source of misogynist text, especially after recognizing the lexical innovations referring to women and others.

5.2 Identity mentions over time (RQ2)

Figure 2 displays the prevalence of identity group mentions in this forum over time, binned every month during the dataset range and identified with the expanded lexicon. To control for any systematic changes in post word count over time, we present log word probability (the logarithm of identity group mention counts normalized by total word count).

Though mentions of women and men are most frequent across the data range, they stay steady or slightly decrease over time. There is a steady rise, however, in mentions of LGBTQ+ identities. Except for a decrease in the latter half of 2019, mentions of Jewish people also steadily rise. There is a significant rise in mentions of Black people in 2020, reaching a peak in June (during the anti-racist uprising against police brutality) and remaining at an increased rate through 2020 and 2021. Mentions of political identities also rise.

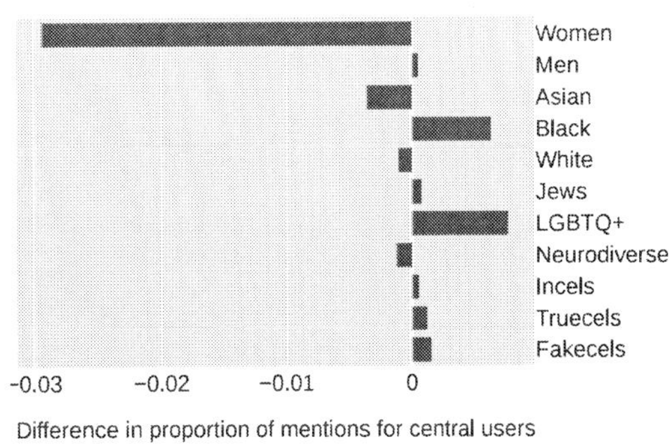

Figure 3: Absolute difference between the proportion of identity mentions used by top 5% central users in the shared thread network for each identity group and the proportion of mentions used by the rest of the users.

5.3 Central users' use of identity terms (RQ3)

Figure 3 shows the absolute difference in proportion of identity term mentions for the top 5% of users ranked by eigenvector centrality, compared to the rest. Proportionally, central users are less likely to mention identity terms for women, but are more likely to mention Black, LGBTQ+, and Jewish people. A concern for incel authenticity is also reflected in this central group's increased use of "truecels" and "fakecels" compared to other users.

Identity		Top PMI^3 terms
Women	*Attr*	white, old, single, fat, young, hot, fucking, ugly, cute, other, ethnic, average
	Act_S	want, get, love, care, go, hate, think, like, fuck, say, give, look, find, wants
	Act_O	get, fuck, hate, fucking, find, getting, having, attracted, see, want, fucked
Men	*Attr*	ugly, white, other, good, looking, average, tall, black, nice, short, chad, young
	Act_S	get, looks, go, need, look, think, want, got, mogs, fuck, going, become, gets
	Act_O	over, see, know, want, fuck, hate, fucking, love, seen, get, against, laid, date
Asian	*Attr*	south, central, >, east, average, half, ugly, other, skinned, northern, full
	Act_S	look, hate, get, cope, worship, go, need, mog, tend, eat, seem, make, want, take
	Act_O	learning, learn, speak, hate, seen, see, mog, killed, against, over, above, know
Black	*Attr*	north, real, west, other, fucking, man, stupid, dumb, ugly, dark, average
	Act_S	get, got, commit, slay, aspire, look, developed, gon, need, go, tend, fuck, run
	Act_O	free, hate, fuck, see, against, say, around, date, prefer, fucking, kill, sand
White	*Attr*	southern, northern, non, eastern, western, pure, white, nordic, other, average
	Act_S	go, get, want, mog, look, hate, invented, need, going, tend, voted, did, age
	Act_O	worship, hate, prefer, against, want, date, after, over, see, sought, towards
Jews	*Attr*	orthodox, fucking, rich, religious, secular, international, anglo, elite, greedy
	Act_S	control, did, created, want, pushing, won, own, pushed, made, win, took, push
	Act_O	hate, blame, ashkenazi, against, because, blaming, gas, kill, hated, hating
LGBTQ+	*Attr*	fucking, it, bluepilled, moral, low, normal, others, larping, stupid, ill, little
	Act_S	get, exist, go, say, need, think, fuck, try, deserve, trying, look, make, want
	Act_O	hate, fucking, coping, fuck, shut, ban, turning, kill, banned, larping, go
Neurodiverse	*Attr*	social, severe, functioning, fucking, extreme, crippling, sentence, complete
	Act_S	exist, makes, worse, causes, affect, get, comes, means, make, sucks, goes, go
	Act_O	because, due, diagnosed, cure, fucking, having, caused, cause, causes
Incels	*Attr*	fellow, other, blackpilled, true, real, actual, white, ugly, bluepilled, blackpill
	Act_S	get, exist, means, need, ascend, go, cope, know, want, say, become, going, look
	Act_O	help, against, hate, coping, create, see, creating, hates, bullying, die, ok, bullied

Table 2: Actions and attributes associated with identity group terms in incels.is dataset. *Attr* refers to attributes, while Act_S are actions for which the identity is a subject and Act_O are actions for which the identity is an object.

5.4 Associations with identities (RQ4)

Terms commonly associated with identity groups are presented in Table 2. Across groups, we find that the most frequent attributes relate to physical features ("ugly," "short," etc.). The use of these descriptors suggest hierarchies based on appearance, race and gender. This focus on physical appearance is apparent in top terms used to describe women, including "young," "fat," and "hot." Example uses show the hierarchies of appearance that incels apply to women: "some can't tell a beta female apart from a hot whore and so lump all types of the female sub species together."[4] Actions for which women are subjects suggest incels' speculation about what women "want," "love," or "hate." Common actions for which women are grammatical objects include "fuck" and "hate"– evidence of the forum's misogyny, casting women as things to be "attracted" or controlled.

Men are also discussed with an emphasis on physical appearance, as well as domination. "Ugly," "looking," "average," and "tall" are all top attributions for men. Top actions include "get," "need," and "mogs," an incel neologism meaning "dominate". An example post that reinforces gender hierarchies reads, "men literally mog femoids across the board, yet the foids whine about it."

Race is relevant in discussions of gendered identities. "White," for example, is a top descriptor for both women and men, as is "black" for men. Top terms suggest a negotiated association of superiority with whiteness. White people are the grammatical objects of "worship" but also of "hate." "Pure" and "nordic," common white supremacist descriptors, are distinctive attributes used for white people.

[4] Quotes are paraphrased for privacy (Williams et al., 2017)

In contrast, Asian people are cast as subjects of actions like "worship" and "cope."

We find a range of common stereotypes for minoritized identities, particularly conspiratorial antisemitic tropes, as evidenced by terms suggesting a global Jewish conspiracy (e.g., "elite" and "control") and derogatory associations with the Holocaust ("gas"). One example post reads, "the endgame is an global Jewish Communist dictatorship," while another mixes antisemitic conspiracy theories with anti-feminism: "feminism is a subversive Jewish movement designed to ruin us."

LGBTQ+ characterizations are negative and associated with inauthenticity (e.g., "larping," or live action role playing). For example, one posts reads, "Lesbians don't exist. They're just bisexual foids who like women but still can't resist Chad."

Violence is associated with Black people ("commit"), for example in one post that reads, "I don't hate blacks because they're ugly, I hate them because no matter where they are they commit crime."

In-group identity associations Victimhood, race and authenticity are common themes associated with identity mentions of incels themselves and "incel" variants on the platform.

The most frequent lexical variations containing the "cel" suffix are in Table 1. Top terms relate to authenticity, including "fakecel," "truecel" and "volcel," ("voluntary celibate"), a focus that has also been observed in incel subreddits (Gothard, 2021). Platform affordances highlight distinctions between frequent and non-frequent posters: "greycels" who have posted less than 500 times have a gray-colored username and are often deemed inauthentic. Variants related to race ("whitecels," "ethnicels") are also frequent, suggesting the importance of race in incel self-classification (Jaki et al., 2019; Farrell et al., 2020). Also visible in these "cel" variations are a set of categories based on the familar theme of physical appearance (e.g., "fatcels" and "youngcels"). "Femcels," or female incels, are frequently mentioned, usually derided as outside the inherent masculinity of inceldom.

Incels are cast as merely "existing" or "coping," (Table 2) while others "hate" them or are "against" them. This victimhood includes common masculine tropes, such as a supposed inability to control themselves. From one post: "we can't control what we want, devaluation of women is a coping mechanism for not being able to elicit a biological response in them." Common far-right narratives of victimhood at the hands of corporations, Jewish people, and the media are also present: "Jews and the media hate incels, and the gaming industry is full of SJWs [social justice warriors]."

Race is also important–and controversial–in associations made with incels. "White" is a top incels attribute on the forum, and both "ethnic" and "white" are associated with truecels (see Table 3 in Appendix A for top terms related to truecels and fakecels on the forum). There is controversy over which races occupy what positions in an assumed hierarchy, often centering around the "just be white" (JBW) theory that white men have access to sexual relationships with women of all races. Some posts support this theory, e.g., "being white is a +3 when it comes to noodles [Asian women], so a 4/10 white is better than a 6/10 ethnic." Others challenge this notion: "a brown man with a chiseled face will mog a white incel everywhere." Still others echo the white supremacist Great Replacement Theory, blaming JBW as a way for incels of color to "get whitecels out so sh**skins can take over."

"Real" and "true" are top attributes associated with talk about incels, echoing a focus on authenticity in the top "cel" variants. This boundary-keeping is also visible in the words associated with fakecels (e.g., "detected" and "ban"). Authentic incels are victims of women's hatred ("if women aren't trying to kill you, you're not a true incel"), post a lot ("graycels are a joke with their tiny post counts") are unattractive ("I'm an incel, of course she said no to my hideous face"), have no female friends ("what true incel has a female friend? stupid newf*g") and do not date ("normie spotted. real incels are doing this all weekend and have no dates"). They also are unable to "ascend" (i.e., have sex and leave inceldom), and are "mogged" by others. Jaki et al. (2019) found similar themes in an earlier incel dataset.

6 Discussion

Across our quantitative analysis of the distribution and associations made with identity terms, we see evidence of an ideology where physical appearance determines human value, as has been found with prior work on incels (Maxwell et al., 2020; Baele et al., 2021; Pruden, 2021). This ideology essentializes social constructs, such as race and gender, as biological physical features impacting desirability, with controversy over the role of race.

We find strong evidence for gender as a central focus of incel discussion; mentions of men and women far surpass the number of mentions of any other identity. We find that this community commonly uses novel identity terms that may not appear in generic lists, including many derogatory terms for women ("foids," "landwhales").

Increases in mentions of LGBTQ+, political, Jewish, and Black identities, often with stereotypes and conspiracy theories, could suggest this community has incorporated broader far-right trends. An increasing politicization is reflected in this example post: "we don't need society to completely accept the incel ideology, we just need to masquerade as normies and keep bashing women, jews and gays." Our evidence from text analysis supports the common user movement that Mamié et al. (2021) found from manosphere content to alt-right content on YouTube and Reddit. We find that many associations on incels.is reinforce stereotypes such as LGBTQ+ identities being fake, Black people being criminals, and antisemitic conspiracy theories. Users who are central in the forum's shared network devote more identity mentions, proportionally, to Black, LGBTQ+, and Jewish people compared to average users, suggesting that leaders on the platform play a role in broadening the discussion to include mentions of marginalized identity groups other than women. We also find more mentions of neurodiversity and mental health in this online community than in a dataset of white supremacist online content, which may be part of a victimhood narrative.

The overarching black-pilled ideology of physical appearance determining human worth also extends to talk about incels themselves on incels.is. Jaki et al. (2019) also find this "negative self-image" on a precursor forum, which is theorized by Nagle (2015) and Ging (2019). Though incels are presented as occupying the lowest status among men, we find fierce gate-keeping around who can claim the identity and its perceived victimhood. This echoes theoretical work by Kleinke and Bös (2015) finding that online communities often disparage less typical members along with out-groups.

Central users are active in discussions of authenticity. Such victimhood could lead "authentic" misogynist incels to pursue symbolic–or material–action against "fake" incels in the community but also against the perceived unjust system and the women they believe benefit from it.

Identities constructed in interaction are negotiated (Bucholtz and Hall, 2010); we find contention around race in inceldom. "White" is associated with both true and fake incels on the platform, often in connection with the folk JBW theory that white men appeal to women of all races.

Implications for automated hate speech detection Central to many hate speech definitions is whether a text denigrates groups based on identity characteristics (Sellars, 2016; Sanguinetti et al., 2018; Poletto et al., 2021). Identity terms are, thus, a major indicator and concern for hate speech detection. In our analysis of identity construction on incels.is, we confirm that mentions of men and women identity terms are much more frequent than in a similar source of unlabeled hate speech: white supremacist data. Incel texts, then, may be a good source of unlabeled or annotated data for misogyny detection. The dangerous black-pilled ideology in particular is missing from current misogyny datasets (Guest et al., 2021). Such data should be considered, but the broader issue is a need for subject matter expertise in building such datasets for automated hate speech detection. Experts should be consulted to know where to look for training data so that specific types of hateful movements, with lexical or other linguistic innovations, are not overlooked.

We find that almost 30% of identity mentions in our dataset involve community-specific neologisms, often derogatory terms against women. Training hate speech classifiers on data that does not include these terms hinders the ability to detect this substantial source of contemporary online misogyny.

Our analysis also draws attention to the ideological associations being made with identities in this discourse space. We find problematic stereotypes against not only women, but also LGBTQ+, Black, and Jewish people. Thus, incel text data is not only a source of misogyny, but also reflects broader trends related to the mainstreaming of far-right beliefs. Particularly pernicious is a black-pilled ideology that physical appearance determines human value, a reinforcement and extension of essentialized gender and racial hierarchies. Hence, fatphobia, homophobia, ableism, and racism are all wrapped up in misogynist incel content. Automatically detecting this broader ideology may be unattainable or extremely difficult with machine learning techniques, but we emphasize practitioners and researchers should be aware of this ideology. A narrow focus on hate against women from these communities will miss these important–and increasing–trends toward politicization and hate against other groups.

7 Conclusion and Future Work

The incel movement and the collective identity around it is a relatively new expression of male supremacism. In this paper, we use quantitative text and network analysis techniques to investigate how identities are constructed in discourse on one of the largest incel forums. We study the identity group mention frequency over time, as well as actions and attributes associated with them.

We find that talk about women and men dominates identity mentions on this forum, though mentions of marginalized identities commonly targeted by far-right groups increase from 2017-2021, appearing in textual contexts that propagate stereotypes. Many of these mentions use novel, community-specific identity terms that would be missed with generic lists of identities or hate speech training data from other contexts. Future work could systematically evaluate the ability of existing hate speech classifiers to handle this jargon, as well as the particularly dangerous black-pilled ideology.

This ideology is apparent in discussions of identities, including in-group ones, that reinforce rigid physical hierarchies based on attractiveness, gender, and race. We find race is a site of contention in discussions of who are "true" incels. Gatekeeping around incel authenticity is common.

Negotiation around race and inceldom, as well as intersectional racism and misogyny in incel forums would be a fruitful avenue for future work. This dataset could also be compared with other incel discussions, such as incels.me and earlier banned subreddits r/incels and r/braincels. The role of platform affordances and informal mentorship on the platform could be further investigated, as Perry and DeDeo (2021) mapped different user pathways in and out of r/TheRedPill. Further network analysis could reveal how the behaviors we identify, including a rise in mentions of marginalized and political identities, were spread in this community and why.

Limitations

Our approaches largely focus on explicit mentions of identity terms. This does not capture whether the identity term is the target of hate speech, which would require further analysis. This approach also does not capture attitudes held toward high-profile members of those groups, which play a role in circulating associations with identities (such as personal attacks on women in gaming or the use of "George Soros" as shorthand for antisemitic conspiracy theories). Future work may try to capture and measure these attitudes.

Incels.is is a large, popular forum for black-pilled incel discourse, which has a unique and extreme ideology that we argue is under-represented in current hate speech datasets. However, our analysis is limited to this forum, and the trends we identify may not apply to more moderate incel discourse (e.g., r/IncelsWithoutHate) or related online male supremacist movements, such as MGTOW and PUAs. Though these communities are known to have related, but distinct jargon (Farrell et al., 2020), we emphasize that researchers should recognize these lexical innovations in their annotations for hate speech and include a variety of these communities in training datasets for misogyny.

Ethics Statement

The Association of Internet Researchers (AoIR) acknowledges internet research is complex, dynamic and often involves many gray areas– specifically related to what constitutes human subjects, private versus public spaces and data versus persons (Markham and Buchanan, 2012). For this reason, the AoIR guidance recommends an inductive, ongoing and context-specific approach to ethics throughout the research process. At all stages, this involves being mindful of the vulnerability of the community under study and taking efforts to protect them where appropriate, while balancing their rights with social benefits and the researcher's right to conduct research.

Following this guidance, we subscribe to a utilitarian philosophy where we focus on doing the greatest good for the greatest number of people. In the case of black-pilled incels, we believe the necessity to better understand this potentially dangerous group outweighs the possible damage to forum members. For this reason, in addition to the AoIR guidance outlined above, we have followed some commonly accepted standards to protect participants and refrain from amplifying misogynist voices.

Data was collected only from publicly available online message boards and no private or identifiable information has been included in this manuscript.

We are not publishing user names, though we did observe them in our analysis of central users. We also did not subscribe to any channels or recirculate any content to ensure our work does not contribute to the monetization of the forum or associated accounts. Following the WOAH recommendation, we paraphrase posts to retain key aspects while protecting users' privacy.

Acknowledgements

This work was supported in part by the Collaboratory Against Hate: Research and Action Center at Carnegie Mellon University and the University of Pittsburgh. The Center for Informed Democracy and Social Cybersecurity at Carnegie Mellon University also provided support.

References

Hind S. Alatawi, Areej M. Alhothali, and Kawthar M. Moria. 2021. Detecting White Supremacist Hate Speech Using Domain Specific Word Embedding with Deep Learning and BERT. *IEEE Access*, 9:106363–106374.

Maria Anzovino, Elisabetta Fersini, and Paolo Rosso. 2018. Automatic Identification and Classification of Misogynistic Language on Twitter. In *Natural Language Processing and Information Systems*, Lecture Notes in Computer Science, pages 57–64. Springer International Publishing.

Stephane J. Baele, Lewys Brace, and Travis G. Coan. 2021. From "Incel" to "Saint": Analyzing the violent worldview behind the 2018 Toronto attack. *Terrorism and Political Violence*, 33(8):1667–1691.

David Bamman, Brendan O'Connor, and Noah A Smith. 2013. Learning Latent Personas of Film Characters. *Proceedings of the 51st Annual Meeting of the Association for Computational Linguistics (ACL 2013)*, pages 352–361.

David Bamman, Ted Underwood, and Noah A. Smith. 2014. A Bayesian Mixed Effects Model of Literary Character. *Proceedings of the 52nd Annual Meeting of the Association for Computational Linguistics (ACL 2014)*, pages 370–379.

Valerio Basile, Cristina Bosco, Elisabetta Fersini, Debora Nozza, Viviana Patti, Francisco Rangel, Paolo Rosso, and Manuela Sanguinetti. 2019. SemEval-2019 Task 5: Multilingual Detection of Hate Speech Against Immigrants and Women in Twitter. In *Proceedings of the 13th International Workshop on Semantic Evaluation (SemEval-2019)*, pages 54–63.

Robert D. Benford and David A. Snow. 2000. Framing Processes and Social Movements: An Overview and Assessment. *Annual Review of Sociology*, 26(1):611–639.

J. M. Berger. 2018. *Extremism*. MIT Press.

Shiladitya Bhattacharya, Siddharth Singh, Ritesh Kumar, Akanksha Bansal, Akash Bhagat, and Yogesh Dawer. 2020. Developing a Multilingual Annotated Corpus of Misogyny and Aggression. In *Proceedings of the Second Workshop on Trolling, Aggression and Cyberbullying*, pages 158–168, Marseille, France. European Language Resources Association (ELRA).

Mary Bucholtz and Kira Hall. 2005. Identity and interaction: A sociocultural linguistic approach. *Discourse Studies*, 7(4-5):585–614.

Mary Bucholtz and Kira Hall. 2010. Locating Identity in Language. In Carmen Llamas and Dominic Watt, editors, *Language and Identities*, pages 18–28. Edinburgh University Press, Edinburgh.

Viv Burr and Penny Dick. 2017. Social Constructionism. In Brendan Gough, editor, *The Palgrave Handbook of Critical Social Psychology*, pages 59–80. Palgrave Macmillan UK, London.

L. Richard Carley, Jeff Reminga, and Kathleen M. Carley. 2018. ORA & NetMapper. In *International Conference on Social Computing, Behavioral-Cultural Modeling and Prediction and Behavior Representation in Modeling and Simulation*, volume 3. Springer.

Béatrice Daille. 1994. *Approche mixte pour l'extraction automatique de terminologie: statistiques lexicales et filtres linguistiques*. Ph.D. Thesis, Paris Diderot University.

Dorottya Demszky, Nikhil Garg, Rob Voigt, James Zou, Matthew Gentzkow, Jesse Shapiro, and Dan Jurafsky. 2019. Analyzing Polarization in Social Media: Method and Application to Tweets on 21 Mass Shootings. In *Proceedings of the 2019 Conference of the North American Chapter of the Association for Computational Linguistics: Human Language Technologies*, pages 2970–3005.

Tracie Farrell, Oscar Araque, Miriam Fernandez, and Harith Alani. 2020. On the use of Jargon and Word Embeddings to Explore Subculture within the Reddit's Manosphere. In *12th ACM Conference on Web Science*, pages 221–230, New York, NY, USA. Association for Computing Machinery.

Tracie Farrell, Miriam Fernandez, Jakub Novotny, and Harith Alani. 2019. Exploring Misogyny across the Manosphere in Reddit. In *Proceedings of the 10th ACM Conference on Web Science*, pages 87–96, New York, NY, USA. Association for Computing Machinery.

Elisabetta Fersini, Debora Nozza, and Paolo Rosso. 2018a. Overview of the Evalita 2018 Task on Automatic Misogyny Identification (AMI). In *Proceedings of the Sixth Evaluation Campaign of Natural Language Processing and Speech Tools for Italian (EVALITA 2018)*, Turin, Italy.

Elisabetta Fersini, Paolo Rosso, and Maria Anzovino. 2018b. Overview of the Task on Automatic Misogyny Identification at IberEval 2018. In *IberEval@SEPLN 2018*, pages 214–228, Seville, Spain.

James Paul Gee. 2011. *An Introduction to Discourse Analysis: Theory and Method*. Routledge, New York.

Debbie Ging. 2019. Alphas, Betas, and Incels: Theorizing the Masculinities of the Manosphere. *Men and Masculinities*, 22(4):638–657.

Kelly Caroline Gothard. 2021. The Incel Lexicon: Deciphering the Emergent Cryptolect of a Global Misogynistic Community. Master's thesis, The University of Vermont and State Agricultural College, Vermont, United States.

Ella Guest, Bertie Vidgen, Alexandros Mittos, Nishanth Sastry, Gareth Tyson, and Helen Margetts. 2021. An Expert Annotated Dataset for the Detection of Online Misogyny. In *Proceedings of the 16th Conference of the European Chapter of the Association for Computational Linguistics: Main Volume*, pages 1336–1350, Online. Association for Computational Linguistics.

Frazer Heritage, Veronika Koller, Alexandra Krendel, and Abi Hawtin. 2019. MANTRaP:A Corpus Approach to Researching Gender in Online Misogynist Communities. In *12th BAAL LGaS SIG*.

Sarah Hewitt, T. Tiropanis, and C. Bokhove. 2016. The problem of identifying misogynist language on Twitter (and other online social spaces). In *Proceedings of the 8th ACM Conference on Web Science*, pages 333–335, New York, NY, USA. Association for Computing Machinery.

Sylvia Jaki, Tom De Smedt, Maja Gwóźdź, Rudresh Panchal, Alexander Rossa, and Guy De Pauw. 2019. Online hatred of women in the Incels.me forum: Linguistic analysis and automatic detection. *Journal of Language Aggression and Conflict*, 7(2):240–268.

Kenneth Joseph, Wei Wei, Matthew Benigni, and Kathleen M. Carley. 2016. A social-event based approach to sentiment analysis of identities and behaviors in text. *The Journal of Mathematical Sociology*, 40(3):137–166.

Sonja Kleinke and Birte Bös. 2015. Intergroup rudeness and the metapragmatics of its negotiation in online discussion fora. *Pragmatics*, 25(1):47–71.

Mirko Lai, Marco Antonio Stranisci, Cristina Bosco, Rossana Damiano, and Viviana Patti. 2021. HaMor at the Profiling Hate Speech Spreaders on Twitter Notebook for PAN at CLEF 2021. Technical report.

Jack LaViolette and Bernie Hogan. 2019. Using platform signals for distinguishing discourses: The case of men's rights and men's liberation on Reddit. In *Proceedings of the 13th International Conference on Web and Social Media, ICWSM 2019*, pages 323–334.

Robin Mamié, Manoel Horta Ribeiro, and Robert West. 2021. Are Anti-Feminist Communities Gateways to the Far Right? Evidence from Reddit and YouTube. In *Proceedings of the 13th ACM Web Science Conference 2021*, pages 139–147, New York, NY, USA. Association for Computing Machinery.

Annette Markham and Elizabeth Buchanan. 2012. Ethical Decision-Making and Internet Research: Recommendations from the AoIR Ethics Working Committee (Version 2.0). Technical report.

December Maxwell, Sarah R. Robinson, Jessica R. Williams, and Craig Keaton. 2020. "A Short Story of a Lonely Guy": A Qualitative Thematic Analysis of Involuntary Celibacy Using Reddit. *Sexuality & Culture*, 24(6):1852–1874.

Tomas Mikolov, Kai Chen, Greg Corrado, and Jeffrey Dean. 2013. Distributed Representations of Words and Phrases and their Compositionality. In *Advances in Neural Information Processing Systems*, pages 3111–3119.

Cynthia Miller-Idriss. 2022. *Hate in the Homeland: The New Global Far Right*. Princeton University Press.

Ioannis Mollas, Zoe Chrysopoulou, Stamatis Karlos, and Grigorios Tsoumakas. 2020. ETHOS: an Online Hate Speech Detection Dataset. ArXiv: 2006.08328.

Angela Nagle. 2015. *An investigation into contemporary online anti-feminist movements*. Ph.D. Thesis, Dublin City University, Dublin, Ireland.

Chloe Perry and Simon DeDeo. 2021. The Cognitive Science of Extremist Ideologies Online. ArXiv:2110.00626.

Fabio Poletto, Valerio Basile, Manuela Sanguinetti, Cristina Bosco, and Viviana Patti. 2021. Resources and benchmark corpora for hate speech detection: a systematic review. In *Language Resources and Evaluation*, volume 55, pages 477–523. Springer Science and Business Media.

Meredith L. Pruden. 2021. *"Maintaining Frame" in the Incelosphere: Mapping the Discourses, Representations and Geographies of Involuntary Celibates Online*. Ph.D. Thesis, Georgia State University, Atlanta, Georgia, USA.

Jing Qian, Anna Bethke, Yinyin Liu, Elizabeth Belding, and William Yang Wang. 2019. A Benchmark Dataset for Learning to Intervene in Online Hate Speech. In *Proceedings of the 2019 Conference on Empirical Methods in Natural Language Processing and the 9th International Joint Conference on Natural Language Processing*, pages 4754–4763.

Manoel Horta Ribeiro, Jeremy Blackburn, Barry Bradlyn, Emiliano De Cristofaro, Gianluca Stringhini, Summer Long, Stephanie Greenberg, and Savvas Zannettou. 2021. The Evolution of the Manosphere across the Web. In *Proceedings of the International AAAI Conference on Web and Social Media*, volume 15, pages 196–207.

François Role and Mohamed Nadif. 2011. Handling the Impact of Low Frequency Events on Co-occurrence based Measures of Word Similarity - A Case Study of Pointwise Mutual Information. In *Proceedings of the International Conference on Knowledge Discovery and Information Retrieval (KDIR-2011)*.

Niloofar Safi Samghabadi, Parth Patwa, Srinivas Pykl, Prerana Mukherjee, Amitava Das, and Thamar Solorio. 2020. Aggression and Misogyny Detection using BERT: A Multi-Task Approach. In *Proceedings of the Second Workshop on Trolling, Aggression and Cyberbullying*, pages 11–16.

Manuela Sanguinetti, Fabio Poletto, Cristina Bosco, Viviana Patti, and Marco Stranisci. 2018. An Italian Twitter Corpus of Hate Speech against Immigrants. In *Proceedings of the Eleventh International Conference on Language Resources and Evaluation (LREC'18)*, pages 2798–2895.

Maarten Sap, Saadia Gabriel, Lianhui Qin, Dan Jurafsky, Noah A. Smith, and Yejin Choi. 2020. Social Bias Frames: Reasoning about Social and Power Implications of Language. In *Proceedings of the 58th Annual Meeting of the Association for Computational Linguistics*, pages 5477–5490.

Joseph Seering, Felicia Ng, Zheng Yao, and Geoff Kaufman. 2018. Applications of Social Identity Theory to Research and Design in Social Computing. In *Proceedings of the ACM Conference on Human-Computer Interaction*, volume 2 of *CSCW*, pages 1–33. Issue: January.

Andrew Sellars. 2016. Defining Hate Speech. Technical report, Berkman Klein Center.

B. Simons and D. B. Skillicorn. 2020. A Bootstrapped Model to Detect Abuse and Intent in White Supremacist Corpora. In *Proceedings - 2020 IEEE International Conference on Intelligence and Security Informatics, ISI 2020*. Institute of Electrical and Electronics Engineers Inc.

Michael Stubbs. 2001. *Words and phrases: Corpus studies of lexical semantics*. Blackwell Publishers Oxford.

Henri Tajfel. 1974. Social identity and intergroup behaviour. *Social Science Information*, 13(2):65–93.

Joshua Uyheng and Kathleen M. Carley. 2020. Bots and online hate during the COVID-19 pandemic: case studies in the United States and the Philippines. *Journal of Computational Social Science*, 3(2):445–468.

Joshua Uyheng and Kathleen M. Carley. 2021. An Identity-Based Framework for Generalizable Hate Speech Detection. In *International Conference on Social Computing, Behavioral-Cultural Modeling and Prediction and Behavior Representation in Modeling and Simulation*, pages 121–130.

Zeerak Waseem and Dirk Hovy. 2016. Hateful Symbols or Hateful People? Predictive Features for Hate Speech Detection on Twitter. In *Proceedings of the NAACL-HLT 2016*, pages 88–93.

Matthew L. Williams, Pete Burnap, and Luke Sloan. 2017. Towards an Ethical Framework for Publishing Twitter Data in Social Research: Taking into Account Users' Views, Online Context and Algorithmic Estimation. *Sociology*, 51(6):1149–1168.

Michael Miller Yoder. 2021. *Computational Models of Identity Presentation in Language*. Ph.D. thesis, Carnegie Mellon University, Pittsburgh, Pennsylvania, USA.

Michael Miller Yoder, Ahmad Diab, David West Brown, and Kathleen M. Carley. 2023. A Weakly Supervised Classifier and Dataset of White Supremacist Language. In *Proceedings of the 61st Annual Meeting of the Association for Computational Linguistics (Volume 2: Short Papers)*.

Michael Miller Yoder, Lynnette Ng, David West Brown, and Kathleen Carley. 2022. How Hate Speech Varies by Target Identity: A Computational Analysis. In *Proceedings of the 26th Conference on Computational Natural Language Learning (CoNLL)*, pages 27–39, Abu Dhabi, United Arab Emirates (Hybrid). Association for Computational Linguistics.

Michael Miller Yoder, Qinlan Shen, Yansen Wang, Alex Coda, Yunseok Jang, Yale Song, Kapil Thadani, and Carolyn P. Rosé. 2020. Phans, Stans and Cishets: Self-Presentation Effects on Content Propagation in Tumblr. In *12th ACM Conference on Web Science (WebSci '20)*, pages 39–48.

A Additional Tables

Table 3 shows actions and attributes associated with "trucels" and "fakecels," common incel variants mentioned in incels.is.

Identity		Top PMI[3] terms
Truecels	*Attr*	biggest, truest, real, actual, giga, ultimate, legit, confirmed, certified, blackpilled, ugly, absolute, genuine, hope, ethnic, white, old, automatic, fellow, bigger, other
	Act_S	ascend, get, post, know, rise, knows, remain, go, looks, confirmed, relate, rot, understand, cope, use, tried, need, browse, make, suicide, spend, ldar, roped, take
	Act_O	pleasure, confirmed, banning, mog, rejected, bluepilled, help, laid, banned, born, save, doomed, over, seen, calling, see, die, excluded, bullying, dude, mock, mocking
Fakecels	*Attr*	fucking, larping, biggest, volcel, inb4, obvious, banned, known, defending, other, massive, fuck, tbh, confirmed, gtfo, potential, normie, likely, one, looking, users
	Act_S	detected, gtfo, confirmed, spotted, get, ascend, post, say, need, banned, try, posting, larping, fuck, smh, come, leave, coming, bragging, go, worry, ruining, invade, piss
	Act_O	ban, calling, banned, gtfo, weed, defending, expose, fucking, larping, spot, call, exposed, defends, exposing, smell, purged, banning, defend, confirmed, found

Table 3: Representative actions and attributes associated with truecels and fakecels identity group terms in the incels.is dataset. *Attr* refers to attributes, while Act_S are actions for which the identity group is a subject and Act_O are actions for which the identity group is an object.

DeTexD: A Benchmark Dataset for Delicate Text Detection

Serhii Yavnyi* **Oleksii Sliusarenko*** **Jade Razzaghi*** **Olena Nahorna***
Yichen Mo* **Knar Hovakimyan*** **Artem Chernodub***
Grammarly
{firstname.lastname}@grammarly.com

Abstract

Over the past few years, much research has been conducted to identify and regulate toxic language.[1] However, few studies have addressed a broader range of sensitive texts that are not necessarily overtly toxic. In this paper, we introduce and define a new category of sensitive text called "delicate text." We provide the taxonomy of delicate text and present a detailed annotation scheme. We annotate DeTexD, the first benchmark dataset for delicate text detection. The significance of the difference in the definitions is highlighted by the relative performance deltas between models trained each definitions and corpora and evaluated on the other. We make publicly available the DeTexD Benchmark dataset, annotation guidelines, and baseline model for delicate text detection.[2] [3] [4]

1 Introduction

The prevalence of user-generated toxic language on online social networks has motivated many to develop automatic methods of detecting such content (Warner and Hirschberg, 2012), (Waseem and Hovy, 2016), (Davidson et al., 2017), (Schmidt and Wiegand, 2017), (ElSherief et al., 2018a), (ElSherief et al., 2018b), (Qian et al., 2018a), (Qian et al., 2018b). These efforts towards moderating toxic language have gained even more momentum as large language models, which have the potential to generate harmful content, have become more mainstream (Welbl et al., 2021), (Bender et al., 2021), (Hovy and Prabhumoye, 2021), (Kocielnik et al., 2023). Much of this work has been constrained to texts that are toxic or otherwise overtly harmful; however, there are many other sensitive texts where interaction with other users or virtual agents may be triggering or offensive. While some studies (Yenala et al., 2018), (Parnell et al., 2020), (Tripathi et al., 2019) have addressed specific sensitive areas (e.g., insults, geopolitics, or illegal activity), to our knowledge, this is the first study that comprehensively analyzes sensitive content in general.

Text	Delicate	Hate speech	Offensive	Profanity
This is f*cking amazing!	no	no	no	yes
Sometimes I have suicidal thoughts but I never talk about it with my mom.	yes	no	no	no
I think you are not a good person and I don't need your toxicity in my life.	yes	no	yes	no
You are full of sh*t, I think you should fuck off now.	yes	no	yes	yes
Why do we allow Mexicans to work in our country!! Send them all back.	yes	yes	yes	no
F*ck them all jews!	yes	yes	yes	yes

Table 1: Examples of delicate texts compared to hate speech, offensive language, and profanity.

In this study, we target a broader set of sensitive texts that we call "delicate texts," an umbrella term covering toxic language as well as lower-severity sensitive texts, with a focus on sensitive texts (Table 1). Delicate text covers many topics which are not necessarily offensive but can still be highly sensitive and triggering. For example, texts where users share challenges regarding their mental health issues, where they discuss their experience of the loss of a loved one, or where they share content about self-harm and suicide. While most of these texts do not contain offensive language or attack certain minority groups, they all contain triggering topics that are emotionally and personally charged. Conversations about these topics can be easily derailed and lead to users experiencing discourteous or offensive behaviors from other users or virtual agents. With delicate text detection, our goal is

* The names of authors are arranged in reverse alphabetical order.

[1] Here, we use the terms "toxic language" and "hate speech" interchangeably.

[2] https://github.com/grammarly/detexd

[3] https://huggingface.co/grammarly/detexd-roberta-base

[4] https://huggingface.co/grammarly/detexd

The 7th Workshop on Online Abuse and Harms (WOAH), pages 14–28
July 13, 2023 ©2023 Association for Computational Linguistics

to identify texts where engagement by other users or agents is most likely to result in harm, rather than focusing only on texts where harmful content has already been generated. Automatic detection of delicate texts is an essential tool for effective monitoring and prevention of potentially harmful content generated by users or AI. This model can be used for practical applications such as content moderation for models that are at high risk of hallucinations or data sampling to efficiently target texts where offensive interactions are most likely to happen.

In this study, we introduce the task of delicate text detection. We present a comprehensive definition of delicate texts and a dataset of 1,023 labeled delicate texts (DeTexD). We share our data collection, annotation, and quality control methods along with the detailed annotation schema. We describe the development of our baseline delicate text detection model. Finally, we demonstrate the difference between delicate text detection and existing content moderation methods by testing our model against toxic language benchmark datasets and testing popular content moderation models against our DeTexD dataset.

2 Related Works

Several studies have investigated the use of various NLP methods to detect inappropriate content; most of these works targeted toxic and offensive language. Some focused on developing more robust models to detect hateful content (Sohn and Lee, 2019), (Caselli et al., 2021), (Yousaf and Nawaz, 2022), while others focused on building better and less biased datasets (Founta et al., 2018), (Zampieri et al., 2019), (Basile et al., 2019), (Davidson et al., 2017), (Kiela et al., 2020), (Mathew et al., 2021), (Xia et al., 2020), (Huang et al., 2020), (Mollas et al., 2022), (Qian et al., 2019). With respect to dataset creation, (Mollas et al., 2022) created ETHOS, a binary and multi-labeled dataset of hate speech, along with a detailed annotation protocol. Their dataset covers various hate speech categories (including race, gender, religion, nationality, sexual orientation and disability), as well as target and whether the texts incited violence. They also examined the quality of their data using both binary and multi-label classification. In another study, (Mathew et al., 2021) created HateXplain, a hate speech dataset that reflects annotators' rationale for their labeling task. Their data went through a three-step annotation process in which a text was first classified as "offensive," "hate," or "normal;" next, the target of the hate was identified as "individual" or "generalized." Last, the annotators were asked to highlight parts of the text that justified their annotation decisions. They reported that models that used annotators' rationale in the training data performed slightly better than those without human rationale. Most studies have targeted hate speech; however, some studies have addressed a more general concept: inappropriate content. While most of these works used the term 'inappropriate content' to refer to hate speech, they also included sensitive topics. For instance, (Yenala et al., 2018) focused on identifying inappropriate content; they defined inappropriate content as impolite and disrespectful posts that offend certain groups, are related to illegal activities, or induce violence. They developed a deep learning-based model to identify inappropriate content in detecting query completion suggestions and user conversation texts. In another study, (Tripathi et al., 2019) focused on detecting sensitive content in user interactions with voice services. They targeted profanity, insult, geopolitical topics, explicit sexual and anatomical content, weapons, war, explicit graphical violence, race, religion, and gender. They focused on binary classification of sensitive content.

In (Basile et al., 2019) SemEval 2019 Task 5 dataset is described, a specific case of hate speech against immigrants and women in Spanish and English Twitter messages. They provide both: a main binary subtask for detecting the presence of hate speech, and a finer-grained one for identifying features such as hate attitude or target. During this competition, over 100 models were submitted. We evaluate our baseline model for delicate text detection on their main dataset.

3 Delicate text

3.1 Definition

We define *delicate text* as any text that is emotionally charged or potentially triggering such that engaging with it has the potential to result in harm. This broad term covers a range of sensitive texts that vary across four major dimensions: 1) riskiness, 2) explicitness, 3) topic, and 4) target. Delicate texts come with varying levels of risk; some can be highly risky such as texts about self-harm or content that promotes violence against certain identity groups, while others can be less risky such as insulting language. Delicate texts can also have various degrees of explicitness: some can be produced explicitly with the use of delicate key terms, while others can be produced implicitly without the presence of delicate lexical terms. Delicate texts cover various subjects, with topics ranging from race, gender, and religion to mental health, socioeconomic status, or political affiliations.

Unlike toxic language that only targets identity groups (Zampieri et al., 2019), (Davidson et al., 2017), delicate texts can target identity groups, non-identity groups, or they can be self-targeted or non-targeted. In addition, delicate texts are not always offensive, unlike toxic language. Table 1 shows how different texts would be treated under our delicate text approach as compared to typical approaches for categorizing hate speech, offensive language, and texts containing profanity.

Table 2 illustrates examples of both delicate and non-delicate texts. The first "non-delicate" text does not contain any references to delicate topics. The rest all reference a delicate subject (mental health), but each has a different level of risk. For example, the "very low risk (1)" delicate text contains a factual statement about mental health, while the "very high risk (5)" text explicitly mentions self-harm. There is a shift in riskiness as content becomes more personal, emotional, and explicit. It is worth noting that none of these examples are offensive or contain vulgar language; however, engagement with these texts, whether by users or virtual agents, can result in harm.

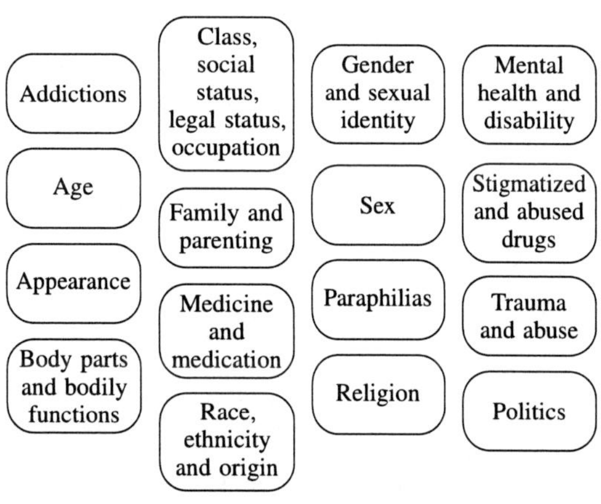

Figure 1: List of delicate text topics.

Figure 1 displays the list of delicate topics. We did not present this list in any hierarchical order as we wanted to highlight the fact that there is not a clear border between toxic language and sensitive language as a text can be both toxic and sensitive. Each of these topics can be used to create risky content. While these topics may be used in various degrees of riskiness, they all are considered delicate. Please see Appendix A for our annotation guidelines and additional examples.

4 DeTexD Benchmark Dataset

4.1 Data Collection

The sparsity of delicate texts in online platforms makes it challenging to target in data collection. To ensure that the data contained sufficient sensitive content, we used a combination of domain specification and keyword-matching when sourcing data. For our DeTexD Benchmark dataset (Table 3), we extracted data from various websites in CommonCrawl[5], where we specifically targeted news websites, forums discussing sensitive topics (e.g., Mental Health Forum[6], and able2know[7] which covers body image), and generally controversial forums (4Chan[8], Stormfront[9]), with the expectation that these would contain a significant amount of sensitive content. To further refine the dataset, we targeted paragraphs containing words from our delicate keyword dictionary. Our dictionary contains keywords related to a wide variety delicate topics which are included as tags in the dictionary metadata (see Table 6 for the full list of topics and examples of keywords). Additionally, each keyword is tagged with one of four severity ratings ranging from highly offensive to potentially offensive. We used these keywords with their metadata as a fine-grained data filtering method to extract delicate texts covering various topics and levels of risk. After analyzing the content of the pilot dataset we confirmed that the targeting methods resulted in a desirable distribution of data and moved forward with extracting 41,000 paragraphs through this method for the main annotation task. This data was split into DeTexD Train dataset containing 40,000 samples (this part is not published) and the DeTexD Benchmark dataset of 1,023 paragraphs. All data was collected from September 2019 to August 2022.

[5] https://commoncrawl.org/
[6] https://www.mentalhealthforum.net/
[7] https://able2know.org/
[8] https://www.4chan.org/
[9] https://www.stormfront.org/forum/

Text	Identification label (step I)	Riskiness label (step II)	Model prediction
A survey-based study of digital media usage shows options covering just about every topic, from true crime to mental health; there's certainly no shortage of options.	non-delicate	non-delicate (0)	NON-DELICATE
Identifying and addressing mental health, especially in the early stages, is highly important.	delicate	very low risk (1)	
Working with children who might have various mental health issues is such a challenging job and people need to understand how hard it can get at times.	delicate	low risk (2)	
One of my patients started having a type of mood swings, and he thought "this is normal for my age group" so he didn't seek help, he was unaware that all the males in his family had bipolar disorder, so the symptoms were left for about a year where they gradually got much worse and far more rapid. Ignorance is not bliss there is no harm in seeing your GP.	delicate	medium risk (3)	DELICATE
So you had a panic attack last night, and it seems that there was an issue with your new pills, and now you have an irrational fear alongside these pills. You imply that you've never had any major problems whilst out, so all I can suggest is to mention it to your GP next time you go.	delicate	high risk (4)	
I am just sick and tired of this life, and there is no hope for me, I am just looking for an easy way to end my life.	delicate	very high risk (5)	

Table 2: Examples of texts and corresponding labels from the DeTexD Benchmark dataset. "Identification" and "riskiness" are labeled by expert annotators (Section 4.2). "Model prediction" illustrates the mapping between 1-5 riskiness labels and binary NON-DELICATE and DELICATE predictions made by our baseline model (Section 5.1). Only predictions with a medium risk (3) or higher rating are converted to a DELICATE prediction.

4.2 Data Annotation

Identifying delicate content is a nontrivial task, as delicate text is a highly subjective concept. To ensure consistent and accurate annotations, we developed a fine-grained annotation scheme to guide expert annotators through the task. The annotation guidelines (Appendix A) contain our definition of delicate text along with a list of delicate categories within delicate text, examples of each category, and labeling samples.

To reduce the impact of subjectivity, we designed a two-step annotation scheme (Table 2):

Step I (identification): Annotators were shown texts and asked to label them as "non-delicate" or "delicate" based on our overall definition of delicate text. This initial binary rating pass allowed us to quickly identify texts most likely to contain delicate content through a relatively low-effort task.

Step II (risk level rating): Texts labeled "delicate" in Step I moved on to Step II, where annotators were asked to rate the risk level of each text on a riskiness scale of 1 ("very low risk") to 5 ("very high risk"). The annotators were instructed to focus on overall sentiment of the texts rather than the lexical meanings of individual keywords. Delicate texts which are more emotional, personal, charged, or those that reference a greater number of delicate topics are considered high risk, whereas texts with more neutral and less personal content are considered low risk (see Table 2 for examples of risk ratings).

Using this labeling process, we stepped away from simple binary labeling of the data, which not only helped to ensure quality, but also allowed us to gain more detailed information about the riskiness of the sensitive data.

Identification label (step I)	# samples	Riskiness label (step II)	# samples
non-delicate	503	non-delicate (0)	503
delicate	520	very low risk (1)	67
		low risk (2)	113
		medium risk (3)	153
		high risk (4)	113
		very high risk (5)	74
TOTAL (step I)	1023	TOTAL (step II)	1023

Table 3: Distribution of annotated texts in the DeTexD Benchmark dataset.

4.3 Quality Control

Each text in the DeTexD Benchmark dataset was annotated following the guidelines (Appendix A). All annotators who participated in this task are expert linguists that had an excellent understanding of delicate texts and had previously completed similar annotation tasks. Each text was annotated by three different annotators, and we took a majority vote as the final label.

To ensure annotation quality, we conducted a pilot annotation. Each snippet was annotated by one annotator, and 500/1,023 labeled snippets were randomly selected and qualitatively analyzed by the team of four expert linguists who designed the task. Each sample was reviewed, and its label was accepted if it matched the guidelines and rejected otherwise. Out of 500 judgments, 426 snippets were accepted, and only 74 labels were rejected (85% acceptance rate). After the pilot, the annotators were provided with feedback for improvement and the guidelines were updated to address common areas of confusion. Annotators who passed the pilot task moved on to annotate the full dataset. We measured the inter-rater agreement and obtained a Krippendorff's alpha score of 0.65 for the final dataset.

5 Experiments

In this section, we share results from a series of experiments. First, we show the potential to create a delicate text detection system which is suitable for practical usage. For this purpose, we developed and evaluated a baseline delicate text detection model. Next, we demonstrate the originality of this task by evaluating the performance of our model on toxic language datasets and evaluating toxic language detection models on DeTexD. Since toxic language detection and delicate text detection are two distinct tasks, DeTexD does not perform well on toxic language benchmarks and other content moderation methods that target mainly toxic language do not perform well on the DeTexD benchmark dataset.

5.1 Baseline Model

Our baseline model is the RoBERTa-based classifier (Liu et al., 2019b), which is fine-tuned on the delicate text detection training dataset of 40,000 samples.[10] The model is trained for 2,000 optimization updates on batches of 256 samples each. We used AdamW as an optimizer with a learning rate of $\alpha = 5e^{-5}$. As a task to learn, we selected a multiclass classification model with binary conversion because it has higher quality than binary classification and ordinal regression (Cheng, 2007). Although we noticed a better diagonal-aligned confusion matrix for ordinal regression, the evaluation result did not show a statistically significant improvement. In our settings, we train a 6-class classification model, where the classes are defined by the riskiness levels from annotation step II. The model's prediction is converted to a binary label using the mapping (Table 2):

i) *NON-DELICATE* = *non-delicate (0)* ∪ *very low risk (1)* ∪ *low risk (2)* and

ii) *DELICATE* = *medium risk (3)* ∪ *high risk (4)* ∪ *very high risk (5)*.

5.2 Baseline Model Performance on Hate Speech Tasks

In order to experimentally confirm that delicate text detection and toxic language detection are distinct tasks, we ran our baseline delicate text detection model (Section 5.1) on popular toxic language datasets (Table 4).

[10]We are not publishing the training portion of our delicate text detection dataset, but it was annotated in exactly the same way as the DeTexD Benchmark dataset (Section 4).

Dataset	Model	Prec.	Rec.	F1
(Davidson et al., 2017),	(Davidson et al., 2017)	91%	90%	90%
hate speech + offensive	(Mozafari et al., 2020)	92%	**92%**	**92%**
	our baseline model	**95.2%**	70.5%	81.0%
(Davidson et al., 2017),	(Davidson et al., 2017)	44%	61%	51%
hate speech only	our baseline model	**60.9%**	**79.5%**	**69.0%**
(Founta et al., 2018)	our baseline model	76.3%	66.6%	71.1%
(Basile et al., 2019)	(Basile et al., 2019)	**56.1%***	77.3%*	**65.0%***
SemEval-2019,	(Caselli et al., 2021)	48.3%	**96.4%**	64.5%
Task 5A	our baseline model	47.5%	89.0%	62.0%
(Zampieri et al., 2019),	(Zampieri et al., 2019)	**78%**	63%	70%
OLID, Task A	(Liu et al., 2019a)	75.8%	**74.6%**	**75.2%**
	our baseline model	48.1%	66.4%	55.8%

Table 4: Performance of our baseline model on toxic language detection tasks as compared to the performance of models from the literature. *For the SemEval-2019 original model, only the accuracy and macro F-score were reported, so we inferred precision and recall values by numerically solving a system of equations with TP, FP, TN, and FN as unknown variables.

The Automated Hate Speech Detection (AHSD) dataset from (Davidson et al., 2017) has separate classes for offensive speech and hate speech, with examples labeled as hate speech representing the minority of the dataset (1,430 examples out of 24,783 total). We evaluate the performance of our model separately on the entire (Davidson et al., 2017) dataset, as well as only on the hate speech subset (which excludes all offensive speech examples). In both cases, after performing error analysis we can see that this dataset is not relevant for our classifier as the task is significantly different. Some false positive prediction examples, such as those mentioning race-related topics or explicitly sexual content, would be categorized as true positives in the DeTexD annotation schema although they are labeled as negative in this dataset. Most of the false negative prediction examples strongly correlate with specific offensive words such as "h*e" or "b*tch." Given the context in which these words are used, these examples would fall under the true negative definition of delicate text. Notably, our classification performance on the hate speech only subset exceeds that of the original work. We attribute the high performance to the fact that there is some overlap in the tasks specifically under the hate speech case, and that we use a more recent model architecture (Liu et al., 2019b), a pre-trained base model and larger model size.

After evaluating our baseline model on the dataset from (Founta et al., 2018) we found that it is not relevant for our classifier as the task is very different from ours. A large proportion of false positives would be classified as delicate under our definition (e.g., sensitive topics such as "killing of thousands..."), while many false negatives would be classified as neutral according to our definition. However, here they are treated as overly emotional like "I'm fu***d up". After evaluating on SemEval-2019, Task 5, Subtask A (Basile et al., 2019) we found that it is not relevant for our classifier as the task is different from ours; it consists mostly of hate speech against migrants and women. As a result, false positives occur in instances where DeTexD detects other delicate topics, even including hate speech that is not targeted at women and migrants. False negatives occur in instances where refugee-directed hate speech is very specific and context-dependent such as "build that wall." Besides that, the dataset is unbalanced: for example, the word "b*tch" appears in half of the texts.

Offensive Language Identification Dataset (OLID), Subtask A (Zampieri et al., 2019) contains examples labeled as "offensive" or "not offensive." Similarly to our other evaluations, we find that the labels in this dataset do not significantly agree with our definition of delicate text. Many of the examples labeled as offensive in this dataset either do not contain enough context to make such a judgment (e.g. "A dying sport") under our definition, or look entirely neutral according to our definition of delicate text (e.g. "Yes. Yes he is!").

These experiments show that there is partial overlap between the definition of delicate text and commonly used definitions of offensive language and hate speech, which results in 70%-90% relative F-score of our baseline model for delicate text detection compared to models trained for toxic language detection (Table 4).

5.3 Comparing our baseline model and hate speech detection methods on the DeTexD Benchmark dataset

In order to evaluate our baseline model's performance and compare it with the most popular existing solutions for hate speech detection, we run them on our DeTexD Benchmark dataset (Table 5).

In our experiments, HateBERT models ("AbusEval", "HatEval", and "OffensEval") are the instances of HateBERT (Caselli et al., 2021), which are fine-tuned on the corresponding dataset. The highest precision is shown by the "HatEval" model,

Method	Prec.	Rec.	F1
HateBERT, AbusEval	86.7%	11.6%	20.5%
HateBERT, AbusEval#	57.0%	70.2%	62.9%
HateBERT, HatEval	**95.2%**	6.0%	11.2%
HateBERT, HatEval#	41.1%	**86.0%**	55.6%
HateBERT, OffensEval	75.4%	31.0%	43.9%
HateBERT, OffensEval#	60.1%	72.6%	65.8%
Google's Perspective API[11]	77.2%	29.2%	42.3%
OpenAI content filter[12]	55.0%	64.0%	58.9%
OpenAI moderation API[13]	91.3%	18.7%	31.1%
Our baseline model	81.4%	78.3%	**79.8%**

Table 5: Comparison of our baseline model for delicate text detection and existing hate speech detection methods on the DeTexD Benchmark dataset. HateBERT model here is from (Caselli et al., 2021).

which is fine-tuned on SemEval 2019 Task 5 dataset that contains hate speech against migrants and women (Basile et al., 2019). These topics are explicitly presented in the DeTexD dataset under "Gender" and "Nationality"/"Race" categories (Fig. 1). "OffensEval" shows the best overall performance among the HateBERT models. We speculate that this is because the definition of offensive language in the training dataset of this model (Basile et al., 2019) ("contains any form of non-acceptable language (profanity) or a targeted offense, which can be veiled or direct") is broader compared to "AbusEval" and "HatEval," and it has greater overlap with our definition of delicate language. All HateBERT models show relatively low recall values because each HateBERT instance targets a narrow range of topics. After receiving valuable feedback from reviewers, we also calibrated optimal thresholds for f-score (marked with hash#). While F-scores got much higher, the precisions got much lower, so we consider this more like metric hacking. In real life, the proportion of positive cases is much lower, so for the future versions it may make sense to get test dataset with more negative cases.

Google's Perspective API is designed to moderate human interaction to support a friendly conversation environment. The Perspective API targets text attributes such as toxicity (rude, disrespectful, or unreasonable comments), severe toxicity (very hateful, aggressive, disrespectful comments), identity attacks (hateful comments targeting someone because of their identity), insults (insulting comments toward people), profanity (swear words), and threat (intention to inflict pain, injury, or violence against people)[14]. This target definition is similar to the "OffensEval" dataset, which could explain why performance is similar to the HatEval model.

[14]https://support.perspectiveapi.com/s/about-the-api-attributes-and-languages

The OpenAI content filter shows strong recall but is lacking precision in our experiments. In error analysis, we see that it misses a large part of examples from mental health and medical topics. In a sample of false-positive predictions, we only see a slight pattern of a tendency to flag texts that contain profane keywords. Surprisingly, during our testing of the OpenAI content filter, we found that for about half of the inputs the predictions are stochastic, with standard deviation on binary prediction reaching as high as 0.5 (across 100 predictions). We expect the presented results for the OpenAI content filter to have a wider than expected confidence interval.

The authors of the OpenAI moderation API suggest it as a replacement for the OpenAI content filter. On our benchmark dataset, the moderation API has higher precision but lower recall as compared to the OpenAI content filter. This can be explained by the difference in the definition of target content between the two models. During error analysis, we find that lower recall can mostly be attributed to medical and mental health topics in our dataset, although some of the examples relating to sexual content were also missed. All examples where the OpenAI moderation API made a false-positive prediction relate to sexual content or socioeconomic status categories. However, the sample is too small (6 out of 687 non-delicate) to make strong conclusions.

In summary, our experiments show that none of the studied toxic language detection methods provide satisfactory detection performance in delicate text detection. Most commonly, the evaluated hate speech detection methods either miss coverage on medical and mental health topics, show lower precision on examples that contain offensive keywords (but aren't deemed delicate according to our definition), or both.

6 Conclusions

We introduced a new type of sensitive language called "delicate text," an umbrella term covering not only toxic language but also sensitive language with a priority focus on the latter. We annotated the DeTexD Benchmark dataset for delicate text detection. The significance of the difference in the definitions is highlighted by the relative performance deltas between models trained each definitions and corpora and evaluated on the other. We make our annotation guidelines, annotated dataset, and baseline model publicly available.

7 Limitations

The presented results only apply to the English language. Both our benchmark dataset and the baseline model target the English language exclusively. Special text sources such as instant messaging or speech-to-text are likely under-represented in our benchmark test set; therefore, we did not evaluate classification performance in those domains. Since we used RoBERTa as the base model, our model inherits the same limitations. Specifically, the length of input sequences is limited to 512 BPE tokens, and additional pre- and post-processing is necessary to run predictions on longer inputs. However, we did not evaluate prediction aggregation methods or classification performance.

7.1 Gender bias

We expect our baseline model to exhibit some amount of gender bias, since it is based on a model that was trained on a wide variety of human-written text. However, in our analysis we only found limited evidence of gender bias. In the counterfactual prediction difference analysis on the DeTexD dataset, we found 6 examples (0.6% of 1023 total) for which the baseline model made a different prediction depending on gender context. The counterfactual texts were created by performing binary gender-swapping (male/female) of the nouns, pronouns and gendered names.

In gender bias evaluation using the Winogender Schemas dataset (Rudinger et al., 2018), we found 4 example triplets (1.7% of 240 total) where the baseline model made different predictions depending on the gender context. We noticed a slight correlation between gender and our model's binary prediction, but consider it negligible at this sample size.

Due to the limited volume of evidence provided by our experiments we cannot make strong conclusions about the presence or absence of gender bias in our baseline model. However, our understanding is that for the best results, bias mitigation methods must be applied. One such method could be the gender-swapping data augmentation of the training data.

7.2 Country bias

The baseline model described in this paper (Section 5.1) treats different countries differently. We

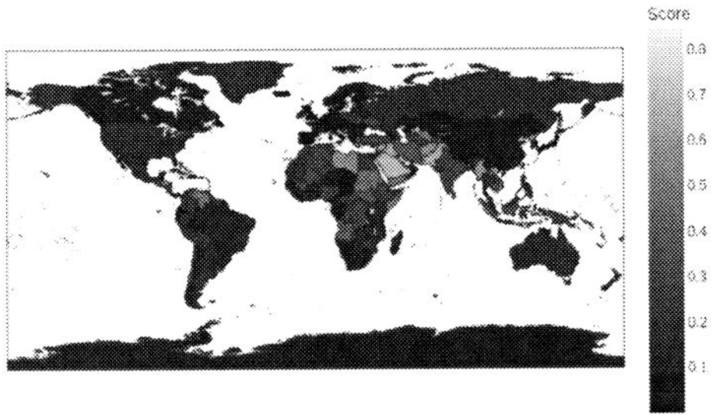

Figure 2: Illustration of country bias.

measure this effect by calculating scores for the template phrase "Unfortunately, the incident happened in {country_name}." The result is illustrated on the colored map on Figure 2. One way to fix this is to replace country names with random others in training data. However, in this case some sentences can become nonsense. For example, "London is the capital of the United Kingdom." In this case, we would need to change all dependent words which would become too complex. From our observation, this situation happens with half of all sentences including country information, so we leave this part as an open question for now.

Ethics Statement

Hate speech, offensive language, and delicate texts are sensitive, and very important matters. Through this work, we try to dive deeper into the challenges and opportunities of any delicate text detection. The goal of this work is to expose the strengths and limitations of different delicate text detection and related techniques and their implications. Some datasets, and models that we work with have been publicly released for a couple of years. All of these artifacts are considered to be in the public sphere from a hate speech perspective. We do not make any recommendations on using these on public or private datasets without proper due diligence for privacy, security, sensitivity, legal, and compliance measures.

Please be advised that due to the nature of the subject matter, the presented DeTexD Benchmark dataset includes a variety of uncensored sensitive content, such as hate speech, violence, threat, self-harm, mental health, sexual, profanity, and others. The text of this work includes keywords and partial text examples of the same type. The most extreme occurrences of such examples in this text are partially obscured with asterisks but the semantics are retained.

8 Acknowledgements

We express our gratitude to our colleagues Cortney Napoles and Leonardo Neves for their valuable advice and to our managers Viktor Zamaruiev and Max Gubin for their constant support. To our communities: While we are writing this, our homeland Ukraine continues to resist the unprovoked Russian invasion. We are grateful to everyone who defends Ukraine, declares support to the people of Ukraine, and is sending aid. Thank you!

References

Valerio Basile, Cristina Bosco, Elisabetta Fersini, Debora Nozza, Viviana Patti, Francisco Manuel Rangel Pardo, Paolo Rosso, and Manuela Sanguinetti. 2019. SemEval-2019 task 5: Multilingual detection of hate speech against immigrants and women in Twitter. In *Proceedings of the 13th International Workshop on Semantic Evaluation*, pages 54–63, Minneapolis, Minnesota, USA. Association for Computational Linguistics.

Emily M Bender, Timnit Gebru, Angelina McMillan-Major, and Shmargaret Shmitchell. 2021. On the dangers of stochastic parrots: Can language models be too big?. In *Proceedings of the 2021 ACM conference on fairness, accountability, and transparency*, pages 610–623.

Tommaso Caselli, Valerio Basile, Jelena Mitrović, and Michael Granitzer. 2021. HateBERT: Retraining BERT for abusive language detection in English. In *Proceedings of the 5th Workshop on Online Abuse and Harms (WOAH 2021)*, pages 17–25, Online. Association for Computational Linguistics.

Jianlin Cheng. 2007. A neural network approach to ordinal regression. *CoRR*, abs/0704.1028.

Thomas Davidson, Dana Warmsley, Michael Macy, and Ingmar Weber. 2017. Automated hate speech detection and the problem of offensive language. In *Proceedings of the international AAAI conference on web and social media*, volume 11, pages 512–515.

Mai ElSherief, Vivek Kulkarni, Dana Nguyen, William Yang Wang, and Elizabeth Belding. 2018a. Hate lingo: A target-based linguistic analysis of hate speech in social media. In *Proceedings of the International AAAI Conference on Web and Social Media*, volume 12.

Mai ElSherief, Shirin Nilizadeh, Dana Nguyen, Giovanni Vigna, and Elizabeth Belding. 2018b. Peer to peer hate: Hate speech instigators and their targets. In *Proceedings of the International AAAI Conference on Web and Social Media*, volume 12.

Antigoni Maria Founta, Constantinos Djouvas, Despoina Chatzakou, Ilias Leontiadis, Jeremy Blackburn, Gianluca Stringhini, Athena Vakali, Michael

Sirivianos, and Nicolas Kourtellis. 2018. Large scale crowdsourcing and characterization of twitter abusive behavior. In *Twelfth International AAAI Conference on Web and Social Media*.

Dirk Hovy and Shrimai Prabhumoye. 2021. Five sources of bias in natural language processing. *Language and Linguistics Compass*, 15(8):e12432.

Xiaolei Huang, Linzi Xing, Franck Dernoncourt, and Michael J Paul. 2020. Multilingual twitter corpus and baselines for evaluating demographic bias in hate speech recognition. *arXiv preprint arXiv:2002.10361*.

Douwe Kiela, Hamed Firooz, Aravind Mohan, Vedanuj Goswami, Amanpreet Singh, Pratik Ringshia, and Davide Testuggine. 2020. The hateful memes challenge: Detecting hate speech in multimodal memes. *Advances in Neural Information Processing Systems*, 33:2611–2624.

Rafal Kocielnik, Shrimai Prabhumoye, Vivian Zhang, R Michael Alvarez, and Anima Anandkumar. 2023. Autobiastest: Controllable sentence generation for automated and open-ended social bias testing in language models. *arXiv preprint arXiv:2302.07371*.

Ping Liu, Wen Li, and Liang Zou. 2019a. NULI at SemEval-2019 task 6: Transfer learning for offensive language detection using bidirectional transformers. In *Proceedings of the 13th International Workshop on Semantic Evaluation*, pages 87–91, Minneapolis, Minnesota, USA. Association for Computational Linguistics.

Yinhan Liu, Myle Ott, Naman Goyal, Jingfei Du, Mandar Joshi, Danqi Chen, Omer Levy, Mike Lewis, Luke Zettlemoyer, and Veselin Stoyanov. 2019b. Roberta: A robustly optimized bert pretraining approach. *arXiv preprint arXiv:1907.11692*.

Binny Mathew, Punyajoy Saha, Seid Muhie Yimam, Chris Biemann, Pawan Goyal, and Animesh Mukherjee. 2021. Hatexplain: A benchmark dataset for explainable hate speech detection. In *Proceedings of the AAAI Conference on Artificial Intelligence*, volume 35, pages 14867–14875.

Ioannis Mollas, Zoe Chrysopoulou, Stamatis Karlos, and Grigorios Tsoumakas. 2022. Ethos: a multi-label hate speech detection dataset. *Complex & Intelligent Systems*, 8(6):4663–4678.

Marzieh Mozafari, Reza Farahbakhsh, and Noel Crespi. 2020. A bert-based transfer learning approach for hate speech detection in online social media. In *Complex Networks and Their Applications VIII: Volume 1 Proceedings of the Eighth International Conference on Complex Networks and Their Applications COMPLEX NETWORKS 2019 8*, pages 928–940. Springer.

Andrew C Parnell, Víctor González-Castro, Rocío Alaiz-Rodríguez, and Gonzalo Molpeceres Barrientos. 2020. Machine learning techniques for the detection of inappropriate erotic content in text. *International Journal of Computational Intelligence Systems*, 13(1):591.

Jing Qian, Anna Bethke, Yinyin Liu, Elizabeth Belding, and William Yang Wang. 2019. A benchmark dataset for learning to intervene in online hate speech. In *Proceedings of the 2019 Conference on Empirical Methods in Natural Language Processing and the 9th International Joint Conference on Natural Language Processing (EMNLP-IJCNLP)*, pages 4755–4764, Hong Kong, China. Association for Computational Linguistics.

Jing Qian, Mai ElSherief, Elizabeth Belding, and William Yang Wang. 2018a. Hierarchical CVAE for fine-grained hate speech classification. In *Proceedings of the 2018 Conference on Empirical Methods in Natural Language Processing*, pages 3550–3559, Brussels, Belgium. Association for Computational Linguistics.

Jing Qian, Mai ElSherief, Elizabeth Belding, and William Yang Wang. 2018b. Leveraging intra-user and inter-user representation learning for automated hate speech detection. In *Proceedings of the 2018 Conference of the North American Chapter of the Association for Computational Linguistics: Human Language Technologies, Volume 2 (Short Papers)*, pages 118–123, New Orleans, Louisiana. Association for Computational Linguistics.

Rachel Rudinger, Jason Naradowsky, Brian Leonard, and Benjamin Van Durme. 2018. Gender bias in coreference resolution. In *Proceedings of the 2018 Conference of the North American Chapter of the Association for Computational Linguistics: Human Language Technologies*, New Orleans, Louisiana. Association for Computational Linguistics.

Anna Schmidt and Michael Wiegand. 2017. A survey on hate speech detection using natural language processing. In *Proceedings of the Fifth International Workshop on Natural Language Processing for Social Media*, pages 1–10, Valencia, Spain. Association for Computational Linguistics.

Hajung Sohn and Hyunju Lee. 2019. Mc-bert4hate: Hate speech detection using multi-channel bert for different languages and translations. In *2019 International Conference on Data Mining Workshops (ICDMW)*, pages 551–559. IEEE.

Rahul Tripathi, Balaji Dhamodharaswamy, Srinivasan Jagannathan, and Abhishek Nandi. 2019. Detecting sensitive content in spoken language. In *2019 IEEE International Conference on Data Science and Advanced Analytics (DSAA)*, pages 374–381. IEEE.

William Warner and Julia Hirschberg. 2012. Detecting hate speech on the world wide web. In *Proceedings of the second workshop on language in social media*, pages 19–26.

Zeerak Waseem and Dirk Hovy. 2016. Hateful symbols or hateful people? predictive features for hate speech detection on Twitter. In *Proceedings of the NAACL Student Research Workshop*, pages 88–93, San Diego, California. Association for Computational Linguistics.

Johannes Welbl, Amelia Glaese, Jonathan Uesato, Sumanth Dathathri, John Mellor, Lisa Anne Hendricks, Kirsty Anderson, Pushmeet Kohli, Ben Coppin, and Po-Sen Huang. 2021. Challenges in detoxifying language models. In *Findings of the Association for Computational Linguistics: EMNLP 2021*, pages 2447–2469, Punta Cana, Dominican Republic. Association for Computational Linguistics.

Mengzhou Xia, Anjalie Field, and Yulia Tsvetkov. 2020. Demoting racial bias in hate speech detection. In *Proceedings of the Eighth International Workshop on Natural Language Processing for Social Media*, pages 7–14, Online. Association for Computational Linguistics.

Harish Yenala, Ashish Jhanwar, Manoj K Chinnakotla, and Jay Goyal. 2018. Deep learning for detecting inappropriate content in text. *International Journal of Data Science and Analytics*, 6:273–286.

Kanwal Yousaf and Tabassam Nawaz. 2022. A deep learning-based approach for inappropriate content detection and classification of youtube videos. *IEEE Access*, 10:16283–16298.

Marcos Zampieri, Shervin Malmasi, Preslav Nakov, Sara Rosenthal, Noura Farra, and Ritesh Kumar. 2019. Predicting the type and target of offensive posts in social media. In *Proceedings of the 2019 Conference of the North American Chapter of the Association for Computational Linguistics: Human Language Technologies, Volume 1 (Long and Short Papers)*, pages 1415–1420, Minneapolis, Minnesota. Association for Computational Linguistics.

A Appendix. Guidelines for building DeTexD.

A.1 Glossary

In these guidelines, you are going to see numerous references to sensitivity in language as well as related notions. Before reading the document, please familiarize yourself with the following terms that will help you get a better understanding of the task:

- **Delicate** (adj. for a text/word/subject matter): referencing a touchy or sensitive subject. This includes texts that are emotionally charged and that cover topics that are potentially triggering, offensive, taboo, intimate, or about marginalized groups.
- **Delicate topics**: topics that are usually delicate. Examples include mental and physical health-related topics, trauma and violence, or identity-related topics. See an the list of sensitive topics in Table 6.
- **Delicate keywords**: words that semantically relate to a certain delicate topic. For example:
  - *democrat, chauvinist, islamo-leftism* are normally used in political language,
  - *able-bodied, autistic, bulimia* will typically refer to the topic of ableism or mental health.

A.2 Delicate topics

Table 6 provides the list of delicate topics and the definitions of their typical language that can be associated with the language of a certain delicate topic.

A.3 Context

This task will ask you to make two judgment steps:

Step I. Identification: decide if a text is delicate or non-delicate using the following definitions:

- A **delicate** sentence contains emotionally-charged references to a sensitive topic.
- A **non-delicate** is fully innocuous and doesn't contain any particularly charged references to a sensitive topic.

Step II. Riskiness estimation: rate how **delicate** texts are using a 5-point scale where 1 stands for "very low risk" and 5 for "very high risk". How delicate a sentence is must be evaluated with regard to its sentiment rather than the lexical meanings of separate keywords. In other words, the more emotional and personal the tone, the more delicate the sentence. The following questions can help you make a decision:

(a) Is the content of the sentence emotionally charged rather than factual?

(b) Can the content of the sentence evoke negative feelings?

(c) Does the content of the sentence pertain to a sensitive topic and show bias against particular groups of people?

If the answer to any of these questions is positive, the sentence will fall on the high end of the riskiness scale. Find a detailed interpretation of the riskiness scale in the next section.

See the examples of annotated texts in Table 8.

A.4 Riskiness estimation

Table 9 provides a description of riskinesses that are likely to fall on certain parts of the rating scale, examples of delicate texts, and explanations.

A.5 Paragraph-level judgments

The paragraphs are annotated holistically. This means that the assigned score is not based on just the individual sentences within a paragraph, but rather the score is reflective of the overall meaning of the paragraph. However, the score can be affected by the number of:

- delicate sentences within a paragraph;
- explicit delicate sentences within a paragraph;
- emotional and personal sentences within a paragraph;
- paragraphs that have a higher number of delicate sentences, higher level of explicitness, and have more emotional and personal weights should get a higher score. A comparative analysis of some examples is presented in the Table 10.

Delicate topic	Description	Examples of related delicate keywords
Addictions	Language associated with addictive behavior.	alcohol, gambling, toxicomania
Age	Language associated with biological age, age identity, and age discrimination.	elderly, elderspeak
Appearance	Language that has to do with physical appearance and prejudice based on physical appearance.	unibrow, humpback
Body parts and bodily functions	Language used to talk about sensitive body parts and bodily functions.	breast, wiener
Class, social status, legal status, occupation	Language used to talk about people in the context of their economic, legal, and cultural factors.	yuppie, unserved, refugee
Crime and violence	Language describing violence, crime, and people who are engaged in it.	murder, arsonist, genocide.
Family and parenting	Language associated with marital status, parental status, adoption.	co-parenting, surrogacy
Gender and sexual identity	Language associated with the lgbtqai+ community or sexual orientation.	heterosexual, agenderfluid, cross-dresser
Medicine and medication	Language associated with diseases, illnesses, and medication.	venereal, abortion, chancre
Mental health and disability	Language used to talk about people and issues related to disability and mental health.	able-bodied, autist, bulimia
Paraphilias	Language related to perversions.	asphyxiophile, frotteurism
Politics	Language associated with political ideas and movements as well as their representatives, advocates, and opponents.	democrat, chauvinist, islamo-leftism
Race, ethnicity, and origin	Language that has to do with racial and ethnic identity.	white, brown
Religion	Language associated with religious ideas and movements as well as their representatives, advocates, and opponents.	bible, burqa, mosque
Sex	Language describing sex-related activities and their participants, sex toys.	cowgirling, penetrate, dildo
Stigmatized and abused drugs	Language used to talk about stigmatized or abused medications.	viagra, clonazepam, barbiturate
Trauma and abuse	Language referencing physical as well as psychological trauma and abuse.	victim, bullying, gaslighting

Table 6: List of delicate topics with descriptions and delicate keywords.

Delicate topics	Count
Hate speech, race, religion, sexual orientation, nationality	45
Mental health, physical and mental issues, disability	166
Socioeconomic status, political affiliation, fake news, misinformation	17
Self-harm	17
Sexual content, pornographic and erotica	81
Crime and violence, threat and incitement to violence	36
Other	30

Table 7: Distribution of delicate topics.

Text	Identification label (step I)	Riskiness label (step II)	Explanation
Both women suspect that Lars has his wife's gold wedding band in the handbag.	non-delicate	non-delicate (0)	No references to delicate topics.
Huh I guess that explains why Zelina's cat is always on Black's cats' Instagram page.	non-delicate	non-delicate (0)	No references to delicate topics.
Ongoing research projects are focused on quantitative methods for evaluating animal systems (production, reproduction, mammary health; the value of milk urea nitrogen (MUN) as a nutrition management tool; feed cost optimization and nutritional economics; and production risks and risk management for dairy farms.	non-delicate	non-delicate (0)	No references to delicate topics
If someone rejects one and believes the other, they are not following science, they are following their personal ideologies.	non-delicate	non-delicate (0)	No references to delicate topics.
On the other hand, some women would question me about how much I enjoyed it and if I were ambitious in it.	non-delicate	non-delicate (0)	No references to delicate topics.
Everyone seems to have an agenda or view point, so it's rarely true science.	non-delicate	non-delicate (0)	No references to delicate topics.
I'd say, "Oh, that seems incorrect to me."	non-delicate	non-delicate (0)	No references to delicate topics.
I know things I've seen talked about in the past are, moving during his ult, or crippling people in his ult.	non-delicate	non-delicate (0)	The sentence includes "crippling" but is low risk.
There is a good expression, "kill with eyes," and I don't mind being killed with their eyes — with their blue, and ever blue eyes.	non-delicate	non-delicate (0)	Just a metaphorical expression.
I wonder if they're stream snipers.	non-delicate	non-delicate (0)	Obvious references to video games.
There isn't a cure for loss.	delicate	very low risk (1)	The sentence contains a subtle reference to a delicate topic, but it's rather an impersonal piece of wisdom.
I found out later they didn't throw it away but packed it up as punishment.	delicate	very low risk (1)	The word "punishment" refers to violence, but the sentence can be subject to multiple interpretations.
Why, am I under arrest?	delicate	very low risk (1)	The sentence may refer to a delicate topic, but 1) the sentence may be interpreted in a number of ways; 2) interrogatory sentences seem to be less risky than statements.
Not really it is the way humans dispose of plastic that is bad although I will say the materials used to make it suck but we use them anyway right now for other things.	delicate	very low risk (1)	The topic of ecology is relatively delicate, and the word "suck" makes the sentence slightly charged. However, the sentence doesn't seem to be particularly risky.
As for OP's question, I think you should come out.	delicate	low risk (2)	The sentence is subject to multiple interpretations.
But they're not outright shit.	delicate	low risk (2)	The sentence is a low-key insult that could apply to anyone. Negation lowers the delicateness.
I am a heterosexual female, married to a heterosexual male.	delicate	low risk (2)	The sentence introduces some facts connected with the author's sexuality that is unlikely to be associated with a stigma.
Women are particularly susceptible to developing depression and anxiety disorders in response to stress compared to men.	delicate	delicate (3)	The sentence is referencing mental health, but the tone is impersonal and academic.
Mumbai, October 17: Rahul Mahajan, the son of former BJP general secretary Pramod Mahajan would sit on a dharna and address a meeting to support the death sentence awarded to Parliament mastermind Mohammed Afzal Guru.	delicate	medium (3)	The sentence covers several delicate topics and refers to a particular person, but it should be counted as moderately risky since it's a news report.
Most importantly, powerless communist labor will always be cheaper than democratic labor because voting and civic education are expensive.	delicate	medium (3)	The sentence is dry and talks about things in the abstract.
The supported employees ranged in age from early twenties to late forties, none were from ethnic minorities and only four of them were women, reflecting the demographics of supported employees in the area.	delicate	medium (3)	The sentence is quite neutral. The density of sensitive references makes the sentence potentially problematic, but given that the sentence is impersonal and not emotional, it doesn't deserve a (4) or (5).
I used to live in that district next to the bank and right across from where that guy got shot last year.	delicate	high risk (4)	The sentence introduces a tragic event.
So people who disapprove of prenatal testing, abortion or reproductive technologies should be under no obligation to undergo any such treatments themselves.	delicate	high risk (4)	The sentence is likely to be presenting the author's attitude towards a delicate topic.
I started to get a little freaked out, thinking maybe a stranger was in the house, but all of a sudden my sister yelled 'Elf', her service dog's name and said there was blood on his tail.	delicate	high risk (4)	Personal experience associated with fear and possibly violence.
I get the euphoria side effects of codeine so I tend to drown myself in that and Xanax on days I know I'll be spending in bed.	delicate	very high risk (5)	The sentence is very personal and emotional. The reference to a delicate topic is undeniable.
This dbag also banged a lot of females that he worked with.	delicate	very high risk (5)	The sentence contains offensive words and introduces face-threatening facts about certain people (even though their names are not disclosed).
wait what happened to your sisters mental health exactly and at what age?	delicate	very high risk (5)	The sentence is mentioning a concrete delicate story associated with close people.
OP, I know it's different dating someone with PTSD especially if you never have or if you don't have it yourself.	delicate	very high risk (5)	A subjective statement about a delicate topic.
There, Elster had plans to do away with his wife under circumstances that falsely implied that she had committed suicide.	delicate	very high risk (5)	Explicit crime-related content.
Difficult to consume enough to get high because of the nausea the drug produces.	delicate	very high risk (5)	The sentence is clearly referencing a delicate topic.

Table 8: Examples of texts which passed two annotation steps: identification (step I) and riskiness estimation (step II). In step I, the annotators were shown a text and were asked first to label the text as "non-delicate" or "delicate." In step II, if the annotators labeled a text as "delicate" in step I, they were asked to estimate the riskiness of the delicate text using a 5-point scale where (1) stands for "very low risk" and (5) for "very high risk."

Delicate text	Riskiness label (step II)	Motivation of riskiness label	Explanation
This is **fucking** amazing!	1	The sentence contains a sensitive keyword, but it doesn't engage with any delicate topics.	The f-word is used as an intensifier of the positive meaning.
God never received a PhD because he had only one major publication. If **Jesus** had had a car, it would have been a Christler.	1	God or Jesus are sensitive keywords that belong to the topic of religion. However, the content of the sentences is inoffensive and does not perpetuate stereotypes. The sentiment is well-meaning and kindly humorous.	The sentence refers to a delicate topic but the sentiment is humorous, and it does not perpetuate stereotypes.
I am a heterosexual female, married to a heterosexual male.	2	The sentence introduces some facts connected with the author's sexuality that is unlikely to be associated with a stigma.	The sentence contains sensitive keywords, but the sentence is not emotionally charged.
Assuming you use lube and don't try to force one that won't slide in.	2	The sentence doesn't allude to the topic of sex, but it may also have other non-sensitive interpretations.	The sentence may or may not relate to a delicate topic since it is subject to multiple interpretations.
30% of the people living in that country have depression. Vaginal cancer accounts for approximately three percent of cancers of the female reproductive system. These summits provide communities with opportunities for strategic planning and collaboration building to combat methamphetamine problems faced in their own communities.	3	Even though the sentences touch upon delicate topics, they present plain facts in an unemotional matter-of-fact way.	The sentences contain references to delicate topics, but its tone is neutral, academic, medical, or legal. It does not perpetuate stereotypes or bias.
Funny how the **conservatives** crying for cutting spending suddenly backtrack when it comes to pet projects they like, right? It was a blast watching my parents and all their friends lose their retirement savings under **Bush** and my cousin go off to war and come back having no clue what they accomplished.	4	The sentences contain notes of sarcasm and ridicule targeted at certain political representatives.	The sentence contains notes of negative sentiment or sarcasm targeted at certain political party.
I've been working on recovery for about 5 years for complex PTSD and was doing ok, but then 'bam' I was in severe physical pain, which amplified all of the emotional pain... I've been there every stage of my handsome man's transition and only get more and more attracted. Afterwards, I was transferred to an orphanage in Temuco called Hogar Mamá Augusta.	5	The examples denote the author's personal sensitive experience.	The sentence contains references to delicate topics, and the author is emotionally involved in it.
Ernest is having urges to use opioids and said you are supporting him with the issue. Years later my friend told me he had survivor's guilt and asked himself why he survived.	5	The sentences tell the story of certain people's sensitive experience.	The sentence narrates a tragic or emotionally charged story of a certain individual or a group of people (e.g., suicide note, doctor's notes, descriptions of abuse, etc.).
MDMA and LSD is an amazing drug combo and it will not do you any damage. Also, get the hell off Atripla, it causes psych issues and is no longer a tier 1 recommended medication.	5	Both sentences are about the author's personal perspective as they explicate strong opinions on delicate matters and offer advice.	The sentence expresses the author's strong stance on a delicate topic.
Fuck you! I will come after you and kill you.	5	The sentence contains a threat.	The sentence contains threats.

Table 9: Examples of delicate texts with explanations for various riskinesses. Note that this list is not exhaustive. If you encounter a text that doesn't match any of the descriptions, make the decision using the questions provided in Section A.3.

Text	Score	Explanation
I just hate talking about my mental issues with people; this makes me feel very uncomfortable. I sometimes think that if I share them with anyone, they will judge me, and I just want to not exist in a situation where people judge me.	5	Delicate sentences within a paragraph. All of the sentences in this paragraph are highly delicate and contain extreme emotional and personal content.
I hate talking about my mental issues with people. However, I am aware of the fact that mental issues are like other issues that need to be addressed and adequately taken care of. People must understand the significance of any mental illness and be able to react appropriately to these issues.	3	Delicate sentences within a paragraph. This paragraph contains one delicate sentence that expresses personal emotion, while the remaining sentences have delicate topics that are more factual.
I f***king hate you and people like you, you ugly piece of s**t. I f***king want to shoot you in the head!	5	Explicit delicate sentences within a paragraph. This is a highly delicate paragraph as it contains threats.
I don't feel comfortable around you and I prefer to not hang out with you. You have a very negative energy.	2	Explicit delicate sentences within a paragraph. This sentence does not have any explicit references to a delicate topic; however, it contains personal/emotional content.
The pain and suffering are so much, and I can barely endure it. I feel that I am being suffocated, and I don't want to live anymore.	5	Emotional and personal sentences within a paragraph. This paragraph is highly delicate with extreme emotional and personal content.
Some trauma can have long-lasting effects; the pain and suffering can become unbearable to the point that the patient might feel suicidal.	3	Emotional and personal sentences within a paragraph. This is an example of a paragraph that contains a very delicate topic; however, the topic is presented through factual statements.

Table 10: Paragraph-level annotations.

Question	Answer
Do definite referents make delicate sentences more sensitive than indefinite ones? E.g., *But they're not outright shit.* vs *But [some particular group] are not outright shit.*	Introducing a definite referent can increase the sensitivity of the sentence. However, it's unlikely to turn a non-delicate sentence into a delicate one. E.g., both *No doubt "nobody" would take the job if he was offered a decent pay* and *No doubt 'Tom the Nobody' would take the job if he was offered a decent pay* are non-delicate.
How should we treat mild second-person insults? E.g. *"You loon!", "Your breath doesn't smell great."*	Delicate but low-sensitivity.
What kind of sentences should we consider to be incomprehensible and discard?	By incomprehensible, we mean anything that doesn't make sense at all. E.g.,*no iea why it wentjlout., USFreighways jodohku.* Fragments like *both manipulative assholes lol* should be judged.
How delicate are news reports? E.g., *Mumbai, October 17: Rahul Mahajan, the son of former BJP general secretary Pramod Mahajan would sit on a dharna and address a meeting to support the death sentence awarded to Parliament attack mastermind Mohammed Afzal Guru.*	We assume that news reports are as delicate as academic/legal/etc. texts.
How does the density of delicate references impact the sensitivity level?	Sentences referencing multiple topics are likely to be more delicate than those referencing only one.
Sentences may be targeted at various addresses. How does that correlate with delicateness?	Pragmatic proximity and definiteness of an addressee escalate the sentence sensitivity. E.g., *I hate you.* would be more problematic than *I hate anyone who does things like that.*
Are sentences containing words like "father," "mom," "etc." is delicate since they refer to the domain of family and parenting?	It's contingent on the context: I went to the theater with *my mon yesterday* is non-delicate. *I'd like to find my biological dad* and *I'm his biological dad. are definitely delicate.*
Are sentences mentioning names associated with historical/religious figures delicate? E.g. *Good morning, Adolph.*	No. "Adolph" can be anyone else's name. However, references to concrete figures (Trump, Obama, Hilary(clearly used in a political context)) make the sentence delicate.
Are passages from religious texts delicate? Are these in-line with academic texts/news articles? E.g., *The Jews did not believe that he had been blind and had received his sight, until they called the parents of the man who had received his sight [21] But how he now sees we do not know, nor do we know who opened his eyes.*	They are delicate, but borderline ("very low risk (1)"). These are in line with academic/legal texts.
Are sentences referencing violence in video games delicate?	Please mark such sentences as non-delicate as long as you find explicit references to video games. *In other words, I've died 3 back to back games on 4 kills.* would be non-delicate as its connection with video games is quite obvious. Other cases (e.g., *I killed him with a sword*) would be delicate.

Table 11: Frequently asked questions about delicate text annotation.

Towards Safer Communities: Detecting Aggression and Offensive Language in Code-Mixed Tweets to Combat Cyberbullying

Nazia Nafis[1], **Diptesh Kanojia**[1,2], **Naveen Saini**[1], **Rudra Murthy**[1]
[1]Indian Institute of Information Technology Lucknow, India.
[2]Surrey Institute for People-Centred AI, University of Surrey, United Kingdom.
[1]{mcs21004, naveen, rudra}@iiitl.ac.in
[2]d.kanojia@surrey.ac.uk

Abstract

Cyberbullying is a serious societal issue widespread on various channels and platforms, particularly social networking sites. Such platforms have proven to be exceptionally fertile grounds for such behavior. The dearth of high-quality training data for multilingual and low-resource scenarios, data that can accurately capture the nuances of social media conversations, often poses a roadblock to this task. This paper attempts to tackle cyberbullying, specifically its two most common manifestations - *aggression* and *offensiveness*. We present a novel, manually annotated dataset of a total of 10,000 English and Hindi-English code-mixed tweets, manually annotated for aggression detection and offensive language detection tasks[1]. Our annotations are supported by inter-annotator agreement scores of 0.67 and 0.74 for the two tasks, indicating substantial agreement. We perform comprehensive fine-tuning of pre-trained language models (PTLMs) using this dataset to check its efficacy. Our challenging test sets show that the best models achieve macro F1-scores of 67.87 and 65.45 on the two tasks, respectively. Further, we perform cross-dataset transfer learning to benchmark our dataset against existing aggression and offensive language datasets. We also present a detailed quantitative and qualitative analysis of errors in prediction, and with this paper, we publicly release the novel dataset, code, and models.

OAG	You wont march against kids being raped in country or the endless stream of migrants maybe cheaper energy no but you would march against @username pathetic fking pathetic!
CAG	Wait a few days sir, you are getting used to hearing harsh words. In future, when all the banks will be of Adani or Ambani, then you will also have to listen to abuses for withdrawing your deposits. #demonetisation
NAG	Well this is pure goosebumps, whenever I see him I feel so proud that he is our PM, a living legend for sure

Table 1: Examples of overtly aggressive (**OAG**), covertly aggressive (**CAG**), and non-aggressive (**NAG**) tweets from our dataset.

1 Introduction

Social media is a group of Internet-based applications that allows the creation and exchange of user-generated content. Lately, it has risen as one of the most popular ways in which people share opinions with each other (Pelicon et al., 2019). With rapid advances in Web 3.0, social media is expected to evolve and emerge as an even more vital and potent means of communication. Simultaneously, there has also been noticed a sharp uptick in bullying behavior - including but not limited to the use of snide remarks, abusive words, and personal attacks, going as far as rape threats (Hardaker and McGlashan, 2016) on such platforms. In this context, by leveraging the technological advancements in machine learning and natural language processing, automatic detection of instances of cyberbullying on social media platforms such as Twitter can help create a safer environment. Here we investigate two forms of cyberbullying - aggression and offensiveness.

Aggression has been defined as any behavior enacted with the intention of harming another person who is motivated to avoid that harm (Anderson et al., 2002; Bushman and Huesmann, 2014). Several studies have noted the proliferation of abusive language and an increase in aggressive content on social media (Mantilla, 2013; Suzor et al., 2019)

[1]https://github.com/surrey-nlp/woah-aggression-detection/blob/main/data/New10kData/cyberbullying_10k.csv

The 7th Workshop on Online Abuse and Harms (WOAH), pages 29–41
July 13, 2023 ©2023 Association for Computational Linguistics

OFF	Bhikaris like u, can u first afford watching movie in threatres? Talk about that first. Just coz internet is cheap does not mean u will do open defecation in social media. MDRCHD bhaag BSDK
NOT	Who doesn't enjoy the daily press briefings? They really ease the tension! We have to find some way to keep ourselves entertained

Table 2: Examples of offensive (**OFF**) and non-offensive (**NOT**) tweets from our dataset.

On the other hand, offensiveness has been described as any word or string of words which has or can have a negative impact on the sense of self or well-being of those who encounter it (Molek-Kozakowska, 2022) – that is, it makes or can make them feel mildly or extremely discomfited, insulted, hurt or frightened.

Motivation The dearth of manually-annotated datasets for the tasks of aggression detection and offensive language detection, especially in the Hindi-English code-mixed setting, necessitated us to work in this area.

This paper investigates the tasks of aggression detection and offensive language detection on Twitter data. We curate politically-themed tweets and perform manual annotation to create a dataset for the tasks. Our annotation schema is in line with the existing aggressive and offensive language detection datasets. With the help of pre-trained language models, we fine-tune pre-trained language models for both tasks and discuss the obtained results regarding precision, recall, and macro F1-scores. The **key contributions** of this work are:

- Introduction of a novel, manually-annotated dataset containing English and Hindi-English code-mixed tweets to model aggression and offensiveness in text.
- Validation of our dataset's efficacy for aggressive and offensive language detection tasks within two subsets of this data, *viz.*, English and Hindi-English code-mixed.
- Cross-validation of dataset efficacy with the help of zero-shot transfer learning-based experiments on existing datasets.
- Quantitative and qualitative analysis of erroneous predictions.

2 Related Work

Our work deals with two different but correlated classification tasks. In the available literature, both have been investigated with the help of various machine learning and deep learning-based methods. Below, we provide a detailed overview of the literature from both tasks in separate subsections.

2.1 Aggression Detection

We model aggression detection as a multi-class classification task where our schema is defined as proposed in the TRAC dataset (Kumar et al., 2018a). However, the earliest approaches used decision trees (Spertus, 1997a) to detect aggression with the help of manual rules. These rules were based on syntactic and semantic features. Later, the focus shifted to feature engineering from text which included features like Bag-of-Words (BOW) (Kwok and Wang, 2013; Liu et al., 2019a), N-grams at the word level (Pérez and Luque, 2019; Liu and Forss, 2014; Watanabe et al., 2018), N-grams at the character level (Gambäck and Sikdar, 2017; Pérez and Luque, 2019), typed dependencies (Burnap and Williams, 2016b), part-of-speech tags (Davidson et al., 2017b), dictionary-based approaches (Molek-Kozakowska, 2022) and lexicons (Burnap and Williams, 2016b; Alorainy et al., 2019).

Word embedding-based approaches for automated extraction of these features from text further improved the detection of aggressive text (Nobata et al., 2016; Zhang et al., 2018; Badjatiya et al., 2017; Kshirsagar et al., 2018; Orăsan, 2018; Pratiwi et al., 2019; Galery et al., 2018). Various deep learning-based architectures proposed in the literature use word embeddings to encode features in the text (Nina-Alcocer, 2019; Ribeiro and Silva, 2019). Authors have proposed the use of Convolutional Neural Networks (Gambäck and Sikdar, 2017; Roy et al., 2018; Huang et al., 2018), Long-Short Term Memory (LSTM) (Badjatiya et al., 2017; Pitsilis et al., 2018; Nikhil et al., 2018), Gated Recurrent Unit (GRU) (Zhang et al., 2018; Galery et al., 2018), or a combination of different Deep Neural Network architectures in an ensemble setting (Madisetty and Sankar Desarkar, 2018).

However, state-of-the-art performance (Bojkovský and Pikuliak, 2019; Ramiandrisoa and

Mothe, 2020; Mozafari et al., 2019) was achieved with the help of pre-trained language models (PTLMs) with encoders like ELMo (Peters et al., 2018) and BERT (Devlin et al., 2019). Further, we also observe the use of these contextual embeddings in SemEval-2019 Task 6 (Zampieri et al., 2019b) for English tweets, and TRAC (Kumar et al., 2018b) for Hindi and English tweets and Facebook comments; further motivating us to explore the use of multiple pre-trained language models to validate the efficacy of our dataset.

2.2 Offensive Language Identification

We model the offensive language identification task as a binary classification problem. Waseem et al. (2017) proposed a typology for abusive language and synthesize the typology with two-fold siders containing whether the abuse is 'generalized' or 'directed' *vs.* when it is 'explicit' or 'implicit'. They discuss the distinction between explicit and implicit in the context of 'denotation' *vs.* 'connotation' as discussed by (Barthes, 1957). A detailed review of hate speech detection (Schmidt and Wiegand, 2017) task has surveyed various approaches deployed in the past. Spertus (1997b) propose a rule-based framework for identifying hostile messages where they use manually constructed rules to identify profanity, condescension, insults and so on. Razavi et al. (2010) utilize a flame annotated corpus which contains a lexicon of hostile and abusive words to detect offensive language in personal and commercial communication. Dictionaries (Liu and Forss, 2015) and bag-of-words (Burnap and Williams, 2016a) have also been proposed as lexical features to detect offensive language.

The use of machine learning algorithms to detect offensive language has been prevalent in the research community (Davidson et al., 2017a; Waseem and Hovy, 2016). Further, the use of word embeddings learned with the help of word2vec or FastText approaches combined with machine/deep learning improved the performance of offensive language identification by a significant margin (Rakib and Soon, 2018; Herwanto et al., 2019; Badri et al., 2022). However, as we point out in the previous subsection, state-of-the-art performance has been achieved with the help of PTLMs.

Pitenis et al. (2020) perform the task specifically for the low-resource Greek language. Similarly, Ranasinghe and Zampieri (2020) show that the use of cross-lingual embeddings for inter-task and inter-language scenarios is beneficial. The authors first train a multilingual PTLM (XLM-R) on the English data, and then further continue the training using saved weights and *softmax* layer, for other languages *viz.* Hindi, Bengali, and Spanish.

Further, there have been a lot of efforts to create datasets for the detection of offensive language and hate speech[2] on social media. Çöltekin (2020) presents a dataset for the Turkish language with a specified target for offense. Díaz-Torres et al. (2020) build the same for Mexican Spanish. A clear majority of studies deal with the English language. *While other Indian language datasets have been proposed, there is a clear dearth of English-Hindi datasets which also address code-mixing*, in the available literature (Chakravarthi et al., 2021, 2022) except a few (Mathur et al., 2018; Saroj and Pal, 2020).

3 Dataset Creation

We create a dataset containing a mix of English and Hindi-English sentences, to ensure that sufficient data is available for our research. We used the official Twitter API to obtain data from Twitter. Initially, we collected 15,000 tweets based on the search results for one of the 52 keywords (listed in Table 10 in Appendix) in our list pertaining to recent political events and popular political personalities.

We filtered out tweets that were in any language other than English or Hindi (or containing a mix of both) using XLM Roberta-base with a classification head on top (Conneau et al., 2020). Next, with the help of HingBERT-LID code-mixed language identification model (Nayak and Joshi, 2022), we created subsets of tweets belonging to one of the two aforementioned categories.

We preprocessed the tweets by masking all usernames to minimize the introduction of bias to the annotators. Finally, after cleaning, we were left with 5,452 English monolingual and 4,548 Hindi-English code-mixed tweets.

3.1 Annotation Setup

The following **guidelines** were supplied to the annotators, which outline the definition and provide a few sample tweets for each Aggression and Offensive Language label.

Task I: Aggression Detection

[2]hatespeechdata.com - a catalog of hate speech datasets

Aggression focuses on the user's intention to be aggressive and harmful, or to incite, in various forms, violent acts against a target. The aggression level in the text is categorized into three classes:

- **Overtly Aggressive (OAG):** This type of aggression shows a direct verbal attack pointing to a particular individual or group.

  For example, in the sample tweet for OAG in Table 1, the person expresses frustration over issues such as child sexual abuse, immigration, and high gas prices while also condemning the apathy of others towards these issues. The aggression here is overt, as also seen by the use of words *"fking"* and *"pathetic"* in the tweet.

- **Covertly Aggressive (CAG):** In this type of aggression, the attack is not direct but hidden, subtle, and more indirect while being stated politely in most cases.

  For example, in the sample tweet for CAG in Table 1, the person harbors angst against the process of demonetization of the Indian currency and privatization of banks, but chooses to display it covertly while conversing over Twitter.

- **Not Aggressive (NAG):** Generally, these types of text lack any kind of aggression. It is used to state facts, express greetings and good wishes occasionally, and show agreeableness and support.

  For example, in the sample tweet for NAG in Table 1, the person does not display any aggression at all - on the contrary, they praise the PM by calling them a *"living legend"*.

Task II: Offensive Language Detection

Offensiveness focuses on the potentially hurtful effect of the tweet content on a given target. Text can be identified as belonging to either of the two offensiveness classes:

- **Offensive (OFF)** This category of text often contains offensive words such as sarcastic remarks, insults, slanders, and slurs.

  For example, in the sample tweet for OFF in Table 2, the person uses words such as *"bhikaris"* ("beggars") for others, while also availing outright derogatory Hindi slang to address them.

	Aggression			Offensiveness	
	OAG	**CAG**	**NAG**	**OFF**	**NOT**
Monolingual	1134	1715	2599	1323	4125
Code-mixed	1150	1322	2080	1749	2803
Combined	2284	3037	4679	3072	6928

Table 3: Aggression and Offensive language statistics of our dataset.

- **Not Offensive (NOT)** In this category, there is either a thorough use of positive and uplifting language, such as salutations or homage, or a neutral tone.

  For example, in the sample tweet for NOT in Table 2, the person makes a remark about how everybody enjoys the daily press briefings, and how they ease tension and keep everybody entertained. There is no offensive tone in this instance.

Setup Our team of annotators consisted of two undergraduate students fluent in both Hindi (native) and English as their second language. The selection of annotators was objective and unbiased. The aforementioned guidelines were made available to them, to refer to while deciding upon the labels for the tweets. This was done to ensure that their political beliefs/loyalties do not play a role in the annotation process. We also recorded their highest level of education and medium of schooling to ensure that the annotations would be of the desired quality, and we informed them about the collection of this data.

All usernames in the data were masked, so at any given point, only the tweet content was visible to the annotators whereas the target personality/organization was hidden from their purview. To ensure the confidentiality of data and to check biases, any metadata too, such as the tweet senders' demographic identity, was not made available to the annotators.

Moreover, since the tweets often contained aggressive and highly abusive language, the annotators were also given a choice to quit whenever they felt uncomfortable with the task.

3.2 Inter Annotator Agreement

While labeling, each annotator had to decide independently which category the comment belonged to, with the help of a set of guidelines. It can be inferred that all the annotators clearly understood the guidelines for annotation, as in most cases, they arrived at the same annotation freely. To quantify how good the annotation decisions were, we calculated **Cohen's Kappa** score to measure the inter-annotator agreement. It may be noted that a high score on this statistical metric does not mean the annotations are accurate. It only shows the homogeneity of agreement among the annotators about the chosen label.

We obtained an agreement score of 0.67 for Task I, and a score of 0.74 for Task II, both of which indicate *"substantial agreement"* (p >0.05). In case of disagreement on any instance, we obtained a label on such instances with the help of a third annotator.

3.3 Dataset Statistics

Table 3 shows the exploratory statistics on our dataset for aggression and offensiveness, respectively. We have a total of $10,000$ data instances in the form of tweets. Out of this, $2,284$ are overtly aggressive (OAG), $3,073$ are covertly aggressive (CAG), and $4,679$ are not aggressive (NAG). Similarly, there are $3,072$ offensive (OFF) and $6,928$ not offensive (NOT) instances in the dataset.

Additionally, the monolingual vs. code-mixed statistics are also mentioned for each class in both tables. We have $1,134$ monolingual and $1,150$ code mixed tweets in the OAG category, $1,715$ monolingual and $1,322$ code mixed tweets in the CAG category, and $2,599$ monolingual and $2,080$ code mixed tweets in the NAG category. Similarly, there are $1,323$ monolingual and $1,749$ code mixed tweets in the OFF category and $4,125$ monolingual and $2,803$ code mixed tweets in NOT.

4 Approach

In recent times, sequence classification via fine-tuning of pre-trained language models has become a standard approach for performing various NLP tasks. We take a similar approach and fine-tune some pre-trained language models for the two tasks, and report the results in the next section. We work with two general-purpose English models, one multilingual model, one model trained specifically on Hindi-English code-mixed data, and one trained exclusively on Twitter data.

Every tweet containing a sequence of words is tokenized into a sequence of sub-words using the model-specific tokenizer. This sequence of sub-word tokens is the input to the model that passes through the Transformer's encoder layers. An encoder representation for each token in the sequence is the output from the transformer. We take the encoder representation of the [CLS] token in the case of BERT or the last encoder hidden states for other models. The output layer is a linear layer followed by the softmax function, which takes in the above representation. The model is trained by optimizing for a custom weighted cross-entropy loss value which we explain in detail in an upcoming subsection.

Experimental Setup We fine-tune for the aforementioned two tasks the following pre-trained language models: BERT (Devlin et al., 2019) and RoBERTa (Liu et al., 2019b) which are trained on English data, XLM-R (Conneau et al., 2020) base which is trained over multilingual data containing both Hindi and English, HingRoBERTa (Nayak and Joshi, 2022), a multilingual language model specifically built for Hindi-English code-mixed language as seen in the Indian context, and Bernice (DeLucia et al., 2022), a multilingual language model trained exclusively on Twitter data.

Data Split and Evaluation Criteria We report macro F1-scores on our complete dataset, as well as on its code-mixed and non-code-mixed subsets individually. For the train/validation/test splits, we choose uniform 80% / 10% / 10% from each dataset to perform the experiments.

Experiment Settings We perform experiments using the Huggingface Transformers library (Wolf et al., 2020). We monitor the validation set's macro F1-scores to find the best hyperparameter values, using the following range of values for selecting the best hyperparameter:

- **Batch Size**: 8, 16, 32
- **Learning Rate**: 1e-5, 1e-6, 3e-5, 3e-6, 5e-5, 5e-6

We repeat each training five times with different random seeds and report the mean macro F1-scores along with their standard deviation. Our experiments were performed using 2 x Nvidia RTX A5000 and a single training run usually takes approximately 1 hour on the dataset. For the subsets, however, the runtime is approximately 30 minutes. The models generated during our experiments see the number of trainable parameters varying from 100M to 200M depending upon the language model used.

	Aggression Detection			Offensive Language Detection		
PTLM	**Monolingual**	**Code mixed**	**Combined**	**Monolingual**	**Code mixed**	**Combined**
BERT$_{base}$	63.58±0.51	65.22±0.77	64.98±0.28	60.99±0.43	61.94±0.14	62.05±0.25
RoBERTa$_{base}$	**66.63±0.12**	65.42±0.61	62.13±0.89	**63.46±0.75**	62.06±0.48	60.21±0.30
XLM-R$_{base}$	65.49±0.73	66.85±0.22	**67.87±0.05**	61.24±0.31	64.42±0.02	65.41±0.73
HingRoBERTa	64.01±0.53	**66.94±0.53**	66.47±0.53	61.92±0.26	**64.97±0.13**	**65.45±0.21**
Bernice	63.49±0.15	61.13±0.43	62.75±0.82	60.88±0.57	59.01±0.38	60.58±0.16

Table 4: Mean macro F1-scores obtained from pre-trained language models on our dataset and its two subsets - English monolingual and Hindi-English code-mixed. The values in **bold** highlight the best-performing language model on each dataset.

	Aggression Detection		Offensive Language	
	D1->D2	**D2->D1**	**D1->D2**	**D2->D1**
BERT$_{base}$	55.63±0.21	52.98±0.56	48.69±0.11	46.49±0.53
RoBERTa$_{base}$	52.13±0.74	50.99±0.47	46.02±0.31	43.64±0.49
XLM-R$_{base}$	**56.81±0.84**	55.33±0.60	50.94±0.55	49.27±0.75
HingRoBERTa	56.29±0.71	54.04±0.10	**51.51±0.28**	49.01±0.24
Bernice	52.05±0.87	49.65±0.57	46.16±0.18	45.88±0.05

Table 5: Cross-dataset Test Set F1-Scores from various language models. **D1** represents our dataset. For Aggression detection, **D2** is the TRAC dataset, whereas for Offensive language detection, **D2** is the OLID dataset.

Custom Weighted Loss As our dataset exhibits class imbalance, we use weighted cross-entropy loss (Lee and Liu, 2003) in all our experiments. We assign a weight to the loss of every instance depending on the class label. Then, we find the percentage of examples by class belonging to each class from the train split and take the inverse of the probability values as the weight for the particular class. In this way, we give more importance to the instances belonging to the minority class.

5 Results

We report the results obtained via fine-tuning pre-trained language models in this section. Table 4 reports the test set macro F1-scores from pre-trained language models for the two tasks of aggression detection and offensive language detection on our dataset. In addition to this, we also present the scores on English monolingual and Hindi-English code-mixed subsets of our dataset.

For aggression, we observe that XLM-R$_{base}$ outperforms other pre-trained language models on our overall dataset, achieving the highest macro F1-score of 67.87. On the English subset, we observe that RoBERTa$_{base}$ performs better than other models with a macro F1-score of 66.63, whereas for the Hindi-English code-mixed subset, Hing-RoBERTa gives the best macro F1-score of 66.94.

For offensive language detection, we observe that Hing-RoBERTa outperforms other pre-trained language models on our overall dataset, achieving the highest macro F1-score of 65.45. On the English subset, we observe that RoBERTa$_{base}$ outperforms other models with a macro F1-score of 63.46. For the Hindi-English code-mixed subset, Hing-RoBERTa once again gives the best performance with a macro F1-score of 64.97.

Cross-dataset Transfer Learning We perform transfer learning experiments to benchmark our dataset against some existing datasets for the same tasks. Results from our transfer learning setup are presented in Table 5.

For the task of aggression detection, we benchmark our dataset against a curated subset of the TRAC (Trolling, Aggression, and Cyberbullying) dataset (Bhattacharya et al., 2020). This subset, (discussed in Table 8 in section 9), contains instances in Hindi (Roman script) and English, and is annotated for aggression (OAG: overtly aggressive, CAG: covertly aggressive, NAG: not aggressive). For the task of Offensive language detection, we use OLID (Offensive Language Identification Dataset) (Zampieri et al., 2019a) to benchmark our dataset. OLID is an English language dataset and we make use of its Level-A labels (OFF: offensive, NOT: not offensive), discussed in Table 9 in section 9. We chose these two datasets because their annotation schema aligned with that of ours, for aggression detection and offensive language detection tasks respectively.

For Aggression detection, the columns D1–>D2 and D2–>D1 in Table 5 present a cross-dataset setup within which we observe the performance of models fine-tuned on D1 (our dataset) and tested on D2 (TRAC dataset), and vice versa. We observe

Tweets I Task: Aggression Detection	GT	M1	M2	M3	Error Cause
Romanticizing open defecation under heavy rain to enjoy the melancholy	**CAG**	NAG	CAG	NAG	**Sarcasm**
@username The way Rahul Gandhi changed his DP to Nehru holding a tricolour, I want to change it to Savarkar or Golwalkar holding the Flag. Can anyone help and share pictures of theirs holding the tricolor..	**CAG**	NAG	NAG	NAG	**Real-world context**
@username You use words like waqf, muslims, mullahs, terrorists, radicals and you will get a block message from twitter, hope Elon buys twitter very soon.	**CAG**	CAG	NAG	NAG	**Hidden Aggression**

Table 6: Prediction on test set instances from resultant models for aggression detection. **GT**: Ground Truth label, **M1**: XLM-R$_{base}$, **M2**: RoBERTa$_{base}$, **M3**: Hing-RoBERTa.

that models trained on our dataset obtain better F1-scores than those trained on the TRAC dataset. Further, we observe that the best performance achieved in this setup is with the help of XLM-R$_{base}$, the same multilingual model which also performs the best on the combined dataset in Table 4.

For Offensive language detection, we examine the results in columns D1–>D2 and D2–>D1 in Table 5, which note the performance of models fine-tuned on D1 (our dataset) and tested on D2 (OLID dataset), and vice versa. As was true with the first task, it is observed here too that models trained on our dataset obtain better F1-scores as compared to the models trained on the OLID dataset. Additionally, we observe a similar correlation between both sets of results. The model fine-tuned on code-mixed data, Hing-RoBERTa, performs the best in this scenario, as was the case with the combined dataset performance in Table 4.

The overall decrease in F1-scores observed across models for the Offensive language detection task can be attributed to the dissimilarities in the composition of the OLID dataset and our dataset, despite both being annotated for the offensive language identification task with the same annotation schema. While our dataset contains English and Hindi-English tweets pertaining specifically to the Indian political scenario, OLID is an English-language dataset with no instances of Hindi-English code-mixing, and little to no emphasis on regional or national politics.

On the contrary, the TRAC dataset contains English and Hindi-English sentences with a clear focus on the conversational data generated within India, which explains why we see a greater harmony in Table 5 between the TRAC dataset and our dataset, as compared to the OLID dataset.

Error Analysis

For error analysis, we pick the best-performing models for monolingual, code-mixed, and combined datasets, which as per our experiments have been RoBERTa$_{base}$, Hing-RoBERTa, and XLM-R$_{base}$ respectively. We report some of the most common error patterns in Table 6 and Table 7.

For the task of aggression detection, instances carrying sarcasm that make heavy use of oxymoronic/ironic language were misclassified the most by all three models. An example of this is the first tweet in Table 6, where the person who made the tweet observes discontent with the practice of open defecation not by attacking it directly but with sarcasm. Another common error we observed was among instances, that seemed to have a neutral tone ostensibly but required some real-world knowledge to understand the context of aggression within. The second tweet in Table 6 is an excellent example of this. By itself, the tweet does not appear to be aggressive, but its true meaning unveils when read along with context. A few wrongful predictions can also be observed because of the aggression being very covert or hidden, as seen in the third tweet in Table 6 where under the garb of advocating for Elon Musk's free speech, the person is expressing an intent to, in fact, be disrespectful and use words on the platform that spread disharmony.

For the task of offensive language detection, the most common error type was observed due to the presence of offensive named entities. The first tweet in Table 7 is an example of this, where the use of *"Khujliwal"* (a pun on *"Kejriwal"* - which is the name of an Indian politician), is the cause of offense, as labeled by our annotators. Another common error was in instances that required real-world knowledge to understand their full context. For

Tweets | Task: Offensive Language Detection	GT	M1	M2	M3	Error Cause
@username It was always very clear that **Khujliwal** is a Godse Lover	**OFF**	NOT	NOT	NOT	**Named entity**
@username @username Dogs are at least loyal bro ..not these **rice bags**	**OFF**	NOT	NOT	NOT	**Real-world context**
@username @username Nah, you need to do Ghar Wapasi to find real Moksha. Else you will remain a **mlechha**	**OFF**	NOT	NOT	OFF	**Code-mixed**

Table 7: Prediction on test set instances from resultant models for offensive language detection. **GT**: Ground Truth label, **M1**: XLM-R$_{base}$, **M2**: RoBERTa$_{base}$, **M3**: Hing-RoBERTa.

example, in the second tweet in Table 7, *"rice bags"* is actually a derogatory slur used quite commonly in the Indian political context. Finally, we also observe misclassified instances due to the code-mixed nature of tweets, as seen in the third tweet in Table 7 where the word *"mlechha"* has derogatory connotations.

6 Conclusion and Future Work

This paper presents a novel dataset to model aggressiveness and offensiveness in text. We analyze this dataset using approaches such as fine-tuning pre-trained language models for the task of aggression detection and offensive language detection and report the results. Our analysis also takes into account the code-mixing phenomenon observed on social media platforms as we report additional results for this task. Since aggression and offense can be subtle, and their identification in the text can sometimes be subjective, it is important to note the limitations of such a study - which we discuss in the next section. We release any data (including any raw data, but only in the form of tweet IDs and their respective labels for the two tasks), code, and models produced during this study publicly for further research by the community. We license this release under CC-BY-SA 4.0.

In the near future, we aim to annotate this data for tasks such as sarcasm detection - to develop a deeper understanding of how it is related to aggression and offensiveness. Additionally, the motivation for collecting the same data instances marked with aggression and offense labels is for a multi-task learning-based model also to be able to identify when 1) the tone of a text is aggressive without being offensive *vs.*, 2) the text is offensive, despite it not being overtly aggressive. We also aim to collect more data and annotate it using weak supervision. Finally, we also aim to expand on the theoretical underpinnings of sublime aggression and offense by attempting to identify these within other more tangential domains, *viz.*, comedy.

7 Limitations

Our work can be considered to have the following limitations:

1. The dataset we introduce contains $10,000$ text instances sampled from a single social media platform. However, we acknowledge this limitation and as noted in section 6, we aim to extend this work by collecting more political data across various social media platforms and using it to model aggressive behavior.

2. We obtained this dataset by crawling for tweets based on 52 keywords (as shown in Table 10). We acknowledge that these keywords may have limited the domains in which political aggression can occur. That being said, we also hope that task generalizability is not compromised due to the presence of pre-trained language models at the helm of our experiments.

8 Ethics Statement

Our dataset of tweets was obtained by scraping Twitter. All tweets have been anonymized, and metadata such as senders' demographic identity is never included in the data used to train our models. We plan to release only the tweet ids and their respective labels for the two tasks as part of our dataset.

References

Wafa Alorainy, Pete Burnap, Han Liu, and Matthew L. Williams. 2019. "the enemy among us": Detecting cyber hate speech with threats-based othering language embeddings. *ACM Trans. Web*, 13(3).

Craig A Anderson, Brad J Bushman, et al. 2002. Human aggression. *Annual review of psychology*, 53(1):27–51.

Pinkesh Badjatiya, Shashank Gupta, Manish Gupta, and Vasudeva Varma. 2017. Deep learning for hate speech detection in tweets. In *Proceedings of the 26th International Conference on World Wide Web Companion - WWW '17 Companion*. ACM Press.

Nabil Badri, Ferihane Kboubi, and Anja Habacha Chaibi. 2022. Combining fasttext and glove word embedding for offensive and hate speech text detection. *Procedia Computer Science*, 207:769–778. Knowledge-Based and Intelligent Information Engineering Systems: Proceedings of the 26th International Conference KES2022.

Roland Barthes. 1957. Mythologies, le seuil. *Points, Paris*.

Shiladitya Bhattacharya, Siddharth Singh, Ritesh Kumar, Akanksha Bansal, Akash Bhagat, Yogesh Dawer, Bornini Lahiri, and Atul Kr. Ojha. 2020. Developing a multilingual annotated corpus of misogyny and aggression. In *Proceedings of the Second Workshop on Trolling, Aggression and Cyberbullying*, pages 158–168, Marseille, France. European Language Resources Association (ELRA).

Michal Bojkovský and Matúš Pikuliak. 2019. STUFIIT at SemEval-2019 task 5: Multilingual hate speech detection on Twitter with MUSE and ELMo embeddings. In *Proceedings of the 13th International Workshop on Semantic Evaluation*, pages 464–468, Minneapolis, Minnesota, USA. Association for Computational Linguistics.

Pete Burnap and Matthew L Williams. 2016a. Us and them: identifying cyber hate on twitter across multiple protected characteristics. *EPJ Data science*, 5:1–15.

Peter Burnap and Matthew Leighton Williams. 2016b. Us and them: identifying cyber hate on twitter across multiple protected characteristics. *Epj Data Science*, 5.

Brad J Bushman and L Rowell Huesmann. 2014. Twenty-five years of research on violence in digital games and aggression revisited: A reply to elson and ferguson (2013).

Bharathi Raja Chakravarthi, Ruba Priyadharshini, Navya Jose, Anand Kumar M, Thomas Mandl, Prasanna Kumar Kumaresan, Rahul Ponnusamy, Hariharan R L, John P. McCrae, and Elizabeth Sherly. 2021. Findings of the shared task on offensive language identification in Tamil, Malayalam, and Kannada. In *Proceedings of the First Workshop on Speech and Language Technologies for Dravidian Languages*, pages 133–145, Kyiv. Association for Computational Linguistics.

Bharathi Raja Chakravarthi, Ruba Priyadharshini, Anand Kumar Madasamy, Parameswari Krishnamurthy, Elizabeth Sherly, and Sinnathamby Mahesan, editors. 2022. *Proceedings of the Second Workshop on Speech and Language Technologies for Dravidian Languages*. Association for Computational Linguistics, Dublin, Ireland.

Çağrı Çöltekin. 2020. A corpus of Turkish offensive language on social media. In *Proceedings of the 12th Language Resources and Evaluation Conference*, pages 6174–6184, Marseille, France. European Language Resources Association.

Alexis Conneau, Kartikay Khandelwal, Naman Goyal, Vishrav Chaudhary, Guillaume Wenzek, Francisco Guzmán, Edouard Grave, Myle Ott, Luke Zettlemoyer, and Veselin Stoyanov. 2020. Unsupervised cross-lingual representation learning at scale.

Thomas Davidson, Dana Warmsley, Michael Macy, and Ingmar Weber. 2017a. Automated hate speech detection and the problem of offensive language. In *Proceedings of the international AAAI conference on web and social media*, volume 11, pages 512–515.

Thomas Davidson, Dana Warmsley, Michael W. Macy, and Ingmar Weber. 2017b. Automated hate speech detection and the problem of offensive language. In *ICWSM*, pages 512–515.

Alexandra DeLucia, Shijie Wu, Aaron Mueller, Carlos Aguirre, Philip Resnik, and Mark Dredze. 2022. Bernice: A multilingual pre-trained encoder for Twitter. In *Proceedings of the 2022 Conference on Empirical Methods in Natural Language Processing*, pages 6191–6205, Abu Dhabi, United Arab Emirates. Association for Computational Linguistics.

Jacob Devlin, Ming-Wei Chang, Kenton Lee, and Kristina Toutanova. 2019. BERT: Pre-training of deep bidirectional transformers for language understanding. In *Proceedings of the 2019 Conference of the North American Chapter of the Association for Computational Linguistics: Human Language Technologies, Volume 1 (Long and Short Papers)*, pages 4171–4186, Minneapolis, Minnesota. Association for Computational Linguistics.

María José Díaz-Torres, Paulina Alejandra Morán-Méndez, Luis Villasenor-Pineda, Manuel Montes-y Gómez, Juan Aguilera, and Luis Meneses-Lerín. 2020. Automatic detection of offensive language in social media: Defining linguistic criteria to build a Mexican Spanish dataset. In *Proceedings of the Second Workshop on Trolling, Aggression and Cyberbullying*, pages 132–136, Marseille, France. European Language Resources Association (ELRA).

Thiago Galery, Efstathios Charitos, and Ye Tian. 2018. Aggression identification and multi lingual word embeddings. In *Proceedings of the First Workshop on Trolling, Aggression and Cyberbullying (TRAC-2018)*, pages 74–79, Santa Fe, New Mexico, USA. Association for Computational Linguistics.

Björn Gambäck and Utpal Kumar Sikdar. 2017. Using convolutional neural networks to classify hate-speech. In *Proceedings of the First Workshop on Abusive Language Online*, pages 85–90, Vancouver, BC, Canada. Association for Computational Linguistics.

Claire Hardaker and Mark McGlashan. 2016. "real men don't hate women": Twitter rape threats and group identity. *Journal of Pragmatics*, 91:80–93.

Guntur Herwanto, Annisa Ningtyas, Kurniawan Nugraha, and I Nyoman Prayana Trisna. 2019. Hate speech and abusive language classification using fast-text. pages 69–72.

Qianjia Huang, Diana Inkpen, Jianhong Zhang, and David Van Bruwaene. 2018. Cyberbullying intervention based on convolutional neural networks. In *Proceedings of the First Workshop on Trolling, Aggression and Cyberbullying (TRAC-2018)*, pages 42–51, Santa Fe, New Mexico, USA. Association for Computational Linguistics.

Rohan Kshirsagar, Tyrus Cukuvac, Kathy McKeown, and Susan McGregor. 2018. Predictive embeddings for hate speech detection on Twitter. In *Proceedings of the 2nd Workshop on Abusive Language Online (ALW2)*, pages 26–32, Brussels, Belgium. Association for Computational Linguistics.

Ritesh Kumar, Atul Kr Ojha, Shervin Malmasi, and Marcos Zampieri. 2018a. Benchmarking aggression identification in social media. In *Proceedings of the first workshop on trolling, aggression and cyberbullying (TRAC-2018)*, pages 1–11.

Ritesh Kumar, Atul Kr. Ojha, Shervin Malmasi, and Marcos Zampieri. 2018b. Benchmarking aggression identification in social media. In *Proceedings of the First Workshop on Trolling, Aggression and Cyberbullying (TRAC-2018)*, pages 1–11, Santa Fe, New Mexico, USA. Association for Computational Linguistics.

Irene Kwok and Yuzhou Wang. 2013. Locate the hate: Detecting tweets against blacks. In *Proceedings of the Twenty-Seventh AAAI Conference on Artificial Intelligence*, AAAI'13, page 1621–1622. AAAI Press.

Wee Sun Lee and Bing Liu. 2003. Learning with positive and unlabeled examples using weighted logistic regression. In *Proceedings of the Twentieth International Conference on International Conference on Machine Learning*, ICML'03, page 448–455. AAAI Press.

Han Liu, Pete Burnap, Wafa Alorainy, and Matthew L. Williams. 2019a. A fuzzy approach to text classification with two-stage training for ambiguous instances. *IEEE Transactions on Computational Social Systems*, 6(2):227–240.

Shuhua Liu and Thomas Forss. 2014. Combining n-gram based similarity analysis with sentiment analysis in web content classification. In *Proceedings of the International Conference on Knowledge Discovery and Information Retrieval - Volume 1: SSTM, (IC3K 2014)*, pages 530–537. INSTICC, SciTePress.

Shuhua Liu and Thomas Forss. 2015. New classification models for detecting hate and violence web content. In *2015 7th international joint conference on knowledge discovery, knowledge engineering and knowledge management (IC3K)*, volume 1, pages 487–495. IEEE.

Yinhan Liu, Myle Ott, Naman Goyal, Jingfei Du, Mandar Joshi, Danqi Chen, Omer Levy, Mike Lewis, Luke Zettlemoyer, and Veselin Stoyanov. 2019b. Roberta: A robustly optimized bert pretraining approach.

Sreekanth Madisetty and Maunendra Sankar Desarkar. 2018. Aggression detection in social media using deep neural networks. In *Proceedings of the First Workshop on Trolling, Aggression and Cyberbullying (TRAC-2018)*, pages 120–127, Santa Fe, New Mexico, USA. Association for Computational Linguistics.

Karla Mantilla. 2013. Gendertrolling: Misogyny adapts to new media. *Feminist studies*, 39(2):563–570.

Puneet Mathur, Rajiv Shah, Ramit Sawhney, and Debanjan Mahata. 2018. Detecting offensive tweets in Hindi-English code-switched language. In *Proceedings of the Sixth International Workshop on Natural Language Processing for Social Media*, pages 18–26, Melbourne, Australia. Association for Computational Linguistics.

Katarzyna Molek-Kozakowska. 2022. Recenzja/review: Jim o'driscoll (2020). offensive language: Taboo, offence and social control. london: Bloomsbury academic. isbn 9781350169678. *Res Rhetorica*, 9:166–169.

Marzieh Mozafari, Reza Farahbakhsh, and Noel Crespi. 2019. A bert-based transfer learning approach for hate speech detection in online social media.

Ravindra Nayak and Raviraj Joshi. 2022. L3Cube-HingCorpus and HingBERT: A code mixed Hindi-English dataset and BERT language models. In *Proceedings of the WILDRE-6 Workshop within the 13th Language Resources and Evaluation Conference*, pages 7–12, Marseille, France. European Language Resources Association.

Nishant Nikhil, Ramit Pahwa, Mehul Kumar Nirala, and Rohan Khilnani. 2018. LSTMs with attention for aggression detection. In *Proceedings of the First Workshop on Trolling, Aggression and Cyberbullying (TRAC-2018)*, pages 52–57, Santa Fe, New Mexico, USA. Association for Computational Linguistics.

Victor Nina-Alcocer. 2019. HATERecognizer at SemEval-2019 task 5: Using features and neural networks to face hate recognition. In *Proceedings of the 13th International Workshop on Semantic Evaluation*, pages 409–415, Minneapolis, Minnesota, USA. Association for Computational Linguistics.

Chikashi Nobata, Joel Tetreault, Achint Thomas, Yashar Mehdad, and Yi Chang. 2016. Abusive language detection in online user content. In *Proceedings of the 25th International Conference on World Wide Web*, WWW '16, page 145–153, Republic and Canton of Geneva, CHE. International World Wide Web Conferences Steering Committee.

Constantin Orăsan. 2018. Aggressive language identification using word embeddings and sentiment features. In *Proceedings of the First Workshop on Trolling, Aggression and Cyberbullying (TRAC-2018)*, pages 113–119, Santa Fe, New Mexico, USA. Association for Computational Linguistics.

Andraž Pelicon, Matej Martinc, and Petra Kralj Novak. 2019. Embeddia at semeval-2019 task 6: Detecting hate with neural network and transfer learning approaches. In *Proceedings of the 13th International Workshop on Semantic Evaluation*, pages 604–610.

Juan Manuel Pérez and Franco M. Luque. 2019. Atalaya at SemEval 2019 task 5: Robust embeddings for tweet classification. In *Proceedings of the 13th International Workshop on Semantic Evaluation*, pages 64–69, Minneapolis, Minnesota, USA. Association for Computational Linguistics.

Matthew E. Peters, Mark Neumann, Mohit Iyyer, Matt Gardner, Christopher Clark, Kenton Lee, and Luke Zettlemoyer. 2018. Deep contextualized word representations. In *Proceedings of the 2018 Conference of the North American Chapter of the Association for Computational Linguistics: Human Language Technologies, Volume 1 (Long Papers)*, pages 2227–2237, New Orleans, Louisiana. Association for Computational Linguistics.

Zesis Pitenis, Marcos Zampieri, and Tharindu Ranasinghe. 2020. Offensive language identification in Greek. In *Proceedings of the 12th Language Resources and Evaluation Conference*, pages 5113–5119, Marseille, France. European Language Resources Association.

Georgios K. Pitsilis, Heri Ramampiaro, and Helge Langseth. 2018. Effective hate-speech detection in twitter data using recurrent neural networks. *Applied Intelligence*, 48:4730–4742.

Nur Indah Pratiwi, Indra Budi, and Ika Alfina. 2019. Hate speech detection on indonesian instagram comments using fasttext approach. In *2018 International Conference on Advanced Computer Science and Information Systems, ICACSIS 2018*, 2018 International Conference on Advanced Computer Science and Information Systems, ICACSIS 2018, pages 447–450, United States. Institute of Electrical and Electronics Engineers Inc. Publisher Copyright: © 2018 IEEE.; 10th International Conference on Advanced Computer Science and Information Systems, ICACSIS 2018 ; Conference date: 27-10-2018 Through 28-10-2018.

Tazeek Bin Abdur Rakib and Lay-Ki Soon. 2018. Using the reddit corpus for cyberbully detection. In *Asian Conference on Intelligent Information and Database Systems*.

Faneva Ramiandrisoa and Josiane Mothe. 2020. Aggression identification in social media: a transfer learning based approach. In *TRAC*.

Tharindu Ranasinghe and Marcos Zampieri. 2020. Multilingual offensive language identification with crosslingual embeddings. In *Proceedings of the 2020 Conference on Empirical Methods in Natural Language Processing (EMNLP)*, pages 5838–5844, Online. Association for Computational Linguistics.

Amir H Razavi, Diana Inkpen, Sasha Uritsky, and Stan Matwin. 2010. Offensive language detection using multi-level classification. In *Advances in Artificial Intelligence: 23rd Canadian Conference on Artificial Intelligence, Canadian AI 2010, Ottawa, Canada, May 31–June 2, 2010. Proceedings 23*, pages 16–27. Springer.

Alison Ribeiro and Nádia Silva. 2019. INF-HatEval at SemEval-2019 task 5: Convolutional neural networks for hate speech detection against women and immigrants on Twitter. In *Proceedings of the 13th International Workshop on Semantic Evaluation*, pages 420–425, Minneapolis, Minnesota, USA. Association for Computational Linguistics.

Arjun Roy, Prashant Kapil, Kingshuk Basak, and Asif Ekbal. 2018. An ensemble approach for aggression identification in English and Hindi text. In *Proceedings of the First Workshop on Trolling, Aggression and Cyberbullying (TRAC-2018)*, pages 66–73, Santa Fe, New Mexico, USA. Association for Computational Linguistics.

Anita Saroj and Sukomal Pal. 2020. An Indian language social media collection for hate and offensive speech. In *Proceedings of the Workshop on Resources and Techniques for User and Author Profiling in Abusive Language*, pages 2–8, Marseille, France. European Language Resources Association (ELRA).

Anna Schmidt and Michael Wiegand. 2017. A survey on hate speech detection using natural language processing. In *Proceedings of the fifth international workshop on natural language processing for social media*, pages 1–10.

Ellen Spertus. 1997a. Smokey: Automatic recognition of hostile messages. In *Proceedings of the Fourteenth National Conference on Artificial Intelligence and Ninth Conference on Innovative Applications of Artificial Intelligence*, AAAI'97/IAAI'97, page 1058–1065. AAAI Press.

Ellen Spertus. 1997b. Smokey: Automatic recognition of hostile messages. In *Aaai/iaai*, pages 1058–1065.

Nicolas Suzor, Molly Dragiewicz, Bridget Harris, Rosalie Gillett, Jean Burgess, and Tess Van Geelen. 2019. Human rights by design: The responsibilities of social media platforms to address gender-based violence online. *Policy & Internet*, 11(1):84–103.

Zeerak Waseem, Thomas Davidson, Dana Warmsley, and Ingmar Weber. 2017. Understanding abuse: A typology of abusive language detection subtasks. *arXiv preprint arXiv:1705.09899*.

Zeerak Waseem and Dirk Hovy. 2016. Hateful symbols or hateful people? predictive features for hate speech detection on twitter. In *Proceedings of the NAACL student research workshop*, pages 88–93.

Hajime Watanabe, Mondher Bouazizi, and Tomoaki Ohtsuki. 2018. Hate speech on twitter: A pragmatic approach to collect hateful and offensive expressions and perform hate speech detection. *IEEE Access*, 6:13825–13835. Publisher Copyright: © 2018 IEEE.

Thomas Wolf, Lysandre Debut, Victor Sanh, Julien Chaumond, Clement Delangue, Anthony Moi, Pierric Cistac, Tim Rault, Remi Louf, Morgan Funtowicz, Joe Davison, Sam Shleifer, Patrick von Platen, Clara Ma, Yacine Jernite, Julien Plu, Canwen Xu, Teven Le Scao, Sylvain Gugger, Mariama Drame, Quentin Lhoest, and Alexander Rush. 2020. Transformers: State-of-the-art natural language processing. In *Proceedings of the 2020 Conference on Empirical Methods in Natural Language Processing: System Demonstrations*, pages 38–45, Online. Association for Computational Linguistics.

Marcos Zampieri, Shervin Malmasi, Preslav Nakov, Sara Rosenthal, Noura Farra, and Ritesh Kumar. 2019a. Predicting the Type and Target of Offensive Posts in Social Media. In *Proceedings of NAACL*.

Marcos Zampieri, Shervin Malmasi, Preslav Nakov, Sara Rosenthal, Noura Farra, and Ritesh Kumar. 2019b. SemEval-2019 task 6: Identifying and categorizing offensive language in social media (OffensEval). In *Proceedings of the 13th International Workshop on Semantic Evaluation*, pages 75–86, Minneapolis, Minnesota, USA. Association for Computational Linguistics.

Z Zhang, D Robinson, and J Tepper. 2018. Detecting hate speech on twitter using a convolution-gru based deep neural network. In A Gangemi, R Navigli, M-E Vidal, P Hitzler, R Troncy, L Hollink, A Tordai, and M Alam, editors, *The Semantic Web: Proceedings of the 15th European Semantic Web Conference (ESWC 2018), Heraklion, Crete, Greece, 3-7 June 2018*, volume 10843 of *Lecture notes in computer science*, pages 745–760. Springer, Cham, Switzerland.

9 Appendix

We note the language-wise class distribution for aggression and offensiveness classes, in the publicly available TRAC and OLID datasets respectively, in Table 8 and Table 9. Next, we list the keywords used for data scraping, during the creation of our novel dataset.

	OAG	CAG	NAG
Monolingual	1114	1693	1820
Code mixed	1058	1581	2529
Combined	2172	3279	4349

Table 8: Aggression statistics of the TRAC dataset.

TRAC Dataset Statistics Table 8 shows the exploratory statistics on TRAC dataset for aggression. There are a total of $9,800$ data instances. Out of this, $2,172$ are overtly aggressive (OAG), $3,279$ are covertly aggressive (CAG), and $4,349$ are not aggressive (NAG).

Additionally, the monolingual vs. code mixed statistics are also mentioned for each class. We have $1,114$ monolingual and $1,058$ code mixed tweets in the OAG category, $1,693$ monolingual and $1,581$ code mixed tweets in the CAG category, and $1,820$ monolingual and $2,529$ code mixed tweets in the NAG category.

	OFF	NOT
Monolingual	2034	3578
Code mixed	1134	2786
Combined	3168	6364

Table 9: Offensive language statistics of the OLID dataset.

OLID Dataset Statistics Table 9 shows the exploratory statistics on OLID dataset for offensive language. There are a total of $9,532$ data instances. Out of this, $3,168$ are offensive (OFF) and $6,364$ are not offensive (NOT).

Additionally, here too we mention the monolingual vs. code mixed statistics for each class. We have $2,034$ monolingual and $1,134$ code mixed tweets in the OFF category and $3,578$ monolingual and $2,786$ code mixed tweets in the NOT category.

Keywords for Scraping Tweets Table 10 contains a list of 52 keywords that were used in the initial scraping of tweets, for creation of our novel dataset. These keywords were obtained from Twitter's top trending keywords list of the previous two years.

nationalism	open defecation	Muslims	marxists	JNU	UPA
demonetization	Farmer's Bill	hijab	maoists	RSS	NDA
inflation	UAPA	triple talaq	Uyghur	PFI	Modi
unemployment	IPL	ghar wapasi	Pakistan	Gandhi	Rahul Gandhi
rape	ISRO	love jihad	Kashmir	Godse	Kejriwal
marital rape	migrants	CAA	China	Nehru	Emergency
secularism	lockdown	Shaheen Bagh	north-east	Sardar Patel	Indira Gandhi
urban floods	Covid-19	undertrials	drugs	Bhagat Singh	
lynching	Dalits	Adivasis	nepotism	Golwalkar	

Table 10: Keywords used for scraping tweets.

Towards Weakly-Supervised Hate Speech Classification Across Datasets

Yiping Jin[1,2], Leo Wanner[3,1], Vishakha Laxman Kadam[2], Alexander Shvets[1]
[1]NLP Group, Pompeu Fabra University, Barcelona, Spain
[2]Knorex, 02-129 WeWork Futura, Pune, India
[3]Catalan Institute for Research and Advanced Studies
{yiping.jin, leo.wanner, alexander.shvets}@upf.edu
vishakha.kadam@knorex.com

Abstract

As pointed out by several scholars, current research on hate speech (HS) recognition is characterized by unsystematic data creation strategies and diverging annotation schemata. Subsequently, supervised-learning models tend to generalize poorly to datasets they were not trained on, and the performance of the models trained on datasets labeled using different HS taxonomies cannot be compared. To ease this problem, we propose to apply extremely weak supervision that only relies on the class name rather than on class samples from the annotated data. We demonstrate the effectiveness of a state-of-the-art weakly-supervised text classification model in various in-dataset and cross-dataset settings. Furthermore, we conduct an in-depth quantitative and qualitative analysis of the source of poor generalizability of HS classification models.

Content Warning: *This document discusses examples of harmful content (hate, abuse, and negative stereotypes). The authors do not support the use of harmful language.*

1 Introduction

Due to a growing concern about its impact on society, hate speech (HS) recognition recently received much attention from the NLP research community (Bilewicz and Soral, 2020). A large number of proposals on how to address HS as a supervised classification task have been put forward; see, among others, (Waseem and Hovy, 2016; Waseem, 2016; Poletto et al., 2021) and several shared tasks have been organized (Basile et al., 2019; Caselli et al., 2020).

However, while Transformer models such as BERT (Devlin et al., 2019) achieved impressive performance on various benchmark datasets (Swamy et al., 2019), recent work demonstrated that state-of-the-art HS classification models generalize poorly to datasets other than the ones they have been trained on (Fortuna et al., 2020, 2021; Yin and Zubiaga, 2021), even when the datasets come from the same data source, e.g., Twitter. This casts a doubt on what we have achieved in the HS classification task.

Fortuna et al. (2022) identify three main challenges related to HS classification: 1. *the definitorial challenge*: while the interpretation of what is HS highly depends on the cultural and social norms of its creator (Talat et al., 2022), state-of-the-art HS research favours a universal definition; 2. *the annotation challenge*: due to the subjective nature of HS, the annotation also often depends on the context, the social bias of the annotator, and their familiarity with the topic (Wiegand et al., 2019), such that the annotators with different backgrounds tend to provide deviating annotations (Waseem, 2016; Olteanu et al., 2018), especially when not only the presence of HS is to be annotated, but also its category and the group it targets (Basile et al., 2019); 3. *the learning and evaluation challenge*: the common evaluation practice of the HS classification models assumes that the distributions of the training data and the data to which the model is applied are identical, which is not the case in reality; real-world HS data is relatively rare, while the strategies applied for the creation of HS datasets favor explicit HS expressions (Sap et al., 2020; Yin and Zubiaga, 2021), using search with explicit target keywords (Waseem and Hovy, 2016; Basile et al., 2019).

In order to address these challenges, we propose the use of extremely weak supervision, which uses category names as the only supervision signal (Meng et al., 2020; Wang et al., 2021): Extremely weak supervision does not presuppose any definition of HS, which would guide the annotation, such that when the interpretation of what is to be considered as HS is modified, we can retrain the model on the same dataset, without the need of re-annotation. Furthermore, when the data distribution changes, the model can learn from unlabeled

The 7th Workshop on Online Abuse and Harms (WOAH), pages 42–59
July 13, 2023

data and adapt to a new domain.

Our contributions can be summarized as follows:

- We apply extremely weak supervision to HS classification and achieve promising performance compared to fully-supervised and weakly-supervised baselines.
- We perform cross-dataset classification under different settings and yield insights on the transferability of HS datasets and models.
- We conduct an in-depth analysis and highlight the potentials and limitations of weak supervision for HS classification.

2 Related Work

Since our goal is to advance the research on HS classification, we focus, in what follows, on the review of related work in this area and refrain from the discussion of the application of weakly supervised supervision models to other problems.

Standardizing different HS taxonomies across datasets is a first step in performing cross-dataset analysis and experiments. To this end, Fortuna et al. (2020) created a category mapping among six publicly available HS datasets. Furthermore, they measured the data similarity of categories in an intra- and inter-dataset manner and reported the performance of a public HS classification API on different datasets and categories.

Other previous work in cross-dataset HS classification followed similar experimental settings by training a supervised classifier on the training set of each dataset and reporting the performance on the corresponding test set and test sets from other datasets. For instance, Karan and Šnajder (2018) trained linear SVM models on 9 different HS datasets. They showed that models performed considerably worse on out-of-domain datasets. They further performed domain adaptation using the FEDA framework (Daumé III, 2007) and demonstrated that having at least some in-domain data is crucial for achieving good performance. Similarly, Swamy et al. (2019) compared Linear SVM, LSTM, and BERT models trained on different datasets. They reported that some pairs of datasets perform well on each other, likely due to a high degree of overlap. They also claimed that a more balanced class ratio is essential for the datasets' generalizability.

Fortuna et al. (2021) conducted a large-scale cross-dataset experiment by training a total of 1,698 classifiers using different algorithms, datasets, and other experimental setups. They demonstrated that the generalizability does not only depend on the dataset, but also on the model. Transformer-based models have a better potential to generalize to other datasets, likely thanks to the wealth of data they have observed during pretraining. Furthermore, they built a random forest classifier to predict the generalizability based on human-engineered dataset features. The experiment revealed that to achieve cross-dataset generalization, the model must first perform well in an intra-dataset scenario. In addition, inconsistency in class definition hampers generalizability.

Wiegand et al. (2019) and Arango et al. (2019) studied the impact of data bias on the generalizability of HS models, with the outcome that popular benchmark datasets possess several sources of biases, such as bias towards explicit HS expressions, topic bias, and author bias. The classification results dropped significantly when the bias is reduced. To this end, they proposed using cross-dataset classification as a way to evaluate models' performance in a more realistic setting.

Gao et al. (2017) argued that the low frequency of online HS impedes obtaining a wide-coverage HS detection dataset. To this end, they proposed a two-path bootstrapping approach involving an explicit slur term learner and an LSTM (Hochreiter and Schmidhuber, 1997) classifier. The slur term learner is initialized with a list of hand-engineered seed slur terms and applies to an unlabeled dataset to automatically label hateful posts, which are used to train the classifier. The slur term learner and the classifier are trained iteratively in a co-training manner (Blum and Mitchell, 1998).

A distinct approach was proposed by Talat et al. (2018). This approach utilized multi-task learning (MTL) to enhance domain robustness. They trained a classifier on three distinct sets of annotations: Waseem and Hovy (2016), Waseem (2016), and Davidson et al. (2017). While MTL helps to prevent overfitting and may provide auxiliary fine-grained predictions, it requires annotating a dataset using different taxonomies, granularities, or aspects.

Our approach is most similar to Jin et al. (2022)'s, which also applied weakly-supervised learning on a target-domain dataset. However, their approach requires mining a list of 30 high-quality keywords for each category from a large labeled source-domain dataset. Moreover, they assume that the source and target datasets are labeled using the same HS taxonomy.

3 Weakly-Supervised HS Classification

In this section, we briefly introduce the basics of weakly supervised text classification and then discuss the cross-dataset classification we aim for.

3.1 Preliminaries: Weakly Supervised Text Classification

Weakly-supervised text classification eliminates the need for a large labeled dataset (Meng et al., 2018; Mekala and Shang, 2020). Instead, it trains classifiers using a handful of labeled seed words and unlabeled documents. While the human annotation effort is significantly reduced, weakly-supervised classification methods are sensitive to the choice of seed words, and the process to nominate high-quality seed words is not trivial (Jin et al., 2021).

More recently, Meng et al. (2020) and Wang et al. (2021) explored *extremely* weak supervision, where the model is given only the category name instead of manually curated seed words. Extremely weak supervision is well suited for hate speech detection because we may not know all the aspects of hate speech for a particular category or target group, or what a user may interpret as a HS statement that falls into a specific category. On top of that, extremely weak supervision often performs semantic expansion on the unlabeled dataset and automatically augments the category representation with new aspects (in the form of seed words).

We choose X-Class (Wang et al., 2021) as the primary weakly-supervised classification method because it matches or outperforms previous state-of-the-art weakly-supervised methods on 7 benchmark datasets. X-Class first estimates category representations by iteratively incorporating words similar to the individual categories. More precisely, it represents each word by its averaged contextualized word embedding across the entire dataset and then adds it to the category with whose representation the obtained embedding shows the highest cosine similarity. The category representation is updated as a weighted average of the expanded keywords. Expressly, the authors of X-Class assume a Zipf's law distribution (Powers, 1998) and weight the j-th keyword by $1/j$.

$$s_\ell = \frac{\sum_{j=1}^{|\kappa_\ell|} 1/j \cdot s_{\kappa_{\ell,j}}}{\sum_{j=1}^{|\kappa_\ell|} 1/j} \qquad (1)$$

where $\kappa_{\ell,j}$ is the j-th keyword of category ℓ and $s_{\kappa_{\ell,j}}$ is its average contextualized embedding. X-Class also performs a consistency check and stops adding new words if a category's nearest words have changed.

Then, X-Class derives the document i's category-oriented representation d_i by weighting each word in the document based on its similarity to the category representations. Afterwards, it clusters the documents using a Gaussian Mixture Model (GMM) (Duda and Hart, 1973) by initializing the category representations as cluster centroids. Finally, the most confident pseudo-labeled documents from each cluster are used to train a text classifier.

In our initial experiments, we observed that while GMM generally improves the pseudo-labeling, the accuracy for some low-frequency categories tends to drop sharply. This is likely because GMM works as a *global* density estimator. Therefore, data of the more frequent categories may "attract" more weights and cause the category representation for low-frequency categories to diverge too much from its initial representation. To address this problem, we introduce an additional *representation*-based prediction, which assigns document i to the category representation which has the highest cosine similarity:

$$\ell_i^{rep} = \arg\max_{\ell \in L} cosine(s_\ell, d_i) \qquad (2)$$

We denote GMM's category assignment for document i as 'ℓ_i^{gmm}'. Instead of pseudo-labeling most confident documents based on GMM only, we take the subset of confident documents to which GMM and representation-based prediction assign the same label ($\ell_i^{gmm} = \ell_i^{rep}$). This ensures that the document is sufficiently close to the original category representation. We denote this modified version as 'X-Class^{Agree}'.

3.2 Cross-Dataset Classification

In this work, we study cross-dataset classification, where we do not have any document labels in the target dataset. A dataset is characterized by its *documents* (and their underlying topics and word distributions) and *taxonomy* (list of categories).[1]

Given a single HS dataset with its corresponding categories, we can straightforwardly apply X-Class using the category names and an unlabeled dataset. On the other hand, both the data distribution and taxonomy may differ when we experiment on different datasets. There are three different cases for the relation between the taxonomies of the source and target datasets.

- **1-to-1:** The target taxonomy is identical to the source taxonomy or a subset of it.
- **N-to-1:** The target taxonomy differs from the source taxonomy, but each target category can be mapped to one or more source categories.
- **N-to-N:** The target taxonomy differs from the source taxonomy, and some target categories cannot be mapped to any of the source categories.

Supervised learning can be applied in the first two cases: We can create a category mapping from the target categories to the source categories, then use this mapping to either *post-process* the model predictions (converting predicted source categories to target categories) or relabel the dataset using the target taxonomy and *retrain* the model. However, in the last case, we cannot directly apply supervised learning without further data collection and annotation because we lack labeled data for at least some categories. In contrast, weakly-supervised methods do not require labeled documents and can readily utilize unlabeled documents in the target dataset to capture the underlying distribution. Furthermore, even when applied to a completely unseen dataset, it can also "relabel" the source dataset using the target taxonomy and bootstrap a classifier.

4 Experiments

4.1 Datasets

We conduct experiments on two popular HS datasets that differ with respect to the data source and taxonomy of HS categories: the Waseem dataset and the SBIC dataset. The Waseem dataset (Waseem and Hovy, 2016)[2] contains 5,355 tweets with sexist and racist content. The dataset was annotated by the authors (inter-annotator agreement $\kappa = 0.84$) and reviewed by a domain expert (a gender studies student who is a non-activist feminist). The SBIC dataset (Sap et al., 2020)[3] contains 44,671 posts collected from different domains: Reddit, Twitter, and hate sites. It was annotated by crowdsource workers on Amazon Mechanical Turk. A small portion of the data is originally from the Waseem dataset (1,816 posts). We exclude these posts to avoid overlap between the two datasets.

SBIC dataset does not set a predefined taxonomy for HS categories. Instead, annotators can indicate the target group with free-text answers. We select the most frequent six target groups that can be mapped to the categories in the Waseem dataset. While our proposed weakly-supervised learning method does not depend on category mapping, we select the SBIC categories that can be mapped to compare with supervised learning baselines. Table 1 shows this category mapping.

Waseem	SBIC
Sexist	Women; LGBT
Racist	Black; Jewish; Muslim; Asian

Table 1: Category mapping between the Waseem and SBIC datasets.

We use the original train/dev/test split (75%/12.5%/12.5%) in the SBIC dataset and randomly split the Waseem dataset to 90%/10% into training and test sets. We apply standard preprocessing following Barbieri et al. (2020), including user mention anonymization and website links and emoji removal. Table 2 presents the distribution of the posts in the two datasets.

4.2 Compared Methods

We compare X-Class with two representative supervised learning baselines which are trained using the full *labeled* training dataset:

- **Support Vector Machines (SVM)** (Cortes and Vapnik, 1995)**:** We use scikit-learn's[4] linear SGD classifier with default hyper-parameters and tf-idf weighting.
- **BERT** (Devlin et al., 2019)**:** We fine-tune the `bert-base-uncased` checkpoint[5] using the exact hyper-parameters to train the final classifier in X-Class (detailed in Section 4.3).

[1] While the term "cross-domain" is more popular than "cross-dataset", it does not suggest that the source and target dataset's taxonomies may differ. The discussion of the related problem of cross-task generalization (Raffel et al., 2020; Sanh et al., 2022), which works for unrelated tasks, is beyond the scope of this work.

[2] `https://github.com/zeeraktalat/hatespeech`

[3] `https://maartensap.com/social-bias-frames/`

[4] `https://scikit-learn.org`

[5] `https://huggingface.co/bert-base-uncased`

Dataset	Category	# Train	# Test
Waseem	Sexist	3,107	323
	Racist	1,799	177
	Subtotal	4,906	500
SBIC	Women	2,594	351
	Black folks	2,512	576
	Jewish folks	847	207
	LGBT folks	490	53
	Muslim folks	412	85
	Asian folks	224	34
	Subtotal	7,079	1,306

Table 2: Distribution of the posts per dataset. The average number of words per post in the Waseem dataset is 17.1 and in the SBIC dataset 20.0.

We also compare the performance of our model with the following baselines that do not require any document labeling:[6]

- **Majority class:** Always predict the most frequent category in the training dataset.
- **Keyword voting (category name):** Assign the category whose category name occurs most frequently in the document. Fall back to the majority class prediction if there is a tie or none of the keywords appear.
- **Keyword voting (X-Class keywords):** Same as above, but use the expanded keywords in X-Class's category representation and their associated weights. Assign the category that receives the highest score.
- **Zero-shot PET** (Schick and Schütze, 2021a): Prompting a pre-trained BERT model using hand-crafted patterns and verbalizers to classify documents. We provide details of this baseline in Appendix B.
- **WeSTClass** (Meng et al., 2018)[7]: CNN-based neural text classifier. It first generates pseudo documents with a generative model seeded with user-provided keywords for pretraining, then conducts self-training to bootstrap from unlabeled documents. We use three manually curated seed words for each category following Meng et al. (2018).
- **LOTClass** (Meng et al., 2020)[8]: A strong baseline using extremely weak supervision. The model first uses a masked language model to expand keywords from the category names, then mines category-indicative words using a novel masked category prediction task. Finally, it generalizes via self-training.

4.3 Experiment Settings

We use the official implementation of X-Class.[9] The `bert-base-uncased` checkpoint is used to calculate the document representation and fine-tune the final classifier; the maximum number of keywords for each category is set to 100; and the 50% most confident pseudo-labeled documents from each category are used to train the final classifier.

To facilitate a fair comparison with supervised learning methods, we reimplemented the final classifier fine-tuning step using the HuggingFace Transformers trainer[10] and performed a minimum manual hyper-parameter tuning (`learning_rate=2e-5`; `num_epochs=6`; `weight_decay=0.05`) on the SBIC dev set and applied them on both datasets. We set the `max_length` and `batch_size` to 64.

We merged the following original target groups in the SBIC corpus into "LGBT folks": "gay men", "lesbian women, gay men", "lesbian women", "trans women, trans men", "trans women". Table 3 presents the category names used by the models. We use the original category name except for "LGBT" because it does not occur in the dataset. Instead, we use "gay", the most frequently targeted subgroup in the dataset. As shown in Appendix A, X-Class expands to keywords representing other subgroups in the LGBT community.

4.4 Results of the Experiments

We report the accuracy and macro P/R/F_1 scores to quantify each method's performance.

In-Dataset Classification. We first validate the efficacy of the methods using the standard in-dataset setting, providing the corresponding training and test datasets. Table 4 displays the result.

As expected, BERT outperformed SVM among the supervised-learning baselines on both datasets. Interestingly, keyword voting using only the category name achieved high precision for the SBIC dataset. However, its recall is much lower than that of X-Class due to variations of expressions

[6]We provide the weakly-supervised learning baselines the full *unlabeled* training dataset for keyword expansion and pseudo-labeling.

[7]`https://github.com/yumeng5/WeSTClass`

[8]`https://github.com/yumeng5/LOTClass`

[9]`https://github.com/ZihanWangKi/XClass`

[10]`https://huggingface.co/docs/transformers/main/training`

Class	Seed	Count	WeSTClass
Sexist	sexist	1,071	sexist sexism misogynist
Racist	racist	33	racist racists racism
Women	women	652	women woman female
Black	black	1,601	black blacks n*gro
Jewish	jewish	142	jewish jews jew
LGBT	gay	209	gay gays homosexual
Muslim	muslim	228	muslim muslims islamic
Asian	asian	121	asian asians chinese

Table 3: Seed words used for each category and their frequency in the training dataset. We manually curated the seed words in X-Class's category representation and select the top-3 ranked keywords to train WeSTClass.

Waseem Dataset		
Model	**Acc**	**P/R/F$_1$**
SVM	97.2	97.1/96.8/96.9
BERT	**98.2**	**98.2/97.8/98.0**
Majority class	64.6	33.2/50.0/39.2
KV (class name)	64.6	57.3/50.1/39.8
KV (X-Class)	67.0	76.9/53.6/47.0
Zero-shot PET	49.2	66.7/59.9/47.3
WeSTClass	77.8	77.8/80.4/77.3
LOTClass	63.2	71.3/70.2/63.2
X-Class	96.2	96.9/94.9/95.8
X-Class^{Agree}	**96.6**	**97.5/95.2/96.2**
SBIC Dataset		
Model	**Acc**	**P/R/F$_1$**
SVM	90.7	93.2/82.5/86.7
BERT	**95.7**	**94.2/95.1/94.6**
Majority class	26.9	4.5/16.7/7.1
KV (class name)	57.7	**85.2**/39.7/41.9
KV (X-Class)	55.2	47.8/45.1/40.8
Zero-shot PET	35.1	38.4/21.6/15.8
WeSTClass	36.4	35.9/34.5/29.9
LOTClass	54.2	29.2/29.3/27.5
X-Class	79.8	74.0/81.8/74.8
X-Class^{Agree}	**81.4**	76.1/**85.3/76.6**

Table 4: In-Dataset performance of various models. We highlight the best performances of supervised and weakly-supervised methods in bold.

within the same category. Using X-Class keywords improved keyword voting's recall by 3.5% and 5.4% on the two datasets. However, the precision dropped significantly on the SBIC dataset, likely due to the noisier keywords.

WeSTClass performs superior to keyword voting baselines on the Waseem dataset, primarily due to its high recall of the "Racist" category. This demonstrates the advantage of semantic representation in neural models. However, its performance pales on the SBIC dataset, revealing its weakness in handling more complex cases that involve class imbalance and overlapping, which has been discussed in Wang et al. (2021) and Jin et al. (2022). LOTClass demonstrates a similar trend, but performs worse on both datasets.[11] We analyze the pseudo-labeling accuracy of weakly-supervised baselines and X-Class in Appendix C.

Comparing X-Class and X-Class^{Agree}, we can see that our modification consistently improved the performance.

Cross-Dataset Classification. We conduct cross-dataset classification using the strongest supervised and weakly-supervised models and show the result in Table 5. Note that for the "Waseem → SBIC" setting, we cannot create a category mapping since the target dataset has more fine-grained categories. Therefore, supervised methods and X-Class using category mapping to post-process the predictions are not applicable.

When we train BERT and X-Class using only source-dataset documents, they both perform worse on the target dataset than the in-dataset results in Table 4. The performance drop is smaller for "SBIC → Waseem", likely because the SBIC dataset contains representative posts for the Waseem categories.

Surprisingly, *retraining* the models using the target taxonomy does not outperform *post-processing* using category mapping. However, when a category mapping is unavailable (as in the "Waseem → SBIC" case), retraining a weakly-supervised classifier using the target taxonomy is the only option for cross-dataset classification without manually annotating more data.

An advantage of weakly-supervised methods is that they can utilize *unlabeled* documents from the target dataset when they are available. Although X-Class^{Agree} still underperforms BERT when both

[11] LOTClass has a higher accuracy on SBIC dataset because it predicts the vast majority of the documents to the most frequent categories "Women" and "Black".

SBIC → Waseem		
Model	**Acc**	**P/R/F$_1$**
BERT (post-process)	**93.6**	**92.4/94.7/93.2**
BERT (retrain)	**93.6**	**92.4**/94.2/**93.2**
X-Class (post-process)	91.6	93.5/88.5/90.3
X-Class (retrain)	84.4	89.9/78.1/80.6
X-Class^{Agree} (post-process)	**92.8**	**94.5**/90.1/**91.8**
X-Class^{Agree} (retrain)	92.6	93.4/**90.4**/91.6
Waseem → SBIC		
Model	**Acc**	**P/R/F$_1$**
X-Class (retrain)	60.7	61.3/59.8/54.5
X-Class^{Agree} (retrain)	**69.8**	**62.7/62.2/58.3**

Table 5: Cross-dataset performance of BERT and X-Class. Both models are trained using source dataset documents and tested on the target dataset. We highlight the best performances of supervised and weakly-supervised methods in bold.

are trained using the source dataset in the "SBIC → Waseem" experiment, it surpasses BERT by 3% in both accuracy and macro F$_1$ score when using unlabeled target-dataset documents [12].

Again, X-Class^{Agree} outperforms X-Class in all cases. Subsequently, we use X-Class to refer to X-Class^{Agree} for brevity.

4.5 Analysis: What Makes Cross-Dataset Classification Challenging?

As shown in Table 5, X-Class's performance dropped significantly in the "Waseem → SBIC" cross-dataset setting compared to the use of the SBIC training set. In this section, we try to uncover the causes of the performance drop.

We first plot the per-category F$_1$ score in Figure 1. We can see that the cross-dataset model achieved comparable performance as the in-dataset model for the four categories {Jewish, Muslim, Women, Black}. However, it failed in the two categories {Asian, LGBT}.

Relevant unlabeled documents. Although the Waseem dataset is labeled using a more coarse-grained taxonomy, it may contain documents relevant to some (but not all) fine-grained SBIC categories. Weak supervision usually pseudo-labels the *unlabeled* dataset to train a final classifier. Therefore, it will likely fail when documents related to a particular category are absent in the unlabeled dataset. We count the frequency of documents con-

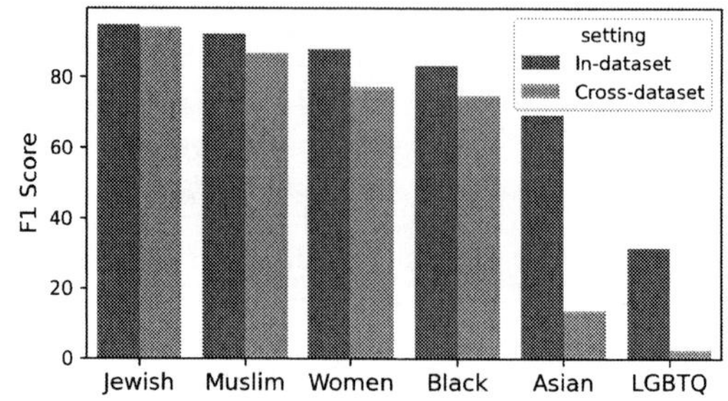

Figure 1: Comparing cross-dataset and in-dataset F$_1$ score of X-Class on the SBIC dataset.

taining each category name in both datasets and present the results in Table 6.

Class	Seed	Waseem %	SBIC %
Sexist	sexist	21.83%	2.70%
Racist	racist	0.67%	1.12%
Women	women	11.94%	9.21%
Black	black	0.63%	22.6%
Jewish	jewish	0.51%	2.00%
LGBT	gay	0.59%	2.95%
Muslim	muslim	10.40%	3.22%
Asian	asian	0.08%	1.71%

Table 6: Frequency of each category name appearing in the Waseem and SBIC training datasets.

We can observe that the "Asian" category (from the SBIC dataset) is severely under-represented in the Waseem dataset. The word "Asian" occurs only 4 times, all in the context of "Asian women/girls".

Waseem and Hovy (2016) conducted a lexical analysis and showed that their "Sexist" category is highly skewed towards *women*, and their "Racist" category is highly skewed towards *Muslims* and *Jews*.[13] Coincidentally, these categories also perform the best in the "Waseem → SBIC" setting.

Category understanding. Jin et al. (2021) argued that weakly-supervised classification and keyword mining are intrinsically related. The failure to identify relevant keywords will harm the category representation and, thus, the classification accuracy. Appendix A presents the full list of keywords X-Class added to the category representations in both in-dataset and cross-dataset settings.

A general observation is that X-Class tends to include fewer keywords in its category representation in the cross-dataset setting. Recall that it stops

[12] We can train weakly-supervised models using unlabeled target dataset, which is equivalent to the in-dataset setting (the X-Class^{Agree} row in Table 4).

[13] Although the term "Jewish" has a low frequency, "Jews" appears in the ten most frequent terms of the "Racist" category.

Model	SBIC → Waseem		Waseem → SBIC	
	Acc	P/P/F$_1$	Acc	P/R/F$_1$
X-Class (src data & src category repr)	92.6	93.4/90.4/91.6	69.8	62.7/62.2/.58.3
X-Class (src data & tgt category repr)	93.4	92.2/94.0/92.9	75.1	65.2/55.5/57.8
X-Class (tgt data & tgt category repr)	96.6	97.5/95.2/96.2	81.4	76.1/85.3/76.6

Table 7: Cross-dataset performance of X-Class using different unlabeled datasets and category representations.

adding keywords once the consistency check is violated. We hypothesize that the mismatch between the dataset and the taxonomy caused the mined keywords to be noisier and more likely to fail the consistency check.

The four categories that perform the best in both in-dataset and out-dataset settings also contain better-quality keywords. In contrast, the "Asian" category's keyword in the cross-dataset setting is entirely off-topic due to its rare occurrence and collocation with words like "women" or "girls". The "LGBT" category contains many vulgar keywords with sexual references, which caused it to confuse with the "Women" category.

Class definition vs. dataset. Previous studies tried to explain why HS classification models generalize poorly across datasets, the most frequently cited reasons being the lack of a standardized definition of hate speech (Waseem and Hovy, 2016; Fortuna et al., 2020, 2021) and biased data distribution (Swamy et al., 2019; Yin and Zubiaga, 2021; Fortuna et al., 2022). It prompts us to wonder *what if* we apply the exact class definition to different datasets or annotate the same dataset using different class definitions. Unfortunately, manual hate speech annotation is time-consuming and very challenging. Waseem (2016) and Caselli et al. (2020) are among the few studies that re-annotated a dataset, providing quantitative analysis or comparing the models' performance. However, such studies focus on a single dataset only. Moreover, the annotation is usually a one-shot effort, influenced by multiple factors related to the annotation task setup and knowledge of annotators. There is no way to assess how much of the performance drop is due to incompatible class definitions and the data distribution *separately*.

In weakly-supervised models, we can interpret the category representation (and associated keywords) as the *class definition*. Therefore, the class definition for the same taxonomy may differ depending on the dataset used to derive the category representation. Furthermore, we can approximate annotating a dataset with a different class definition by altering the category representation.

We designed an ablation study to train X-Class models using different combinations of datasets and class definitions. In Table 7, we present the results of three configurations in this study:[14] 1) Using *source*-dataset documents and category representations derived from the *source* dataset ("X-Class^{Agree} retrain" in Table 5); 2) Using *source*-dataset documents and category representations derived from the *target* dataset; 3) Using *target*-dataset documents and category representations derived from the *target* dataset ("X-Class^{Agree}" in Table 4).

X-Class's cross-dataset performance substantially improved when provided with the category representation derived from the target dataset.[15] Only one factor is altered (either the category representation or the unlabeled training dataset) between the rows in Table 7. Therefore, we can conclude that the performance difference between rows #1 and #2 is due to different *class definitions*, while the performance difference between rows #2 and #3 is due to different *data distributions*.

5 Conclusions and Future Work

We applied extremely weakly-supervised methods to HS classification. We analyzed the transferability of HS classification models through comprehensive in-dataset and cross-dataset experiments and confirmed that weakly-supervised classification has several advantages over the traditional supervised classification paradigm. First, we can apply the algorithm across various HS datasets and domains with taxonomies that cannot be standardized using category mapping. Second, weakly-supervised models can readily utilize unlabeled documents in

[14]All experiments use the target taxonomy, and all documents are unlabeled.

[15]Its average recall in the "Waseem → SBIC" experiment decreased sharply mainly because the category representation for the "Asian" category is far from the document representation (the Waseem dataset does not contain documents related to "Asian"). The model did not predict any document as "Asian".

the target domain and do not suffer from domain mismatch problems. Lastly, weak supervision allows us to "reannotate" a labeled dataset using a different class definition to facilitate cross-dataset comparison, which was previously possible only at the cost of expensive manual annotation.

The presented work is only the beginning of applying weak supervision to HS detection. We can utilize richer category representations than bag-of-keywords. However, such representations should be derived in an unsupervised or weakly-supervised manner to avoid depending on manually labeled datasets. A promising approach in this direction is (Shvets et al., 2021), which extracts HS targets and aspects relying on open-domain concept extraction.

Lastly, we can study how well the model can generalize to previously unknown categories, a more challenging task often known as zero-shot classification (Yin et al., 2019) or open-world classification (Shu et al., 2017).

Limitations

This study utilizes a monolingual pre-trained language model (PLM) in the English language (`bert-base-uncased`). Although the weakly-supervised classification methods are not limited to a particular language, we have not explored applying the method to another language. Social media language use may differ significantly from the data used to train the PLM. Moreover, the presence of code-switching (Doğruöz et al., 2021) may also degrade a monolingual PLM's performance. We explored a RoBERTa checkpoint continually trained with 60M English tweets (Barbieri et al., 2020).[16] However, it does not yield better performance than BERT. We have not investigated whether it is due to the training regime or the dataset.

Moreover, in this work, we focus on classifying hate speech (HS) categories/target groups instead of HS detection (detecting whether a post contains hate speech or not). To perform hate detection and classification, we can either combine our method with another HS detection model in a pipeline or use an adaptation of weakly-supervised text classification incorporating the "Others" category such as Li et al. (2018) or Li et al. (2021).

Due to limited space, we prioritized in-depth analysis instead of a comprehensive evaluation. Therefore, we selected only two datasets (and two-way cross-dataset classification). We are working in parallel on extending this work to a longer-form journal article to cover more datasets and experimental results.

Recent work on large language models (LLMs) demonstrated that when the parameters scale to a certain level, language models exhibit a drastically-increased performance in zero-shot classification (Zhao et al., 2023). We reported the performance of a moderately-sized `bert-large-uncased` zero-shot model because of limited computational resources and lack of access to commercial APIs. Larger language models will likely perform much better than this baseline.

Lastly, understanding HS sometimes requires cultural understanding or background knowledge. It may be difficult to determine the presence and category of HS when we take the post out of its context. For example, many "Sexist" posts in Waseem dataset are tweets related to the Australian TV show *My Kitchen Rules* (MKR), and below is a tweet labeled as "Sexist":

> Everyone else, despite our commentary, has fought hard too. It's not just you, Kat. #mkr

Ethics Considerations

Although weak supervision requires only unlabeled documents, we demonstrated that the model might fail when the training dataset does not contain data related to a particular category or target group. It is especially concerning because the target groups are often minorities and under-represented. Therefore, we recommend against "throwing" a weakly-supervised algorithm on a dataset and hope the model will work. Instead, we should evaluate a model thoroughly before applying it to the real world, such as manually examining the model's predictions, behavioral testing the model using a checklist (Ribeiro et al., 2020) or conducting unsupervised error estimation (Jin et al., 2021).

References

Aymé Arango, Jorge Pérez, and Barbara Poblete. 2019. Hate speech detection is not as easy as you may think: A closer look at model validation. In *Proceedings of the 42nd international acm sigir conference on research and development in information retrieval*, pages 45–54.

Francesco Barbieri, Jose Camacho-Collados, Luis Espinosa Anke, and Leonardo Neves. 2020. TweetEval:

[16] `https://huggingface.co/cardiffnlp/twitter-roberta-base`

Unified benchmark and comparative evaluation for tweet classification. In *Findings of the Association for Computational Linguistics: EMNLP 2020*, pages 1644–1650, Online. Association for Computational Linguistics.

Valerio Basile, Cristina Bosco, Elisabetta Fersini, Debora Nozza, Viviana Patti, Francisco Manuel Rangel Pardo, Paolo Rosso, and Manuela Sanguinetti. 2019. SemEval-2019 task 5: Multilingual detection of hate speech against immigrants and women in Twitter. In *Proceedings of the 13th International Workshop on Semantic Evaluation*, pages 54–63, Minneapolis, Minnesota, USA. Association for Computational Linguistics.

Michał Bilewicz and Wiktor Soral. 2020. Hate speech epidemic. the dynamic effects of derogatory language on intergroup relations and political radicalization. *Political Psychology*, 41:3–33.

Avrim Blum and Tom Mitchell. 1998. Combining labeled and unlabeled data with co-training. In *Proceedings of the eleventh annual conference on Computational learning theory*, pages 92–100.

Tommaso Caselli, Valerio Basile, Jelena Mitrović, Inga Kartoziya, and Michael Granitzer. 2020. I feel offended, don't be abusive! implicit/explicit messages in offensive and abusive language. In *Proceedings of the Twelfth Language Resources and Evaluation Conference*, pages 6193–6202, Marseille, France. European Language Resources Association.

Corinna Cortes and Vladimir Vapnik. 1995. Support-vector networks. *Machine learning*, 20(3):273–297.

Hal Daumé III. 2007. Frustratingly easy domain adaptation. In *Proceedings of the 45th Annual Meeting of the Association of Computational Linguistics*, pages 256–263, Prague, Czech Republic. Association for Computational Linguistics.

Thomas Davidson, Dana Warmsley, Michael Macy, and Ingmar Weber. 2017. Automated hate speech detection and the problem of offensive language. In *Proceedings of the eleventh international AAAI conference on web and social media*, 1, pages 512–515.

Jacob Devlin, Ming-Wei Chang, Kenton Lee, and Kristina Toutanova. 2019. BERT: Pre-training of deep bidirectional transformers for language understanding. In *Proceedings of the 2019 Conference of the North American Chapter of the Association for Computational Linguistics: Human Language Technologies, Volume 1 (Long and Short Papers)*, pages 4171–4186, Minneapolis, Minnesota. Association for Computational Linguistics.

A. Seza Doğruöz, Sunayana Sitaram, Barbara E. Bullock, and Almeida Jacqueline Toribio. 2021. A survey of code-switching: Linguistic and social perspectives for language technologies. In *Proceedings of the 59th Annual Meeting of the Association for Computational Linguistics and the 11th International Joint Conference on Natural Language Processing (Volume 1: Long Papers)*, pages 1654–1666, Online. Association for Computational Linguistics.

Richard O Duda and Peter E Hart. 1973. Pattern classification and scene analysis. *A Wiley-Interscience Publication*.

Paula Fortuna, Monica Dominguez, Leo Wanner, and Zeerak Talat. 2022. Directions for nlp practices applied to online hate speech detection. In *Proceedings of the 2022 Conference on Empirical Methods in Natural Language Processing*, page 11794–11805, Abu Dhabi, United Arab Emirates. Association for Computational Linguistics.

Paula Fortuna, Juan Soler, and Leo Wanner. 2020. Toxic, hateful, offensive or abusive? what are we really classifying? an empirical analysis of hate speech datasets. In *Proceedings of the Twelfth Language Resources and Evaluation Conference*, pages 6786–6794, Marseille, France. European Language Resources Association.

Paula Fortuna, Juan Soler-Company, and Leo Wanner. 2021. How well do hate speech, toxicity, abusive and offensive language classification models generalize across datasets? *Information Processing & Management*, 58(3):102524.

Lei Gao, Alexis Kuppersmith, and Ruihong Huang. 2017. Recognizing explicit and implicit hate speech using a weakly supervised two-path bootstrapping approach. In *Proceedings of the Eighth International Joint Conference on Natural Language Processing (Volume 1: Long Papers)*, pages 774–782, Taipei, Taiwan. Asian Federation of Natural Language Processing.

Sepp Hochreiter and Jürgen Schmidhuber. 1997. Long short-term memory. *Neural computation*, 9(8):1735–1780.

Yiping Jin, Akshay Bhatia, and Dittaya Wanvarie. 2021. Seed word selection for weakly-supervised text classification with unsupervised error estimation. In *Proceedings of the 2021 Conference of the North American Chapter of the Association for Computational Linguistics: Student Research Workshop*, pages 112–118, Online. Association for Computational Linguistics.

Yiping Jin, Dittaya Wanvarie, and Phu TV Le. 2022. Learning from noisy out-of-domain corpus using dataless classification. *Natural Language Engineering*, 28(1):39–69.

Mladen Karan and Jan Šnajder. 2018. Cross-domain detection of abusive language online. In *Proceedings of the 2nd Workshop on Abusive Language Online (ALW2)*, pages 132–137, Brussels, Belgium. Association for Computational Linguistics.

Yoon Kim. 2014. Convolutional neural networks for sentence classification. In *Proceedings of the*

2014 Conference on Empirical Methods in Natural Language Processing (EMNLP), pages 1746–1751, Doha, Qatar. Association for Computational Linguistics.

Chenliang Li, Wei Zhou, Feng Ji, Yu Duan, and Haiqing Chen. 2018. A deep relevance model for zero-shot document filtering. In *Proceedings of the 56th Annual Meeting of the Association for Computational Linguistics (Volume 1: Long Papers)*, pages 2300–2310, Melbourne, Australia. Association for Computational Linguistics.

Peiran Li, Fang Guo, and Jingbo Shang. 2021. "misc"-aware weakly supervised aspect classification. In *Proceedings of the 2021 SIAM International Conference on Data Mining (SDM)*, pages 468–476. SIAM.

Dheeraj Mekala and Jingbo Shang. 2020. Contextualized weak supervision for text classification. In *Proceedings of the 58th Annual Meeting of the Association for Computational Linguistics*, pages 323–333, Online. Association for Computational Linguistics.

Yu Meng, Jiaming Shen, Chao Zhang, and Jiawei Han. 2018. Weakly-supervised neural text classification. In *Proceedings of the 27th ACM International Conference on Information and Knowledge Management*, pages 983–992, Turin, Italy.

Yu Meng, Yunyi Zhang, Jiaxin Huang, Chenyan Xiong, Heng Ji, Chao Zhang, and Jiawei Han. 2020. Text classification using label names only: A language model self-training approach. In *Proceedings of the 2020 Conference on Empirical Methods in Natural Language Processing (EMNLP)*, pages 9006–9017, Online. Association for Computational Linguistics.

Alexandra Olteanu, Carlos Castillo, Jeremy Boy, and Kush Varshney. 2018. The effect of extremist violence on hateful speech online. In *Proceedings of the twelfth international AAAI conference on web and social media*, 1, Stanford, California, USA.

Long Ouyang, Jeffrey Wu, Xu Jiang, Diogo Almeida, Carroll Wainwright, Pamela Mishkin, Chong Zhang, Sandhini Agarwal, Katarina Slama, Alex Ray, et al. 2022. Training language models to follow instructions with human feedback. *Advances in Neural Information Processing Systems*, 35:27730–27744.

Fabio Poletto, Valerio Basile, Manuela Sanguinetti, Cristina Bosco, and Viviana Patti. 2021. Resources and benchmark corpora for hate speech detection: a systematic review. *Language Resources and Evaluation*, 55(2):477–523.

David MW Powers. 1998. Applications and explanations of zipf's law. In *Proceedings of the Joint Conferences on New Methods in Language Processing and Computational Natural Language Learning*, pages 151–160, Sydney, NSW, Australia.

Colin Raffel, Noam Shazeer, Adam Roberts, Katherine Lee, Sharan Narang, Michael Matena, Yanqi Zhou, Wei Li, and Peter J Liu. 2020. Exploring the limits of transfer learning with a unified text-to-text transformer. *Journal of Machine Learning Research*, 21:1–67.

Marco Tulio Ribeiro, Tongshuang Wu, Carlos Guestrin, and Sameer Singh. 2020. Beyond accuracy: Behavioral testing of NLP models with CheckList. In *Proceedings of the 58th Annual Meeting of the Association for Computational Linguistics*, pages 4902–4912, Online. Association for Computational Linguistics.

Victor Sanh, Albert Webson, Colin Raffel, Stephen Bach, Lintang Sutawika, Zaid Alyafeai, Antoine Chaffin, Arnaud Stiegler, Teven Le Scao, Arun Raja, et al. 2022. Multitask prompted training enables zero-shot task generalization. In *The Tenth International Conference on Learning Representations*.

Maarten Sap, Saadia Gabriel, Lianhui Qin, Dan Jurafsky, Noah A. Smith, and Yejin Choi. 2020. Social bias frames: Reasoning about social and power implications of language. In *Proceedings of the 58th Annual Meeting of the Association for Computational Linguistics*, pages 5477–5490, Online. Association for Computational Linguistics.

Timo Schick and Hinrich Schütze. 2021a. Exploiting cloze-questions for few-shot text classification and natural language inference. In *Proceedings of the 16th Conference of the European Chapter of the Association for Computational Linguistics: Main Volume*, pages 255–269, Online. Association for Computational Linguistics.

Timo Schick and Hinrich Schütze. 2021b. It's not just size that matters: Small language models are also few-shot learners. In *Proceedings of the 2021 Conference of the North American Chapter of the Association for Computational Linguistics: Human Language Technologies*, pages 2339–2352, Online. Association for Computational Linguistics.

Lei Shu, Hu Xu, and Bing Liu. 2017. DOC: Deep open classification of text documents. In *Proceedings of the 2017 Conference on Empirical Methods in Natural Language Processing*, pages 2911–2916, Copenhagen, Denmark. Association for Computational Linguistics.

Alexander Shvets, Paula Fortuna, Juan Soler, and Leo Wanner. 2021. Targets and aspects in social media hate speech. In *Proceedings of the 5th Workshop on Online Abuse and Harms (WOAH 2021)*, pages 179–190, Online. Association for Computational Linguistics.

Steve Durairaj Swamy, Anupam Jamatia, and Björn Gambäck. 2019. Studying generalisability across abusive language detection datasets. In *Proceedings of the 23rd Conference on Computational Natural Language Learning (CoNLL)*, pages 940–950, Hong Kong, China. Association for Computational Linguistics.

Zeerak Talat, Aurélie Névéol, Stella Biderman, Miruna Clinciu, Manan Dey, Shayne Longpre, Sasha Luccioni, Maraim Masoud, Margaret Mitchell, Dragomir Radev, Shanya Sharma, Arjun Subramonian, Jaesung Tae, Samson Tan, Deepak Tunuguntla, and Oskar Van Der Wal. 2022. You reap what you sow: On the challenges of bias evaluation under multilingual settings. In *Proceedings of BigScience episode #5 – workshop on challenges & perspectives in creating large language models*, pages 26–41, virtual+Dublin. Association for Computational Linguistics.

Zeerak Talat, James Thorne, and Joachim Bingel. 2018. Bridging the gaps: Multi task learning for domain transfer of hate speech detection. In *Online harassment*, pages 29–55. Springer.

Zihan Wang, Dheeraj Mekala, and Jingbo Shang. 2021. X-class: Text classification with extremely weak supervision. In *Proceedings of the 2021 Conference of the North American Chapter of the Association for Computational Linguistics: Human Language Technologies*, pages 3043–3053, Online. Association for Computational Linguistics.

Zeerak Waseem. 2016. Are you a racist or am I seeing things? annotator influence on hate speech detection on Twitter. In *Proceedings of the First Workshop on NLP and Computational Social Science*, pages 138–142, Austin, Texas. Association for Computational Linguistics.

Zeerak Waseem and Dirk Hovy. 2016. Hateful symbols or hateful people? predictive features for hate speech detection on Twitter. In *Proceedings of the NAACL Student Research Workshop*, pages 88–93, San Diego, California. Association for Computational Linguistics.

Michael Wiegand, Josef Ruppenhofer, and Thomas Kleinbauer. 2019. Detection of Abusive Language: the Problem of Biased Datasets. In *Proceedings of the 2019 Conference of the North American Chapter of the Association for Computational Linguistics: Human Language Technologies, Volume 1 (Long and Short Papers)*, pages 602–608, Minneapolis, Minnesota. Association for Computational Linguistics.

Wenjie Yin and Arkaitz Zubiaga. 2021. Towards generalisable hate speech detection: a review on obstacles and solutions. *PeerJ Computer Science*, 7:e598.

Wenpeng Yin, Jamaal Hay, and Dan Roth. 2019. Benchmarking zero-shot text classification: Datasets, evaluation and entailment approach. In *Proceedings of the 2019 Conference on Empirical Methods in Natural Language Processing and the 9th International Joint Conference on Natural Language Processing (EMNLP-IJCNLP)*, pages 3914–3923, Hong Kong, China. Association for Computational Linguistics.

Wayne Xin Zhao, Kun Zhou, Junyi Li, Tianyi Tang, Xiaolei Wang, Yupeng Hou, Yingqian Min, Beichen Zhang, Junjie Zhang, Zican Dong, et al. 2023. A survey of large language models. *arXiv preprint arXiv:2303.18223*.

A Full List of Keywords in X-Class's Category Representation

Table 9 shows the list of keywords in X-Class's category representation in the in-dataset setting (using the unlabeled documents and list of categories from the same dataset). Table 10 shows the list of keywords in X-Class's category representation in the cross-dataset setting (using the unlabeled Waseem dataset documents to induce category representations of SBIC dataset categories and vice versa).

B Reproducibility

Table 11 presents the hyper-parameters and their corresponding values to facilitate reproducing our result.

We use the `bert-large-uncased` model in HuggingFace as the base pre-trained language model for the zero-shot PET baseline. PET combines a *pattern* (or prompt/instruction) with the input text and prompts the model to predict the mask token. Unlike open-ended prompting, PET uses a list of hand-crafted *verbalizers* (candidate tokens). It classifies documents by assigning the category whose associated verbalizer receives the highest predicted probability. PET-style classification is especially beneficial for smaller PLMs, which do not possess a strong capability of instruction following (Schick and Schütze, 2021b; Ouyang et al., 2022).

We hand-crafted patterns and verbalizers based on our understanding of the tasks (without fine-tuning). For Waseem dataset, we use the pattern "<text> This hate speech is based on <mask>" (verbalizers: gender/race), and for SBIC dataset "<text> The target group of this hate speech is <mask>" (verbalizers: women/black/Jews/gay/Muslims/Asian).

C Pseudo-Labeling

Being able to accurately pseudo-label documents is crucial to the success of weak supervision. We report the accuracy of pseudo-labeling by various weakly-supervised methods in Table 8.

We can see that the accuracy of pseudo-labeled documents is consistent with the model's performance on the test dataset (Table 4). Moreover, LOTClass and X-Class use the same underlying pre-trained language model (`bert-base-uncased`) in their final classifier, while WeSTClass uses a more traditional convolutional neural networks architecture (Kim, 2014). The data pseudo-labeled by

Dataset (Method)	Acc	P/R/F$_1$
Waseem	**99.1**	**98.4/99.2/98.9**
- WeSTClass	77.8	77.9/80.1/77.4
- LOTClass	64.4	72.7/70.9/64.3
SBIC	**93.0**	**89.1/92.8/91.1**
- WeSTClass	35.4	34.8/35.6/29.9
- LOTClass	51.8	32.4/26.3/24.5
SBIC → Waseem	91.2	92.1/90.9/91.0

Table 8: Pseudo-labeled dataset accuracy calculated against the gold-standard labels. The default method is X-Class unless otherwise specified. For the "SBIC → Waseem" setting, we use the category mapping in Table 1 to derive the gold labels. We omit the "Waseem → SBIC" setting because we do not have gold labels.

X-Class is substantially more accurate than the two baselines in both datasets. Comparing Table 8 and Table 4, we can observe that the pseudo-labeling accuracy has a more significant impact on the final classifier's accuracy than the model architecture.

We provide randomly sampled pseudo-labeled documents by X-Class in Table 12 (in-dataset) and Table 13 (cross-dataset). In general, the SBIC dataset contains more diverse and nuanced data. On the other hand, the Waseem dataset sometimes contains trivial slurs like "... I'm not sexist ...". The samples in the cross-dataset setting revealed that X-Class tends to wrongly categorize original "Sexist" posts in the Waseem dataset (which mainly target women) as "LGBT" and "Asian".

Class	Keywords
Sexist	sexist sexism misogynist sl*ts sl*t hypocrisy bigotry c*nts hypocrite bigoted pedophile filth c*nt phony barbarity scum bigot genocidal barbaric raping bitchy bigots rapist rapists blasphemy feminists mongering apostacy delusional trashy bimbos a*sholes skank retarded idiotic morons illiterate behead being sexual gays extremists sex islamophobia apostates whining self islamofascists beheads b*tches rape dudes beheading s*cking an enslave pure up common of a sassy vandaliser gender by feminist
Racist	racist racists racism naziphobia fascist oppression hateful hatred semitic imperialist hating race imperialism genocide inhuman vile ideology violent murderous violence anti nazism vileness brutal propaganda nazis terrorist filthy disgusting radical murdering terrorists hate abuse attacking islamists islamolunatic islamolunatics minority murderers domination jihad terrorism islamist westerners evil killing attack against hated atheists political terror murder culture minorities religious lunatics human conspiracy population hatewatch killings secular religion force cult
Women	women woman female females girls ladies ch*cks wives men feminist lady girl chick feminists feminine males male gender feminism whores blonde virgins bitches guys hookers prostitutes sl*ts mens wh*re sl*t b*tch p*ssy prostitute virgin couples d*cks breast moms c*nts girlfriend wife sisters dudes attractive sexy betas partners she her beautiful genders lovers normies mothers boys man chads adult couple them fathers mensrights normie assholes they body someone bodies looking v*ginas loser dyk*y sister ones femaloid self mate material raped hooker
Black	black white colored blacks whites n*gro african negroes negros racial race racist races minorities color africans n*groids minority n*groid racism mixed brown n*ggers skinned blackman slaves peoples ghetto discrimination n*gger people whitey africa red yellow dark savages individuals civil poor disabled blind gorillas savage human folk nonwhite left lynching slavery diversity worthless folks south gorilla majority violent dirty green cotton slave
Jewish	jewish jews jew synagogue rabbi israel zionist semitic holocaust kosher auschwitz nazi goyim german aryan germans nazis ethiopian germany hitler concentration ash
LGBT	gay homosexual gays homosexuals homosexuality lesbian lesbians queer transgender homophobic sexuality sexual h*mo queers transgenders masculine sexism sexist trans sex sexually straight dating anal dyke dykes penis marriage rape erection pubic openly pedophile porn nude hiv aids raping interracial relationships relationship genitals boyfriends pedophilia objectifying bi std naked d*ck cocks date misogynist misogyny threesome masturbating shaming stoned v*gina assault bestiality c*nt f*cks rapist genital hot c*ck
Muslim	muslim muslims islamic islam mosque mosques arabic quran arab muhammad mohammed shia prophet religion terrorists christian religious allah saudi christians terrorist pakistani arabia ali terrorism pakistan prophets bombers isis syria al qaeda banislam radical camels mass bomber bombing church refugees iran suicide iraq middle faith mosul abdul converted jesus akbar military bomb nations militant pray god kkk militia attacks bible propaganda attack
Asian	asian asians chinese oriental korean japanese american vietnamese indian ethnic mexican americans english latina china eastern foreign exotic european koreans pacific russian north indians spanish russians thai east korea japan country america french cultural western irish countries cuban international nigerian chinaman culture british primitive aged ape inner refugee alien older states europe united animal fat nationality usa russia armed old ignorant special city iq traitor eating animals hungarian food intelligent modern state vietnam rice

Table 9: Full list of keywords in X-Class's category representation mined from *in-dataset* setting.

Class	Keywords
Sexist	sexist sexism homophobic misogyny misogynist hypocrisy sl*ts sl*t c*nts sl*tty degenerate pedophile pedophilia lesbians sexual masculinity bestiality stereotypical shaming whores feminists masturbating mutilation trashy objectifying homosexuals sexually patriarchy misandry raping c*nt rapist hypocritical gays discriminated genital degeneracy unoriginal a*sholes retarded queers virgins disgusting cannibalism self kinky barbarity promiscuity genitals f*cks rape
Racist	racist racism racial discrimination race ethnic races blacks black colored white whites n*gro african negroes minority asians minorities oppression diversity negros ghetto n*groid n*groids mixed cultural peoples africans n*ggers color semitic americans american culture asian individuals people savages savage violence slavery n*gger mixing transgenders mass skinned worthless queer slaves
Women	women woman female females ladies girls feminine feminist feminists feminism womens gender male men girl lady ch*cks blonde blondes males femininity mens wives guys ch*ck wife yesallwomen b*tches daughters her she stars b*tchy girlfriend body b*tch sister feminismisawful announcers promogirls sportscasters bodies models they themselves refs ones them couples someone diva their sjw mother
Black	black white blacks whites racists racist race minorities minority racism africans oppressed americans oppression people population human
Jewish	jewish jews jew judaism israel palestinian zionist palestinians israelis israeli palestine semitic semitism hamas gaza holocaust nazis nazi egyptians
LGBT	gay gays sexual sex sexism sexists sexist rape raping misogynist rapists reproductive misogyny pedophile rapist genitals sl*ts sl*t raped c*nts assault dudes masculinity porn boys shaming c*nt hypocrisy v*gina bigotry rapes bigoted hypocrites hateful haters stereotype openly bimbos wh*re abuse misandrist
Muslim	muslim muslims islamic islam islamist sunni religious islamists jihadi jihadis arab arabs mosques shia quran jihad religion muhammad mohammed taqiyya allah terrorist terrorists prophet believers religions christian hadiths sharia baghdadi secular caliphate hadith saudis saudi pakistani imam christians terrorism islamolunatics isis islamofascists arabian arabia umar extremists hindus pakistan taquiyya medina qurans mullah sunnah westerners
Asian	asian intelligent attractive ignorant young pretty dumb hot rich fat ugly stupid smart tough looking crazy insane blond selfish common brainwashed correct biased clever annoying childish being most hating seeing old beautiful terrible killer self innocent a everydaysexism friendly average ridiculous idiotic extremely poor good bad flawed decent great low simple nice an legit out safe trash doing useless awful corrupt funny sick strong other known working many making best no

Table 10: Full list of keywords in X-Class's category representation mined from *cross-dataset* setting.

Hyper-parameter	Value	Description
random_seed	42	The fixed random seed. Used to split the dataset and initialize parameters.
lm_ckp	bert-base-uncased	The pre-trained language model checkpoint used to derive document representations.
clf_ckp	bert-base-uncased	The pre-trained language model checkpoint used to fine-tune the final classifier. Used in both supervised and weakly-supervised settings.
min_freq	5	Minimum frequency of a word to be included in the vocabulary.
T	100	Maximum terms to include in the category representation.
cluster_method	gmm	Method to perform document class alignment in X-Class. We use the default Gaussian Mixture Model with tied covariance.
pca_dim	64	Dimension of principal component analysis before performing clustering.
conf_threshold	0.5	The percentage of most confident documents assigned by GMM to include in the pseudo-labeled training set.
max_len*	64	The maximum number of tokens of the input posts. Input longer than it will be truncated.
batch_size‡	64	The training batch size.
n_epochs‡	6	The number of training epochs.
learning_rate‡	2e-5	
weight_decay‡	0.05	
lr_schedule†	cosine w/ warmup	Learning rate schedule. Cosine learning rate schedule with 1/3 steps warm-up.

Table 11: Full list of hyper-parameters. The first block is hyper-parameters related to X-Class. The second block is hyper-parameters related to the classifier fine-tuning. * denotes values set based on data analysis. ‡ denotes values set by manual hyperparameter tuning. † denotes values chosen based on our experience but are not tuned. All the rest of the parameters default from the X-Class repo.

Class	Posts	Correct?
Sexist	AbuserDynamics Girls should count themselves lucky if they got a guy that still shouts when his mad, means he cares	✓
	I have a stupid man crush on Lloyd and I can't help it. mkr2015 mkr sexylloydmkr	✓
	RT This lady is a terrible official. Not because she's a lady though. I'm not sexist. But because she's a stupid b*tch. Cavs	✓
Racist	RT CNN reports on the murders of homosexuals by the Islamic State, but the problem isn t just ISIS, it s Islam	✓
	Yes, there is even more rape in Muslim countries but it is not reported.	✓
	For example, the Quran says leaving Islam is not accepted. The Hadiths say kill anyone who leaves.	✓
Women	Molly make b*tches crazy	✓
	The emoji I use when I'm flirting wit b*tches gt	✓
	Rule number two don't trust nobody especially a b*tch with a hookers body	✓
Black	It's funny when u get a black female mad they start acting ghetto then a b*tch	✓
	White bitches be lovin da colored men	✗
	Those ratchet broads don't represent me but YOUR white a*s can't talk trash about them 'cause you on racist sh*t "Black"'	✓
Jewish	What was the Jewish pirate's nickname? Hooknose.	✓
	Do you know why do Jewish kids wait behind the chimney? Because they're waiting for their parents .	✓
	Why do Jews hate a*sholes? The can't stand gas chambers.	✓
LGBT	Any man even considering plastic surgery is gay gay gay imagine ya boy say "I'd get more hoes then u after I get these new lips"	✓
	do it i f*cking dare you f*ggot	✓
	What do you call a gay drive by? A fruit roll up.	✓
Muslim	RT Fuck Islam you pigfucking trash troll.	✓
	Bomb your house, Then f*ck your b*tch. All hail Al Qaeda	✓
	What did the Muslim say after eating a bacon sandwich? That's the way Allah Allah I like it.	✓
Asian	My economics professor just called these asians retards	✓
	Korean idols are perfectly handsome, cute, funny, stylish, hot, know how to dance, have a wonderful voices.	✗
	The Stock Exchange I like the NYSE just like the Ethiopian population count. Going down faster than ever.	✗

Table 12: Randomly sampled pseudo-labeled examples for each category in the in-dataset setting.

Class	Posts	Correct?
Sexist	on sale a*s hoes	✓
	Molly make b*tches crazy	✓
	This n*ggga said I be branding b*tches	✗
Racist	RT Wow the stupid n*gger in LeBron really came out there	✓
	My Moor friends,no not black friends,but Moor friends said N*gger came from Nigeria...You are so lost..Stop tagging me...	✓
	RT Remember the "yellow badge" Nazis used? Israel is making Muslim women carry a yellow badge order to pray in Al Aqsa. h	✓
Women	RT I'm no sexist but the last thing I wanna read about is women's, football or cricket on the sky sports news app! controve	✓
	RT Then I guess Feminism is just a sideshow as much as WWE wrestling in general.. Irony is off the c	✓
	Are you even a real person? I'm not sexist. But Men are superior to women	✓
Black	Can't forget it...never heard about it...	✗
	...with a flat face. The nose a bay window.	✗
	But look at the reality disconnect. Burak says he is for freedom and against all slavery while at the ...	✓
Jewish	Max Blumenthal is bad mouthing you. Not enough room at the top for all the self genocidal Jews. Israel Palestine	✓
	The job Mohammed set Muslims is not done while Israel exists.	✓
	The Jews of Europe should just come to the US. Then the Europeans can allow Islam to take them backwards.	✓
LGBT	RT I'm not sexist but right now I hate girls !!!!	✗
	RT This is not sexist but I want to punch both of the girls from broad city workaholics	✗
	RT This is why girls don't play football. Someone's feelings get hurt and boom, it's out of hand. Go ahead and call me sexist,	✗
Muslim	You didn't recognize the irony of me using your method because you are an ignorant Muslim.	✓
	And you lie again. The majority of Muslims were forced into it.	✓
	RT Arab slave trade 140 to 200 million non Muslim slaves from all colors and nationalities still happening today!	✓
Asian	Someone really needs to get the sniffer dogs onto Kat offherlips MKR	✗
	MKR anyone can cook from a can girls.	✗
	Kat you don't look suspicious at all! MKR	✗

Table 13: Randomly sampled pseudo-labeled examples for each category in the cross-dataset setting.

Respectful or Toxic?
Using Zero-Shot Learning with Language Models to Detect Hate Speech

Flor Miriam Plaza-del-Arco, Debora Nozza, Dirk Hovy
Bocconi University
Via Sarfatti 25
Milan, Italy
{flor.plaza, debora.nozza, dirk.hovy}@unibocconi.it

Abstract

Hate speech detection faces two significant challenges: 1) the limited availability of labeled data and 2) the high variability of hate speech across different contexts and languages. Prompting brings a ray of hope to these challenges. It allows injecting a model with task-specific knowledge without relying on labeled data. This paper explores zero-shot learning with prompting for hate speech detection. We investigate how well zero-shot learning can detect hate speech in 3 languages with limited labeled data. We experiment with various large language models and verbalizers on 8 benchmark datasets. Our findings highlight the impact of prompt selection on the results. They also suggest that prompting, specifically with recent large language models, can achieve performance comparable to and surpass fine-tuned models, making it a promising alternative for under-resourced languages. Our findings highlight the potential of prompting for hate speech detection and show how both the prompt and the model have a significant impact on achieving more accurate predictions in this task.

1 Introduction

The rising prevalence of online hate speech and its harmful effects have made hate speech detection a central task in natural language processing (NLP). Despite progress, the prevalent supervised learning approaches encounter significant challenges: many languages or contexts have little or no labeled data (Poletto et al., 2021). Hate speech is also subjective and context-dependent, as it is influenced by factors such as demographics, social norms, and cultural backgrounds (Talat and Hovy, 2016).

To overcome these challenges, approaches like zero-shot learning (ZSL) and prompting of large language models (LLMs) have emerged.[1] Both use a *template* to process the original text and the class labels as *verbalizers*. This approach leverages the LLM's knowledge to predict the likelihood of the (class) verbalizers in the template. These verbalizers guide the model's understanding of a specific task. For binary hate speech detection, the template might be "`<text>`. This text is `<verbalizer>`", where `<verbalizer>` can be "`hateful`" or "`non-hateful`". For the input, "I hate you. This text is", the LLM should associate a higher likelihood with the verbalizer completion "`hateful`". By picking the more likely completion, this approach requires no training data. It has shown promising results in various NLP applications (Zhao et al., 2023; Su et al., 2022; Wei et al., 2022; Brown et al., 2020).However, to date, its effectiveness for hate speech detection remains largely unexplored.

We comprehensively evaluate ZSL with prompting for hate speech detection to better understand its capabilities. The choice of appropriate verbalizers is a key factor in the effectiveness of prompting (Plaza-del-Arco et al., 2022; Liu et al., 2023). To this end, we systematically compare various verbalizers across multiple models. We evaluate the performance of conventional transformer models and more recent instruction fine-tuned LLMs on 8 benchmark datasets to assess their robustness. Furthermore, we test our approach on two languages with limited labeled data (Italian and Spanish). Our results show that ZSL with prompting matches or surpasses the performance of fine-tuned models, particularly in instruction fine-tuned models.

Contributions 1) We investigate the effectiveness of ZSL with prompting for hate speech detection 2) We conduct a systematic exploration and comparison of various verbalizers across 5 models 3) We extend our investigation to two languages with limited labeled data. Our code is publicly available at `https://github.com/MilaNLProc/prompting_hate_speech`.

[1] Note that ZSL could be used with various models, whereas prompting is specific to LLMs. Here, we use ZSL to prompt LLMs without additional labeled examples in the prompt (few-shot learning), but only the target sentence.

The 7th Workshop on Online Abuse and Harms (WOAH), pages 60–68
July 13, 2023 ©2023 Association for Computational Linguistics

2 Datasets

We compare our results on 8 benchmark datasets using binary classification. See Table 1 for details. They differ in terms of size, corpus source, and labels. More details are in Appendix A.

Dataset	Size	Source
DAVIDSON	24,802	Twitter
DYNABENCH	41,255	Synthetic
GHC	27,665	Gab
HATEVAL	13,000	Twitter
HATEXPLAIN	20,148	Twitter and Gab
MHS	50,000	Youtube, Twitter and Reddit
MLMA	5,647	Twitter
HSHP	16,914	Twitter

Table 1: Datasets used in our experiments.

3 Prompting for Zero-Shot Hate Speech Classification

We use ZSL with prompting to evaluate the models' ability to detect hate speech. First, we test various encoder models to select the best verbalizers. We then test those verbalizers on recent instruction fine-tuned LLMs and compare to encoder models.

Encoder-based Language Models For our experiments, we use the following prompt template: "`<text>` This text is `<verbalizers>`". We then check the LLM likelihood of hateful and non-hateful verbalizers and select the most probable completion as final prediction. We test all 25 possible pairs from the following lists. For hate: `harmful`, `abusive`, `offensive`, `hateful`, `toxic`, and for non-hate `respectful`, `kind`, `polite`, `neutral`, `positive`.

We compare three different language models: BERT (Devlin et al., 2019), RoBERTa (Liu et al., 2019), and DeBERTa (He et al., 2020). We use OpenPrompt (Ding et al., 2022), a standard framework for prompt learning over pre-trained language models.

Instruction Fine-tuned Language Models We experiment with recent instruction fine-tuned language models. They are fine-tuned on a large set of varied instructions that use an intuitive description of the downstream task to answer natural language prompts. In this approach, we formulate the prompt template as "Classify this text as <verb$_{\text{non-hate}}$> or <verb$_{\text{hate}}$>. <text>. Answer:", for the *verbalizers* (verb$_{\text{non-hate}}$, verb$_{\text{hate}}$) we consider the best pair obtained with the encoder models, and for the prompt models, we use the Fine-tuned Language Net (FLAN-T5) model (Chung et al., 2022) and mT0 (Muennighoff et al., 2022). Note that FLAN-T5 has been trained for toxic language detection.

Baseline We used (1) a RoBERTa model fine-tuned with supervised training on each hate speech dataset and (2) the commercial Perspective API.[2]

4 Results

4.1 Encoder models

Table 2 shows the results of several encoder models on multiple hate speech detection benchmark datasets. Overall, the best-performing encoder model across different datasets is $\text{RoBERTa}_{\text{LARGE}}$ obtained the best macro-F1 score in 5 out of 8 datasets. Regarding the verbalizers, the pair `positive` and `polite` yield the best results in identifying non-hateful speech, while `hateful` and `toxic` prove best for detecting hate speech. This highlights the need for careful selection of verbalizers to achieve optimal performance in this task.

Identifying Best Verbalizers To select the best pair of verbalizers that work well across models and datasets for hate speech detection, we averaged the different performance metrics by model and dataset across all folds. As shown in Table 3, the best-performing verbalizer pair is `respectful-toxic`, which achieves the highest macro-F1 score of 42.74. The verbalizers most commonly associated with the non-hate speech class are `respectful` and `polite`, while `toxic` and `hateful` are more commonly associated with hate speech. We select the best verbalizer pair (`respectful-toxic`) to conduct additional experiments.

4.2 Encoder vs. Instruction Fine-tuned LLMs

In this section, we compare the results obtained by prompting the encoder-based models and the instruction fine-tuned models. The results are shown in Table 4. These models are prompted using the best pair of verbalizers we found in the encoder-based models, which is `respectful-toxic`. In general, the recent models mT0 and FLAN-T5 outperform the encoder-based models by a large margin showing an average improvement of 39.75% and 65.33% over the encoder models, respectively. In particular, FLAN-T5 exhibits remarkable performance in detecting hate speech across various datasets, which can be attributed to its prior fine-tuning for toxic detection. This suggests that the

[2] `https://www.perspectiveapi.com/`

Dataset	Model	Verb$_{\text{non-hate}}$	Verb$_{\text{hate}}$	F1$_{\text{non-hate}}$	F1$_{\text{hate}}$	Macro-F1
DAVIDSON	RoBERTa$_{\text{LARGE}}$	positive	hateful	41.38	69.15	55.26
DYNABENCH	RoBERTa$_{\text{LARGE}}$	positive	harmful	52.96	57.36	55.16
GHC	RoBERTa$_{\text{LARGE}}$	positive	hateful	45.03	68.85	56.94
HATEVAL	BERT$_{\text{BASE-uncased}}$	polite	toxic	61.52	58.05	59.78
HATEXPLAIN	RoBERTa$_{\text{LARGE}}$	polite	toxic	24.36	86.23	55.30
MHS	RoBERTa$_{\text{LARGE}}$	positive	hateful	66.91	73.68	70.30
MLMA	DeBERTa$_{\text{V3-BASE}}$	polite	hateful	12.32	93.53	52.93
HSHP	RoBERTa$_{\text{BASE}}$	positive	hateful	73.79	54.64	64.21

Table 2: Class and macro-F1 score of encoder models on different benchmark datasets.

Verb-nh	Verb-h	F1-nh	F1-h	Macro-F1
respectful	toxic	27.28	58.19	42.74
polite	hateful	24.37	59.42	41.89
positive	hateful	34.58	48.84	41.71
positive	offensive	19.37	63.94	41.66
neutral	toxic	31.17	52.11	41.64
respectful	hateful	18.60	63.91	41.25
polite	toxic	28.30	53.79	41.04

Table 3: Verbalizer pairs across encoder models and datasets by Macro-F1 score.

knowledge learned from detecting toxic language is transferable and can be leveraged to improve hate speech detection in other datasets. In addition, we conduct a comparison between the supervised learning upper bound, a fine-tuned RoBERTa$_{\text{BASE}}$ model, and the instruction fine-tuned models in our ZSL experiments. Our findings show that the instruction fine-tuned models achieve comparable performance, and FLAN-T5 even surpasses the RoBERTa$_{\text{BASE}}$ fine-tuned model in some datasets, such as GHC, HATEXPLAIN, and MLMA. Overall, the DAVIDSON dataset achieves the highest performance among all the datasets, with a macro-F1 score of 83.30. In contrast, the MLMA dataset obtains the lowest macro-F1 score of 54.35, which is expected given its complexity arising from the low inter-annotator agreement. Notably, the performance on the HATEVAL dataset (65.38) exhibits an improvement over the participant results' mean (44.84) in the competition (Basile et al., 2019). On the DYNABENCH dataset, the FLAN-T5 model's result (58.08) is similar to that of fine-tuning the RoBERTa$_{\text{BASE}}$ fine-tuned model (61.76), despite the dataset's complexity with a large number of challenging perturbations that make it harder for models to detect hate speech accurately. Finally, we compared our approach with Perspective API, the most popular commercial tool for toxicity detection. FLAN-T5 is outperforming it in 6 cases out of 8, demonstrating prompting to be a more accurate solution. While the varying degrees of difficulty across datasets in hate speech detection is demonstrated in these results, the potential of instruction fine-tuned models to achieve state-of-the-art performance on various benchmarks without requiring fine-tuning on a specific dataset is highlighted. This insight is especially valuable for subjective tasks like hate speech, where the complex nature of labeling this phenomenon can make it challenging to find labeled datasets.

5 Results on Multi-Lingual Datasets

We also investigated the effectiveness of ZSL with prompting in a multilingual context, which is often more challenging due to the scarcity or unavailability of data. We present the outcomes achieved by multilingual models: multilingual XLM-R (Conneau et al., 2020) as encoder model and mT0 and FLAN-T5 as instruction fined-tuned models. The prompt has been written in English following the same templates presented in Section 3 and using the best-performing verbalizer pair `respectful-toxic`. We use the experimental settings adopted in Nozza (2021), comparing our method with their fine-tuned XLM-R model. Thus, the dataset comprises English (EN), Spanish (ES), and Italian (IT). The HatEval (Basile et al., 2019) shared task dataset on hate speech against immigrants and women on Twitter is adopted for English and Spanish. For Italian, two different corpora proposed for Evalita shared tasks (Caselli et al., 2018) are considered: the automatic misogyny identification challenge (AMI) (Fersini et al., 2018) for hate speech towards women, and the hate speech detection shared task on Facebook and Twitter (HaSpeeDe) (Bosco et al., 2018) for hate speech towards immigrants.

The results are shown in Table 5. Regarding the ZSL approaches, the instruction fine-tuned models outperform XLM-R, with FLAN-T5 achieving the highest macro-F1 score on all languages. The

Dataset	ZSL Prompting							API	Fine-tuning
	RoBERTa$_B$	RoBERTa$_L$	BERT$_B$	DeBERTa$_B$	DeBERTa$_L$	mT0	FLAN-T5	Perspective API	RoBERTa$_B$
DAVIDSON	42.46	40.87	52.33	46.67	25.99	54.46	<u>83.30</u>	79.20	**91.28**
DYNABENCH	36.68	36.08	45.87	51.38	37.57	54.11	<u>58.08</u>	55.50	**61.76**
GHC	42.02	41.43	53.13	50.13	35.36	56.07	61.53	**62.35**	<u>59.59</u>
HATEVAL	31.89	29.90	59.69	55.82	36.68	57.76	<u>65.38</u>	60.77	**70.98**
HATEXPLAIN	49.38	46.11	48.93	51.67	20.88	56.68	**67.11**	58.86	<u>60.34</u>
MHS	44.60	36.16	62.23	57.38	43.29	74.70	79.38	<u>87.90</u>	**90.50**
MLMA	47.90	47.65	<u>49.47</u>	49.10	28.23	44.97	**54.35**	43.91	47.47
HSHP	27.50	24.77	43.10	44.17	40.37	53.97	<u>64.36</u>	56.30	**76.82**
Avg.% ↑	—	—	—	—	—	39.75 ↑	65.33 ↑	—	—

Table 4: Macro-F1 scores for different models on benchmark datasets using *respectful-toxic* verbalizer. B = base model, L = large model. Best model in bold, second-best underlined. Last row shows the average improvement of Flan-T5 and mT0 over encoder models.

Lang	XLM-R	mT0	FLAN-T5	Nozza (2021)
EN	29.80	<u>57.85</u>	**65.34**	41.6
ES	29.42	53.75	<u>62.61</u>	**75.2**
IT	31.34	43.25	<u>57.29</u>	**80.4**

Table 5: Macro-F1 scores on different languages. Best model in bold, second-best underlined.

ZSL models, as expected, did not outperform the fine-tuned XLM-R. However, the results obtained from the ZSL models are still considered adequate. Spanish, in particular, achieves comparable results with FLAN-T5 to the fine-tuned XLM-R. FLAN-T5 achieves better results in English because it is not affected by overfitting issues that arise during training (Nozza, 2021). These findings suggest that prompting with instruction fine-tuned LLMs is a promising method for hate speech detection in both mono and multilingual settings, without language-specific fine-tuning.

6 Related Work

Hate speech classification received increased attention in recent years. Supervised learning methods are the most common (Poletto et al., 2021; Fortuna et al., 2022). Among these methods, fine-tuning transformer-based LLMs emerged as the dominant paradigm (Plaza-del-Arco et al., 2020; Sarkar et al., 2021; Singh and Li, 2021; Caselli et al., 2021; Kirk et al., 2022, inter alia). However, they face significant challenges, like the limited availability of labeled data, especially in languages other than English (Schmidt and Wiegand, 2017; Fortuna and Nunes, 2018), and the subjective nature of hate speech, which varies based on cultural background, personal experiences, and individual beliefs.

LLMs have led to innovative techniques like prompting (Liu et al., 2023) that use zero-shot and few-shot learning paradigms without needing labeled data. Recent works have explored these new techniques for hate speech detection. Chiu et al. (2021) use the prompts "Is the following text sexist? Answer yes or no" and "Classify the following texts into racist, sexist, or neither" to detect hate speech, with GPT-3 showing that LLMs have a role to play in hate speech detection. Schick et al. (2021) explore toxicity in LLMs using comparable prompts to self-diagnose toxicity during the decoding. They use the RealToxicityPrompts dataset (Gehman et al., 2020). (Goldzycher and Schneider, 2022) develop NLI-based zero-shot hate speech detection approaches using prompts as a hypothesis as proposed by Yin et al. (2019). Their results outperform fine-tuned models. Our work ZSL for hate speech classification differs from previous approaches as follows. (1) We provide a comprehensive evaluation of ZSL with prompting on multiple benchmark datasets, offering new insights into the effectiveness of this technique. (2) We explore the impact of the selection of verbalizers and models for the task, and (3) we compare the performance of encoder models with the recent LLMs based on instruction fine-tuning.

7 Conclusion

This paper presents a comprehensive evaluation of ZSL with prompting for hate speech classification. We have compared both encoder and instruction fine-tuned LLMs. Our experiments across different benchmark data sets showed that ZSL with prompting is a promising option to address the challenges presented in supervised learning systems. However, it also highlights the importance of carefully selecting the model and appropriate verbalizers, as they can significantly affect performance. Our results also show that recent LLMs based on instruction fine-tuning play an essential role in hate speech detection. Further exploration of prompt formulation could lead to their continued growth in this area. Additionally, our multilingual experiments show that our proposed methods can be applied to other languages with comparable results.

Future research could investigate the bias presence (Dixon et al., 2018; Attanasio et al., 2022) and robustness (Röttger et al., 2021, 2022) of ZSL prompting for hate speech detection models, also in multilingual settings.

Limitations

While promising, our work presents limitations that need to be acknowledged. Firstly, we did not explore the best verbalizers for instruction fine-tuned language models, which could have further enhanced the performance of the models explored in this study, due to computational cost and the specific goals of the research. Secondly, we selected benchmark datasets based on their popularity and diversity, which might not be representative of all possible datasets in hate speech detection. We also acknowledge that, in addition to the languages examined in this paper, there are a number of other languages that may present unique challenges and characteristics for detecting hate speech. Our decision as to which languages to include in the multilingual experiment was based on a direct comparison with state-of-the-art research. Finally, we utilized the latest open-source language models for our experiments, but we did not explore other recent language models, such as the GPT family, primarily because they are not open and reasonably reproducible[3], and therefore the community may encounter challenges in replicating our results. These limitations provide directions for future research to improve and expand upon our work.

Ethics Statement

To ensure data privacy and protection, we use publicly available benchmark datasets for hate speech detection and do not collect any personal or sensitive information. Additionally, we acknowledge that the detection of hate speech can be a sensitive topic; therefore, we report the results of our experiments in a responsible and appropriate manner. Lastly, we acknowledge that language models trained on large datasets have the potential to perpetuate bias and discrimination, and we strive to mitigate these risks by carefully selecting and evaluating our models and verbalizers to ensure fairness and impartiality.

[3]https://hackingsemantics.xyz/2023/closed-baselines/

Acknowledgements

This project has in part received funding from Fondazione Cariplo (grant No. 2020-4288, MONICA). The authors are members of the MilaNLP group and the Data and Marketing Insights Unit of the Bocconi Institute for Data Science and Analysis.

References

Giuseppe Attanasio, Debora Nozza, Dirk Hovy, and Elena Baralis. 2022. Entropy-based attention regularization frees unintended bias mitigation from lists. In *Findings of the Association for Computational Linguistics: ACL 2022*, pages 1105–1119, Dublin, Ireland. Association for Computational Linguistics.

Valerio Basile, Cristina Bosco, Elisabetta Fersini, Debora Nozza, Viviana Patti, Francisco Manuel Rangel Pardo, Paolo Rosso, and Manuela Sanguinetti. 2019. SemEval-2019 task 5: Multilingual detection of hate speech against immigrants and women in Twitter. In *Proceedings of the 13th International Workshop on Semantic Evaluation*, pages 54–63, Minneapolis, Minnesota, USA. Association for Computational Linguistics.

Cristina Bosco, Dell'Orletta Felice, Fabio Poletto, Manuela Sanguinetti, and Tesconi Maurizio. 2018. Overview of the EVALITA 2018 hate speech detection task. In *Proceedings of the Sixth Evaluation Campaign of Natural Language Processing and Speech Tools for Italian. Final Workshop (EVALITA 2018)*, volume 2263, pages 1–9, Turin, Italy. CEUR.org.

Tom Brown, Benjamin Mann, Nick Ryder, Melanie Subbiah, Jared D Kaplan, Prafulla Dhariwal, Arvind Neelakantan, Pranav Shyam, Girish Sastry, Amanda Askell, et al. 2020. Language Models are Few-Shot Learners. *Advances in neural information processing systems*, 33:1877–1901.

Tommaso Caselli, Valerio Basile, Jelena Mitrović, and Michael Granitzer. 2021. HateBERT: Retraining BERT for abusive language detection in English. In *Proceedings of the 5th Workshop on Online Abuse and Harms (WOAH 2021)*, pages 17–25, Online. Association for Computational Linguistics.

Tommaso Caselli, Nicole Novielli, Viviana Patti, and Paolo Rosso. 2018. EVALITA 2018: Overview of the 6th Evaluation Campaign of Natural Language Processing and Speech Tools for Italian. In *Proceedings of Sixth Evaluation Campaign of Natural Language Processing and Speech Tools for Italian. Final Workshop (EVALITA 2018)*, Turin, Italy. CEUR.org.

Ke-Li Chiu, Annie Collins, and Rohan Alexander. 2021. Detecting Hate Speech with GPT-3. *arXiv preprint arXiv:2103.12407.*

Hyung Won Chung, Le Hou, Shayne Longpre, Barret Zoph, Yi Tay, William Fedus, Yunxuan Li, Xuezhi Wang, Mostafa Dehghani, Siddhartha Brahma, Albert Webson, Shixiang Shane Gu, Zhuyun Dai, Mirac Suzgun, Xinyun Chen, Aakanksha Chowdhery, Alex Castro-Ros, Marie Pellat, Kevin Robinson, Dasha Valter, Sharan Narang, Gaurav Mishra, Adams Yu, Vincent Zhao, Yanping Huang, Andrew Dai, Hongkun Yu, Slav Petrov, Ed H. Chi, Jeff Dean, Jacob Devlin, Adam Roberts, Denny Zhou, Quoc V. Le, and Jason Wei. 2022. Scaling instruction-finetuned language models.

Alexis Conneau, Kartikay Khandelwal, Naman Goyal, Vishrav Chaudhary, Guillaume Wenzek, Francisco Guzmán, Edouard Grave, Myle Ott, Luke Zettlemoyer, and Veselin Stoyanov. 2020. Unsupervised cross-lingual representation learning at scale. In *Proceedings of the 58th Annual Meeting of the Association for Computational Linguistics*, pages 8440–8451, Online. Association for Computational Linguistics.

Thomas Davidson, Dana Warmsley, Michael W. Macy, and Ingmar Weber. 2017. Automated Hate Speech Detection and the Problem of Offensive Language. In *International Conference on Web and Social Media.*

Jacob Devlin, Ming-Wei Chang, Kenton Lee, and Kristina Toutanova. 2019. BERT: Pre-training of Deep Bidirectional Transformers for Language Understanding. In *Proceedings of the 2019 Conference of the North American Chapter of the Association for Computational Linguistics: Human Language Technologies.*

Ning Ding, Shengding Hu, Weilin Zhao, Yulin Chen, Zhiyuan Liu, Haitao Zheng, and Maosong Sun. 2022. OpenPrompt: An open-source framework for prompt-learning. In *Proceedings of the 60th Annual Meeting of the Association for Computational Linguistics: System Demonstrations*, pages 105–113, Dublin, Ireland. Association for Computational Linguistics.

Lucas Dixon, John Li, Jeffrey Sorensen, Nithum Thain, and Lucy Vasserman. 2018. Measuring and mitigating unintended bias in text classification. In *Proceedings of the 2018 AAAI/ACM Conference on AI, Ethics, and Society*, AIES '18, page 67–73, New York, NY, USA. Association for Computing Machinery.

Elisabetta Fersini, Debora Nozza, and Paolo Rosso. 2018. Overview of the EVALITA 2018 task on automatic misogyny identification (AMI). *Proceedings of the 6th evaluation campaign of Natural Language Processing and Speech tools for Italian (EVALITA 2018)*, 12:59.

Paula Fortuna, Monica Dominguez, Leo Wanner, and Zeerak Talat. 2022. Directions for NLP Practices Applied to Online Hate Speech Detection. In *Proceedings of the 2022 Conference on Empirical Methods in Natural Language Processing*, pages 11794–11805, Abu Dhabi, United Arab Emirates. Association for Computational Linguistics.

Paula Fortuna and Sérgio Nunes. 2018. A survey on automatic detection of hate speech in text. 51(4).

Samuel Gehman, Suchin Gururangan, Maarten Sap, Yejin Choi, and Noah A. Smith. 2020. RealToxicityPrompts: Evaluating neural toxic degeneration in language models. In *Findings of the Association for Computational Linguistics: EMNLP 2020*, pages 3356–3369, Online. Association for Computational Linguistics.

Janis Goldzycher and Gerold Schneider. 2022. Hypothesis engineering for zero-shot hate speech detection. In *Proceedings of the Third Workshop on Threat, Aggression and Cyberbullying (TRAC 2022)*, pages 75–90, Gyeongju, Republic of Korea. Association for Computational Linguistics.

Pengcheng He, Xiaodong Liu, Jianfeng Wang, Weizhu Li, Yelong Liu, and Jianfeng Chen. 2020. DeBERTa: Decoding-enhanced BERT with Disentangled Attention. *arXiv preprint arXiv:2006.03654.*

Brendan Kennedy, Mohammad Atari, Aida Mostafazadeh Davani, Leigh Yeh, Ali Omrani, Yehsong Kim, Kris Coombs, Shreya Havaldar, Gwenyth Portillo-Wightman, Elaine Gonzalez, et al. 2022. Introducing the Gab Hate Corpus: defining and applying hate-based rhetoric to social media posts at scale. *Language Resources and Evaluation*, pages 1–30.

Brendan Kennedy, Xisen Jin, Aida Mostafazadeh Davani, Morteza Dehghani, and Xiang Ren. 2020a. Contextualizing hate speech classifiers with post-hoc explanation. In *Proceedings of the 58th Annual Meeting of the Association for Computational Linguistics*, pages 5435–5442, Online. Association for Computational Linguistics.

Chris J Kennedy, Geoff Bacon, Alexander Sahn, and Claudia von Vacano. 2020b. Constructing interval variables via faceted Rasch measurement and multitask deep learning: a hate speech application. *arXiv preprint arXiv:2009.10277.*

Hannah Kirk, Bertie Vidgen, and Scott Hale. 2022. Is more data better? re-thinking the importance of efficiency in abusive language detection with transformers-based active learning. In *Proceedings of the Third Workshop on Threat, Aggression and Cyberbullying (TRAC 2022)*, pages 52–61, Gyeongju, Republic of Korea. Association for Computational Linguistics.

Pengfei Liu, Weizhe Yuan, Jinlan Fu, Zhengbao Jiang, Hiroaki Hayashi, and Graham Neubig. 2023. Pre-train, prompt, and predict: A systematic survey of prompting methods in natural language processing. *ACM Computing Surveys*, 55(9):1–35.

Yinhan Liu, Myle Ott, Naman Goyal, Jingfei Du, Mandar Joshi, Danqi Chen, Omer Levy, Mike Lewis, Luke Zettlemoyer, and Veselin Stoyanov. 2019. RoBERTa: A Robustly Optimized BERT Pretraining Approach. *arXiv preprint arXiv:1907.11692*.

Binny Mathew, Punyajoy Saha, Seid Muhie Yimam, Chris Biemann, Pawan Goyal, and Animesh Mukherjee. 2021. HateXplain: A Benchmark Dataset for Explainable Hate Speech Detection. In *Proceedings of the AAAI Conference on Artificial Intelligence*, volume 35, pages 14867–14875.

Niklas Muennighoff, Thomas Wang, Lintang Sutawika, Adam Roberts, Stella Biderman, Teven Le Scao, M Saiful Bari, Sheng Shen, Zheng-Xin Yong, Hailey Schoelkopf, Xiangru Tang, Dragomir Radev, Alham Fikri Aji, Khalid Almubarak, Samuel Albanie, Zaid Alyafeai, Albert Webson, Edward Raff, and Colin Raffel. 2022. Crosslingual generalization through multitask finetuning.

Debora Nozza. 2021. Exposing the limits of zero-shot cross-lingual hate speech detection. In *Proceedings of the 59th Annual Meeting of the Association for Computational Linguistics and the 11th International Joint Conference on Natural Language Processing (Volume 2: Short Papers)*, pages 907–914, Online. Association for Computational Linguistics.

Nedjma Ousidhoum, Zizheng Lin, Hongming Zhang, Yangqiu Song, and Dit-Yan Yeung. 2019. Multilingual and multi-aspect hate speech analysis. In *Proceedings of the 2019 Conference on Empirical Methods in Natural Language Processing and the 9th International Joint Conference on Natural Language Processing (EMNLP-IJCNLP)*, pages 4675–4684, Hong Kong, China. Association for Computational Linguistics.

Flor Miriam Plaza-del-Arco, María-Teresa Martín-Valdivia, and Roman Klinger. 2022. Natural language inference prompts for zero-shot emotion classification in text across corpora. In *Proceedings of the 29th International Conference on Computational Linguistics*, pages 6805–6817, Gyeongju, Republic of Korea. International Committee on Computational Linguistics.

Flor-Miriam Plaza-del-Arco, M. Dolores Molina-González, L. Alfonso Ureña López, and M. Teresa Martín-Valdivia. 2020. Detecting Misogyny and Xenophobia in Spanish Tweets Using Language Technologies. *ACM Trans. Internet Technol.*, 20(2).

Fabio Poletto, Valerio Basile, Manuela Sanguinetti, Cristina Bosco, and Viviana Patti. 2021. Resources and benchmark corpora for hate speech detection: a systematic review. *Language Resources and Evaluation*, 55:477–523.

Paul Röttger, Haitham Seelawi, Debora Nozza, Zeerak Talat, and Bertie Vidgen. 2022. Multilingual HateCheck: Functional tests for multilingual hate speech detection models. In *Proceedings of the Sixth Workshop on Online Abuse and Harms (WOAH)*, pages 154–169, Seattle, Washington (Hybrid). Association for Computational Linguistics.

Paul Röttger, Bertie Vidgen, Dong Nguyen, Zeerak Talat, Helen Margetts, and Janet Pierrehumbert. 2021. HateCheck: Functional tests for hate speech detection models. In *Proceedings of the 59th Annual Meeting of the Association for Computational Linguistics and the 11th International Joint Conference on Natural Language Processing (Volume 1: Long Papers)*, pages 41–58, Online. Association for Computational Linguistics.

Diptanu Sarkar, Marcos Zampieri, Tharindu Ranasinghe, and Alexander Ororbia. 2021. fBERT: A neural transformer for identifying offensive content. In *Findings of the Association for Computational Linguistics: EMNLP 2021*, pages 1792–1798, Punta Cana, Dominican Republic. Association for Computational Linguistics.

Timo Schick, Sahana Udupa, and Hinrich Schütze. 2021. Self-Diagnosis and Self-Debiasing: A Proposal for Reducing Corpus-Based Bias in NLP. *Transactions of the Association for Computational Linguistics*, 9:1408–1424.

Anna Schmidt and Michael Wiegand. 2017. A survey on hate speech detection using natural language processing. In *Proceedings of the Fifth International Workshop on Natural Language Processing for Social Media*, pages 1–10, Valencia, Spain. Association for Computational Linguistics.

Sumer Singh and Sheng Li. 2021. Exploiting auxiliary data for offensive language detection with bidirectional transformers. In *Proceedings of the 5th Workshop on Online Abuse and Harms (WOAH 2021)*, pages 1–5, Online. Association for Computational Linguistics.

Hongjin Su, Jungo Kasai, Chen Henry Wu, Weijia Shi, Tianlu Wang, Jiayi Xin, Rui Zhang, Mari Ostendorf, Luke Zettlemoyer, Noah A Smith, and Tao Yu. 2022. Selective annotation makes language models better few-shot learners. *arXiv preprint arXiv:2209.01975*.

Zeerak Talat and Dirk Hovy. 2016. Hateful symbols or hateful people? predictive features for hate speech detection on Twitter. In *Proceedings of the NAACL Student Research Workshop*, pages 88–93, San Diego, California. Association for Computational Linguistics.

Bertie Vidgen, Tristan Thrush, Zeerak Talat, and Douwe Kiela. 2021. Learning from the worst: Dynamically generated datasets to improve online hate detection. In *Proceedings of the 59th Annual Meeting of the Association for Computational Linguistics and the 11th International Joint Conference on Natural Language Processing (Volume 1: Long Papers)*, pages 1667–1682, Online. Association for Computational Linguistics.

Jason Wei, Yi Tay, Rishi Bommasani, Colin Raffel, Barret Zoph, Sebastian Borgeaud, Dani Yogatama, Maarten Bosma, Denny Zhou, Donald Metzler, Ed H. Chi, Tatsunori Hashimoto, Oriol Vinyals, Percy Liang, Jeff Dean, and William Fedus. 2022. Emergent abilities of large language models. *arXiv preprint arXiv:2206.07682*.

Wenpeng Yin, Jamaal Hay, and Dan Roth. 2019. Benchmarking zero-shot text classification: Datasets, evaluation and entailment approach. *CoRR*, abs/1909.00161.

Wayne Xin Zhao, Kun Zhou, Junyi Li, Tianyi Tang, Xiaolei Wang, Yupeng Hou, Yingqian Min, Beichen Zhang, Junjie Zhang, Zican Dong, Yifan Du, Chen Yang, Yushuo Chen, Zhipeng Chen, Jinhao Jiang, Ruiyang Ren, Yifan Li, Xinyu Tang, Zikang Liu, Peiyu Liu, Jian-Yun Nie, and Ji-Rong Wen. 2023. A survey of large language models. *arXiv preprint arXiv:2303.18223*.

A Dataset Details

Vidgen et al. (2021) (DYNABENCH) introduced a novel framework for dynamically creating benchmark corpora. The task assigned to the annotators involved identifying adversarial examples, which are instances that would be classified incorrectly by the target model and are particularly challenging to detect. The dataset contains a significant proportion of hateful entries, accounting for 54% of the dataset.

Kennedy et al. (2020b) (MHS) gathered a large collection of comments from diverse social media platforms (YouTube, Twitter, and Reddit). To label the comments, they used a crowdsourcing platform where four different ratings were given to each comment. To ensure a comprehensive assessment, the authors made certain that every annotator evaluated comments that spanned the entire hate speech scale. Since the dataset is annotated with a continuous hate score, we used a threshold set to binarise the problem: if value $< -1 \rightarrow 0$ and if value $> 0.5 \rightarrow 1$.

Kennedy et al. (2022) (GHC) presented the Gab Hate Corpus, a multi-label English dataset of posts sourced from gab.com, a social networking platform. To label the comments, at least three annotators labeled them under one of the following categories: Call for Violence, Assault on Human Dignity, or Not Hateful. Following Kennedy et al. (2020a), we aggregate the first two for obtaining the hateful class.

Basile et al. (2019) (HATEVAL) created the HatEval corpus for the HatEval campaign in SemEval. The dataset consists of tweets that were manually annotated via crowdsourcing for hate speech. To collect the tweets, they follow three different strategies: (1) monitoring potential victims of hate accounts, (2) downloading the history of identified haters, and (3) filtering Twitter streams with keywords, i.e., words, hashtags, and stems. The corpus contains a total of 24,802 tweets.

Talat and Hovy (2016) (HSHP) provided a dataset consisting of 16,914 tweets that were collected using Twitter's streaming API and filtered using a set of hate speech-related keywords related to religious, sexual, gender, and ethnic minorities. The tweets were then manually annotated by two annotators for the presence of hate speech.

Davidson et al. (2017) (DAVIDSON) created a dataset of 24,802 tweets annotated for the presence of hate speech and offensive language. The tweets were crawled using keywords related to a hate speech lexicon. Each tweet was labeled by three or more people into one of three categories: hate speech, offensive language, or neither. We aggregate the first two for obtaining the hateful class.

Mathew et al. (2021) (HATEXPLAIN) collected English posts from Twitter and Gab social media platforms. Afterward, a crowdsourcing platform was employed to categorize each post into three categories: hate speech, offensive speech, or normal speech. In addition to this, the annotators were tasked with identifying the target communities mentioned in the posts, as well as the specific portions of the post which formed the basis of their labeling decision. Finally, the majority voting decision was used to determine the final label. By combining the hate and offensive targets, the hateful class was formed. We combine the hate and offensive posts to obtain the hateful class.

Ousidhoum et al. (2019) (MLMA) presented a multilingual multi-aspect hate speech dataset comprising English, French, and Arabic tweets that encompass various targets and hostility types. Each tweet is labeled by 5 annotators, and then the majority vote is used to decide the final label. The average Krippendorff scores for inter-annotator agreement (IAA) are 0.153, 0.244, and 0.202 for English, French, and Arabic, respectively.

B Implementation Details

We implement the fine-tuned version of RoBERTa$_{\text{BASE}}$ with the following hyperparameter configuration for training: epochs are set to 3, batch size to 8, and the number of epochs to 3. For the ZSL models, we used the default hyperparameters presented in Hugging Face. We fine-tune $RoBERTa_{BASE}$ for three epochs. We perform 5-fold partitions and report the results on the test set.

Hugging Face model cars $BERT_{BASE\text{-}uncased}$[4], $RoBERTa_{BASE}$[5], $RoBERTa_{LARGE}$[6], $DeBERTa_{V3\text{-}BASE}$[7], $DeBERTa_{V3\text{-}LARGE}$[8], XLM-$RoBERTa_{LARGE}$[9], mT0[10], and FLAN-T5[11].

Computing Infrastructure We run the experiments on one machine with the following characteristics: it is equipped with three NVIDIA RTX A6000 and has 48GB of RAM.

[4] https://huggingface.co/bert-base-uncased

[5] https://huggingface.co/roberta-base

[6] https://huggingface.co/roberta-large

[7] https://huggingface.co/microsoft/deberta-v3-base

[8] https://huggingface.co/microsoft/deberta-v3-large

[9] https://huggingface.co/xlm-roberta-large

[10] https://huggingface.co/bigscience/mT0-xxl

[11] https://huggingface.co/google/flan-t5-xl

Benchmarking Offensive and Abusive Language in Dutch Tweets

Tommaso Caselli and **Hylke van der Veen**
CLCG, University of Groningen
t.caselli@rug.nl | hylkevdveen@gmail.com

Abstract

We present an extensive evaluation of different fine-tuned models to detect instances of offensive and abusive language in Dutch across three benchmarks: a standard held-out test, a task-agnostic functional benchmark, and a dynamic test set. We also investigate the use of data cartography to identify high quality training data. Our results show a relatively good quality of the manually annotated data used to train the models while highlighting some critical weakness. We have also found a good portability of trained models along the same language phenomena. As for the data cartography, we have found a positive impact only on the functional benchmark and when selecting data per annotated dimension rather than using the entire training material.

1 Introduction

Being able to correctly detect instances of offensive and abusive language plays a pivotal role in creating safer and more inclusive environments, especially on Social Media platforms. Since current methods for these phenomena are based on supervised techniques, a pending issue is represented by the quality of the data used to train the corresponding systems. Standard evaluation methods based on held-out test sets only provide a partial picture of the actual robustness of fine-tuned models while being silent about potential annotators' bias, topic and author biases (Wiegand et al., 2019). Recent work has show that held-out tests may result in overly optimistic performance estimates which do not translate into real-world performance (Gorman and Bedrick, 2019; Søgaard et al., 2021). To get a realistic performance estimate, models should be evaluated on out-of-corpus data, i.e. a different data distribution but within the same language variety (Ramponi and Plank, 2020), or even on a held-out test set from a different but related domain. Out-of-corpus evaluation requires the development of multiple datasets which can be expensive, time consuming, and, in the case of less- or poor-resources languages, unfeasible.

A complementary solution is the use of functional tests, i.e., sets of systematically generated test cases aiming at evaluating in a task-agnostic methodology trained models (Ribeiro et al., 2020; Lent et al., 2021; Sai et al., 2021; Röttger et al., 2021; Manerba and Tonelli, 2021). Functional testing enables more targeted insights and diagnostics on multiple levels. For instance, the systematic categorisation as hateful of messages containing a protected identity term (e.g., "gay", "trans", among others) of a system trained to detect hate speech against LGBTQIA+ people is an indicator of the weakness of the model(s) as well as of biases in the training data.

Although limited in terms of number of datasets and annotated phenomena, Dutch covers a peculiar position in the language resource panorama: it has a comprehensively annotated corpus for offensive and abusive language whose standard held-out test set does not present any overlap with the training set; it includes a dynamic benchmark for offensive language, OP-NL (Theodoridis and Caselli, 2022); and it presents a functional benchmark, HATECHEK-NL, that extends MULTILINGUAL HATECHEKCK (Röttger et al., 2022). This puts us is an optimal position to conduct an extensive benchmarking of different models for offensive and abusive language in Dutch and reflect on the potential shortcomings of the Dutch Abusive Language Corpus v2.0 (DALC-v2.0) (Ruitenbeek et al., 2022). In addition to this, we apply data cartography (Swayamdipta et al., 2020) to carve out different subsets of training materials to investigate whether this method is valid on DALC-v2.0 to identify robust and good quality training data.

Our contributions Our major contributions are the followings: (i) we present and discuss our ex-

The 7th Workshop on Online Abuse and Harms (WOAH), pages 69–84
July 13, 2023 ©2023 Association for Computational Linguistics

tensions of HATECHEK-NL (Section 2); (ii) we apply data cartography (Swayamdipta et al., 2020) to DALC-v2.0 to investigate whether we can identify robust subsets of training data (Section 3); (iii) we conduct an extensive evaluation of different systems based on a monolingual pre-trained language model, namely BERTje (de Vries et al., 2019), against multiple test sets (Section 4).[1]

2 Data

In this section, we present the data we use to fine-tune and evaluate the models based on BERTje (de Vries et al., 2019).

DALC-v2.0 DALC-v2.0 contains 11,292 messages from Twitter in Dutch, covering a time period between November 2015 and August 2020. Messages have been annotated using a multi-layer annotation scheme compliant with Waseem et al. (2017) for two dimensions: offensive and abusive language. Offensive language in DALC-v2.0 is the same as in Zampieri et al. (2019), i.e., messages "containing any form of non-acceptable language (profanity) or a targeted offence, which can be veiled or direct". Abusive language corresponds to "impolite, harsh, or hurtful language (that may contain profanities or vulgar language) that result in a debasement, harassment, threat, or aggression of an individual or a (social) group, but not necessarily of an entity, an institution, an organisations, or a concept." (Caselli et al., 2021, 56–57). Each dimension is further annotated along two layers: explicitness and target. The explicitness layer is used to annotate whether a message is belonging to the positive category or not. In the former case, the values explicit (EXP) and implicit (IMP) are used to distinguish the way the positive category is realised. The target layer is used to annotate towards who or what the offence, or abuse, is directed to. Target layers inherit values from Zampieri et al. (2019), namely individual (IND), group (GRP), other (OTH).

Here we focus only on the explicitness layer, considering each dimension separately and jointly. In particular, when addressing each dimension separately, we frame the task as a binary classification by collapsing the explicit and implicit labels either into OFF and ABU for the offensive and abusive dimension, respectively. When working on both dimensions jointly, we face a multi-class classification where systems must distinguish between two positive classes (OFF and ABU) and one negative (NOT). Table 1 illustrates the distribution of the data for the dimensions in analysis across the Train/Dev and standard held-out test splits.

Annotated Dimension	Label	Train	Dev	Test	Total
Offensive	OFF	2,477	439	867	3,783
	NOT	4,340	766	2,403	7,509
Abusive	ABU	1,391	243	463	2,097
	NOT	5,426	962	2,807	9,195
Offensive & Abusive	OFF	1,086	196	404	1,686
	ABU	1,391	243	463	2,097
	NOT	4,304	766	2,403	7,473

Table 1: DALC-v2.0 : Distribution of labels (binary and multi-class settings) in Train, Dev, and official held-out Test splits for each annotated dimension independently and jointly.

Labels are skewed towards the negative class as in previous work (Basile et al., 2019; Davidson et al., 2017; Zampieri et al., 2019, 2020). When considering each dimension separately, the offensive dimension is larger than the abusive one (*approx* 33% of the total *vs.* $\approx$ 19%, respectively). In the joint setting, the OFF messages drop to $\approx$ 15%. This reflects the definitions of offensive and abusive language and how the two phenomena interact: abusive language is more specific and subject to a stricter set of criteria for its identification (e.g., a target must always be present), resulting in a "specialized instance" of offensive language (Poletto et al., 2020). In other words, while every abusive message is also offensive, the contrary does not hold. In their analysis of the corpus, the authors do not report evidence of any specific topic bias and they state that train and test splits have no overlap (Caselli et al., 2021; Ruitenbeek et al., 2022).

HATECHEK-NL HATECHEK-NL extends MULTILINGUAL HATECHEKCK (MHC) (Röttger et al., 2022). MHC defines hate speech as "abuse that is targeted at a protected group or at its members for being a part of that group." (Röttger et al., 2022, 155). This definition is more specific than the language phenomena in DALC-v2.0, although it is compatible. MHC has 27 common functionalities for 10 languages, including Dutch, 18 specific for *expressions of hate* and nine non-hateful to *contrast the hateful cases*. Each test is realised by a short text uniquely identifying a gold label (e.g.,

[1]All code, data, and trained models are available via `https://github.com/tommasoc80/DALC`

hateful *vs.* non-hateful). To massively generate tests, MHC makes use of templates (Ribeiro et al., 2020). We have extended the functionalities in MHC with two extra tests to include the use of reclaimed slurs and profanities in a non hateful way (**F8**, **F9**). These two functional tests are present in the original English HATECHECK (Röttger et al., 2021) but they were excluded from MHC to maintain a more homogeneous distribution of functional tests across all languages. Röttger et al. (2022) observe that these functionalities have no direct equivalents in most of the languages in MHC, but this is not the case for Dutch. For the functionality **F8** (non-hateful homonyms of slurs), we have identified four slurs that are each aimed at one of the target identities and have a non-hateful homonym. For instance, the term "f*****r" is used to refer to gay men or as a verb meaning flickering of a light, to fall or to drop something. Reclaimed slurs (**F9**) have been partially translated from English, excluding terms such as "n****r" and "b***h" for which we have not found evidence of their use in Dutch nor have we identified corresponding terms.

HATECHEK-NL contains 3,835 functional tests across the 29 functionalities. A total of 2,640 (68.83%) tests are hateful and 1,195 (31.16%) are non-hateful, a distribution in line with the original HATECHECK. An overview of all the functionalities in HATECHEK-NL is in Table A.1 in Appendix A. On the basis of the annotated dimensions in DALC-v2.0, we expect that models trained on offensive language may overgeneralise the identification of hateful messages, also for challenging non-hateful cases (e.g., **F8**, **F9**). On the other hand, we expect models trained on abusive language (both in isolation and jointly) to perform better, although the emphasis on "protected group and its members" in HATECHEK-NL may present an extra challenge since no specific protected group is part of DALC-v2.0.

OP-NL Offend the Politicians Benchmark (OP-NL) is a dynamic test set composed by 1,500 tweets collected in March 2021 containing at least one mention of a Dutch politician from the *Tweede Kamer* (i.e., the Dutch House of Representatives). The messages have been annotated for offensive language using the same definition of DALC-v2.0, making OP-NL perfectly compatible and suitable as a dynamic benchmark. The labels in OP-NL are distributed as follows: 961 messages (64%) are not offensive (NOT) and 539 (36%) are offensive (OFF). The ratio between non-offensive and offensive messages is 1.78 : 1, very close to the label distribution in DALC-v2.0. In this case, we expect offensive language models (in isolation or jointly with abusive language) to obtain good performances, i.e., in-line with those on DALC-v2.0 for offensive language. On the contrary, models trained for abusive language are expected to struggle, mainly on the recall for the positive class.

3 Experiment settings

We have designed three sets of experiments for each annotated dimension to fine-tune a monolingual pre-trained language model for Dutch, BERTje, with varying training splits. All fine-tuned models are evaluated both on the official DALC-v2.0 held-out test set, HATECHEK-NL, and OP-NL. All pre-processing steps and fine-tuning (hyper)parameters are detailed in Appendix B for replicability.

The first block of experiment has a standard setting: for each annotated dimension (in isolation or jointly) we fine-tuned BERTje using all available training data in DALC-v2.0. We will refer to these models as standard (**std**).

For the second block, we use data cartography (Swayamdipta et al., 2020). The cartography approach uses a model's confidence in the true class and the variability of this confidence across multiple training epochs (i.e., training dynamics) to identify a subset of training instances that qualify as more reliable and informative. In this way, it is possible to train a model using less data and still achieve state-of-the-art results, if not better. When plotting statistics from the training dynamics into a map, they result into a spectrum of data points: some *easy* (high-confidence, low variability), some *hard* (low-confidence, low variability), and some *ambiguous* (mid-range confidence, high variability). Previous work (Swayamdipta et al., 2020; Bhargava et al., 2021) has shown that, in classification tasks, the use of *ambiguous* data points at training time results in better models than those obtained when using the entire training split. Our goal is to test the validity of this method on DALC-v2.0, a smaller dataset than those where data cartography has been successfully applied.

To identify the ambiguous data points, we have used the training dynamics from the fine-tuned models from each classification task from DALC-v2.0. Given its skewed distribution and size, we

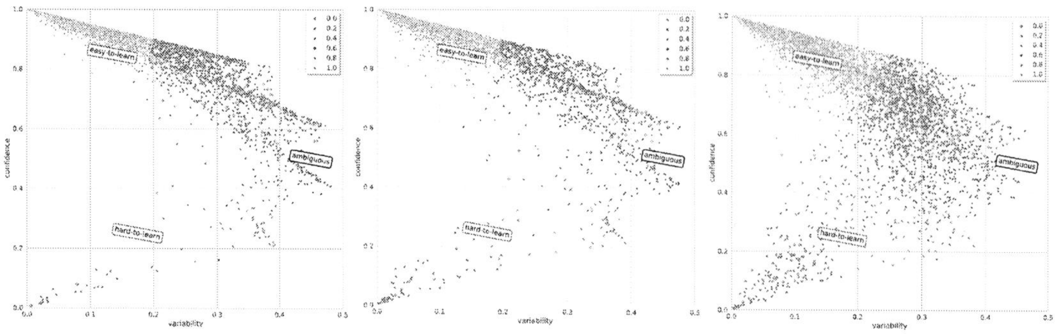

(a) Offensive data map (b) Abusive data map (c) Offensive and abusive data map

Figure 1: DALC-v2.0: data maps from training dynamics for each annotated dimension with BERTje.

Split	Dimension	Labels	Avg. Variability
amb-dim	Offensive	OFF 1,192 NOT 1,080	$0.255_{.089}$
	Abusive	ABU 1,136 NOT 1,136	$0.225_{.101}$
	Offensive & Abusive	OFF 894 ABU 714 NOT 664	$0.280_{.057}$
amb-class	Offensive	OFF 1,136 NOT 1,136	$0.123_{.120}$
	Abusive	ABU 1,136 NOT 1,136	$0.142_{.131}$
	Offensive & Abusive	OFF 757 ABU 757 NOT 758	$0.182_{.115}$

Table 2: Ambiguous train splits per annotated dimensions (**amb-dim**) or per class per dimension (**amb-class**). Numbers in subscript report standard deviations.

Split	Dimension	Labels	Avg. Variability
rand-1	Offensive	OFF 821 NOT 1,451	$0.114_{.116}$
	Abusive	ABU 458 NOT 1,814	$0.091_{.110}$
	Offensive & Abusive	OFF 363 ABU 458 NOT 1451	$0.139_{.089}$
rand-2	Offensive	OFF 814 NOT 1,458	$0.114_{.116}$
	Abusive	ABU 458 NOT 1,814	$0.094_{.112}$
	Offensive & Abusive	OFF 356 ABU 458 NOT 1,458	$0.147_{.097}$
rand-3	Offensive	OFF 855 NOT 1,417	$0.116_{.116}$
	Abusive	ABU 476 NOT 1,796	$0.095_{.112}$
	Offensive & Abusive	OFF 379 ABU 476 NOT 1,417	$0.143_{.087}$

Table 3: Random train splits (**rdm**) per annotated dimensions. Number in subscripts report standard deviations.

have investigated two methods to select the ambiguous data: the first (**amb-dim**) follows the approach in Swayamdipta et al. (2020) by retaining 1/3 of the original training data (i.e., 2,272 examples) corresponding to the top ambiguous cases per annotated dimension (separately and jointly). The second (**amb-class**) independently retains the top ambiguous examples for *each class*. In particular, we have carved three training splits of 2,272 examples where the distribution of instances per class is perfectly balanced (50-50 for binary settings, and 1/3 each for the multi-class setting). As the figures in Table 2 show, the class distribution is less skewed when compared to the original DALC-v2.0 training. For the abusive dimension, the distribution of the labels is perfectly balanced also when using the **amb-dim** method. The variability, across all data selection methods, is not particularly high. However, we observe a systematic difference between the values of the **amb-dim** and the **amb-class** data, with the latter being always lower of ≈ 0.1 points. Although in both cases the selected data instances qualifies as "ambiguous", the relatively low variability questions their efficacy as more robust training instances.

Figures 1a, 1b, and 1c illustrate the data maps of the training examples for the offensive and abusive dimension, separately and jointly. We can observe a consistent overlap between the easy and the ambiguous cases which questions the use of the ambiguous instances as effective training material from DALC-v2.0. At the same time, we observe that the hard examples are limited and well clustered for each dimension separately (Figures 1a and 1b), while this does not hold in the joint case (Figure 1c). In this case, the overlap between the hard and the ambiguous instances is larger, indicating, on one side, that the classification task is more challenging and, on the other side, that the distinction among the three classes is less clear than it seems.

The last set of training data has the same size of the ambiguous data (2,272 instances) but it is randomly extracted from the original training set (**rand**). It is a control to better asses the effectiveness of the data cartography on DALC-v2.0. Random splits have been sampled three times with different seeds and no substitution. Table 3 illustrates their distribution. In this case, the data are skewed towards the negative class and their variability is consistently lower than that of the ambiguous ones, suggesting that the corresponding fine-tuned models should obtain worst results.

4 Results

For the analysis of the results we first focus on DALC-v2.0, and subsequently on HATECHEK-NL and OP-NL. All fine-tuned models are compared against a baseline. For DALC-v2.0 and OP-NL, we use a dummy classifier that always assigns the most frequent class, i.e., NOT; for HATECHEK-NL, we use a random classifier (balanced for the hateful and non-hateful class distribution). The random classifier for HATECHEK-NL represents a more realistic baseline than a majority label classifier given the nature of the benchmark. Detailed results for each dataset are illustrated in Appendix C.

DALC-v2.0 Table 4 summarises the results on DALC-v2.0. All models largely outperform the baselines. When compared to previous work based on data cartography (Swayamdipta et al., 2020; Bhargava et al., 2021), we cannot find the same trends. Across all annotated dimensions and classification tasks (binary *vs.* multi-class), the use of the full training set (**std**) returns the best results, with a macro-F1 of 79.93 for offensive language, 72.33 for abusive language, and 58.90 for the two dimensions in conjunction. The identification of offensive and abusive language separately clearly returns better results than when the two dimensions are predicted jointly. This confirms the observations from the data maps (Figure 1c). In this latter case, the system mostly struggles to distinguish between the two positive classes. As it appears from the analysis of the predictions using a confusion matrix, for the abusive class the largest number of errors are messages classified as OFF (125 out of 463 instances), while for the offensive class most of the messages are wrongly classified either as ABU (137 out 404 instances) or as NOT (159 out 404 instances).

	DALC		
Train split	**Offensive**	**Abusive**	**Off. & Abu.**
baseline	42.35	46.19	28.24
std	**79.93**	**72.23**	**58.90**
amb-dim	68.85	66.31	43.74
amb-class	77.66	67.21	53.58
rdm	$77.64_{1.7}$	$70.70_{1.0}$	$57.26_{1.26}$

Table 4: Experiments results for each annotated dimension in DALC-v2.0 against the held-out test sets (per annotated dimension). Best scores per training split are marked in bold. Scores correspond to macro-F1. We report the average and standard deviations for the **rdm** splits.

The use of random subsets for training (**rdm**) is unexpectedly competitive when compared to the **std** split and both ambiguous subsets from the data maps. A better impact of selecting ambiguous data per class (**amb-class**) to generate balanced training sets is evident for all dimensions. A further unexpected behaviour is the better performances of low variability training sets (i.e., **amb-class** and **rdm**). While the results of the **amb-class** set may suggest a different way of selecting robust sub-samples using data maps, the **rdm** blocks question the validity of data maps with small datasets.

When narrowing down the analysis to the differences between the reduced training data, we identify a peculiar behaviour of the data map splits. In particular, **amb-dim** and **amb-class** tend to overgeneralise the positive classes, with higher recall values at the cost of precision. Given the distribution of the labels (see Table 2), it is difficult to explain this behaviour in terms of class imbalance. On the other hand, this effect appears to be directly related to the use of the data maps. The impression is that the selected training data for the positive classes are too "ambiguous" for the system resulting in overgeneralisations to the detriment (mainly) of the negative class. Support in this direction comes from the results of the **rdm** splits where precision and recall are more balanced.

HATECHEK-NL Table 5 reports the performances of the trained models on HATECHEK-NL.

Train Split	HATECHECK-NL Offensive	HATECHECK-NL Abusive	HATECHECK-NL Off. & Abusive	OP-NL Offensive	OP-NL Abusive	OP-NL Off. & Abusive
baseline	57.08	57.08	57.08	39.04	39.04	39.04
std	61.40	60.19	60.94	**73.56**	57.57	**71.85**
amb-dim	59.35	**62.72**	61.22	54.23	63.19	51.83
amb-class	**64.52**	62.42	**63.21**	69.91	**68.75**	66.41
rdm	$61.05_{19.56}$	$55.28_{20.55}$	$52.78_{26.96}$	$69.07_{0.83}$	$55.50_{4.28}$	$69.91_{2.51}$

Table 5: Results of the fine-tuned models against HATECHEK-NL and OP-NL. Best scores per model are in bold. Scores correspond to Accuracy for HATECHEK-NL and macro-F1 for OP-NL. We report the average and standard deviation for the **rdm** splits.

At evaluation time, for the joint model we have considered valid only the predictions for the ABU class, with the OFF labels as non-hateful messages.

In general, all fine-tune models outperform the baseline with the exceptions of the models fine-tuned on the **rdm** training data for abusive language and for offensive and abusive language jointly.

Models fine-tuned on offensive language obtain a better global accuracy. The sole deviation is represented by the model fine-tuned using the **amb-dim** data (59.35). This is mainly due to an overgeneralisation of the positive class in each functional test due to the broader and encompassing definition of offensive language. Being HATECHEK-NLunbalanced for the hateful labels, this gives the false impression of dealing with better models. To put things in perspective, consider that the average accuracy based on the majority label (i.e., all hateful) would be 68.83% - a score that no fine-tuned model can beat. Furthermore, these models fail the majority of the non-hateful functional tests, as we have predicted: in this cases, the accuracy ranges from 28.77% for **amb-class** to 52.57% for **rdm**, with only the model fine-tuned on **rdm** being above 50% (see also Table C.1). In particular, for the most challenging non-hateful tests, such as **F9** (reclaimed slurs), **F11** (not hateful use of profanities), **F21** (quotation of hate speech to counteract hate speech), **F23–24** (non hateful messages with individual or group targets), the accuracy is consistently below 50% across all training splits. At the same time, this is an indirect positive feedback on the quality of the annotation for offensive language in DALC-v2.0: the non-hateful tests may contain language and expressions that can be perceived as offensive, and thus are flagged by the models. This is particular evident with the results for **F11** where accuracy ranges between 15% and 33.67% since the presence of a profanity is flagged as offensive.

As for the use of abusive language as training, models have a more balanced behaviour between the hateful and the non-hateful cases. In particular, across all non-hateful tests, accuracy ranges from 36.29% for **amb-dim** to 65.72% for **rdm**, with one extra model, **std**, being above 50% (see Table C.2). For the challenging non-hateful tests, there is only one case where the performance is consistently below 50% across all training splits, namely **F16** (hate expressed via a question). For all the other non-hateful tests, the behaviour of the models is more varied with at least one or two models achieving results above 50%. To make a direct comparison with the offensive training splits, on **F9** and **F11** only two out four models are below 50% (**amb-dim**, and **amb-class**), while on **F21** and **F23–24**, three out of four are below 50% (**std**, **amb-dim**, and **amb-class**). In addition, the accuracy of these models is consistently higher when compared to their counterparts fine-tuned using offensive language. Again, this provides an indirect feedback on the quality of the annotated data and the compatibility of the definition of abusive language in DALC-v2.0 with that of hate speech in HATECHEK-NL. The results for **std** and **rdm** on **F9–F11** are particularly relevant. These functional tests are very useful to assess the generalisation functionalities of fine-tune models to distinguish between abusive/hateful content and the mere presence of slurs or swear words. Although half of the models achieve a score which is higher than 50%, there is still room for improvement: the best results for **F9** is only 66.70% (with **std**) and that for **F11** is 62.67 (with **rdm**).

When focusing on the joint models, the picture that emerges is more complex than it seems at a first look. First, the joint models have a lower overall accuracy. Yet, these are the models that achieve the best results for all non-hateful tests, with the accuracy ranging between 47.77% for **amb-class** to 76.50% for **rdm**, and with only one model, **amb-dim** below 50% (see also Table C.3). While struggling on the positive classes - in a way that is similar to models fine-tuned on abusive language only - the pattern on the non-hateful tests indicates that the presence of an extra dimension (i.e., offensive language) seems to improve the overall precision. Although the behaviour on the DALC-v2.0 held-out test may suggest that this could be due by chance rather than robustness, the performance on the challenging functionalities **F9–F11** cautiously indicates the contrary. Indeed, this is the only case where only one fine-tuned model has performance below 50% (**amb-class** for both tests). For **F11**, the best accuracy (70.00% - **amb-dim**) is better than that of the models trained on abusive language only. Further improvements can be seen for **F21** with two models above 50% (**amb-dim** and **rdm**), and **F24**, with three models (**std**, **amb-dim** and **rdm**). At the same time, issues persist on other functionalities. In particular, for **F23** we observe a downgrade of the accuracy when compared to the abusive language models, and for **F16**, where all models are well below the 50% threshold.

A notable difference, when compared to DALC-v2.0, concerns the behaviour of the data maps training splits. With the sole exception of the **amb-dim** from the offensive dimension, in all the other cases they help to achieve better results when compared to the use of the full training set as well as the use of random training splits. In particular, the selection of ambiguous data per dimension (**amb-dim**) consistently outperforms all other settings, a trend already observed for DALC-v2.0. Although for the abusive dimension we observe a better results for the **amb-dim** setting, the difference is not statistically significant.

Focusing on the best models, the use of offensive data allows the model to achieve 85.50% accuracy on all hateful tests on average, while it only obtains 76.88% with abusive data and 72.64% for the joint model. In only two functionalities, namely **F5** (direct threat) and **F7** (hateful slurs), the use of abusive language obtains better results. As for the joint model, the best results are mainly on the non-hateful functionalities, namely **F19** (use of protected group identifiers in a positive statement), **F20** (denouncement of hate via quote) and **F22** (abuse at objects). The only hateful functionality where it obtains the best score is **F26** (change of hateful term by eliminating characters).

Finally, it is clear that the annotations in DALC-v2.0, and consequently the fine-tuned models, have limits that emerge with HATECHEK-NL while being hidden by looking at their performances of the respective DALC-v2.0 test sets. Even the use of abusive language data, which are the most similar to hate speech to fine-tune models, does not allow to properly pass all the tests. From the analysis of the results of every single functional test, it appears evident that very good results are obtained on the easy cases: as soon the expressions of hate become more subtle or fine-grained, models fine-tuned on DALC-v2.0, regardless of the training split and annotated dimension used, fail.

OP-NL Results for OP-NL are also reported on Table 5. Differently from HATECHEK-NL, we have converted the prediction for the ABU class of the joint model into offensive labels.

Like in the previous cases, all fine-tuned models outperform the baselines. The use of the full training data (**std**) results in the best scores only for the offensive and the joint models, while the model fine-tuned on abusive language only underperforms. This is actually a positive result: abusive language is more specific than its offensive counterpart, and the lower results further confirm the quality of the annotated data for each language phenomenon in DALC-v2.0. On the other hand, the results for the joint model are quite disappointing. Although competitive with the offensive dimension model, the results are ≈ 2 points lower. By looking at the distribution of the errors, we observe that the biggest sources of errors are offensive messages misclassified as NOT, a behaviour in-line with what we have observed when the same model is evaluated against the DALC-v2.0 held-out test set.

Similarly to the other evaluation settings, the **amd-class** data maps for the offensive and abusive models in isolation obtain competitive results when compared to the **std** models. When using the abusive language dimension as training material, the model fine-tuned with **amd-class** achieves the best macro F1 (68.75). Only for the joint model, we observe better results for the **rdm** splits. Lastly, the only model which across all training splits overgeneralises the positive class is the joint model. On the basis of the errors observed in DALC-v2.0 for this model, it appears that the overgeneralisation is a consequence of the conversion process of the labels for offensiveness to make the predictions compatible with OP-NL.

5 Discussion

Concerning data maps, we observe inconsistent behaviours of the fine-tuned models: on DALC-v2.0, they are unsuccessful while they achieve either the best performances or very competitive results on HATECHEK-NL and OP-NL. By analysing the variability per class across **amb-dim**, **amb-class**, and **rdm**, we can see that **amb-dim** is the data split that contains core ambiguous cases for all classes, separately and jointly. The ambiguity for the positive class remain relatively high also in **amb-class**, but we observe a drop in the values for the NOT class (0.096 for offensive language, 0.062 for abusive language, and 0.095 when the two dimensions jointly). This means that in the negative class we mainly have easy examples and relatively ambiguous cases for the positive classes. A similar distribution can be observed for the variability for all **rdm** splits, where the variability for the negative class is substantially lower than that of the positive classes. When compared to our expectations on the behaviour of the models based on the ambiguous and the random splits, these observations help to explain the results of these models. Overall, the use of ambiguous examples only on the positive class(es) forces models to pay more attention towards the challenging cases and "disregard" the contributions of the easy ones. This confirms our explanation for the overgeneralisation of the positive class(es). As for the randomly extracted data (**rdm**), it appears that their better performances on DALC-v2.0 is an effect of the distribution of the training instances closer to those in the held-out test data. As for the **amb-dim**, there is a consistent pattern of underperformance across all test data. Rather than issues in the variability scores, i.e., not very "strong" ambiguous cases, it appears that the culprit for the low results should be found in the size of the original DALC-v2.0 training data which makes it difficult to identify good ambiguous cases with respect to the easy (or hard) ones. A similar pattern has been identified by Richburg and Carpuat (2022) when applying data cartography to low- and very-low Machine Translation settings. Furthermore, across all the test sets, we found that only for HATECHEK-NL the use of ambiguous training instances leads to improved out-of-domain performance as reported by Swayamdipta et al. (2020).

When comparing the results of our models against the English HATECHECK for a BERT model fine-tuned on Davidson et al. (2017), the core set of non-hateful functional tests (i.e., **F9**, **F20–21**, **F23–24**) are consistently failed in both languages. Things are quite different for MHC. In this case, the tested model is fine-tuned by concatenating three datasets whose definitions of hate speech perfectly matches the one adopted in MHC. While for **F9** results are excellent, the model still struggles for **F20–21**, **F23–24**[2]

6 Conclusions and Future Directions

In this paper we have presented an extensive benchmarking of models fine-tuned with DALC-v2.0 across three test portions: an internal held-out test, a functional benchmark, HATECHEK-NL, and a dynamic test, OP-NL. Our experiments have investigated the reliability of DALC-v2.0 as a training set for three classification tasks: offensive and abusive language detection in isolation and jointly. Overall, addressing each task in isolation results in better performances than when running a joint experiment. The challenge here lies both in the strict connections between the two language phenomena in analysis and in the limited training data. When the fine-tuned models are applied on the out-of-corpus test sets, we observe a good performance on OP-NL and less satisfying results on HATECHEK-NL. The compatibility of the annotated phenomena in the training data actually plays a major role on this behaviour and it indicates that the quality of the annotated data in DALC-v2.0 contributes to develop robust models.

We have further investigated the effectiveness of the use of data cartography to identify more informative subsets of training materials. Unlike previous work, we observe a limited beneficial effects of this data selection method with DALC-v2.0. While the size of the dataset appears limited for an effective application of this method, we have found that selecting training subsets on the basis of the training dynamics of each annotated dimension results in better systems than when using training dynamics of the whole training split.

The results on HATECHEK-NL clearly identify limitations of the use of DALC-v2.0 to detect hate speech. While its abusive dimension can be considered a good proxy, all fine-tuned models systematically fails on core non-hateful functional tests, indicating limitations in the annotated data.

Future work will focus on extending DALC-v2.0 with multiple hate speech datasets and further

[2]These correspond to **F18–19**, **F21–22** in MHC.

validate the functionalities of HATECHEK-NL.

Ethical statement

Limitations HATECHECK-NL is based on MHC and it inherits its limits. However, as we have discussed in Section 2, we failed to fully implement some functional tests (e.g., reappropriation of slurs) because we were not able to find evidence during our research. To address these limitations, we plan to conduct focused interviews with Dutch organizations such as The Black Archives[3].

Intended use HATECHEK-NLis a diagnostic tool for hate speech against specific protected groups. We have shown its functionalities and its impact on the evaluation of models trained both on a different language phenomenon, e.g., offensive language, and on related and comparable one, e.g., abusive language. The results have shown critical weaknesses mainly on the non-hateful tests rather than showing the strengths of the systems/models on the hateful examples. Similarly, OP-NL is a dynamic test for offensive language whose use is to help assessing the robustness and portability of models trained for offensive language detection.

Goodness of data DALC-v2.0 is the only publicly available resource for investigating the behavior of models on offensive and abusive language phenomena in Dutch. None of the annotated dimensions in DALC-v2.0 explicitly address hate speech as we discussed in Section 2. The results of the fine-tuned models on HATECHEK-NL for the abusive language dimension indicate a compatibility between abusive language in DALC-v2.0 and hate speech. The use of offensive training data on HATECHEK-NL better highlights the limitations of the data, especially as pointed out by the systematic failure on the functions **F23–24**. At the same time, the results on OP-NL for offensive language show a relatively good portability of the models for this language phenomenon.

References

Valerio Basile, Cristina Bosco, Elisabetta Fersini, Debora Nozza, Viviana Patti, Francisco Manuel Rangel Pardo, Paolo Rosso, and Manuela Sanguinetti. 2019. SemEval-2019 task 5: Multilingual detection of hate speech against immigrants and women in Twitter. In *Proceedings of the 13th International Workshop on Semantic Evaluation*, pages 54–63, Minneapolis, Minnesota, USA. Association for Computational Linguistics.

Prajjwal Bhargava, Aleksandr Drozd, and Anna Rogers. 2021. Generalization in NLI: Ways (not) to go beyond simple heuristics. In *Proceedings of the Second Workshop on Insights from Negative Results in NLP*, pages 125–135, Online and Punta Cana, Dominican Republic. Association for Computational Linguistics.

Tommaso Caselli, Arjan Schelhaas, Marieke Weultjes, Folkert Leistra, Hylke van der Veen, Gerben Timmerman, and Malvina Nissim. 2021. DALC: the Dutch abusive language corpus. In *Proceedings of the 5th Workshop on Online Abuse and Harms (WOAH 2021)*, pages 54–66, Online. Association for Computational Linguistics.

Thomas Davidson, Dana Warmsley, Michael Macy, and Ingmar Weber. 2017. Automated hate speech detection and the problem of offensive language. In *Proceedings of the International AAAI Conference on Web and Social Media*, volume 11, pages 512–515.

Wietse de Vries, Andreas van Cranenburgh, Arianna Bisazza, Tommaso Caselli, Gertjan van Noord, and Malvina Nissim. 2019. Bertje: A dutch bert model. *arXiv preprint arXiv:1912.09582*.

Kyle Gorman and Steven Bedrick. 2019. We need to talk about standard splits. In *Proceedings of the 57th Annual Meeting of the Association for Computational Linguistics*, pages 2786–2791, Florence, Italy. Association for Computational Linguistics.

Heather Lent, Semih Yavuz, Tao Yu, Tong Niu, Yingbo Zhou, Dragomir Radev, and Xi Victoria Lin. 2021. Testing cross-database semantic parsers with canonical utterances. In *Proceedings of the 2nd Workshop on Evaluation and Comparison of NLP Systems*, pages 73–83, Punta Cana, Dominican Republic. Association for Computational Linguistics.

Marta Marchiori Manerba and Sara Tonelli. 2021. Fine-grained fairness analysis of abusive language detection systems with CheckList. In *Proceedings of the 5th Workshop on Online Abuse and Harms (WOAH 2021)*, pages 81–91, Online. Association for Computational Linguistics.

Fabio Poletto, Valerio Basile, Manuela Sanguinetti, Cristina Bosco, and Viviana Patti. 2020. Resources and benchmark corpora for hate speech detection: a systematic review. *Language Resources and Evaluation*, pages 1–47.

Alan Ramponi and Barbara Plank. 2020. Neural unsupervised domain adaptation in NLP—A survey. In *Proceedings of the 28th International Conference on Computational Linguistics*, pages 6838–6855, Barcelona, Spain (Online). International Committee on Computational Linguistics.

[3]https://www.theblackarchives.nl/over-ons.html

Marco Tulio Ribeiro, Tongshuang Wu, Carlos Guestrin, and Sameer Singh. 2020. Beyond accuracy: Behavioral testing of NLP models with CheckList. In *Proceedings of the 58th Annual Meeting of the Association for Computational Linguistics*, pages 4902–4912, Online. Association for Computational Linguistics.

Aquia Richburg and Marine Carpuat. 2022. Data cartography for low-resource neural machine translation. In *Findings of the Association for Computational Linguistics: EMNLP 2022*, pages 5594–5607, Abu Dhabi, United Arab Emirates. Association for Computational Linguistics.

Paul Röttger, Haitham Seelawi, Debora Nozza, Zeerak Talat, and Bertie Vidgen. 2022. Multilingual HateCheck: Functional tests for multilingual hate speech detection models. In *Proceedings of the Sixth Workshop on Online Abuse and Harms (WOAH)*, pages 154–169, Seattle, Washington (Hybrid). Association for Computational Linguistics.

Paul Röttger, Bertie Vidgen, Dong Nguyen, Zeerak Waseem, Helen Margetts, and Janet Pierrehumbert. 2021. HateCheck: Functional tests for hate speech detection models. In *Proceedings of the 59th Annual Meeting of the Association for Computational Linguistics and the 11th International Joint Conference on Natural Language Processing (Volume 1: Long Papers)*, pages 41–58, Online. Association for Computational Linguistics.

Ward Ruitenbeek, Victor Zwart, Robin Van Der Noord, Zhenja Gnezdilov, and Tommaso Caselli. 2022. "zo grof !": A comprehensive corpus for offensive and abusive language in Dutch. In *Proceedings of the Sixth Workshop on Online Abuse and Harms (WOAH)*, pages 40–56, Seattle, Washington (Hybrid). Association for Computational Linguistics.

Ananya B. Sai, Tanay Dixit, Dev Yashpal Sheth, Sreyas Mohan, and Mitesh M. Khapra. 2021. Perturbation CheckLists for evaluating NLG evaluation metrics. In *Proceedings of the 2021 Conference on Empirical Methods in Natural Language Processing*, pages 7219–7234, Online and Punta Cana, Dominican Republic. Association for Computational Linguistics.

Anders Søgaard, Sebastian Ebert, Jasmijn Bastings, and Katja Filippova. 2021. We need to talk about random splits. In *Proceedings of the 16th Conference of the European Chapter of the Association for Computational Linguistics: Main Volume*, pages 1823–1832, Online. Association for Computational Linguistics.

Swabha Swayamdipta, Roy Schwartz, Nicholas Lourie, Yizhong Wang, Hannaneh Hajishirzi, Noah A. Smith, and Yejin Choi. 2020. Dataset cartography: Mapping and diagnosing datasets with training dynamics. In *Proceedings of the 2020 Conference on Empirical Methods in Natural Language Processing (EMNLP)*, pages 9275–9293, Online. Association for Computational Linguistics.

Dion Theodoridis and Tommaso Caselli. 2022. All that glitters is not gold: Transfer-learning for offensive language detection in dutch. *Computational Linguistics in the Netherlands Journal*, 12:141–164.

Zeerak Waseem, Thomas Davidson, Dana Warmsley, and Ingmar Weber. 2017. Understanding abuse: A typology of abusive language detection subtasks. In *Proceedings of the First Workshop on Abusive Language Online*, pages 78–84.

Michael Wiegand, Josef Ruppenhofer, and Thomas Kleinbauer. 2019. Detection of Abusive Language: the Problem of Biased Datasets. In *Proceedings of the 2019 Conference of the North American Chapter of the Association for Computational Linguistics: Human Language Technologies, Volume 1 (Long and Short Papers)*, pages 602–608, Minneapolis, Minnesota. Association for Computational Linguistics.

Marcos Zampieri, Shervin Malmasi, Preslav Nakov, Sara Rosenthal, Noura Farra, and Ritesh Kumar. 2019. SemEval-2019 task 6: Identifying and categorizing offensive language in social media (OffensEval). In *Proceedings of the 13th International Workshop on Semantic Evaluation*, pages 75–86, Minneapolis, Minnesota, USA. Association for Computational Linguistics.

Marcos Zampieri, Preslav Nakov, Sara Rosenthal, Pepa Atanasova, Georgi Karadzhov, Hamdy Mubarak, Leon Derczynski, Zeses Pitenis, and Çağrı Çöltekin. 2020. SemEval-2020 task 12: Multilingual offensive language identification in social media (OffensEval 2020). In *Proceedings of the Fourteenth Workshop on Semantic Evaluation*, pages 1425–1447, Barcelona (online). International Committee for Computational Linguistics.

A HateCheck-NL: List of Functional Tests

	Functionality	Description from Röttger et al. (2021)	Label	Count	
				templ	**cases**
F1	derog_neg_emote_h	Strong negative emotions explicitly expressed about a protected group or its members	hateful	20	140
F2	derog_neg_attrib_h	Explicit descriptions of a protected group or its members using very negative attributes	hateful	20	140
F3	derog_dehum_h	Explicit dehumanisation of a protected group or its members	hateful	20	140
F4	derog_impl_h	Implicit derogation of a protected group or its members	hateful	20	140
F5	threat_dir_h	Direct threats against a protected group or its members	hateful	20	140
F6	threat_norm_h	Threats expressed as normative statements	hateful	20	140
F7	slur_h	Hate expressed using slurs	hateful	10	170
F8	slur_homonym_nh	Non-hateful homonyms of slurs	non-hate	25	25
F9	slur_reclaimed_nh	Use of reclaimed slurs	non-hate	45	45
F10	profanity_h	Hate expressed using profanity	hateful	20	140
F11	profanity_nh	Non-hateful uses of profanity	non-hate	100	100
F12	ref_subs_clause_h	Hate expressed through pronoun reference in subsequent clauses	hateful	20	140
F13	ref_subs_sent_h	Hate expressed through pronoun reference in subsequent sentences	hateful	20	140
F14	negate_pos_h	Hate expressed using negated positive statements	hateful	20	140
F15	negate_neg_nh	Non-hate expressed using negated hateful statements	non-hate	20	140
F16	phrase_question_h	Hate phrased as a question	hateful	20	140
F17	phrase_opinion_h	Hate phrased as an opinion	hateful	20	140
F18	ident_neutral_nh	Neutral statements using protected group identifiers	non-hate	20	140
F19	ident_pos_nh	Positive statements using protected group identifiers	non-hate	30	210
F20	counter_quote_nh	Denouncements of hate that quote it	non-hate	20	170
F21	counter_ref_nh	Denouncements of hate that make direct reference to it	non-hate	20	170
F22	target_obj_nh	Abuse targeted at objects	non-hate	65	65
F23	target_indiv_nh	Abuse targeted at individuals not referencing membership in a protected group	non-hate	65	65
F24	target_group_nh	Abuse targeted at non-protected groups (e.g. professions)	non-hate	65	65
F25	spell_char_swap_h	Swaps of adjacent characters	hateful	20	140
F26	spell_char_del_h	Missing characters	hateful	20	140
F27	spell_space_del_h	Missing word boundaries	hateful	20	170
F28	spell_space_add_h	Added spaces between characters	hateful	20	170
F29	spell_leet_h	Leet speak	hateful	20	170
	Total		**hateful**	**350**	**2,640**
			non-hate	**475**	**1,195**
			all	**825**	**3,835**

Table A.1: HATECHECK-NL functionality overview

B Replicability: Preprocessing and Hyperparameters

Preprocessing All experiments have been conducted with common pre-processing steps, namely:

- lowercasing of all words
- all users' mentions have been substituted with a placeholder (MENTION);
- all URLs have been substituted with a with a placeholder (URL);
- all ordinal numbers have been replaced with a placeholder (NUMBER);
- emojis have been replaced with text (e.g. 😹 → `:cat_face_joy:`) using Python `emoji` package;
- hashtag symbol has been removed from hasthtags (e.g. #kadiricinadalet → kadiricinadalet);
- extra blank spaces have been replaced with a single space;
- extra blank new lines have been removed.

Models' hyperparameters All hyperparamters used for the experiments are reported in Table B.1.

Model	Task	Hyperparm.	Value
BERTje	Offensive Abusive Offensive & Abusive	Learning rate	2e-5
		Training Epochs	5
		Optimzer	AdamW
		Adam epsilon	1e-8
		Max sequence length	280
		Batch size	16
		Num. warmup steps	2

Table B.1: Hyperparameters used to fine-tune BERTje.

C Detailed Results

System	Train	Class	P	R	Macro-F1
Dummy	n.a.	OFF	0.0	0.0	0.4230
		NOT	0.7340	1.0	
BERTje	std	OFF	0.7214	0.6864	0.7993
		NOT	0.8881	0.9047	
	amb-dim	OFF	0.5031	0.6459	0.6885
		NOT	0.8577	0.7699	
	amb-class	OFF	0.6575	0.6932	0.7766
		NOT	0.8871	0.8697	
	rand	OFF	0.7139	0.6294	0.7764
		NOT	0.8723	0.9064	

Table C.1: DALC-v2.0 **offensive language**: binary classification; **rand** reports the averages of the results obtained using three different training splits.

Model	Train	Class	P	R	Macro-F1
Dummy	n.a.	ABU	0.0	0.0	0.4619
		NOT	0.8584	1.0	
BERTje	std	ABU	0.5741	0.4687	0.7223
		NOT	0.9149	0.9426	
	amb-dim	ABU	0.3783	0.5270	0.6631
		NOT	0.9166	0.8571	
	amb-class	ABU	0.3693	0.7106	0.6721
		NOT	0.9434	0.7852	
	rand	ABU	0.5534	0.4527	0.7070
		NOT	0.9104	0.9417	

Table C.2: DALC-v2.0 **abusive language**: binary classification; **rand** reports the averages of the results obtained using three different training splits.

Model	Train	Class	P	R	Macro-F1
Dummy	n.a.	OFF	0.0	0.0	0.2824
		ABU	0.0	0.0	
		NOT	0.7348	1.0	
BERTje	std	OFF	0.3301	0.3391	0.5890
		ABU	0.5696	0.5011	
		NOT	0.8971	0.9800	
	amb-dim	OFF	0.1933	0.4158	0.4374
		ABU	0.2718	0.4773	
		NOT	0.8822	0.5830	
	amb-class	OFF	0.2194	0.4653	0.5358
		ABU	0.4491	0.5529	
		NOT	0.9371	0.7187	
	rand	OFF	0.3343	0.2953	0.5725
		ABU	0.5778	0.4672	
		NOT	0.8682	0.9159	

Table C.3: DALC-v2.0 **offensive and abusive language**: multi-class classification; **rand** reports the averages of the results obtained using three different training splits.

	Functionality	Label	# Inst.	std	amb-dim	amb-class	rdm
F1	derog_neg_emote_h	hateful	140	77.10	61.40	**93.60**	69.77
F2	derog_neg_attrib_h	hateful	140	85.00	95.00	**98.60**	87.37
F3	derog_dehum_h	hateful	140	78.60	**91.40**	85.70	69.53
F4	derog_impl_h	hateful	140	37.10	**65.70**	56.40	31.63
F5	threat_dir_h	hateful	140	58.60	57.90	**77.90**	47.87
F6	threat_norm_h	hateful	140	57.90	78.60	**88.60**	53.80
F7	slur_h	hateful	170	71.20	**90.60**	79.40	67.47
F8	slur_homonym_nh	non-hate	25	68.00	40.00	64.00	**73.33**
F9	slur_reclaimed_nh	non-hate	45	46.70	33.30	26.70	49.63
F10	profanity_h	hateful	140	**98.60**	93.60	**98.60**	97.60
F11	profanity_nh	non-hate	100	29.00	15.00	19.00	33.67
F12	ref_subs_clause_h	hateful	140	75.00	85.00	**98.60**	73.80
F13	ref_subs_sent_h	hateful	140	88.60	95.70	**99.30**	85.27
F14	negate_pos_h	hateful	140	40.70	65.70	**77.10**	31.17
F15	negate_neg_nh	non-hate	140	65.70	50.70	12.90	**65.93**
F16	phrase_question_h	hateful	140	52.90	11.40	**69.30**	49.50
F17	phrase_opinion_h	hateful	140	67.90	65.70	**82.10**	55.50
F18	ident_neutral_nh	non-hate	140	83.60	42.90	69.30	**91.47**
F19	ident_pos_nh	non-hate	210	65.20	57.60	40.50	**73.80**
F20	counter_quote_nh	non-hate	170	38.20	37.10	28.20	**50.77**
F21	counter_ref_nh	non-hate	170	27.10	14.10	11.80	31.73
F22	target_obj_nh	non-hate	65	61.50	15.40	38.50	**64.63**
F23	target_indiv_nh	non-hate	65	41.50	18.50	12.30	46.67
F24	target_group_nh	non-hate	65	26.20	26.20	12.30	30.27
F25	spell_char_swap_h	hateful	140	57.10	68.60	**82.10**	60.93
F26	spell_char_del_h	hateful	140	72.10	**89.30**	87.10	76.20
F27	spell_space_del_h	hateful	170	82.90	84.70	**95.90**	86.07
F28	spell_space_add_h	hateful	170	55.90	**78.80**	78.20	42.77
F29	spell_leet_h	hateful	170	70.60	**91.20**	87.10	72.37
	Average			61.40	59.35	**64.52**	61.05
	Average - Hateful			68.86	76.57	**85.50**	64.57
	Average - Non-hateful			47.61	30.53	28.77	52.57

Table C.1: HATECHEK-NL: results using training data from DALC-V2.0 annotated for **offensive language**. Best results across training splits are marked in bold. We have marked in red results below 50%.

	Functionality	Label	# Inst.	std	amb-dim	amb-class	rdm
F1	derog_neg_emote_h	hateful	140	57.10	**69.30**	64.30	48.33
F2	derog_neg_attrib_h	hateful	140	77.10	**93.60**	83.60	65.00
F3	derog_dehum_h	hateful	140	61.40	**80.00**	**80.00**	53.10
F4	derog_impl_h	hateful	140	35.70	**55.00**	27.90	24.53
F5	threat_dir_h	hateful	140	65.70	**86.40**	67.10	56.20
F6	threat_norm_h	hateful	140	61.40	**80.00**	70.00	43.33
F7	slur_h	hateful	170	63.50	**91.20**	78.20	44.10
F8	slur_homonym_nh	non-hate	25	**80.00**	32.00	48.00	78.67
F9	slur_reclaimed_nh	non-hate	45	**66.70**	44.40	48.90	58.53
F10	profanity_h	hateful	140	85.00	**95.70**	**95.70**	79.27
F11	profanity_nh	non-hate	100	50.00	29.00	34.00	**62.67**
F12	ref_subs_clause_h	hateful	140	73.60	80.00	**80.70**	53.83
F13	ref_subs_sent_h	hateful	140	84.30	86.40	**94.30**	69.53
F14	negate_pos_h	hateful	140	36.40	**67.90**	49.30	20.00
F15	negate_neg_nh	non-hate	140	67.90	49.30	60.70	**74.77**
F16	phrase_question_h	hateful	140	24.30	14.30	30.00	11.90
F17	phrase_opinion_h	hateful	140	57.90	**77.90**	54.30	25.23
F18	ident_neutral_nh	non-hate	140	85.00	61.40	80.70	**91.20**
F19	ident_pos_nh	non-hate	210	63.30	35.20	62.40	**81.90**
F20	counter_quote_nh	non-hate	170	47.10	52.90	59.40	**76.87**
F21	counter_ref_nh	non-hate	170	48.80	39.40	37.10	**59.40**
F22	target_obj_nh	non-hate	65	86.20	52.30	70.80	**93.30**
F23	target_indiv_nh	non-hate	65	43.10	13.80	33.80	**51.80**
F24	target_group_nh	non-hate	65	43.10	18.50	27.70	**56.43**
F25	spell_char_swap_h	hateful	140	51.40	**83.60**	71.40	40.70
F26	spell_char_del_h	hateful	140	60.70	82.90	**84.30**	51.43
F27	spell_space_del_h	hateful	170	79.40	87.60	**92.40**	55.67
F28	spell_space_add_h	hateful	170	33.50	**74.10**	47.10	30.40
F29	spell_leet_h	hateful	170	55.90	**84.70**	76.50	45.07
	Average			60.19	**62.72**	62.43	55.28
	Average - Hateful			59.58	**76.88**	69.16	45.70
	Average - Non-hateful			57.38	36.29	48.14	**65.72**

Table C.2: HATECHEK-NL: results using training data from DALC-V2.0 annotated for **abusive language**. Best results across training splits are marked in bold. We have marked in red results below 50%.

	Functionality	Label	# Inst.	std	amb-dim	amb-class	rdm
F1	derog_neg_emote_h	hateful	140	59.30	63.60	**77.90**	30.27
F2	derog_neg_attrib_h	hateful	140	77.10	65.70	**83.60**	50.27
F3	derog_dehum_h	hateful	140	62.90	77.90	**78.60**	49.30
F4	derog_impl_h	hateful	140	31.40	**50.00**	49.30	19.27
F5	threat_dir_h	hateful	140	57.10	77.10	**80.70**	41.20
F6	threat_norm_h	hateful	140	57.10	59.30	**67.10**	34.03
F7	slur_h	hateful	170	64.70	72.40	**77.60**	46.07
F8	slur_homonym_nh	non-hate	25	80.00	64.00	56.00	**82.67**
F9	slur_reclaimed_nh	non-hate	45	51.10	**62.20**	35.60	61.47
F10	profanity_h	hateful	140	88.60	72.10	**91.40**	70.23
F11	profanity_nh	non-hate	100	55.00	**70.00**	40.00	66.00
F12	ref_subs_clause_h	hateful	140	75.00	76.40	**80.00**	46.90
F13	ref_subs_sent_h	hateful	140	82.10	87.10	**90.70**	63.80
F14	negate_pos_h	hateful	140	56.40	**67.90**	17.87	20.00
F15	negate_neg_nh	non-hate	140	75.00	60.70	50.00	**85.93**
F16	phrase_question_h	hateful	140	32.90	25.00	21.40	11.20
F17	phrase_opinion_h	hateful	140	49.30	41.40	**60.70**	21.90
F18	ident_neutral_nh	non-hate	140	80.70	46.40	67.90	**89.77**
F19	ident_pos_nh	non-hate	210	65.20	39.00	53.80	**83.17**
F20	counter_quote_nh	non-hate	170	62.40	**84.40**	64.10	84.13
F21	counter_ref_nh	non-hate	170	48.20	50.60	36.50	**69.40**
F22	target_obj_nh	non-hate	65	87.70	86.20	75.40	**92.30**
F23	target_indiv_nh	non-hate	65	36.90	27.70	15.40	**57.43**
F24	target_group_nh	non-hate	65	61.50	56.90	30.80	**69.23**
F25	spell_char_swap_h	hateful	140	46.40	58.60	**72.90**	31.90
F26	spell_char_del_h	hateful	140	66.40	62.10	**84.30**	47.37
F27	spell_space_del_h	hateful	170	73.50	65.90	**85.90**	48.07
F28	spell_space_add_h	hateful	170	42.40	45.90	**75.90**	21.57
F29	spell_leet_h	hateful	170	58.20	72.40	**75.30**	37.83
	Average			60.94	61.22	**63.21**	52.78
	Average - Hateful			59.09	62.74	**72.64**	38.28
	Average - Non-hateful			63.97	58.74	47.77	**76.50**

Table C.3: HATECHEK-NL: results using training data from DALC-V2.0 annotated for **offensive and abusive language**. Best results across training splits are marked in bold. We have marked in red results below 50%.

System	Train	Class	P	R	Macro-F1
Dummy	n.a.	OFF	0.0	0.0	0.3904
		NOT	0.6406	1.0	
BERTje	std	OFF	0.6772	0.6345	0.7356
		NOT	0.8020	0.8304	
	amb-dim	OFF	0.4293	0.8219	0.5423
		NOT	0.7949	0.3871	
	amb-class	OFF	0.6527	0.5510	0.6991
		NOT	0.7684	0.8356	
	rand	OFF	0.6761	0.5028	0.6907
		NOT	0.7562	0.8625	

Table C.4: OP-NL **offensive language**: binary classification; **rand** reports the averages of the results obtained using three different training splits.

Model	Train	Class	P	R	Macro-F1
Dummy	n.a.	OFF	0.0	0.0	0.3904
		NOT	0.6406	1.0	
BERTje	std	OFF	0.8582	0.2134	0.5757
		NOT	0.6896	0.9802	
	amb-dim	OFF	0.6773	0.3544	0.6319
		NOT	0.7143	0.9053	
	amb-class	OFF	0.6446	0.5250	0.6875
		NOT	0.7587	0.8377	
	rand	OFF	0.8217	0.1911	0.5500
		NOT	0.6829	0.9761	

Table C.5: OP-NL **abusive language**: binary classification; **rand** reports the averages of the results obtained using three different training splits.

Model	Train	Class	P	R	Macro-F1
Dummy	n.a.	OFF	0.0	0.0	0.3904
		NOT	0.6406	1.0	
BERTje	std	OFF	0.6606	0.6030	0.7185
		NOT	0.7877	0.8262	
	amb-dim	OFF	0.4002	0.6809	0.5183
		NOT	0.7050	0.4277	
	amb-class	OFF	0.5278	0.7570	0.6641
		NOT	0.8198	0.6202	
	rand	OFF	0.7045	0.4990	0.6991
		NOT	0.7591	0.8824	

Table C.6: OP-NL **offensive and abusive language**: binary classification; **rand** reports the averages of the results obtained using three different training splits.

Relationality and Offensive Speech: A Research Agenda

Razvan Amironesei*
Unaffiliated
amironesei@gmail.com

Mark Díaz*
Google Research
markdiaz@google

Abstract

We draw from the framework of relationality as a pathway for modeling social relations to address gaps in text classification, generally, and offensive language classification, specifically. We use minoritized language, such as queer speech, to motivate a need for understanding and modeling social relations– both among individuals and among their social communities. We then point to socio-ethical style as a research area for inferring and measuring social relations as well as propose additional questions to structure future research on operationalizing social context.

1 Introduction

In this paper, we build on NLP-based approaches to defining and classifying offensive speech to lay out research directions for robustly incorporating social context into the ways text classification tasks are conceptualized and operationalized. Our motivation lies in classifying sociolinguistic norms of minoritized communities, such as the use of reclaimed slurs, which current classification approaches often fail to distinguish from language which is abusive, toxic, or hateful. To achieve a robust understanding of social context, we consider offensive speech in terms of relationality– or the social relations that inform how language is used and interpreted. At a conceptual level we defined offensiveness as a property of social relations rather than as a property of specific language terms. At an operational level, we discuss initial insights and open research directions for how social relations can be measured in practice.

Reclaimed language use and other aspects of minoritized language, such as queer speech and Black American vernacular have proven challenging for text classification (Dias Oliva et al., 2021; Sap et al., 2019). This language use reflects a plurality of language meaning and non-normative use that many NLP approaches currently fail to capture. The research directions we propose are oriented toward text classification for potentially harmful or undesirable speech, such as toxicity detection or hate speech detection. While we consider offensive speech to be distinct from hate speech or toxic language, they have important similarities that help to clarify a definition of offensive speech as well as point to approaches for improving classification tasks (Diaz et al., 2022). That is to say, while we use a definition of offensive speech that overlaps with definitions of hate speech and other abusive language, a sociological understanding of offensive speech indicates that it is distinct in ways that current classification approaches do not reflect. Our overarching goal is to provide research directions toward contextually-informed modeling and annotation to appropriately capture sociolinguistic norms used within minoritized groups. A key underlying postulate of our research is that speech, and in particular offensive speech, is not divorced from "doing". On the contrary, offensive speech has practical effects that enact and perform subjective formations (Butler, 2021).

Although a range of definitions and labels have been used to operationalize offensive language, they share a goal of classifying undesirable language that stands to harm or deteriorate discourse. Concepts for classification have included, "abusive language" (Nobata et al., 2016), "harmful speech" (Faris et al., 2016), and "hate speech" (Schmidt and Wiegand, 2017), among others. These tasks do not use identical definitions of offensiveness but often use similar labels and share similar goals. Definitional differences can be observed in the label schema for each task. For example, Van Hee et al. (2015) define 'racist' and 'sexist' as subsets of 'insults', and Wulczyn et al. (2017) include a specific label for personal attacks.

Importantly, researchers have identified issues and challenges related to the variety of social

*Authors contributed equally

The 7th Workshop on Online Abuse and Harms (WOAH), pages 85–95
July 13, 2023

contexts in which classification tools are applied, namely those involving satire and nonstandard use of language, such as reclaimed speech (Davidson et al., 2017). These challenges are rooted in nuanced use and understanding of language that rely heavily on aspects of social context including, culture, place, and power. Additionally, they point to a need for better incorporation of social context in the ways that NLP tasks are conceptualized and operationalized (Hovy and Yang, 2021a).

We refine this line of research by emphasizing that a socio-ethical account of offensive speech should be attentive to a diversity of contextual uses and the variety of forms it can take. This requires a basic understanding that the offensiveness of speech is dependent upon 1) the background of social and cultural conditions that surround it; 2) the social dynamics between the subjects and objects of offense; 3) the in-group/out-group language norms surrounding language use; and 4) the different types of outcomes of offensive speech, including the resulting potential and actual harms associated with the previous considerations. Our approach expands from (Diaz et al., 2022), who use conceptual analysis to evaluate specific components of how hate speech and toxicity are defined in order to form the basis for an expanded definition of offensive speech. Rather than an exhaustive review of definitions, they identify those which help to build a more robust approach to defining offensiveness, with specific attention toward identifying and operationalizing its relational qualities. Building from their work, we propose relationality as a conceptual bridge to more robustly operationalize social context and, in particular, the social relations that differentiate minoritized speech from antagonistic forms of speech. In addition, we point to existing work on style measurement as an avenue to do so.

In the following sections we draw from the framework of relationality to motivate a need for modeling social relations to address gaps in text classification, generally, and offensive language classification, specifically. Second, we propose research domains and questions to structure future research on operationalizing social context. Third, we point to and discuss examples for how we can begin to better model social relations. We do not provide a closed or exhaustive set of techniques for applying a relational lens, however we discuss style and its use in NLP as a jumping off point for addressing ethical concerns surrounding offensive language classification that others have raised (e.g., (Dias Oliva et al., 2021; Diaz et al., 2022).

2 A Relational Framework for Contextual Analysis of Offensive Speech

Relationality operates as a general analytic tool that helps to unveil and disambiguate specific contextual uses of offensive speech from others. A relational lens in the context of NLP refers to a focus on the social relations that influence the production, meaning, reception, and outcomes of language among interlocutors. In this way, relationality is a means of analysis to conceptually organize social context. Hovy and Yang (2021) propose to shift NLP analysis toward a contextual understanding of speech that consists in the following seven factors: 1) speaker and 2) receiver, 3) social relations, 4) context, 5) social norms, 6) culture and ideology, and 7) communicative goals (Hovy and Yang, 2021a). We argue that contextual analysis of offensive speech can be achieved through a focus on the social relations inherent in language, its use, and its outcomes.

Diaz et al. (2022) point out a distinction between treating offensiveness as a property of an utterance rather than as a relation between individuals or communities and that utterance. Treating offensiveness as a property of a linguistic token, such as by registering a term to a blocklist, ignores the very real ways in which language meaning is not fixed or inherent to its orthography but rather is constructed socially via a network of meanings among social actors. For this reason, when we refer to "offensive speech" we refer not only to the content of an utterance, but also the confluence of social relations and context that surround the production of that utterance. In other words, "offensive speech" entails time, place, by whom, and to whom, in addition to orthography. Relationality also reflects a move away from locating offensiveness exclusively at the level of words and instead locates offensiveness in an individual or group's relation to a word or concept. This, in turn, helps to distinguish why a term might produce offense when used between members of different communities but not when used between members of the same community, as in the example of reclaimed slurs.

Through relationality our focus is on accounting for patterns inherent in the social relations that produce offensive speech. In this respect, our work overlaps with prior work that effectively operationalizes aspects of relationality through analyses of interactional patterns and discourse (e.g., (Danescu-Niculescu-Mizil et al., 2011)). Relationality itself does not provide a comprehensive list of all the contextual elements that influence how communication is understood between social actors, however, it emphasizes how to conceptually organize social context– namely around social relations between and surrounding subjects. As such, applying relationality rests on further research and validation of the relevant aspects of social relations that must be accounted for across text classification tasks.

While Hovy and Yang (2021b) have laid important groundwork for addressing this question and Diaz et al. (2022) explore social context more specifically in the context of offensive language classification tasks, we propose several research directions for bringing relationality into practice for classification tasks. There has not been explicit work on detailing the aspects of social context most operative for distinguishing the range and differential impacts of offensive language. Each of these directions has overlapping components but address open questions about what a relational lens means for 1) how offensive language can be conceptualized in a way that is responsive to minoritized speech and 2) how offensive language is operationalized through annotation task design and language modeling.

2.1 Minoritized Speech

A problem we draw from that exemplifies the need for a relational lens is that posed by minoritized speech, which classification systems have been shown to misclassify or classify in systematically biased ways. For example, scholars in NLP have high error rates for African American English (AAE) in part-of-speech tagging and language identification (Jørgensen et al., 2015; Blodgett et al., 2016), and disproportionately toxic ratings of speech containing features of AAE compared with speech that does not (Sap et al., 2021). Another example is that of drag queen speech, which Dias Oliva et al. showed was rated more likely to be 'toxic' compared with tweets from white supremacists in a comparative study (Dias Oliva et al., 2021). As Dias Oliva et al. (2021). discuss, the discourse used by drag queens on Twitter is expressed through shared slang, references, and linguistic norms. Diaz et al. (2022) point out that using this language relies on shared assumptions about the use of slurs, mutual consent to break normative rules of language "decency", and an understanding that manners of speaking used in an in-group context can be qualitatively distinct from the use of those manners of speaking in an out-group context.

We understand minoritized speech as a type of speech that emerges as a result of a power asymmetry that is produced by dominant and widely accepted forms of expression within a language. Both Dias Oliva et al. (2021) and Diaz et al. (2022) note that communication in the queer community involves the reappropriation of offensive language as a means to "self-inoculate" community members against social attacks from out-group members. The same cannot be said about white supremacist speech which is defined by objectifying and demeaning historically marginalized groups and incitement of hate and violence (Blazak, 2009). The problem they raise, however, is not limited to the minoritization of drag queen speech. They argue that addressing the risk of increased censorship for minoritized language is an ethical imperative because of the socially productive role that non-normative language plays in the survival of minoritized groups (Diaz et al., 2022).

3 Relationality through Style

In response to the challenges posed by minoritized speech, we turn to linguistic style and its measurement in NLP as a means of both describing and applying relationality. In doing so, we draw from style as an artifact of social context that specifies how social relations are structured. Work on linguistic style in NLP has typically focused on individual communication style, such as in investigating author attribution (Safin and Ogaltsov, 2018) or making inferences about author psychological state and demographics (Pennebaker, 2011). Notably, measurements of style are usually pursued in contrast to explorations of language content. Khalid and Srinivasan (2020) bridge the gap between structure and content by applying style measurement to understand an individual's relationship to a broader community. The authors use style to explicate a social relation that is not necessarily explicit in an utterance itself. This moves from simply applying style to characterize individuals to understanding a broader social relation and orientation to community language norms.

Our contention is that NLP accounts of style must explicitly contend with the social, historical, and practical conditions from which styles of speech emerge. Thus, work on style in NLP needs to be attuned to the underlying ethical questions associated with the technical measurement of styles of speech. First and foremost, this means that style needs to be understood as embedded in specific contexts of production with distinct practical outcomes. For example, at an ethical level, style can be understood: (1) as the reflexive practice of styles of existence via the exercise of specific technologies of the self (Martin et al., 1988; Hadot, 1995), such as practices of self writing (Foucault, 2019) and practices of truthful speech (Foucault, 2011); (2) as a work of forming and transforming one's existence (Foucault, 2012; McWhorter, 1999) via somatoaesthetic projects that are not reducible to the purely individual and voluntaristic manifestations of heroic self-distinction (Heyes, 2007) and moral quests for universal wisdom predicated on self-possession (Amironesei, 2014). However, an ethical grounding of style is related yet distinct from a strictly sociological (Fleck, 2012; Zittel, 2012), historical (Crombie, 1994) and an epistemological account of styles of thinking (Hacking, 1992). From an ethical standpoint style is conceptualized as a practice of the self and others while at a sociological level, style is the product of community language norms that reflect hierarchical patterns of discourse that are interwoven with social identity formation and relational dynamics (Labov, 1973). In both cases, a socio-ethical account of style is context-dependent, "relational and dynamic" (Ekström et al., 2018) and a key feature of an individual or a group's self-expression. One aspect that we emphasize here is that style has irreducible ethical, social and political conditions, expressions and manifestations which refer to speech that an individual or a group produce in relation to others, rather than as a fixed property of an individual, their words or given images. In this way, analyses of style can be robust to code-switching or the range of styles individuals may use in changing social contexts.

Thus, given the contingent and contextual production of style we propose relationality through style as an analytic or a mode of analysis that seeks to account for the historically and socially constituted matrices of power relations where style works as an interactive feature which opens to spaces of contestation in the formation of both individuals and collectives. For our purposes, while style provides general indications of social context, its relational significance lies in its potential for disentangling minoritized forms of speech from abusive language. For example, mock impoliteness, which features in drag queen speech, plays a central role in group identity formation and resistance against oppressive social systems (McKinnon, 2017). Style's significance for minoritized communities emerges through "contextualized repertoires of speaking and behaving through which identities and sociocultural affiliations are claimed and communicated" (Ekström et al., 2018).

A key takeaway is that a common style among interlocutors can suggest shared norms or social or cultural proximity. Because style is an artifact of social norms, and thus social relations, it can be used to infer shared context among individuals involved in an interaction being assessed for offensive content. In this way, comparisons of linguistic form can be a tool to unveil the relations among which offensive language is couched. While style can vary from individual to individual, Khalid and Srinivasan (2020) show that style can reliably predict group membership, independent of language content (Khalid and Srinivasan, 2020). Indeed, earlier work has shown that style can indicate social demographic information about a speaker (Eckert and Rickford, 2001). In the context of offensive speech classification, this means that style provides useful information for assessing whether individuals share a sociolect or dialect. This carries significance not only for disambiguating language use within a given minoritized sociolect and improving upon weaknesses in offensive speech classification.

3.1 Style and Common Sense

By failing to disambiguate language uses, particularly those that are minoritized, current classification approaches implicitly force a generalized or 'common sense' interpretation of language, whether at train time (i.e., via annotation) or at inference time. Using style measurement, or other relational approaches, to situate language explicitly in its social relations puts into practice the understanding that the same language can carry different connotations or meanings. A pluralistic understanding of language is not possible through approaches that ignore relations between individuals and the communities they belong to. This is because, in the absence of explicit, familiar sociolinguistic cues or relational context, a reader or model must interpret the language using generalized language norms as a primary point of reference thus concealing the differential relations (Deleuze, 1994; Boven, 2014) that occur between various ways that individuals and communities engage with language.

From a ML fairness perspective, applying generalized language norms is to rely on dominant, prescriptivist views that often treat minoritized speech as improper and contribute to biased system performance. One example of stigmatized speech, AAE, has been characterized as incorrect, devaluing not only its use, but also the communities that speak it. As Pullum demonstrates, AAE "is not Standard English with mistakes," rather its "speakers use a different grammar clearly and sharply distinguished from Standard English at a number of points" (Pullum, 1999). In NLP, Sap et al. (2019) show that "AAE tweets are twice as likely to be labeled offensive compared to others" and recommend paying special attention to the effect of a speaker's dialect and social identity to mitigate negative and disparate impacts. Aside from being ethically dubious, applying generalized language norms drawn from prescriptivist views of language use ignores nuances and distinctions between uses of AAE in in-group and out-group contexts.

We eschew any analysis that treats language as offensive based on guidelines grounded in notions of common sense or, in the case of offensive language classification, notions of common decency or civility. This is precisely because notions of common decency, like notions of generalized language norms, stand to devalue minoritized sociolinguistic norms. Civility is not always explicitly defined in text classification contexts, but has been articulated as "concerned with communicating attitudes of respect, tolerance and consideration to one another' (Calhoun, 2000). While common sense can indicate general, accepted uses of speech, it is culturally and contextually dependent, and thus falls within the set of factors that a relational lens is needed to disambiguate, including the subjects and relations that they are embedded in. Without disambiguation, applying generalized language norms stands to be exclusionary by reflecting stigmatizing beliefs about non-standard language. At the same time, notions of common sense are vague and difficult to define as well as ignore the variety of conditions and contexts in which language is used.

The conceptual distinction between a relational and a common sense approach to language processing is not a mere abstraction that NLP researchers should simply be aware of. On the contrary, it has major implications for language modeling processes. For example, annotating the presence of offensive language in a rating task, with limited social context posits that there is a widely understood corpus of offensive language that a rater can draw upon that is distinct from another corpus of non-offensive language that represents decent, and civil discourse. The problem with this distinction is that offensive speech is historically constituted, that is, offensive terms change over time, and are defined by societal and cultural norms and power relations between groups. Annotators may draw from overlapping notions of civil language, however a variety of speech exists outside of these norms.

The measurement of style to study an individual's relationship to a broader community and its communication norms in the way that Khalid and Srinivasan (2020) do provides motivation for measuring the relationships among speakers across different communities. While style does not necessarily speak to specific relationships between individuals, overlaps in style can suggest some degree of shared norms or values. Still further research is needed to better understand how style might be used alongside other information collected or inferred in NLP tasks. For example, in their study of bias in toxicity ratings for AAE, Sap et al. (2019) showed raters an estimation of a tweet's likelihood to contain elements of AAE as well as primed raters to consider dialect in relation to the author's likely racial identity. They found that raters provided less biased toxicity annotations of AAE tweets after their intervention. It is not known whether the score caused raters to re-interpret the text examples according to AAE norms or if raters adjusted their annotations out of fear of appearing racist. However questions remain about why exactly the intervention succeeded and whether rater subgroups were similarly impacted by the intervention. Determining how relational approaches can best be applied to operationalize social context raises a number of research directions that we outline in the following sections.

4 Operationalizing Relational Context

In practice, the primary challenge of applying a relational approach to offensive language lies in defining its scope and operationalizing its component parts. As others have pointed out, identifying social context and integrating it into NLP models is both needed for more robust and successful NLP as well as nontrivial (Hovy and Yang, 2021a). Measuring linguistic style provides one way of applying a relational lens, however other features may be leveraged to infer relational context.

A relational focus in classification tasks requires determining a set of measurable features that provide information about social relations, as well as work to prioritize features that most improve task performance, particularly with respect to language norms missed by current techniques. Identifying and predicting aspects of social context as a part of classifying offensive speech brings its own, deep set of research questions and challenges. Although offensive speech detection and related tasks have largely been framed as text classification tasks, we break down research questions for future work into those that focus on linguistic features and those that focus on extra-linguistic features surrounding text and its production. In doing so, we implicitly shift offensive language classification from a text classification task to one that expands to include non-textual inferences in addition to linguistic content. Through a relational lens, language is one artifact produced by the social relation of offense between social actors. Framing language in this way allows us to consider other artifacts that result or shift as a consequence of offense. This broadens the range of features at our disposal to infer social context, including user behavior (e.g., "liking" comments), networks of user accounts, the post structure of dialogue, and histories of interactions. Taking advantage of this broadened set of features, we propose areas for research that build both from established approaches in language modeling, such as text annotation, as well as modeling approaches focused on non-text data, such as conversation structure, can serve as a clue to the nature of the relationship between two social actors (Zhang et al., 2018).

4.1 Context through Linguistic Features

As previously described, existing NLP techniques for modeling linguistic style and language dialect implicitly carry information about cultural context and community membership and should be further explored for the relational insights they bring. However, prior challenges in text classification, such as classifying reclaimed speech or satire, also bring to light research opportunities with respect to capturing social context at the data annotation step. Though not exhaustive of all opportunities for improving capture of social context, text annotation and annotation task design are ripe for additional work. Further research in these areas will be key to operationalizing relational aspects of language, precisely because human annotation is well-suited for capturing explicit social dynamics and interpretations that automated methods struggle with.

4.2 Context through Annotation

We bring a focus to annotation because the complexity of social context provides an opportunity to leverage human inference. Annotation tasks are typically designed in such a way that they isolate examples from the social context in which they were produced. This modularity makes the annotation of large volumes of data more efficient, but also introduces difficulties for data annotators who may lack important context in order to select an appropriate label for a given example. This also effectively takes a problematic common sense approach.

With respect to queer vernacular and erroneous classifications of toxicity, one reason for these misclassifications likely lies in idiosyncratic uses of otherwise offensive language in queer vernacular, such as the use "b*tch" or "f*ggot" as consensual terms of endearment. Idiosyncratic uses of language, including reclaimed speech, raise questions about how this language use can be made apparent to workers and distinguished from language use in other sociolects. As McKinnon notes, failing to distinguish this language brings with it ethical issues rooted in the fact that this language constitutes a means of queer survival (McKinnon, 2017). As a first direction of research focused on data annotation we ask: **How can additional context be provided in annotation tasks to support raters in understanding the original relations surrounding text examples?** Moreover, **what influence does additional information have on both annotation behavior and model performance?**

Some researchers have experimented with reintroducing social context into annotation tasks with varying degrees of success, such as by providing multiple turns in a conversation or exchange (Gao and Huang, 2017; Sap et al., 2019; Pavlopoulos et al., 2020). This stands in contrast to typical annotation approaches, which require raters to judge whether an utterance is offensive without context apart from what is contained within it. Utterances may often name the target and receiver, and can offer some cultural, demographic, and ideological context if it is named explicitly; however the social relations are particularly difficult to infer from an isolated message. There are opportunities to experiment with other kinds of social context, such as the website or origins of text examples and temporal information about when the interaction occurred. At the same time, it is important to explore the limits to what kinds of social context can be provided to raters, whether due to knowability or privacy preserving limitations.

Thus far investigations of providing social context in annotation tasks have taken a quantitative focus to measure if and how additional context changed the resulting annotations collected. Simply providing raters with more context may be of little value if the raters themselves lack social or cultural awareness of specific domains, such as queer life and vernacular. Thus, it is unclear how annotators use additional context when it is provided, the role their own social experiences play in their ability to understand sociolects or cultural references, as well as which kinds of examples require additional context for annotators to make confident assessments. Thus, as a complementary annotation research direction to the first we ask: **How do annotators understand and use contextual cues provided to them?**

This research direction builds, in part, from ongoing work in NLP and ML considering annotator diversity, social identity and their influence on the annotations raters provide (Díaz et al., 2022; Prabhakaran et al., 2021; Davani et al., 2022), as well as work that qualitatively investigates annotation work practices. For example, scholars such as (Miceli et al., 2020) have provided rich accounts of how organizational structures influence how annotators are able to conduct their work. As a result, researchers seeking to understand annotation behavior must consider factors beyond what they can measure through typical metrics such as inter-rater reliability. This work is undertaken with a motivation to understand variation in annotation behavior and its potential roots in the social experiences, sociodemographics, and labor contexts of workers. In the context of queer vernacular, it would be intuitive to expect that a queer rater is more likely to understand the social context of a text example involving queer speech compared with a non-queer rater, provided they are given sufficient context to begin with. (Díaz et al., 2022; Prabhakaran et al., 2021) make calls for reporting transparency for crowdsourced data collection so that dataset users can investigate systematic disagreements and representation.

However, there remain open questions regarding how raters might apply their 'interpretive lens' and, more broadly, how these perspectives might be incorporated reliably into data collection efforts given the sensitivity of questions regarding membership to minoritized communities. We propose this direction with a specific eye toward research that incorporates qualitative approaches and understandings of annotation work. Relational considerations regarding data annotation include not only the relations embedded in data examples, but also the social relations between annotators and content embedded in the data they annotate.

4.3 Context through Extra-Linguistic Features

In addition to research on annotation task design, we propose expanded exploration of modeling techniques. A relational approach on offensive language brings into focus not just the specific language used in an interaction, but also behaviors and context that surround an offensive interaction. These include the behaviors, such as an individual's past interactions with content (e.g., 'liking' or downvoting) and other users, and metadata that captures temporal and geocultural situatedness. Using these features and techniques as windows into social context, there are opportunities to additionally model extra-linguistic features to more robustly infer social context.

Features apart from those specifically embedded in the text of an utterance can be used to provide clues into relevant social context in an interaction. (Mishra et al., 2019) do precisely this in incorporating author profiles in their modeling of racist and sexist tweets. From author profiles, they were able to model user-specific information, such as their network of followers. This approach effectively ties a given utterance to be classified to the particular individual who produced it. This stands apart from approaches which implicitly assume that an utterance carries the same offensive nature independent of who produced it. Mishra et al. specifically call out this shortcoming, arguing that deviations from sociolinguistic norms within communities is important for understanding the varied forms that abusive language can take (Mishra et al., 2021). Building from this work we ask:

What additional features become useful for identifying offensive content in the shift from targeting offensive speech to targeting offensive relations? and **How might extra-linguistic features, such as conversation structure and non-textual content, be used to infer social context?**

4.3.1 Interaction Outcomes

With the notable exception of work on toxicity, little work has focused on measurable outcomes of offensive interactions. Toxicity is a prediction of whether a tweet or excerpt of text will cause its audience to disengage from an interaction. This provides a proxy for determining the inappropriate or offensive nature of text that can be measured through behavior. (Diaz et al., 2022) point out that maintaining user engagement may not be desirable and may have disproportionately negative consequences for minoritized users. We focus, however, on the incorporation of non-textual observations that toxicity inspires. These include outcomes of interactions, such as downvotes and blocking user profiles, as well as behaviors that precede a given interaction, such as a user's past posting behavior. Additionally, (Zhang et al., 2018) use conversation structure in modeling whether user interactions on Facebook Pages will result in users blocking one another. Using an extended conversation as a unit of analysis opens up opportunities for modeling interactions and additional social context. As a complement to work on how text should be annotated we propose another research direction that asks: **What are relevant interaction outcomes that can be measured and used to model interactions that produce offense?**

(Mishra et al., 2019)'s work points to additional opportunities to assess individuals' communication history in relation to one another. For example, patterns in individuals' communication history may indicate repeated, antagonistic behavior. A related area of work lies in online trolling detection, which has been pursued through user-based methods, post-based methods, thread-based methods and social network analysis (Tomaiuolo et al., 2020). While not all offensive language falls under the umbrella of trolling, techniques used to detect trolling highlights avenues for measuring behaviors in relation to offensive language use.

5 Conclusion

Our chief claim is that relationality and its sociological and ethical formulations of linguistic style are a promising guiding analytic for achieving a more robust contextual analysis of offensive speech. Motivated by the challenges posed by minoritized language norms, we propose avenues for research that take aim at operationalizing it in practice. Because style patterns can be used to unveil social relations among individuals and communities, we point to its measurement as an example for operationalizing our approach. Ultimately, offense is produced through social relations that must be ethically and sociologically understood in order to accurately model and classify language content. Focusing on social relations and their potential to help distinguish sociolinguistic norms generates the following research questions:

- What are the relevant aspects of social relations that must be accounted for across text classification tasks?
- How might structural elements of style, which have been measured in various ways, be complemented by measurements of sociological and ethical aspects of style?

In the context of data annotation:

- How can additional context be provided in annotation tasks to support raters in understanding the relations surrounding text examples?
- Moreover, what influence does additional information have on both annotation behavior and how do annotators use contextual cues provided to them?

With respect to modeling language and social interactions:

- What additional features become useful for identifying offensive content in the shift from targeting offensive speech to targeting offensive relations?
- How might extra-linguistic features, such as conversation structure and non-textual content, be used to infer social context?

- What are relevant interaction outcomes that can be measured and used to model interactions that produce offense?

Importantly, we must also explore the limitations of a relational approach rooted in style. While style has important connections to the formation of individual and collective identities, it has different uses, such as to comply with institutional (e.g., workplace) norms, which may not necessarily align with community norms or social identification processes. In addition, style can be deployed in adversarial ways, such as with mockery, intent to impersonate, exploit trust, or arguably 'inauthentic' uses of accent or dialect (e.g., appropriative use of a "blaccent" (Lockhart, 2021)). It is unclear, at least at an operational level, how relationality might account for these uses of style. Another complication lies in the fact that in many digital contexts, one's "true" identity is often not verifiable. For our purposes, this means that a person can communicate online using styles of speech that may align with offline specific manners of speaking (e.g., AAE) but that may not align with the styles they use in other contexts. Underlining all of the above limitations is a greater tension regarding the ethical risks of inferring social identity and the extent to which inferring an individual's social identity is meaningful for classification. Hamidi et al. (2018) studied trans* and gender nonconforming individuals' perceptions of automatic gender recognition systems, demonstrating how automated systems can contribute to misgendering harms and undermine individual autonomy. Thus, inferences about social context that rely on further inferences about social identity

Still, relationality can work as a frame of analysis for the design of NLP approaches, including annotation practices and modeling decisions that can unveil specific relational context. We have identified minoritized speech as a motivating example to show how current, generalized approaches are inadequate for classifying language that deviates from dominant sociolinguistic norms. Providing sound criteria to disambiguate and classify a plurality of modes of speech grounded in a deep social understanding of their formation is key to ensure a more just and ethical approach to offensive speech.

References

Razvan Amironesei. 2014. La déprise de soi comme pratique de désubjectivation: Sur la notion de "stultitia" chez michel foucault. *Journal of French and Francophone Philosophy*, 22(2):104–122.

Randy Blazak. 2009. Toward a working definition of hate groups. *Hate crimes*, 3(1):133–162.

Su Lin Blodgett, Lisa Green, and Brendan O'Connor. 2016. Demographic dialectal variation in social media: A case study of african-american english. *arXiv preprint arXiv:1608.08868*.

Martijn Boven. 2014. 11 a system of heterogenesis: Deleuze on plurality. In *Phenomenological Perspectives on Plurality*, pages 175–194. Brill.

Judith Butler. 2021. *Excitable speech: A politics of the performative*. routledge.

Cheshire Calhoun. 2000. The virtue of civility. *Philosophy & public affairs*, 29(3):251–275.

Alistair Cameron Crombie. 1994. *Styles of scientific thinking in the European tradition: The history of argument and explanation especially in the mathematical and biomedical sciences and arts*, volume 2. Duckworth.

Cristian Danescu-Niculescu-Mizil, Michael Gamon, and Susan Dumais. 2011. Mark my words! linguistic style accommodation in social media. In *Proceedings of the 20th international conference on World wide web*, pages 745–754.

Aida Mostafazadeh Davani, Mark Díaz, and Vinodkumar Prabhakaran. 2022. Dealing with disagreements: Looking beyond the majority vote in subjective annotations. *Transactions of the Association for Computational Linguistics*, 10:92–110.

Thomas Davidson, Dana Warmsley, Michael Macy, and Ingmar Weber. 2017. Automated hate speech detection and the problem of offensive language. In *Proceedings of the International AAAI Conference on Web and Social Media*, volume 11.

Gilles Deleuze. 1994. *Difference and repetition*. Columbia University Press.

Thiago Dias Oliva, Marcelo Antonialli Dennys, and Alessandra Gomes. 2021. Fighting hate speech, silencing drag queens? artificial intelligence in content moderation and risks to lgbtq voices online. *Sexuality & culture*, 25(2):700–732.

Mark Diaz, Razvan Amironesei, Laura Weidinger, and Iason Gabriel. 2022. Accounting for offensive speech as a practice of resistance. In *Proceedings of the Sixth Workshop on Online Abuse and Harms (WOAH)*, pages 192–202, Seattle, Washington (Hybrid). Association for Computational Linguistics.

Mark Díaz, Ian Kivlichan, Rachel Rosen, Dylan K. Baker, Razvan Amironesei, Vinodkumar Prabhakaran, and Emily Denton. 2022. Crowdworksheets: Accounting for individual and collective identities underlying crowdsourced dataset annotation. In *Proceedings of the 2022 ACM Conference on Fairness, Accountability, and Transparency*, FAccT '22. Association for Computing Machinery.

Penelope Eckert and John R Rickford. 2001. *Style and sociolinguistic variation*. Cambridge University Press.

Mats Ekström, Marianna Patrona, and Joanna Thornborrow. 2018. Right-wing populism and the dynamics of style: a discourse-analytic perspective on mediated political performances. *Palgrave Communications*, 4(1):1–11.

Robert Faris, Amar Ashar, and Urs Gasser. 2016. Understanding Harmful Speech Online. *SSRN Electronic Journal*.

Ludwik Fleck. 2012. *Genesis and development of a scientific fact*. University of Chicago Press.

Michel Foucault. 2011. *The courage of truth*. Springer.

Michel Foucault. 2012. *The history of sexuality, vol. 2: The use of pleasure*. Vintage.

Michel Foucault. 2019. *Ethics: subjectivity and truth: essential works of Michel Foucault 1954-1984*. Penguin UK.

Lei Gao and Ruihong Huang. 2017. Detecting Online Hate Speech Using Context Aware Models. In *RANLP 2017 - Recent Advances in Natural Language Processing Meet Deep Learning*, pages 260–266. Incoma Ltd. Shoumen, Bulgaria.

Ian Hacking. 1992. 'style'for historians and philosophers. *Studies in History and Philosophy of Science Part A*, 23(1):1–20.

Pierre Hadot. 1995. Philosophy as a way of life: Spiritual exercises from socrates to foucault.

Foad Hamidi, Morgan Klaus Scheuerman, and Stacy M Branham. 2018. Gender recognition or gender reductionism? the social implications of embedded gender recognition systems. In *Proceedings of the 2018 chi conference on human factors in computing systems*, pages 1–13.

Cressida J Heyes. 2007. *Self-transformations: Foucault, ethics, and normalized bodies*. Oxford University Press.

Dirk Hovy and Diyi Yang. 2021a. The Importance of Modeling Social Factors of Language: Theory and Practice. In *Proceedings of the 2021 Conference of the North American Chapter of the Association for Computational Linguistics: Human Language Technologies*, pages 588–602, Online. Association for Computational Linguistics.

Dirk Hovy and Diyi Yang. 2021b. The importance of modeling social factors of language: Theory and practice. In *Proceedings of the 2021 Conference of the North American Chapter of the Association for Computational Linguistics: Human Language Technologies*, pages 588–602, Online. Association for Computational Linguistics.

Anna Jørgensen, Dirk Hovy, and Anders Søgaard. 2015. Challenges of studying and processing dialects in social media. In *Proceedings of the workshop on noisy user-generated text*, pages 9–18.

Osama Khalid and Padmini Srinivasan. 2020. Style matters! investigating linguistic style in online communities. In *Proceedings of the International AAAI Conference on Web and Social Media*, volume 14, pages 360–369.

William Labov. 1973. *Sociolinguistic patterns*. 4. University of Pennsylvania press.

Amirah Lockhart. 2021. A stolen culture: The harmful effects of cultural appropriation.

Luther H Martin, Huck Gutman, and Patrick H Hutton. 1988. *Technologies of the self: A seminar with Michel Foucault*. Tavistock.

Sean McKinnon. 2017. "Building a thick skin for each other": The use of 'reading'as an interactional practice of mock impoliteness in drag queen backstage talk. *Journal of Language and Sexuality*, 6(1):90–127.

Ladelle McWhorter. 1999. *Bodies and pleasures: Foucault and the politics of sexual normalization*. Indiana University Press.

Milagros Miceli, Martin Schuessler, and Tianling Yang. 2020. Between subjectivity and imposition: Power dynamics in data annotation for computer vision. *Proceedings of the ACM on Human-Computer Interaction*, 4(CSCW2):1–25.

Pushkar Mishra, Marco Del Tredici, Helen Yannakoudakis, and Ekaterina Shutova. 2019. Author profiling for hate speech detection. *arXiv preprint arXiv:1902.06734*.

Pushkar Mishra, Helen Yannakoudakis, and Ekaterina Shutova. 2021. Modeling users and online communities for abuse detection: A position on ethics and explainability. In *Findings of the Association for Computational Linguistics: EMNLP 2021*, pages 3374–3385, Punta Cana, Dominican Republic. Association for Computational Linguistics.

Chikashi Nobata, Joel Tetreault, Achint Thomas, Yashar Mehdad, and Yi Chang. 2016. Abusive Language Detection in Online User Content. In *Proceedings of the 25th International Conference on World Wide Web*, pages 145–153, Montréal Québec Canada. International World Wide Web Conferences Steering Committee.

John Pavlopoulos, Jeffrey Sorensen, Lucas Dixon, Nithum Thain, and Ion Androutsopoulos. 2020. Toxicity detection: Does context really matter? *arXiv preprint arXiv:2006.00998*.

James W Pennebaker. 2011. The secret life of pronouns. *New Scientist*, 211(2828):42–45.

Vinodkumar Prabhakaran, Aida Mostafazadeh Davani, and Mark Diaz. 2021. On Releasing Annotator-Level Labels and Information in Datasets. In *Proceedings of The Joint 15th Linguistic Annotation Workshop (LAW) and 3rd Designing Meaning Representations (DMR) Workshop*, pages 133–138, Punta Cana, Dominican Republic. Association for Computational Linguistics.

Geoffrey K Pullum. 1999. African american vernacular english is not standard english with mistakes. *The workings of language: From prescriptions to perspectives*, pages 59–66.

Kamil Safin and Aleksandr Ogaltsov. 2018. Detecting a change of style using text statistics. *Working Notes of CLEF*.

Maarten Sap, Dallas Card, Saadia Gabriel, Yejin Choi, and Noah A. Smith. 2019. The Risk of Racial Bias in Hate Speech Detection. In *Proceedings of the 57th Annual Meeting of the Association for Computational Linguistics*, pages 1668–1678, Florence, Italy. Association for Computational Linguistics.

Maarten Sap, Swabha Swayamdipta, Laura Vianna, Xuhui Zhou, Yejin Choi, and Noah A Smith. 2021. Annotators with Attitudes: How Annotator Beliefs And Identities Bias Toxic Language Detection. *arXiv preprint arXiv:2111.07997*.

Anna Schmidt and Michael Wiegand. 2017. A Survey on Hate Speech Detection using Natural Language Processing. In *Proceedings of the Fifth International Workshop on Natural Language Processing for Social Media*, pages 1–10, Valencia, Spain. Association for Computational Linguistics.

Michele Tomaiuolo, Gianfranco Lombardo, Monica Mordonini, Stefano Cagnoni, and Agostino Poggi. 2020. A survey on troll detection. *Future internet*, 12(2):31.

Cynthia Van Hee, Ben Verhoeven, Els Lefever, Guy De Pauw, Véronique Hoste, and Walter Daelemans. 2015. Guidelines for the fine-grained analysis of cyberbullying.

Ellery Wulczyn, Nithum Thain, and Lucas Dixon. 2017. Ex Machina: Personal Attacks Seen at Scale. In *Proceedings of the 26th International Conference on World Wide Web*, pages 1391–1399, Perth Australia. International World Wide Web Conferences Steering Committee.

Justine Zhang, Jonathan P Chang, Cristian Danescu-Niculescu-Mizil, Lucas Dixon, Yiqing Hua, Nithum Thain, and Dario Taraborelli. 2018. Conversations gone awry: Detecting early signs of conversational failure. *arXiv preprint arXiv:1805.05345*.

Claus Zittel. 2012. Ludwik fleck and the concept of style in the natural sciences. *Studies in East European Thought*, 64:53–79.

Cross-Platform and Cross-Domain Abusive Language Detection with Supervised Contrastive Learning

Md Tawkat Islam Khondaker[♠] **Muhammad Abdul-Mageed**[♠◇] **Laks V.S. Lakshmanan**[♠]

[♠]The University of British Columbia, [◇]MBZUAI

{tawkat@cs.,muhammad.mageed@,laks@cs.}ubc.ca

Abstract

The prevalence of abusive language on different online platforms has been a major concern that raises the need for automated cross-platform abusive language detection. However, prior works focus on concatenating data from multiple platforms, inherently adopting Empirical Risk Minimization (ERM) method. In this work, we address this challenge from the perspective of domain generalization objective. We design SCL-Fish, a supervised contrastive learning integrated meta-learning algorithm to detect abusive language on unseen platforms. Our experimental analysis shows that SCL-Fish achieves better performance over ERM and the existing state-of-the-art models. We also show that SCL-Fish is data-efficient and achieves comparable performance with the large-scale pre-trained models upon finetuning for the abusive language detection task.[1]

1 Introduction

Abusive language is defined as any form of microaggression, condescension, harassment, hate speech, trolling, and the like (Jurgens et al., 2019). Use of abusive language online has been a significant problem over the years. Although a plethora of works has explored automated detection of abusive language, it is still a challenging task due to its evolving nature (Davidson et al., 2017; Müller and Schwarz, 2017; Williams et al., 2019). In addition, a standing challenging in tackling abusive language is linguistic variation as to how the problem manifests itself across different platforms (Karan and Šnajder, 2018; Swamy et al., 2019; Salminen et al., 2020).

We provide examples illustrating variation of abusive language on different platforms in Figure 1.[2] For example, user comments in broadcasting media such as Fox News do not directly contain any strong words but can implicitly carry abusive messages. Meanwhile, people on social media such as on Twitter employ an abundance of strong words that can be outright personal bullying and spread of hate speech. On an extremist public forum such as Gab, users mostly spread abusive language in the form of identity attacks. For these reasons, it is an unrealistic assumption to train an abusive language detector on data from one platform and expect the model to exhibit equally satisfactory performance on another platform.

Figure 1: Examples of abusive language on different platforms.

Prior Works on cross-platform abusive language detection (Karan and Šnajder, 2018; Mishra et al., 2018; Corazza et al., 2019; Salminen et al., 2020) usually concatenate examples from multiple sources, thus inherently applying Empirical Risk Minimization (ERM) (Vapnik, 1991). These models capture platform-specific spurious features, and lack generalization (Shi et al., 2021). Fortuna et al. (2018), on the other hand, incorporate out-of-platform data into training set and employ domain-adaptive techniques. Other works such as Swamy et al. (2019) and Gallacher (2021) develop one model for each platform and ensemble them to improve overall performance.

None of the prior works, however, attempt to generalize task-oriented features across the platforms to improve performance on an unseen platform. In this work, we introduce a novel method

[1]Source code: https://github.com/Tawkat/SCL-Fish-Abusive-Language

[2]This paper contains several examples of abusive language and strong words for the purpose of demonstration.

The 7th Workshop on Online Abuse and Harms (WOAH), pages 96–112
July 13, 2023

for learning domain-invariant features to fill this gap. Our approach initially adopts an first-order derivative of meta-learning algorithm (Andrychowicz et al., 2016; Finn et al., 2017), *Fish* (Shi et al., 2021), that attempts to capture domain-invariance. We then propose a supervised contrastive learning (*SCL*) (Khosla et al., 2020) to impose an additional constraint on capturing task-oriented features that can help the model to learn semantically effective embeddings by pulling samples from the same class close together while pushing samples from opposite classes further apart. We refer to our new method as **SCL-Fish** and conduct extensive experiments on a wide array of platforms representing social networks, public forums, broadcasting media, conversational chatbots, and synthetically-generated data to show the efficacy of our method over other abusive language detection models (and specially ERM that prior works on cross-platform abusive language detection applied).

To summarize, we offer the following contributions in this work:

1. We propose SCL-Fish, a novel supervised contrastive learning augmented domain generalization method for cross-platform abusive language detection.

2. Our method outperforms prior works on cross-platform abusive language detection, thus demonstrating superiority to ERM (the core idea behind these previous models). Additionally, we show that SCL-Fish outperforms platform-specific state-of-the-art abusive/hate speech detection models.

3. Our analysis reveals that SCL-Fish can be data-efficient and exhibit comparable performance with the state-of-the-art models upon finetuning on the abusive language detection task.

2 Related Works

2.1 What is Abusive Language?

The boundary between hate speech, offensive, and abusive language can be unclear. Davidson et al. (2017) define *hate speech* as "language that is used to express hatred towards a targeted group or is intended to be derogatory, to humiliate, or to insult the members of the group"; whereas,. Zampieri et al. (2019a) define *offensive language* as "any form of non-acceptable language (profanity) or a targeted offense, which can be veiled or direct". In this paper, we adopt the definition of abusive language provided by Jurgens et al. (2019) and consider both offensive and hate speech as abusive language in general, since distinguishing between offensive and hate speech is often deemed as subjective (Sap et al., 2019; Koh et al., 2021).

2.2 Domain Generalization

In the domain generalization task, training and test sets are sampled from different distributions (Quiñonero-Candela et al., 2008). In recent years, domain-shifted datasets have been introduced by synthetically corrupting the samples (Hendrycks and Dietterich 2019, Xiao et al. 2020, Santurkar et al. 2020). To improve the capability of a learner on distributional generalization, Vapnik (1991) proposes Empirical Risk Minimization (ERM) approach which is widely used as the standard for the domain generalization tasks (Koh et al. 2021). ERM concatenates data from all the domains and focuses on minimizing the average loss on the training set. However, Pezeshki et al. (2021) state that a learner can overestimate its performance by capturing only one or a few dominant features with the ERM approach. Several other algorithms have been proposed to generalize models on unseen domains. Sagawa et al. (2019) attempt to develop distributionally robust algorithm, where the domain-wise losses are weighted inversely proportional to the domain performance. Krueger et al. (2021) propose to minimize the variation loss across the domains during the training phase and Arjovsky et al. (2020) aim to penalize the models if the performance varies among the samples from the same domain.

2.3 Contrastive Learning

Contrastive learning aims to learn effective embedding by pulling semantically close neighbors together while pushing apart non-neighbors (Hadsell et al. 2006). This method uses cross-entropy-based similarity objective to learn the embedding representation in the hyperspace (Chen et al., 2017; Henderson et al., 2017). In computer vision, Chen et al. (2020) proposes a framework for contrastive learning of visual representations without specialized architectures or a memory bank. Khosla et al. (2020) shows that supervised contrastive loss can outperform cross-entropy loss on ImageNet (Russakovsky et al., 2015). In NLP, similar methods have been explored in in the context of sentence representation learning (Karpukhin et al., 2020; Gillick et al., 2019; Logeswaran and Lee, 2018). Among of the most notable works, Gao et al. (2021) proposes unsupervised contrastive learning framework, *SimCSE* that predicts input sentence itself by augmenting it with dropout as noise.

2.4 Abusive Language Detection

Over the years, the task of abusive language detection have been studied in NLP in the form of hate speech (Davidson et al., 2017; Founta et al., 2018; Golbeck et al., 2017), sexism/racism (Waseem and Hovy, 2016), cyberbulling (Xu et al., 2012; Dadvar et al., 2013). Earlier works in abusive language detection depend on feature-based approaches to identify lexical difference between abusive and non-abusive language (Warner and Hirschberg, 2012; Waseem and Hovy, 2016; Ribeiro et al., 2018). Although inclusion of neural network architecture improves the performance (Mitrović et al., 2019; Kshirsagar et al., 2018; Sigurbergsson and Derczynski, 2020), the models still misclassify a large number of samples in false-positive and false-negative categories when abusive language is intentionally manipulated (Gitari et al., 2015). Recently, Transformer-based (Vaswani et al., 2017) architectures like BERT (Devlin et al., 2018), RoBERTa (Liu et al., 2019b) have been introduced in the abusive language detection task (Liu et al., 2019a; Swamy et al., 2019).

However, most of the prior works on abusive language detection focus on a single platform due to the inaccessibility to multiple platforms (Vidgen and Derczynski, 2020) and thus, do not scale well on other platforms Schmidt and Wiegand (2017). As a result, the models are not suitable to apply to other platforms due to the lack of generalization (Karan and Šnajder, 2018; Gröndahl et al., 2018). In this work, we aim to address this challenge by introducing an augmented domain generalization method that captures task-oriented domain-generalized features across multiple platforms.

3 Method

3.1 Challenge & Proposed Solution

As shown in Figure 1, the nature of offensive language can vary from one platform to another. Therefore, it is important to design a model that can capture platform-generalized representations. This inspires us to adopt a domain-generalization algorithm that can maximize feature generalization while avoiding dependence on domain-specific, spurious features. To learn platform-invariant features, we adopt first-order derivative of *Inter-domain Gradient Matching (IDGM)* Shi et al. (2021), a Model Agnostic Meta-Learning (MAML) (Andrychowicz et al., 2016; Finn et al., 2017), algorithm, *Fish*, that aims to reduce sample complexity of new, unseen domains and increase domain-generalized feature selection across those domains.

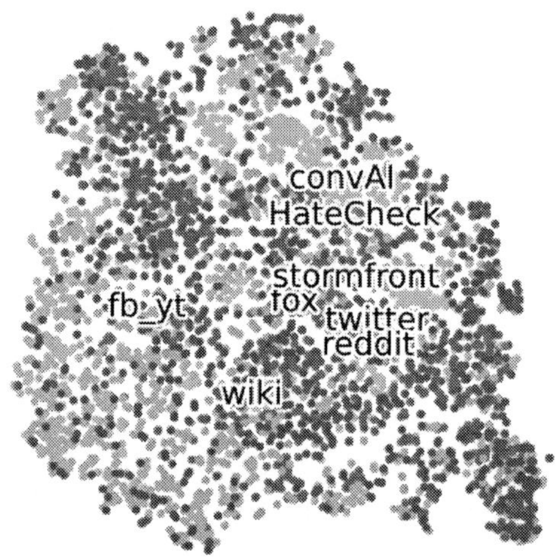

Figure 2: tSNE representations of platforms. We plot the embedding of [CLS] token from pre-trained BERT.

However, if we look at Figure 2, the representation of abusive language across the platforms is overlapping and scattered. Hence, the model should also learn some platform-specific and overlapping features that can help to capture task-oriented representations. Therefore, we need to impose a constraint on the learning objective of the model so that in one direction, it should learn platform-invariant features for better generalization, and in the other direction, it should also learn only those task-oriented overlapping features that pass positive signals to those platform-generalized features for the abusive language detection task.

To learn task-oriented features we introduce **SCL-Fish**, method for supervised contrastive learning (SCL) (Khosla et al., 2020) with Fish. The rationale behind integrating SCL is that we seek to find commonalities between the examples of each class (abusive/normal) irrespective of the platforms and contrast them with examples from the other class.

3.2 SCL-Fish

Assuming we have a training dataset of abusive language detection consisting of samples from two platforms $\mathbf{P_1}$ and $\mathbf{P_2}$ where $\mathbf{P_k} = \{(\mathbf{X}^k, \mathbf{Y}^k)\}$. Given a model θ and loss function l, the empirical risk minimization (ERM) (Vapnik, 1991) objective is to minimize the average loss across the given platform:

$$L_{ERM} = \min_{\theta} \mathbb{E}_{(x,y) \sim P \in (P_1, P_2)} \frac{\delta l((x, y); \theta)}{\delta \theta}$$

The expected gradients for these two platforms are expressed as

$$\begin{aligned} G_1 &= \mathbb{E}_{(x,y) \sim P_1} \frac{\delta l((x, y) ; \theta)}{\delta \theta} \\ G_2 &= \mathbb{E}_{(x,y) \sim P_2} \frac{\delta l((x, y) ; \theta)}{\delta \theta} \end{aligned}$$

If the directions of G_1 and G_2 are same ($G_1.G_2 > 0$), then we can say that the model is improving on both platforms. Therefore, IDGM algorithm attempts to align the direction of the gradients G_1 and G_2 by maximizing their inner dot product. Hence, given the total number of training platforms S, the final objective function of IDGM is obtained by subtracting gradient dot product (GIP) from ERM loss:

$$\begin{aligned} L_{IDGM} &= L_{ERM} \\ &- \gamma \frac{2}{S(S-1)} \sum_{i,j \in S}^{i \neq j} G_i.G_j \end{aligned} \tag{1}$$

Here, γ is a scaling term and GIP can be computed in linear time by $\widehat{G} = ||\sum_i G_i||^2 - \sum_i ||G_i||^2$

However, the derivation of $\widehat{G}$ is computationally expensive, as it is a dot product of two gradients. Adopting from Nichol et al. (2018), Shi et al. (2021) work around this issue by proposing a first-order derivative version of IDGM, namely, Fish. Shi et al. (2021) show that given the gradient of ERM $\bar{G}$ and a clone of original model $\tilde{\theta}$,

$$G_f = \mathbb{E}[\theta - \tilde{\theta}] - \alpha S.\bar{G} \text{ and } G_g = \frac{d\widehat{G}}{d\theta},$$

$$\lim_{\alpha \to 0} \frac{G_f.G_g}{||G_f|| \,.\, ||G_g||} = 1 \tag{2}$$

In other words, if we ignore the ERM objective, we can substitute the second-order derivative G_g with a computationally less expensive G_f.

Although, this method exhibits impressive performance on the domain-generalization task, as mentioned in Section 3.1, it may capture only platform-invariant features without much focus on *task-relevant* features. To overcome this issue, we augment Fish with a supervised contrastive learning (SCL) objective, which will teach the model to select the features such that the representation of an abusive sample and a non-abusive sample are located far from each other in the hyperspace,

$$\begin{aligned} L_{SCL} &= -\sum_{j=1}^{N} 1_{y_i = y_j} \\ &\log \frac{exp(f(x_i) \,.\, f(x_j) \,/\, \tau)}{\sum 1_{i \neq k} \, exp(f(x_i) \,.\, f(x_k) \,/\, \tau)} \end{aligned} \tag{3}$$

Here, $f(.)$ is an encoder and N is the number of samples summing all the platforms. Therefore, the model will be encouraged to learn only those task-oriented features that are invariant across the platforms *and* can be used to distinguish abusive and non-abusive examples.

Algorithm 1 SCL-Fish

1: **for** iteration = 1, 2,... **do**
2: $\quad \tilde{\theta} \leftarrow \theta$
3: $\quad$ **for** $P_i \in \{P_1, P_2, ..., P_S\}$ **do**
4: $\quad\quad$ Sample minibatch $p_i \sim P_i$
5: $\quad\quad \tilde{g}_i = \mathbb{E}_{(x,y) \sim p_i} \left[\frac{\delta l((x, y) ; \tilde{\theta})}{\delta \tilde{\theta}} \right]$
6:
7: $\quad\quad$ Update $\tilde{\theta} \leftarrow \tilde{\theta} - \alpha \tilde{g}_i$
8: $\quad$ **end for**
9:
10: $\quad$ Update $\theta \leftarrow \theta - \epsilon(\tilde{\theta} - \theta)$ ▷ Updating Fish
11:
12: $\quad P_{scl} \leftarrow \{P_1 \cup P_2 \cup ... \cup P_S\}$
13: $\quad$ **for** Sample minibatch $p_{scl} \sim P_{scl}$ **do**
14: $\quad\quad$ ▷ Calculate gradient for SCL from (3):
15: $\quad\quad g_{scl} = \mathbb{E}_{(x,y) \sim p_{scl}} \left[\frac{\delta l((x, y) ; \tilde{\theta})}{\delta \tilde{\theta}} \right]$
16:
17: $\quad\quad$ Update $\theta \leftarrow \theta - \alpha' \, g_{scl}$
18: $\quad$ **end for**
19: **end for**

We present SCL-Fish in Algorithm 1. For each training platform, Fish performs inner-loop (*l3-l8*) update steps with learning rate α on a clone of the original model $\tilde{\theta}$ in a minibatch. Subsequently, the original model θ is updated by a weighted difference between the cloned model and the original model $\tilde{\theta} - \theta$. After performing, platform-generalized update, the trained samples of this iteration(*l12*) are queued and sampled in a minibatch

Dataset	Platform	Source	Offnsv/normal
wiki	Wikipedia	Wulczyn et al. (2017)	14880 / 117935
twitter	Twitter	*Multiple**	77656 / 55159
fb-yt	Facebook & Youtube	Salminen et al. (2018)	2364 / 858
stormfront	Stormfront	de Gibert et al. (2018)	1364 / 9507
fox	Fox News	Gao and Huang (2017)	435 / 1093
twi-fb	Twitter & Facebook	Mandl et al. (2019)	6840 / 11491
reddit	Reddit	Qian et al. (2019)	2511 / 11073
convAI	ELIZA & CarbonBot	Cercas Curry et al. (2021)	128 / 725
hateCheck	Synthetic. Generated	Röttger et al. (2021)	2563 / 1165
gab	Gab	Qian et al. (2019)	15270 / 656
yt_reddit	Youtube & Reddit	Mollas et al. (2020)	163 / 163

Table 1: List of experimental datasets with corresponding platforms. * *Twitter* dataset is collected from Waseem and Hovy (2016), Davidson et al. (2017), Jha and Mamidi (2017), ElSherief et al. (2018), Founta et al. (2018), Mathur et al. (2018), Basile et al. (2019), Mandl et al. (2019), Ousidhoum et al. (2019), and Zampieri et al. (2019a).

to update θ with supervised contrastive loss (*l13-l18*).

4 Experiments

4.1 Datasets

To experiment with the efficacy of SCL-Fish, we compile datasets from a wide range of platforms. We collect source of the datasets primarily from (Risch et al., 2021) and (Vidgen and Derczynski, 2020). We provide meta-information of the datasets in Table 1. Description of each dataset is presented in Appendix F.

4.2 Methods Comparison

We compare performance of **SCL-Fish** with **Fish**, also using **ERM** as a sensible baseline. We also conduct experiments on an SCL version of ERM **(SCL-ERM)**. Additionally, we compare SCL-Fish with two of the benchmark models for abusive/hate speech detection, HateXplain (Mathew et al., 2021) and HateBERT (Caselli et al., 2021). **HateXplain** is finetuned on hate speech detection datasets collected from Twitter and Gab[3] for a three-class classification (hate, offensive, or normal) task. It incorporates human-annotated explainability with BERT to gain better performance by reducing unintended bias towards target communities. While conducting our experiments, we consider both *hate* and *offensive* classes as one category (*abusive*). **HateBERT** pre-trains BERT with Masked Language Modeling (MLM) objective on more than one million offensive and hate messages from banned Reddit community. It results in a shifted BERT model that has learned language variety and hate polarity (e.g. *hate, abuse*). Finetuning on different abusive language detection tasks has shown that HateBERT achieves the best/comparable performance.

[3]https://gab.com

4.3 Experimental Setup

We train the models (ERM, SCL-ERM, Fish, and SCL-Fish) on *fb-yt, twitter*, and *wiki* datasets (in-platform datasets) and use *stromfront* as validation set. We use the same hyperparameters on all the models for fair comparisons. We present the list of hyperparameters in Appendix A. The rest of the datasets from Table 1 are used for cross-platform evaluation. As evident from Table 1, the datasets are highly imbalanced. Hence, we report *F_1-score* for abusive class (we denote it as *positive-F_1*) and *macro-averaged F_1-score*. For completeness, we also provide performance in *accuracy*. We train and evaluate our models on Nvidia A100 40GB GPU.

5 Results on Cross-Platform Datasets

We show results of our models for cross-platform performance in Table 2. We observe that SCL-Fish outperforms other methods in macro-F_1 and positive-F_1 scores while maintaining comparable performance with the best method on the other datasets (*reddit, hatecheck*). In overall average performance, SCL-Fish achieves best macro-F_1 and positive-F_1 scores. More specifically, user comments on broadcasting media (*Fox News*), SCL-Fish achieves a gain of 3.2% positive-F_1 and 0.5% macro-F_1 over the other methods. On public forums (*Youtube* and *Reddit*), SCL-Fish achieves a total gain of 2.0% in positive-F_1 but SCL-ERM outperforms SCL-Fish by 1.3% in macro-F_1 score. On AI bot conversation (*CarbonBot* and *ELIZA*), SCL-Fish achieves a gain of 1.4% positive-F_1 and 1.0% macro-F_1 over other methods. On the synthetically-generated platform (*HateCheck*), ERM outperforms SCL-Fish by 1.2% in positive-F_1 score and Fish outperforms SCL-Fish by 0.1% in macro-F_1 score. On Gab, all the methods (ERM and Fish-based, including SCL-Fish) achieve high positive-F_1 score because of the highly imbalanced dataset. Hence, for a fair comparison among all methods, we report performance on sampled balanced datasets in Appendix B. We also discuss the performance on the in-platform datasets in Appendix C.

Platform	HateXplain			HateBERT			ERM			SCL-ERM			Fish			SCL-Fish		
(% of hate)	Acc	Pos. F_1	Macro F_1	Acc	Pos. F_1	Macro F_1	Acc	Pos F_1	Macro F_1	Acc	Pos. F_1	Macro F_1	Acc	Pos. F_1	Macro F_1	Acc	Pos. F_1	Macro F_1
stormfront (12.5)	**88.1**	44.1	67.2	87.3	34.6	63.8	85.3	**44.2**	67.7	86.0	43.0	67.5	85.5	42.0	66.9	85.1	**44.2**	**67.8**
fox (28.5)	**73.9**	29.4	56.7	68.7	31.5	63.8	73.6	42.3	62.6	73.6	42.3	62.6	73.6	44.3	63.5	72.2	**47.5**	**64.3**
twi-fb (37.3)	63.4	09.3	43.2	**65.0**	27.9	52.4	61.3	35.7	54.0	60.2	33.6	52.6	53.7	36.9	50.2	61.8	**38.2**	**55.3**
reddit (18.5)	**83.7**	38.0	64.3	81.0	45.5	**66.9**	76.9	43.0	64.3	77.7	43.9	65.1	76.7	44.6	64.9	76.6	**46.3**	65.7
convAI (15.0)	86.4	26.6	59.5	**87.9**	56.9	74.9	86.6	66.3	78.9	86.8	65.9	78.8	86.3	64.7	78.1	87.3	**67.7**	**79.9**
hateCheck (68.8)	38.4	26.9	36.9	58.9	64.3	57.9	**67.3**	**77.4**	59.0	65.4	75.3	58.6	67.1	76.6	**60.5**	66.7	76.2	60.4
gab (95.9)	75.6	85.7	50.6	75.9	86.0	50.4	91.1	95.3	**59.1**	91.4	95.5	57.9	90.9	95.2	58.8	**92.0**	**95.8**	57.4
yt-reddit (50.0)	65.3	54.3	63.2	70.9	69.3	70.8	72.4	75.7	71.9	**74.5**	**77.1**	**74.2**	73.6	76.6	73.2	73.0	76.7	72.3
avg.	71.9	38.9	55.2	74.5	52.0	61.6	76.8	59.9	64.7	**76.9**	59.6	64.7	75.9	60.1	64.5	76.8*	**61.6**	**65.4**

Table 2: Performance on cross-platform datasets. **Bold** font represents the best performance for a particular metric. Gray cells indicate performance on the datasets from identical or overlapping platforms but different sources and distributions. * Although SCL-Fish exhibits comparable accuracy with other competitive models on this imbalanced dataset, it achieves better accuracy on the balanced dataset (Appendix B).

Most notably, HateBERT achieves the highest macro-F_1 scores on *reddit*, which is expected since HateBERT is pre-trained on *reddit* and so has an advantage over other methods since these are trained on data from other platforms. However, all the models including HateXplain and HateBERT are trained on the datasets from Twitter platform. Hence, we analyze performance of the models on *twi-fb* dataset. Our rationale is that although twi-fb involves data from Twitter and Facebook, these data do not necessarily have the same distribution as data used to train all the models. The distribution of datasets from the same platform can still defer due to the variations in the timestamps, topics, locations, demographic attributes (e.g. age, race, gender, ethnicity). Although it is not possible to extract all this information from the textual contents, we provide a quantitative comparison between in-domain and out-domain datasets for Twitter in Appendix D. We refer the readers to Koh et al. (2021) for more detailed analysis. We find that performance of the models deteriorates significantly (under 56% macro-F_1) even on datasets from overlapping platforms but of different distributions. This demonstrates effect of distribution shift in the data, even if we train on date from the same platform. We further discuss possible rationales for this performance gap across the platforms in Appendix E.

6 Analysis

In this section, we conduct qualitative and quantitative analysis on the experimental results.

6.1 Diversity over Quantity

It is worth noting that HateBERT has been pre-trained on $1,478,348$ Reddit messages, almost five times more data than SCL-Fish. However, as Table 2 shows, performance of HateBERT on cross-platform datasets suffers significant drops which is not the case for SCL-Fish. Even on *yt-reddit* dataset, which is collected from *Youtube* and *Reddit* (the latter being the platform whose data HateBERT is trained on), HateBERT fails to outperform the baseline ERM method. This shows that, for the purpose of creating platform/domain-invariant models, it is more important to employ training data with different distributions than simply using huge amounts of training data from the same platform but that may have limited distribution.

6.2 Finetuning SCL-Fish

Since we show SCL-Fish exhibits better performance than other methods on most of the cross-platform datasets, we further investigate whether the platform-generalization capability of SCL-Fish helps it improve performance on a specific platform (*Twitter*) upon finetuning. For this purpose, we use two benchmark datasets, namely, OLID (Zampieri et al., 2019a) dataset from SemEval-2019 Task 6 (Zampieri et al., 2019b) and AbusEval (Caselli et al., 2020). Please note that we use OLID dataset for training our methods (Appendix F). Now we are finetuning with the same dataset for this experiment.

We present results for this set of experiments in Table 3. Performance of NULI (BERT-based

Datasets	Models	Macro F_1	Pos. F_1
OffensEval	BERT	80.3	71.5
	HateBERT	80.9	72.3
	NULI	**82.9**	**75.2**
	SCL-Fish	<u>81.6</u>	<u>72.6</u>
AbusEval	BERT	72.7	55.2
	HateBERT	**76.5**	**62.3**
	Caselli et al. (2020)	71.6	53.1
	SCL-Fish	<u>75.2</u>	<u>59.4</u>

Table 3: Performance of models after finetuning. **Bold** and *underline* represent best and second best performance for a particular metric, respectively.

model secured first position in SemEval-2019 Task 6 (Zampieri et al., 2019b)) in the table is from Liu et al. (2019a) and BERT, HateBERT from Caselli et al. (2021).

As Table 3 shows, NULI (Liu et al., 2019a) achieves the best performance for OLID dataset. Although SCL-Fish gets a lower score than NULI[4], SCL-Fish outperforms BERT and HateBERT on both in positive-F_1 and macro-F_1. This is important because HateBERT uses five times more data from one specific platform (*Reddit*). This proves that our proposed SCL-Fish is useful not only in platform generalized zero-shot setting but also for finetuning, and emphasizes the importance of *diversity* of the data (which translates into varied distributions) over data *size*.

For AbusEval dataset, SCL-Fish performs better than BERT and the prior work (Caselli et al., 2020), but it cannot outperforms HateBERT. We suspect that the reason is due to the different annotation process followed during the earlier training phase of SCL-Fish and HateBERT. Because, although OLID and AbusEval contain identical tweets in the training and the testing sets, the annotation scheme of AbuseEval is different from OLID. While Zampieri et al. (2019a) uses the definition of offensive language as "Posts containing any form of non-acceptable language (profanity) or a targeted offense, which can be veiled or direct" to annotate OLID dataset, Caselli et al. (2020) uses the definition of abusive language as "hurtful language that a speaker uses to insult or offend another individual or a group of individuals based on their personal qualities, appearance, social status, opinions, statements, or actions" to annotate AbusEval dataset. More comprehensively, AbusEval excludes any kind of untargeted messages from the hate speech category. During the training phase of SCL-Fish, we consider any targeted or non-targeted strong language as offensive. Therefore, finetuning on AbusEval causes misalignment with the earlier training phase of SCL-Fish, and may result in performance deterioration.

[4]Please note that Caselli et al. (2021) reports positive-F_1 of NULI as 59.9% which is lower than positive-F_1 of SCL-Fish. But the positive-F_1 we compute from Liu et al. (2019a) is different from the one reported in Caselli et al. (2021). Therefore, we consider our computed positive-F_1 for NULI.

6.3 Explainability with Attention Visualization

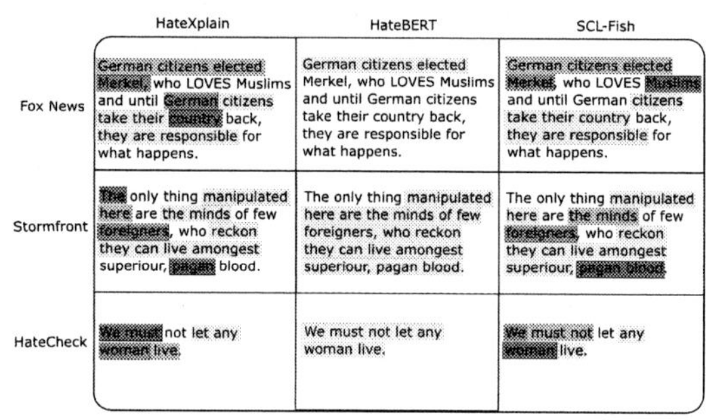

Figure 3: Attention visualization for different platforms. Deeper color indicates higher attention.

We investigate how platform generalization helps the model attend to the right context on 'out-of-platform' datasets. For this purpose, we analyze attention vectors of SCL-Fish, HateXplain, and HateBERT in an attempt to better understand their performance. We use BertViz (Vig, 2019) to compute and visualize the final layer attention vectors from `[CLS]` to other tokens. We select three out-of-platform datasets (*fox*, *stormfront*, and *hateCheck*) and randomly sample one abusive example from each where SCL-Fish correctly identifies the example as abusive, but HateXplain and HateBERT misclassify it. Figure 3 shows the attention visualization for each of the examples. As we can see, in the example from Fox News user comments, although the text does not explicitly contain any strong or offensive words, it is seemingly offensive towards 'Muslims' and 'Merkel'. Hence, our models should attend to these two words with the highest priority, which SCL-Fish does. On the other hand, although HateXplain gives higher attention to 'Merkel', it fails to attend the word 'Muslims'. Surprisingly, HateBERT does not assign priority to any context for the misclassified examples. On the example from StormFront, both SCL-Fish and HateXplain, correctly assign priority to the words 'foreigners' and 'pegan' unlike HateBERT. However,

HateXplain also confuses other words e.g. 'The' as a highly prioritized token. Finally, the example from synthetically-generated dataset *hateCheck* is challenging because of the linguistic complexity (e.g. negations, hedging terms) language models typically struggle to address (Hossain et al., 2020; Ettinger, 2020; Kassner and Schütze, 2020). We observe that SCL-Fish highly prioritizes 'women' and also attends to the token 'not'. On the other hand, HateXplain mistakenly provides the highest attention to 'We must' and ignores the negation term 'not'.

Overall, our analysis shows that model trained on platform-generalized settings improves on identifying the targeted community and right context on an out-domain offensive text. On the contrary, platform-specific models may not be able to attend to the targeted community in a different platform, because these models are trained on target specific to particular platforms.

6.4 SCL Improves Fish

From Table 2 and Table 8, it is evident that integrating SCL with Fish empirically improves performance across the platforms. Now, we substantiate the empirical result with the visual justification for Fish and SCL-Fish on different platforms. For all the platforms, we pass an equal number of abusive and non-abusive samples to the models and plot the [CLS] embeddings in Figure 4.

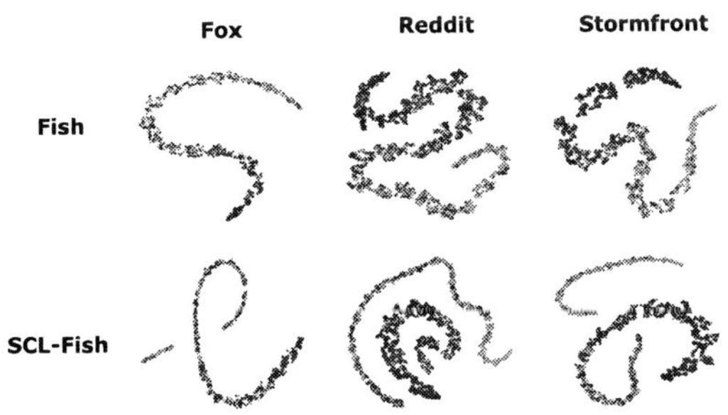

Figure 4: tSNE plot for Fish vs. SCL-Fish on Fox News Comment, Reddit, and StormFront. Abusive samples are presented in *orange* and non-abusive samples are presented in *blue*.

We observe that, SCL-Fish forms more compact clusters of abusive (majority from *orange* samples) and non-abusive (majority from *blue* samples) examples than Fish. Supervised contrastive learning attempts to learn task-oriented features that help bring representations of the same class closer to each other while pushing representations of different classes further apart. As a result, distinct clusters are formed for each class in Figure 4. Therefore, incorporating SCL helps Fish reduce the confusion between abusive and non-abusive representations and improves overall performance of the model.

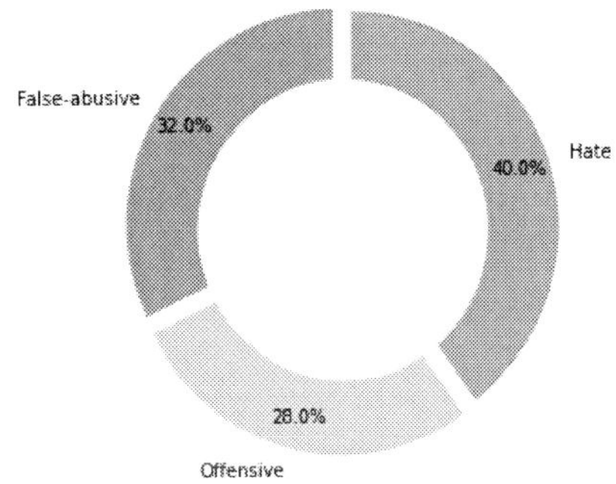

Figure 5: Percentage of error categories in a randomly sampled 50 misclassified examples.

7 Error Analysis

We conduct an error analysis on the examples that SCL-Fish misclassified. We randomly sample 50 misclassified examples and divide them into three categories:

False-abusive: Examples that are normal but SCL-Fish categorizes them as abusive.

Offensive: Examples that are degrading, harassing to an individual or untargeted abuse, trolling but SCL-Fish categorizes them as normal.

Hate: Examples that contain targeted attacks towards a particular group or identity.

We provide examples for each category in Table 4. Figure 5 shows that SCL-Fish misclassify 32% normal examples as false-abusive. Most of the examples of this category contain some sort of slang words that the model confuses as abusive. On other hand, SCL-Fish misclassifies 28% of the offensive examples as normal. This is because the examples may contain some positive words (e.g. 'please') or do not contain any profanity. Therefore, the model considers them as normal speech. Lastly, around 40% of the hate speech is misclassified as normal by SCL-Fish. Similar to the reason for offensive, the model confuse because of some sarcastic positive words and lack of expected profanity. This analysis shows that detecting implicit abusive language that does not contain direct profanity is still challenging and a direction to be explored in the future.

Category	Example	Predicted Class
False-abusive	Once at work, I accidentally checked out some dragons f*cking cars. Didn't know that would be an issue.	Abusive
Offensive	The girl on the left looks like a Jewish pizza.	Normal
Hate	The Blacks and Browns are destroying Sweden and nobody does anything about it!	Normal
False-abusive	I've been out for years and it hasn't been easy, but I also love being a f*g.	Abusive
Offensive	Why do you not think so? Feck off. Please go on. You annoy me.	Normal
Hate	All we have is Blacks and a few Mestizos and all are pretty well behaved, we keep them that way around here.	Normal
False-abusive	I truly am a bada*s motherf*cker.	Abusive
Offensive	Oh yeah, she's so annoying I had mentally blocked out her existence.	Normal
Hate	As opposed to Reddit, which is composed mainly of Communists jacking each other off about child drag queens?	Normal

Table 4: Sample of misclassified examples from *False-abusive*, *Offensive*, and *Hate* category.

8 Conclusion

In this work, we addressed the problem of cross-platform abusive language detection from the domain generalization perspective. We proposed SCL-Fish, a supervised contrastive learning augmented meta-learning method to learn generalized task-driven features across platforms. We showed that SCL-Fish achieves better performance compared to the other state-of-the-art models and models adopting ERM for cross-platform abusive language detection. Our analysis also reveals that SCL-Fish achieves comparable performance on finetuning with much smaller data for cross-platform training than other data-intensive methods. Our work demonstrates progress on both platform and domain generalization in the context of abusive language detection, which we hope future research can be extended to other areas of language understanding.

9 Limitations

Although SCL-Fish achieves improvement over Fish, training SCL-Fish takes longer time than Fish. Empirically, we find that SCL-Fish is approximately 1.2x slower than Fish. Moreover, we believe that the subjective nature of abusive language (Sap et al., 2019) affects the annotation process of different datasets and possibly negatively impact performance.

Acknowledgements

MAM acknowledges support from Canada Research Chairs (CRC), the Natural Sciences and Engineering Research Council of Canada (NSERC; RGPIN-2018-04267), the Social Sciences and Humanities Research Council of Canada (SSHRC; 435-2018-0576; 895-2020-1004; 895-2021-1008), Canadian Foundation for Innovation (CFI; 37771), and Digital Research Alliance of Canada.[5]

References

Marcin Andrychowicz, Misha Denil, Sergio Gómez, Matthew W Hoffman, David Pfau, Tom Schaul, Brendan Shillingford, and Nando de Freitas. 2016. Learning to learn by gradient descent by gradient descent. In *Advances in Neural Information Processing Systems*, volume 29. Curran Associates, Inc.

Martin Arjovsky, Léon Bottou, Ishaan Gulrajani, and David Lopez-Paz. 2020. Invariant risk minimization. In *International Conference on Machine Learning*.

Valerio Basile, Cristina Bosco, Elisabetta Fersini, Debora Nozza, Viviana Patti, Francisco Manuel Rangel Pardo, Paolo Rosso, and Manuela Sanguinetti. 2019. SemEval-2019 task 5: Multilingual detection of hate speech against immigrants and women in Twitter. In *Proceedings of the 13th International Workshop on Semantic Evaluation*, pages 54–63, Minneapolis, Minnesota, USA. Association for Computational Linguistics.

[5]https://alliancecan.ca

Tommaso Caselli, Valerio Basile, Jelena Mitrović, and Michael Granitzer. 2021. HateBERT: Retraining BERT for abusive language detection in English. In *Proceedings of the 5th Workshop on Online Abuse and Harms (WOAH 2021)*, pages 17–25, Online. Association for Computational Linguistics.

Tommaso Caselli, Valerio Basile, Jelena Mitrović, Inga Kartoziya, and Michael Granitzer. 2020. I feel offended, don't be abusive! implicit/explicit messages in offensive and abusive language. In *Proceedings of the 12th Language Resources and Evaluation Conference*, pages 6193–6202, Marseille, France. European Language Resources Association.

Amanda Cercas Curry, Gavin Abercrombie, and Verena Rieser. 2021. ConvAbuse: Data, analysis, and benchmarks for nuanced abuse detection in conversational AI. In *Proceedings of the 2021 Conference on Empirical Methods in Natural Language Processing*, pages 7388–7403, Online and Punta Cana, Dominican Republic. Association for Computational Linguistics.

Ting Chen, Simon Kornblith, Mohammad Norouzi, and Geoffrey Hinton. 2020. A simple framework for contrastive learning of visual representations. In *Proceedings of the 37th International Conference on Machine Learning*, volume 119 of *Proceedings of Machine Learning Research*, pages 1597–1607. PMLR.

Ting Chen, Yizhou Sun, Yue Shi, and Liangjie Hong. 2017. On sampling strategies for neural network-based collaborative filtering. In *Proceedings of the 23rd ACM SIGKDD International Conference on Knowledge Discovery and Data Mining*, KDD '17, page 767–776, New York, NY, USA. Association for Computing Machinery.

Michele Corazza, Stefano Menini, Elena Cabrio, Sara Tonelli, and Serena Villata. 2019. Cross-platform evaluation for italian hate speech detection. In *CLiC-it*.

M. Dadvar, Rudolf Berend Trieschnigg, Roeland J.F. Ordelman, and Franciska M.G. de Jong. 2013. Improving cyberbullying detection with user context. In *Proceedings of the 35th European Conference on IR Research, ECIR 2013*, Lecture Notes in Computer Science, pages 693–696, Netherlands. Springer.

Thomas Davidson, Dana Warmsley, Michael Macy, and Ingmar Weber. 2017. Automated hate speech detection and the problem of offensive language. *Proceedings of the International AAAI Conference on Web and Social Media*, 11(1):512–515.

Ona de Gibert, Naiara Perez, Aitor García-Pablos, and Montse Cuadros. 2018. Hate speech dataset from a white supremacy forum. In *Proceedings of the 2nd Workshop on Abusive Language Online (ALW2)*, pages 11–20, Brussels, Belgium. Association for Computational Linguistics.

Jacob Devlin, Ming-Wei Chang, Kenton Lee, and Kristina Toutanova. 2018. Bert: Pre-training of deep bidirectional transformers for language understanding.

Mai ElSherief, Vivek Kulkarni, Dana Nguyen, William Yang Wang, and Elizabeth Belding. 2018. Hate lingo: A target-based linguistic analysis of hate speech in social media. *Proceedings of the International AAAI Conference on Web and Social Media*, 12(1).

Allyson Ettinger. 2020. What bert is not: Lessons from a new suite of psycholinguistic diagnostics for language models. *Transactions of the Association for Computational Linguistics*, 8(0):34–48.

Chelsea Finn, Pieter Abbeel, and Sergey Levine. 2017. Model-agnostic meta-learning for fast adaptation of deep networks. In *Proceedings of the 34th International Conference on Machine Learning*, volume 70 of *Proceedings of Machine Learning Research*, pages 1126–1135. PMLR.

Paula Fortuna, José Ferreira, Luiz Pires, Guilherme Routar, and Sérgio Nunes. 2018. Merging datasets for aggressive text identification. In *Proceedings of the First Workshop on Trolling, Aggression and Cyberbullying (TRAC-2018)*, pages 128–139, Santa Fe, New Mexico, USA. Association for Computational Linguistics.

Antigoni Founta, Constantinos Djouvas, Despoina Chatzakou, Ilias Leontiadis, Jeremy Blackburn, Gianluca Stringhini, Athena Vakali, Michael Sirivianos, and Nicolas Kourtellis. 2018. Large scale crowdsourcing and characterization of twitter abusive behavior. *Proceedings of the International AAAI Conference on Web and Social Media*, 12(1).

John D Gallacher. 2021. Leveraging cross-platform data to improve automated hate speech detection.

Lei Gao and Ruihong Huang. 2017. Detecting online hate speech using context aware models. In *Proceedings of the International Conference Recent Advances in Natural Language Processing, RANLP 2017*, pages 260–266, Varna, Bulgaria. INCOMA Ltd.

Tianyu Gao, Xingcheng Yao, and Danqi Chen. 2021. SimCSE: Simple contrastive learning of sentence embeddings. In *Proceedings of the 2021 Conference on Empirical Methods in Natural Language Processing*, pages 6894–6910, Online and Punta Cana, Dominican Republic. Association for Computational Linguistics.

Daniel Gillick, Sayali Kulkarni, Larry Lansing, Alessandro Presta, Jason Baldridge, Eugene Ie, and Diego Garcia-Olano. 2019. Learning dense representations for entity retrieval. In *Proceedings of the 23rd Conference on Computational Natural Language Learning (CoNLL)*, pages 528–537, Hong Kong, China. Association for Computational Linguistics.

Njagi Dennis Gitari, Zhang Zuping, Zuping Zhang, Hanyurwimfura Damien, and Jun Long. 2015. A lexicon-based approach for hate speech detection. In *International Journal of Multimedia and Ubiquitous Engineering*.

Jennifer Golbeck, Zahra Ashktorab, Rashad O. Banjo, Alexandra Berlinger, Siddharth Bhagwan, Cody Buntain, Paul Cheakalos, Alicia A. Geller, Quint Gergory, Rajesh Kumar Gnanasekaran, Raja Rajan Gunasekaran, Kelly M. Hoffman, Jenny Hottle, Vichita Jienjitlert, Shivika Khare, Ryan Lau, Marianna J. Martindale, Shalmali Naik, Heather L. Nixon, Piyush Ramachandran, Kristine M. Rogers, Lisa Rogers, Meghna Sardana Sarin, Gaurav Shahane, Jayanee Thanki, Priyanka Vengataraman, Zijian Wan, and Derek Michael Wu. 2017. A large labeled corpus for online harassment research. In *Proceedings of the 2017 ACM on Web Science Conference*, WebSci '17, page 229–233, New York, NY, USA. Association for Computing Machinery.

Tommi Gröndahl, Luca Pajola, Mika Juuti, Mauro Conti, and N. Asokan. 2018. All you need is "love": Evading hate speech detection. AISec '18, page 2–12, New York, NY, USA. Association for Computing Machinery.

Raia Hadsell, Sumit Chopra, and Yann LeCun. 2006. Dimensionality reduction by learning an invariant mapping. *2006 IEEE Computer Society Conference on Computer Vision and Pattern Recognition (CVPR'06)*, 2:1735–1742.

Matthew Henderson, Rami Al-Rfou, Brian Strope, Yunhsuan Sung, Laszlo Lukacs, Ruiqi Guo, Sanjiv Kumar, Balint Miklos, and Ray Kurzweil. 2017. Efficient natural language response suggestion for smart reply.

Dan Hendrycks and Thomas Dietterich. 2019. Benchmarking neural network robustness to common corruptions and perturbations. *Proceedings of the International Conference on Learning Representations*.

Md Mosharaf Hossain, Venelin Kovatchev, Pranoy Dutta, Tiffany Kao, Elizabeth Wei, and Eduardo Blanco. 2020. An analysis of natural language inference benchmarks through the lens of negation. In *Proceedings of the 2020 Conference on Empirical Methods in Natural Language Processing (EMNLP)*, pages 9106–9118, Online. Association for Computational Linguistics.

Akshita Jha and Radhika Mamidi. 2017. When does a compliment become sexist? analysis and classification of ambivalent sexism using twitter data. In *Proceedings of the Second Workshop on NLP and Computational Social Science*, pages 7–16, Vancouver, Canada. Association for Computational Linguistics.

David Jurgens, Libby Hemphill, and Eshwar Chandrasekharan. 2019. A just and comprehensive strategy for using NLP to address online abuse. In *Proceedings of the 57th Annual Meeting of the Association for Computational Linguistics*, pages 3658–3666, Florence, Italy. Association for Computational Linguistics.

Mladen Karan and Jan Šnajder. 2018. Cross-domain detection of abusive language online. In *Proceedings of the 2nd Workshop on Abusive Language Online (ALW2)*, pages 132–137, Brussels, Belgium. Association for Computational Linguistics.

Vladimir Karpukhin, Barlas Oguz, Sewon Min, Patrick Lewis, Ledell Wu, Sergey Edunov, Danqi Chen, and Wen-tau Yih. 2020. Dense passage retrieval for open-domain question answering. In *Proceedings of the 2020 Conference on Empirical Methods in Natural Language Processing (EMNLP)*, pages 6769–6781, Online. Association for Computational Linguistics.

Nora Kassner and Hinrich Schütze. 2020. Negated and misprimed probes for pretrained language models: Birds can talk, but cannot fly. In *Proceedings of the 58th Annual Meeting of the Association for Computational Linguistics*, pages 7811–7818, Online. Association for Computational Linguistics.

Prannay Khosla, Piotr Teterwak, Chen Wang, Aaron Sarna, Yonglong Tian, Phillip Isola, Aaron Maschinot, Ce Liu, and Dilip Krishnan. 2020. Supervised contrastive learning. In *Advances in Neural Information Processing Systems*, volume 33, pages 18661–18673. Curran Associates, Inc.

Pang Wei Koh, Shiori Sagawa, Henrik Marklund, Sang Michael Xie, Marvin Zhang, Akshay Balsubramani, Weihua Hu, Michihiro Yasunaga, Richard Lanas Phillips, Irena Gao, Tony Lee, Etienne David, Ian Stavness, Wei Guo, Berton Earnshaw, Imran Haque, Sara M Beery, Jure Leskovec, Anshul Kundaje, Emma Pierson, Sergey Levine, Chelsea Finn, and Percy Liang. 2021. Wilds: A benchmark of in-the-wild distribution shifts. In *Proceedings of the 38th International Conference on Machine Learning*, volume 139 of *Proceedings of Machine Learning Research*, pages 5637–5664. PMLR.

David Krueger, Ethan Caballero, Joern-Henrik Jacobsen, Amy Zhang, Jonathan Binas, Dinghuai Zhang, Remi Le Priol, and Aaron Courville. 2021. Out-of-distribution generalization via risk extrapolation (rex). In *International Conference on Machine Learning*, pages 5815–5826. PMLR.

Rohan Kshirsagar, Tyrus Cukuvac, Kathy McKeown, and Susan McGregor. 2018. Predictive embeddings for hate speech detection on Twitter. In *Proceedings of the 2nd Workshop on Abusive Language Online (ALW2)*, pages 26–32, Brussels, Belgium. Association for Computational Linguistics.

Ping Liu, Wen Li, and Liang Zou. 2019a. NULI at SemEval-2019 task 6: Transfer learning for offensive language detection using bidirectional transformers. In *Proceedings of the 13th International Workshop* on Semantic Evaluation, pages 87–91, Minneapolis, Minnesota, USA. Association for Computational Linguistics.

Yinhan Liu, Myle Ott, Naman Goyal, Jingfei Du, Mandar Joshi, Danqi Chen, Omer Levy, Mike Lewis, Luke Zettlemoyer, and Veselin Stoyanov. 2019b. Roberta: A robustly optimized bert pretraining approach. *arXiv preprint arXiv:1907.11692*.

Lajanugen Logeswaran and Honglak Lee. 2018. An efficient framework for learning sentence representations. In *International Conference on Learning Representations*, volume abs/1803.02893.

Thomas Mandl, Sandip Modha, Prasenjit Majumder, Daksh Patel, Mohana Dave, Chintak Mandlia, and Aditya Patel. 2019. Overview of the hasoc track at fire 2019: Hate speech and offensive content identification in indo-european languages. FIRE '19, page 14–17, New York, NY, USA. Association for Computing Machinery.

Binny Mathew, Punyajoy Saha, Seid Muhie Yimam, Chris Biemann, Pawan Goyal, and Animesh Mukherjee. 2021. Hatexplain: A benchmark dataset for explainable hate speech detection. *Proceedings of the AAAI Conference on Artificial Intelligence*, 35(17):14867–14875.

Puneet Mathur, Ramit Sawhney, Meghna Ayyar, and Rajiv Shah. 2018. Did you offend me? classification of offensive tweets in Hinglish language. In *Proceedings of the 2nd Workshop on Abusive Language Online (ALW2)*, pages 138–148, Brussels, Belgium. Association for Computational Linguistics.

Pushkar Mishra, Helen Yannakoudakis, and Ekaterina Shutova. 2018. Neural character-based composition models for abuse detection. In *Proceedings of the 2nd Workshop on Abusive Language Online (ALW2)*, pages 1–10, Brussels, Belgium. Association for Computational Linguistics.

Jelena Mitrović, Bastian Birkeneder, and Michael Granitzer. 2019. nlpUP at SemEval-2019 task 6: A deep neural language model for offensive language detection. In *Proceedings of the 13th International Workshop on Semantic Evaluation*, pages 722–726, Minneapolis, Minnesota, USA. Association for Computational Linguistics.

Ioannis Mollas, Zoe Chrysopoulou, Stamatis Karlos, and Grigorios Tsoumakas. 2020. Ethos: an online hate speech detection dataset. *Complex & Intelligent Systems*.

Karsten Müller and Carlo Schwarz. 2017. Fanning the flames of hate: Social media and hate crime. *SSRN Electronic Journal*.

Alex Nichol, Joshua Achiam, and John Schulman. 2018. On first-order meta-learning algorithms. *arXiv preprint arXiv:1803.02999*.

Nedjma Ousidhoum, Zizheng Lin, Hongming Zhang, Yangqiu Song, and Dit-Yan Yeung. 2019. Multilingual and multi-aspect hate speech analysis. In *Proceedings of the 2019 Conference on Empirical Methods in Natural Language Processing and the 9th International Joint Conference on Natural Language Processing (EMNLP-IJCNLP)*, pages 4675–4684, Hong Kong, China. Association for Computational Linguistics.

Mohammad Pezeshki, Sékou-Oumar Kaba, Yoshua Bengio, Aaron C. Courville, Doina Precup, and Guillaume Lajoie. 2021. Gradient starvation: A learning proclivity in neural networks. In *35th Conference on Neural Information Processing Systems (NeurIPS)*.

Jing Qian, Anna Bethke, Yinyin Liu, Elizabeth Belding, and William Yang Wang. 2019. A benchmark dataset for learning to intervene in online hate speech. In *Proceedings of the 2019 Conference on Empirical Methods in Natural Language Processing and the 9th International Joint Conference on Natural Language Processing (EMNLP-IJCNLP)*, pages 4755–4764, Hong Kong, China. Association for Computational Linguistics.

Joaquin Quiñonero-Candela, Masashi Sugiyama, Anton Schwaighofer, and Neil D Lawrence. 2008. *Dataset shift in machine learning*. Mit Press.

Manoel Horta Ribeiro, Pedro H Calais, Yuri A Santos, Virgílio AF Almeida, and Wagner Meira Jr. 2018. Characterizing and detecting hateful users on twitter. In *Twelfth international AAAI conference on web and social media*.

Julian Risch, Philipp Schmidt, and Ralf Krestel. 2021. Data integration for toxic comment classification: Making more than 40 datasets easily accessible in one unified format. In *Proceedings of the 5th Workshop on Online Abuse and Harms (WOAH 2021)*, pages 157–163, Online. Association for Computational Linguistics.

Paul Röttger, Bertie Vidgen, Dong Nguyen, Zeerak Waseem, Helen Margetts, and Janet Pierrehumbert. 2021. HateCheck: Functional tests for hate speech detection models. In *Proceedings of the 59th Annual Meeting of the Association for Computational Linguistics and the 11th International Joint Conference on Natural Language Processing (Volume 1: Long Papers)*, pages 41–58, Online. Association for Computational Linguistics.

Olga Russakovsky, Jia Deng, Hao Su, Jonathan Krause, Sanjeev Satheesh, Sean Ma, Zhiheng Huang, Andrej Karpathy, Aditya Khosla, Michael Bernstein, Alexander C. Berg, and Li Fei-Fei. 2015. Imagenet large scale visual recognition challenge.

Shiori Sagawa, Pang Wei Koh, Tatsunori B. Hashimoto, and Percy Liang. 2019. Distributionally robust neural networks for group shifts: On the importance of regularization for worst-case generalization. In *International Conference on Learning Representations*.

Joni Salminen, Hind Almerekhi, Milica Milenković, Soon-gyo Jung, Jisun An, Haewoon Kwak, and Bernard Jansen. 2018. Anatomy of online hate: Developing a taxonomy and machine learning models for identifying and classifying hate in online news media. *Proceedings of the International AAAI Conference on Web and Social Media*, 12(1).

Joni O. Salminen, Maximilian Hopf, S. A. Chowdhury, Soon-Gyo Jung, Hind Almerekhi, and Bernard Jim Jansen. 2020. Developing an online hate classifier for multiple social media platforms. *Human-centric Computing and Information Sciences*, 10:1–34.

Shibani Santurkar, Dimitris Tsipras, and Aleksander Madry. 2020. BREEDS: benchmarks for subpopulation shift. *CoRR*, abs/2008.04859.

Maarten Sap, Dallas Card, Saadia Gabriel, Yejin Choi, and Noah A. Smith. 2019. The risk of racial bias in hate speech detection. In *Proceedings of the 57th Annual Meeting of the Association for Computational Linguistics*, pages 1668–1678, Florence, Italy. Association for Computational Linguistics.

Anna Schmidt and Michael Wiegand. 2017. A survey on hate speech detection using natural language processing. In *Proceedings of the Fifth International Workshop on Natural Language Processing for Social Media*, pages 1–10, Valencia, Spain. Association for Computational Linguistics.

Yuge Shi, Jeffrey Seely, Philip H. S. Torr, N. Siddharth, Awni Hannun, Nicolas Usunier, and Gabriel Synnaeve. 2021. Gradient matching for domain generalization. *arXiv preprint arXiv:2104.09937*.

Gudbjartur Ingi Sigurbergsson and Leon Derczynski. 2020. Offensive language and hate speech detection for Danish. In *Proceedings of the 12th Language Resources and Evaluation Conference*, pages 3498–3508, Marseille, France. European Language Resources Association.

Steve Durairaj Swamy, Anupam Jamatia, and Björn Gambäck. 2019. Studying generalisability across abusive language detection datasets. In *Proceedings of the 23rd Conference on Computational Natural Language Learning (CoNLL)*, pages 940–950, Hong Kong, China. Association for Computational Linguistics.

V. Vapnik. 1991. Principles of risk minimization for learning theory. In *Advances in Neural Information Processing Systems*, volume 4. Morgan-Kaufmann.

Ashish Vaswani, Noam Shazeer, Niki Parmar, Jakob Uszkoreit, Llion Jones, Aidan N Gomez, Ł ukasz Kaiser, and Illia Polosukhin. 2017. Attention is all you need. In *Advances in Neural Information Processing Systems*, volume 30. Curran Associates, Inc.

Bertie Vidgen and Leon Derczynski. 2020. Directions in abusive language training data, a systematic review: Garbage in, garbage out. *PLoS ONE*, 15(12):e0243300.

Jesse Vig. 2019. A multiscale visualization of attention in the transformer model. In *Proceedings of the 57th Annual Meeting of the Association for Computational Linguistics: System Demonstrations*, pages 37–42, Florence, Italy. Association for Computational Linguistics.

William Warner and Julia Hirschberg. 2012. Detecting hate speech on the world wide web. In *Proceedings of the Second Workshop on Language in Social Media*, LSM '12, page 19–26, USA. Association for Computational Linguistics.

Zeerak Waseem and Dirk Hovy. 2016. Hateful symbols or hateful people? predictive features for hate speech detection on Twitter. In *Proceedings of the NAACL Student Research Workshop*, pages 88–93, San Diego, California. Association for Computational Linguistics.

Matthew L Williams, Pete Burnap, Amir Javed, Han Liu, and Sefa Ozalp. 2019. Hate in the Machine: Anti-Black and Anti-Muslim Social Media Posts as Predictors of Offline Racially and Religiously Aggravated Crime. *The British Journal of Criminology*, 60(1):93–117.

Ellery Wulczyn, Nithum Thain, and Lucas Dixon. 2017. Ex machina: Personal attacks seen at scale. In *Proceedings of the 26th International Conference on World Wide Web*, pages 1391–1399.

Kai Yuanqing Xiao, Logan Engstrom, Andrew Ilyas, and Aleksander Madry. 2020. Noise or signal: The role of image backgrounds in object recognition. *CoRR*, abs/2006.09994.

Jun-Ming Xu, Kwang-Sung Jun, Xiaojin Zhu, and Amy Bellmore. 2012. Learning from bullying traces in social media. In *Proceedings of the 2012 Conference of the North American Chapter of the Association for Computational Linguistics: Human Language Technologies*, pages 656–666, Montréal, Canada. Association for Computational Linguistics.

Marcos Zampieri, Shervin Malmasi, Preslav Nakov, Sara Rosenthal, Noura Farra, and Ritesh Kumar. 2019a. Predicting the type and target of offensive posts in social media. In *Proceedings of the 2019 Conference of the North American Chapter of the Association for Computational Linguistics: Human Language Technologies, Volume 1 (Long and Short Papers)*, pages 1415–1420, Minneapolis, Minnesota. Association for Computational Linguistics.

Marcos Zampieri, Shervin Malmasi, Preslav Nakov, Sara Rosenthal, Noura Farra, and Ritesh Kumar. 2019b. SemEval-2019 task 6: Identifying and categorizing offensive language in social media (OffensEval). In *Proceedings of the 13th International Workshop on Semantic Evaluation*, pages 75–86, Minneapolis, Minnesota, USA. Association for Computational Linguistics.

A Hyperparameter Configuration

The detailed configuration of hyperparameters for the training phase of the cross-platform experiments is shown in Table 5. We run each experiment three times and report the average performance of the models.

Hyperparameters	Values
LM model variant	BERT-base-uncased
Token length	512
Optimizer	Adam
AdamW epsilon	1e-8
AdamW betas	(0.9, 0.999)
Fish meta lr. (ϵ)	0.05
SCL temperature (τ)	0.05
Learning rate	5e-6
Batch size	8
Epochs	10

Table 5: Hyperparameters for cross-platform experiments.

Table 6 presents the configuration of hyperparameters during the finetuning (Section 6.2).

Hyperparameters	Values
LM model variant	BERT-base-uncased
Token length	100
Optimizer	AdamW
AdamW epsilon	1e-8
AdamW betas	(0.9, 0.999)
Learning rate	1e-5
Batch size	32
Epochs	5

Table 6: Hyperparameters for finetuning.

B Performance on Cross-Platform Balanced Datasets

We sample an equal number of examples from abusive and normal classes for each dataset. The result is shown in Table 7.

C In-Platform Performance

Table 8 shows the performance of the methods on the in-platform datasets. Unsurprisingly, ERM-based methods outperform Fish-based methods on all the datasets and in all the metrics. ERM method learns platform-specific features, while the Fish-based method tends to learn platform-invariant features. Therefore, evaluating the in-platform datasets yield better performance for ERM-based methods. Notably, as the percentage of abusive speech decreases from the top row to the bottom row in Table 8, positive-F_1 scores also drop accordingly. But Fish-based methods suffer least performance deterioration (10.1% drop from *fb-yt* to *wiki* for SCL-Fish, 7.2% drop from *fb-yt* to *wiki* for Fish) than the other methods (12.3% drop from *fb-yt* to *wiki* for ERM, 12.7% drop from *fb-yt* to *wiki* for SCL-ERM). This shows that domain generalization helps the methods to learn more robust platform-invariant features, which in turn, results in more accurate detection of abusive speech on cross-platform datasets.

D Quantitative Comparison for *Twitter* In-Domain and Out-Domain Datasets

We compare *twitter* (in-domain) and *twi-fb* (out-domain) datasets based on linguistic features and sentiment analysis. For each dataset, we compute average sentiment scores, average number of words, and characters for both abusive and non-abusive classes.

Table 9 reflects the difference in sentiments scores and linguistic features between the datasets. We see that the number of words and the number of characters are higher for the out-domain (*twi-fb*) dataset than the in-domain (*twitter*) dataset for both abusive and non-abusive classes. Additionally, the examples of out-domain datasets have more negative sentiment on average than the examples of in-domain dataset. These types of variation can shift the distribution of the datasets, as a result, the models may struggle to perform better on an out-domain dataset (Table 2).

E Rationale for Performance Gap across Platforms

To this end, we aim to study the reason for the performance gap of the models across different platforms through a qualitative analysis of linguistic variance. We sample abusive texts from the platforms and plot the word frequency in Figure 6.

We observe that the type of abusive texts varies along with the linguistic features across the platforms. For example, on social networks like Twitter, most appeared words in abusive texts are 'f*cking', 'gun', 'a*s', which mostly imply violence and personal attack. Meanwhile, an extremist forum like Stormfront contains words like 'black',

Platform	HateXplain			HateBERT			ERM			SCL-ERM			Fish			SCL-Fish		
	Acc	Pos. F_1	Macro F_1	Acc	Pos. F_1	Macro F_1	Acc	Pos. F_1	Macro F_1	Acc	Pos. F_1	Macro F_1	Acc	Pos. F_1	Macro F_1	Acc	Pos. F_1	Macro F_1
stormfront	64.7	48.5	60.9	61.9	41.2	56.5	69.2	60.1	67.5	67.5	56.4	65.3	67.3	56.1	65.0	**69.5**	**60.6**	**67.8**
fox	57.0	30.7	49.8	55.6	36.3	51.1	61.5	46.9	58.4	61.6	46.9	58.4	61.8	49.1	59.3	**63.3**	**54.6**	**61.9**
twi-fb	51.6	09.4	38.2	55.5	29.0	48.3	54.7	38.9	51.5	53.4	36.6	49.9	50.0	**42.1**	49.1	**55.8**	41.6	**53.0**
reddit	61.6	41.4	56.4	66.1	55.8	64.2	65.9	57.9	64.6	66.1	58.1	64.8	67.1	60.6	66.2	**68.2**	**63.2**	**67.6**
convAI	57.8	28.0	49.1	73.4	66.7	72.3	87.1	87.2	87.1	86.3	86.2	86.3	85.5	85.3	85.5	**87.9**	**87.9**	**87.9**
hateCheck	52.3	27.5	45.9	**63.4**	60.9	**63.3**	59.5	**67.3**	57.1	59.1	65.7	57.6	60.9	67.1	59.5	60.8	66.8	59.5
gab	33.8	41.0	32.8	33.9	42.7	32.3	64.1	72.8	**60.1**	62.2	72.1	56.7	**64.3**	**72.9**	**60.1**	60.2	71.1	53.6
yt-reddit	65.3	54.3	63.2	70.9	69.3	70.8	72.4	75.7	71.9	**74.5**	**77.1**	**74.2**	73.6	76.6	73.2	73.0	76.7	72.3
avg.	55.5	35.1	49.5	60.1	50.2	57.4	66.8	63.3	64.8	66.4	62.4	64.2	66.3	63.7	64.7	**67.3**	**65.3**	**65.5**

Table 7: Performance on the **balanced** cross-platform datasets. **Bold** font represents best performance for a particular metric. Gray cells indicates performance on the datasets from identical or overlapping platforms but different sources and distributions.

Platform (% of hate)	ERM			SCL-ERM			Fish			SCL-Fish		
	Acc	Pos. F_1	Macro F_1	Acc	Pos. F_1	Macro F_1	Acc	Pos. F_1	Macro F_1	Acc	Pos. F_1	Macro F_1
fb-yt (73.4)	**94.1**	**95.8**	**92.9**	92.9	94.9	91.4	79.9	85.1	77.1	90.1	92.8	88.5
twitter (58.5)	**89.2**	90.7	**88.9**	**89.2**	**90.8**	88.8	84.0	85.8	83.8	**89.2**	90.7	**88.9**
wiki (11.2)	**96.2**	**83.5**	**90.7**	96.0	82.2	89.9	95.1	77.9	87.6	95.9	82.7	90.2
avg.	**93.2**	**90.0**	**90.8**	92.7	89.3	90.1	86.3	82.9	82.8	91.8	88.7	89.2

Table 8: Performance on in-platform datasets. **Bold** font represents best performance for a particular metric.

Class	Features	*twitter*	*twi-fb*
Abusive	No. of Words	15.49	29.64
	No. of Characters	96.53	168.46
	Sentiment Score	-0.75	-0.83
Non-Abusive	No. of Words	18.51	26.84
	No. of Characters	118.41	172.09
	Sentiment Score	-0.49	-0.71

Table 9: Comparison between in-domain (*twitter*) and out-domain (*twi-fb*) datasets. Features are computed averaging the examples for a particular class (abusive/non-abusive).

'white', 'jews' which indicate abusive comments towards a particular community or ethnicity. Linguistic features from a public forum like Reddit reveal that abusive comments on this platform are mostly targeted attacks and slang. Abusive conversation with AI bots mostly contains strong words in the form of personal attacks. On the other hand, user comments on broadcasting media like Fox News do not contain any strong words but rather implicit abuse focused towards a particular race like 'black', person like 'Obama', or sexual orientations like 'gay'. Finally, abusive texts on Wikipedia include both targeted and untargeted slang words toward a specific entity.

The variation of abuse across different platforms shows that training models on a specific platform are not enough to address the issue of mitigating abusive language on another platform. This also implies the importance of the platform-generalized study of abusive language detection.

F Datasets Description

In this section, we briefly describe the datasets we compile for our cross-platform experiments.

F.1 wiki

wiki dataset represents Wikipedia platform. We collect this dataset from Wulczyn et al. (2017). The corpus contains 63M comments from discussions relating to user pages and articles dating from 2004 to 2015. Human annotations were used to label personal attack, aggressiveness, and harassment. The authors find that almost 1% of Wikipedia comments contain personal attacks. We randomly sample 132,815 examples from the initial corpus to make it compatible in size with other training sets.

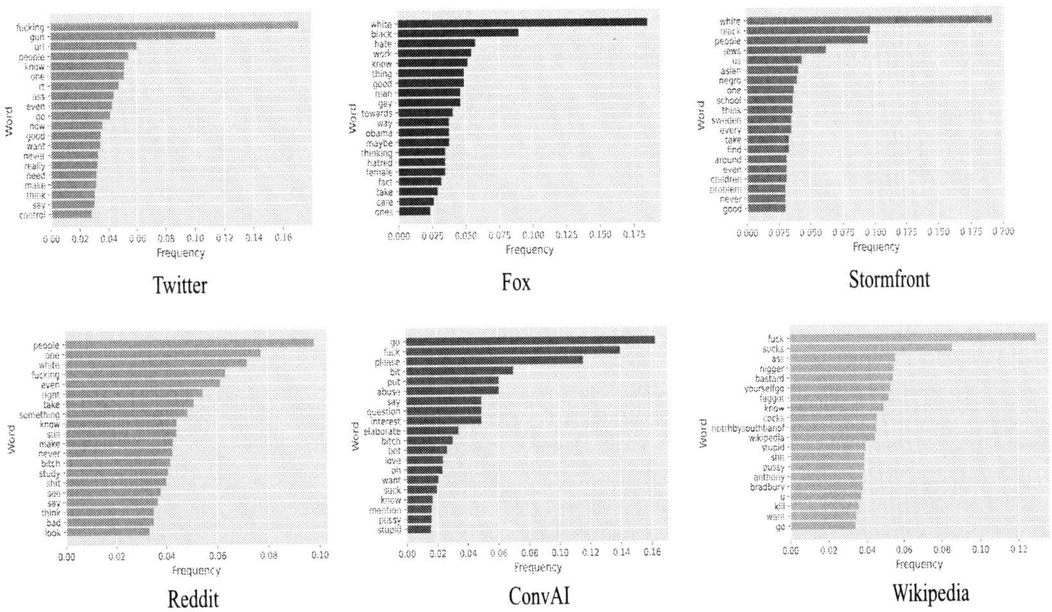

Figure 6: Top-20 normalized word frequency of abusive language for different platforms (ignoring *stopwords* and *non-alphabetic* characters).

Of these examples, 14,880 contain abusive (personal attack, aggressiveness, harassment) language.

F.2 twitter

We collect *twitter* dataset from a variety of sources. Waseem and Hovy (2016) annotate around 16k tweets that contain sexist/racist language. Initially, the authors bootstrap the corpus based on common slurs, then manually annotate the whole corpus to identify tweets that are offensive but do not contain any slur. Similarly, Davidson et al. (2017) crawled tweets with lexicon containing words and phrases identified by internet users as hate speech. Then crowdsourcing is performed to distinguish the category of hate, offensive, and normal tweets, resulting in around 25k annotated tweets. Jha and Mamidi (2017) crawled Twitter with the terms that generally exhibit positive sentiment but sexist in nature (e.g. 'as good as a man', 'like a man', 'for a girl'). The authors also annotate tweets that are aggressively sexist. The final corpus contains around 10k tweets of implicit/explicit sexist and normal tweets. ElSherief et al. (2018) adopt multi-step data collection process that include collecting tweets based on lexicon, *hashtag*, and other existing works (Waseem and Hovy, 2016; Davidson et al., 2017). Then, crowdsourcing is applied to annotate targeted and untargeted hate speech. Founta et al. (2018) build an annotated corpus of 80k tweets with seven classes (offensive, abusive, hateful speech, aggressive, cyberbullying, spam, and normal). Mathur et al. (2018) annotate a corpus of around 3k tweets containing hate, abusive, and normal tweets. Basile et al. (2019) crawled 13k tweets containing abusive language against women and immigrants. The authors applied crowdsourcing to annotate if the tweets contain individual/ group hate speech or aggressiveness. Mandl et al. (2019) develop a corpus of 7k English examples with the category of hate, offensive, and profanity. Ousidhoum et al. (2019) build a corpus of multilingual and multi-aspect hate speech. The English corpus (5,647 tweets) covers a wide range of hate speech categories including the level of directness, hostility, targeted theme, and targeted group. Zampieri et al. (2019a) develop an offensive corpus of 14,100 tweets based on hierarchical modelings, such as whether a tweet is offensive/targeted, if it is targeted towards a group or individual.

Our final *twitter* dataset contains 132.815 examples of which 77,656 are abusive.

F.3 fb-yt

fb-yt represent both Facebook and Youtube platforms. We collect this dataset from Salminen et al. (2018). Salminen et al. (2018) crawled the comments from Facebook and Youtube videos and annotate them into hateful, non-hateful categories. The authors also subcategorize hateful comments into 21 classes including accusation, promoting violence, and humiliation.

F.4 stormfront

stormfront dataset is collected from de Gibert et al. (2018). The authors crawled around 10k examples from Stormfront and categorize them into hate/normal speech. The authors further investigate whether joining subsequent seemingly normal sentences result in hate speech. Our final dataset contains 1364 hateful speech from Stormfront.

F.5 fox

fox dataset represents user comments on the broadcasting platform Fox News. We collect this dataset from Gao and Huang (2017). The authors find that the hateful comments are more implicit and creative and such hateful comments detection requires context-dependency.

F.6 twi-fb

twi-fb dataset contains user posts from Twitter and Facebook. We collect this dataset from Mandl et al. (2019). The authors initially collect the corpus by crawling keywords and hashtags. Later, they annotate the corpus into targeted/untargeted hate speech, offense, and profane.

F.7 reddit

reddit dataset contains conversations from Reddit. Qian et al. (2019) compiled a list of toxic subreddit and crawled user conversations from those subreddits. Additionally, the authors provide hate speech intervention, where the goal is to automatically generate responses to intervene during online conversations that contain hate speech. The final dataset contains 2511 examples of hate/abusive speech.

F.8 convAI

Cercas Curry et al. (2021) collect *convAI* dataset from the user conversation with an AI assistant, CarbonBot, hosted on Facebook Messenger and a rule-based conversational agent, ELIZA. The authors categorize the dataset based on the severity and the type of abusiveness, directness, and target. We collected 853 examples from this dataset of which 128 are abusive speech.

F.9 hateCheck

hateCheck is a synthetically-generated dataset collected from Röttger et al. (2021). The authors develop 29 functionality through prior research and human interview and generate test case to evaluate test case for each of the functionalities. The dataset contains 2563 examples of hate speech.

F.10 gab

We collect *gab* dataset from Qian et al. (2019). Unlike other datasets, Qian et al. (2019) provide the full conversation which helps the models to understand the context. We collect 15,926 examples from the original corpus of which 15,270 are hate speech.

F.11 yt-reddit

yt-reddit dataset is collected from Mollas et al. (2020). The authors develop the dataset, namely, ETHOS sampling from Youtube and Reddit comments. The authors emphasize reducing any kinds of bias (e.g. gender) in the annotation process and annotate the dataset into various forms of targeted hate speech (e.g. origin, race, disability). We sample an equal number of hate and normal speech from this dataset.

Aporophobia: An Overlooked Type of Toxic Language Targeting the Poor

Svetlana Kiritchenko,[1] Georgina Curto,[2] Isar Nejadgholi,[1] Kathleen C. Fraser[1]
[1]National Research Council Canada, Ottawa, Canada
[2]University of Notre Dame, Notre Dame, USA
{svetlana.kiritchenko, isar.nejadgholi, kathleen.fraser}@nrc-cnrc.gc.ca, gcurtore@nd.edu

Abstract

Content Warning: *This paper presents textual examples that may be offensive or upsetting.*

While many types of hate speech and online toxicity have been the focus of extensive research in NLP, toxic language stigmatizing poor people has been mostly disregarded. Yet, *aporophobia*, a social bias against the poor, is a common phenomenon online, which can be psychologically damaging as well as hindering poverty reduction policy measures. We demonstrate that aporophobic attitudes are indeed present in social media and argue that the existing NLP datasets and models are inadequate to effectively address this problem. Efforts toward designing specialized resources and novel socio-technical mechanisms for confronting aporophobia are needed.

1 Introduction

Online toxicity includes language that is offensive, derogatory, or perpetuates harmful social biases. Significant research effort has been devoted to addressing the problem of toxic language targeting several social groups, including women, immigrants, and ethnic minorities (Fortuna and Nunes, 2018; Kiritchenko et al., 2021). Yet, other groups (e.g., based on age, physical appearance, and socio-economic status) also regularly experience stigmatization with severe consequences to the groups and to society at large. In this work, we focus on aporophobia—"rejection, aversion, fear and contempt for the poor" (Cortina, 2022). Cortina, the philosopher who coined the term in 1990s, argues that aporophobia is even more common than other forms of discrimination, such as xenophobia and racism. Moreover, aporophobia often aggravates intersectional bias (e.g., it is not the same to be a *rich* woman from an ethnic minority than a *poor* woman from the same ethnic group) (Hoffmann, 2019; Hellgren and Gabrielli, 2021).

In meritocratic societies, the rhetoric of equal opportunities—according to which everyone is provided with the same chances for success—assigns the responsibility for one's welfare to each individual and results in blaming the poor for their fate (Mounk, 2017; Sandel, 2020). However, this principle does not reflect reality since every person has different abilities and disabilities, backgrounds, and experiences (Fishkin, 2014). In fact, economic indicators unveil a completely different picture: the overwhelming majority of poor people are those born into poverty (United Nations, 2018). Global levels of inequality are increasingly growing (Chancel and Piketty, 2021), social mobility is as low as 7% both in the United States and in Europe (Chetty et al., 2014; OECD, 2018), and the perception of social mobility in the US is higher than the actual opportunities to climb up the ladder, exacerbating even more the blamefulness and criminalization of the poor (Alesina et al., 2018).

Crucially, this bias has an impact on the actual poverty levels: if society considers the poor responsible for their situation and, therefore, "undeserving of help", then measures for poverty mitigation would not be supported, thwarting the efforts towards achieving the first sustainable development goal of the United Nations to end poverty (Arneson, 1997; Applebaum, 2001).

Cortina (2022) states that evolutionary pressure has resulted in innate tendencies toward the search for reciprocity, which in market economies penalizes the poor when they are perceived as benefiting from social programs while offering nothing in return. These tendencies are further aggravated in the current Western capitalist context, where wealth is a symbol of success (Fraser and Honneth, 2003). What has been described as a "tyranny of merit" (Sandel, 2020) manifests unconsciously in our speech and writing as subtle and implicit stereotyping and rejection of the poor. Such implicit biased language can be challenging for NLP

The 7th Workshop on Online Abuse and Harms (WOAH), pages 113–125
July 13, 2023

models that were not specifically trained to recognize this type of abuse (Wiegand et al., 2019; Nejadgholi et al., 2022).

To date, aporophobia has received little attention in NLP (Curto et al., 2022). In this position paper, we intend to raise awareness of this phenomenon in the community and advocate for the need to study such online behavior, its motivations and expressions, as well as its persistence and spread across online communications, and to design technologies to actively counter aporophobic attitudes. In particular, our goals are as follows:

- Characterize aporophobia as a distinct discriminatory phenomenon with significant societal impact, based on social science literature;
- Demonstrate that aporophobic attitudes are common in society and prominent in social media;
- Show that existing toxic language datasets are ill-suited for training automatic systems to address this type of prejudice due to (1) the lack of adequate sample of aporophobic instances, and (2) the failure of human annotators to recognize implicit aporophobic statements and attitudes as part of a general definition of harmful language.

The creation of resources and techniques to effectively confront aporophobia will contribute to both the safety and inclusiveness of online and offline spaces and to the effectiveness of poverty reduction efforts.

2 Societal Impact of Aporophobia

The current debate on bias and fairness mostly focuses on race and gender-based discrimination. Only recently, prejudice and bias against the poor, or aporophobia, has been described as a key distinctive discriminatory phenomenon in the social science literature (Cortina, 2022). However, international organizations have been denouncing the discrimination and criminalization of the poor for a long time (United Nations, 2018). Aporophobic attitudes have significant impact at different societal levels. At the micro (personal) level, stigmatization of the poor can inflict significant psychological harm, lead to the internalization of the continuous message of one's inferiority, and contribute to a self-fulfilling prophecy of failure (Habermas, 1990; Honneth, 1996). At the meso (institutional) level, policies for poverty reduction can be hindered by societal beliefs that the poor are responsible for their own fate and, therefore, undeserving of social assistance (Applebaum, 2001; Everatt, 2008; Nunn and Biressi, 2009). Finally, at the macro (international) level, aporophobic views are extended to blaming developing countries for their poverty, and prevent reaching fairer deals in international trade and financial markets (Reis et al., 2005; Yapa, 2002).

Aporophobia affects people across races, genders, and countries. In "Voices of the Poor," a series of publications that present poor people's own voices in 60 countries (Narayan and Petesch, 2002), a common concern has been raised that poor individuals face widespread social disapproval even from people of their own communities, races, genders, and religions. The testimonies describe situations in which "the mere fact of being poor is itself cause for being isolated, left out, looked down upon, alienated, pushed aside, and ignored by those who are better off. This ostracism and voicelessness tie together poor people's experiences across very different contexts" (Narayan and Petesch, 2002).

The impact of aporophobia is starting to be recognized by national and international organizations. Spain was the first country to include aporophobia as a distinct aggravation of hate crimes in the legal framework (Spanish Criminal Code, article 22.4), and aporophobia observatories are being created in several countries, in coordination with the United Nations. Examining and quantifying aporophobia provides NGOs and government officials with new approaches for poverty reduction policy making, acting on public awareness (in addition to redistribution of wealth) and treating poverty as a societal problem, as opposed to a problem of the poor. Mitigating aporophobia contributes to the fight against poverty for all ethnic groups and genders (Everatt, 2008) and NLP can play a key role in the identification, tracking and countering of online aporophobia.

3 Presence of Aporophobia in Twitter

In the first part of the study, we investigated the presence of aporophobia in Twitter. For this, we collected and analyzed tweets containing terms related to 'poor people' and contrasted them with tweets related to 'rich people'. Then, we performed topic modeling on tweets mentioning the group

giftofhome, encampments, encampment, sauda, dera, unsheltered, sacha, nudist, ***defecating, feces****, blankets, shelters,* ***druggies****, sidewalk,* ***crackheads, addicts****, doorways, tents, shelter, hostels, sidewalks, vagrants, gurmeet,* ***needles****, evicting, rahim, sweeps, sleepers, tent, vets, skid,* ***junkies****, toothless, outreach, camping, sacramento, sindh,* ***schizophrenic****, portland, panhandling,* ***pooping****, hobo, evict, motel, fatherless,* ***sodom****, hud, isaiah, evicted, housed,* ***addict****, motels, veterans, servicemen, fran, denver, camps, hemp, pdx, cashapp, eviction, downtown, accommodation,* ***meth****, seattle, subways, depape, streets,* ***junkie****, brettfavre, chinatown, unhoused, ebt, shalt, venice, hostel, freeway, newsom, sheltering, francisco, benches,* ***overdoses****, surfing, huddled, rv,* ***overdose****, reverend, homelessness, euthanasia,* ***addictions, heroin****, stray, houseless, belongings, cardboard, rendered,* ***urine, alcoholics****, favre, evictions*

Table 1: Top 100 words with the highest PMI-based association score (Eq. 1) for the group 'poor'. The words are presented in the decreasing order of the association score. The scores for the shown words range between 9.18 and 3.32. Words related to substance abuse, mental disorders, and health and environmental hazards associated with the homeless population are in bold.

'poor' and examined topics related to aporophobia. In the following, we discuss these steps in detail.

3.1 Tweet Collection

We polled the Twitter API to collect English tweets for a period of three months, from 25 August 2022 to 23 November 2022, using query terms related to poor and homeless people. The initial set of query terms was assembled from the social science literature on the "undeserving poor" (Everatt, 2008; Narayan and Petesch, 2002; Applebaum, 2001) and aporophobia (Cortina, 2022; Comim et al., 2020). The set was expanded with synonyms and related terms. Then, a one-week sample of tweets collected using this set of terms was manually examined. Terms that resulted in very small numbers of retrieved tweets or in many irrelevant tweets were discarded. We also excluded explicitly offensive and derogatory terms, such as *trailer trash, scrounger*, or *redneck*, which tend to be used in personal insults. The final list of query terms for the group 'poor' was: *the poor* (used as a noun as opposed to an adjective as in 'the poor performance'), *poor people, poor ppl, poor folks, poor families, homeless, on welfare, welfare recipients, low-income, underprivileged, disadvantaged, lower class.*

As a contrasting set, we also collected tweets related to the group 'rich' using the following query terms: *the rich* (used as a noun), *rich people, rich ppl, rich kids, rich men, rich folks, rich guys, rich elites, rich families, wealthy, well-off, upper-class, upper class, millionaires, billionaires, elite class, privileged, executives.* The single words *poor* and *rich* were not part of the search due to their polysemy (e.g., 'poor results', 'rich dessert'). Using the selected terms, we were able to collect a large amount of relevant tweets without costly manual filtering.

We excluded re-tweets, tweets with URLs to external websites, tweets with more than five hashtags, and tweets from user accounts that have the word *bot* in their user or screen names. This filtering step helped to remove advertisements, spam, news headlines, and so on. Further, tweets containing query terms from both 'poor' and 'rich' groups were also excluded. In the remaining tweets, user mentions were replaced with '@user' and query terms were masked with '<target>' to reduce the bias from the query terms in the analysis. In total, there were 1.3M tweets for the group 'poor' and 1.8M tweets for the group 'rich'.

3.2 Word Analysis

Words which are often used in tweets describing 'poor people', but rarely used in tweets describing 'rich people', are expected to be the most representative words associated with the group 'poor'. Thus, we calculated the score of association with the group 'poor' using the following formula:

$$s\,(w) = PMI\,(w, C_{poor}) - PMI\,(w, C_{rich}) \quad (1)$$

where PMI stands for Pointwise Mutual Information and was calculated as follows:

$$PMI\,(w, C) = log_2\,\frac{freq\,(w, C) * N(T)}{freq\,(w, T) * N(C)} \quad (2)$$

where $freq\,(w, C)$ is the number of times the word w occurs in corpus C, $freq\,(w, T)$ is the number of times the word w occurs in corpus $T = C_{poor} \cup C_{rich}$, $N(C)$ is the total number of words in corpus C, and $N(T)$ is the total number of words in corpus T. Stopwords and low-frequency ($<$ 300 occurrences in C_{poor}) words were disregarded.

Table 1 shows 100 words with the highest association to the group 'poor'. Note that these words include many terms related to alcohol and drug abuse (e.g., *addicts, meth, alcoholics*) and mental disorders (*schizophrenic*). Many tweeters also complained about unsanitary environments often

Topic words	# of tweets in topic	Example tweets
drug, addicts, mental, drugs, mentally, ill, addiction, health, addicted, addict	9,705	Homeless men are homeless because they are on drugs, got charges, are violent and up to no good. Most homeless are mentally ill, just put them into a home for the mentally ill.
crime, police, cops, criminals, jail, crimes, prison, arrest, commit, criminal	5,807	Crimes committed by the homeless against non-homeless or other homeless people occur weekly in our city. Put the homeless in jail and make work camps.
war, military, wars, army, soldiers, fight, join, recruitment, peace, die	1,687	The military preys on poor people to fight their wars. No rich kids go to war. They need more poor people to sign up to die for the state.
drunk, beer, drink, drinking, alcohol, cigarette, drunks, drinks, liquor, smoking	882	Poor folks can't run without alcohol. Drinks and deadbeat are the most beloved members of poor families.
fear, scared, scary, anxiety, afraid, terrified, scare, terrifying, fears, mongering	680	There are more homeless creeps hanging around a bicycle path than ever. People are scared they might need to walk past a homeless person when going to the mall.

Table 2: Examples of tweets expressing or discussing aporophobic views. The tweet texts were paraphrased to protect the privacy of the users.

surrounding homeless encampments and city sidewalks occupied by homeless people. Further, *euthanasia* appears in this list since many users were concerned (or some users supported) that it could become a solution to end the suffering of the poor.

3.3 Topic Modeling

Next, we analyzed the thematic content of tweets mentioning the group 'poor'. For this, we employed an unsupervised topic modeling toolkit, BERTopic (Grootendorst, 2022). The core component of BERTopic is a density-based clustering technique HDBSCAN (Campello et al., 2013), which can produce clusters of arbitrary shapes and leave documents that do not fit any clusters as outliers. This suited our case well as we wanted to discover the most commonly discussed topics in tweets mentioning poor people. The discovered topics are then represented with topic words, which are identified using class-based TF-IDF (c-TF-IDF). The 'topic words' are the words that tend to appear frequently in the topic of interest, and less frequently in the other topics.

To reduce computational costs, we applied topic modeling on a random subsample of 600K sentences from C_{poor}. For converting text to numerical representations, we used the sentence transformers method based on the *all-MiniLM-L6-v2* pre-trained embedding model.[1] For the vectorizer model, we used the CountVectorizer method,[2] and removed English stopwords and terms that appeared in less than 5% of the sentences ($min\_df = 0.05$). For the HDBSCAN clustering algorithm, we specified the minimum size of the clusters as $min\_cluster\_size = 500$. For all the other parameters, the default settings of the BERTopic package were used.

There were 142 topics extracted. We found a number of expected topics discussing the issues of homeless encampments in city parks and streets, the lack of affordable housing, the need to provide shelter and free meals to the homeless, (un)fair distribution of taxes among the socio-economic classes, Christian dogmas of helping the poor, criticism or support of government policies, and various related local issues. We also observed a number of topics with more derogatory and vilifying attitudes, portraying the poor, and especially the homeless, as drug addicts, drunkards, criminals, mentally disabled, and expendable, or expressing general feelings of fear and rejection of the group. Table 2 shows example tweets for some of these topics. Several topics tie the issues of poverty and homelessness with specific communities, such as Black people, immigrants and refugees, and veterans. Not all tweets on these topics express aporophobic views. Some report aporophobic situations, and many actually oppose such attitudes and criticize individuals and policies that hurt the poor. However, even when stereotypes are negated (e.g., 'not all homeless people are drug addicts'), the syntactic form preserves the stereotype-consistent

[1] https://www.sbert.net/docs/pretrained_models.html

[2] https://scikit-learn.org/stable/modules/generated/sklearn.feature_extraction.text.CountVectorizer.html

information (here: 'all homeless people are drug addicts'), confirming the stereotypic association (Beukeboom and Burgers, 2019). That is, the existence of such counter-speech is indirect evidence that such stereotypes and biases exist.

4 Unsuitability of Existing Datasets for Studying Aporophobia

Groups based on socio-economic status have been mostly overlooked in NLP research on toxic and biased language. Current lexicons designed to identify various types of social biases do not usually include status or socio-economic class categories, and in rare cases when they do, these lexicons are not tailored to identify aporophobia (Nicolas et al., 2021; Kozlowski et al., 2019; Smith et al., 2022).

Most existing datasets collected for specific targets of abuse (e.g., women, immigrants) do not include poor and low-income subpopulations as a target, with the exception of the dataset for patronizing and condensending language by Perez Almendros et al. (2020). To investigate whether these groups appear in datasets collected to study general toxicity (and its various forms), we examined nine frequently used, large, English-language toxicity datasets:

1. Civil Comments Dataset (Borkan et al., 2019): a dataset of public comments from English-language news sites annotated through crowd-sourcing for toxicity and six toxicity subtypes (severe toxicity, obscene, threat, insult, identity attack, and sexual explicit) with real-valued scores that represent the fraction of annotators who assigned the category to the comment. We considered a comment 'toxic' if it had score > 0.5 for at least one of the seven toxic categories.

2. Wiki Toxicity (Wulczyn et al., 2017): a dataset of comments from Wikipedia talk page edits annotated through crowd-sourcing for six categories of toxicity: toxic, severe toxic, obscene, threat, insult, and identity attack. We considered a comment 'toxic' if it was labeled with any of the six categories of toxicity.

3. Abusive and Hateful tweet corpus by Founta et al. (2018): a large corpus of tweets annotated through crowd-sourcing for hateful, abusive, spam, and normal language. We considered a tweet 'toxic' if it was labeled as 'hateful' or 'abusive'.

4. Social Bias Inference Corpus (SBIC) (Sap et al., 2020): a collection of tweets, Reddit posts, posts from the hate communities Stormfront and Gab, and posts from a corpus of microaggressions annotated through crowd-sourcing for offensiveness, intent to offend, sexual content, target group, whether the speaker is part of the target group, and the implied statement. We considered a text 'toxic' if it was labeled as 'offensive'.

5. Unhealthy Comments Corpus (Price et al., 2020): a dataset of public comments from the Globe and Mail news website annotated through crowd-sourcing for 'healthy' vs. 'unhealthy' and for six potentially 'unhealthy' categories: (1) hostile; (2) antagonistic, insulting, provocative or trolling; (3) dismissive; (4) condescending or patronising; (5) sarcastic; and (6) an unfair generalisation. We considered a comment 'toxic' if it was labeled as 'unhealthy'.

6. Hate Speech and Offensive Language tweet corpus by Davidson et al. (2017): a dataset of tweets annotated through crowd-sourcing for three categories: (1) hate speech, (2) offensive language, and (3) neither hate speech nor offensive. We considered a tweet 'toxic' if it was labeled as either 'hate speech' or 'offensive language'.

7. Contextual Abuse Dataset (CAD) (Vidgen et al., 2021): a dataset of posts and comments from Reddit annotated for identity-directed abuse, affiliation-directed abuse, person-directed abuse, counter-speech, non-hateful slurs, and neutral. The annotations were done by two annotators, and the disagreements were resolved through an expert-driven group adjudication process. We considered a text 'toxic' if it was labeled as 'identity-directed abuse', 'affiliation-directed abuse', or 'person-directed abuse'.

8. Offensive Language Identification Dataset (OLID) (Zampieri et al., 2019a): a dataset of tweets annotated through crowd-sourcing for offensiveness (offensive or not), type of offense (targeted insult or untargeted), and target of offense (individual, group, or other). We considered a tweet 'toxic' if it was labeled as 'offensive'.

Dataset	Data source	Categories considered 'toxic'	Total # of instances	# of instances mentioning 'poor'	
				all classes	'toxic'
Civil Comments	news site comments	score > 0.5 for 'toxicity' or its subtype	1,999,515	19,140	867
Wiki Toxicity	Wikipedia comments	toxic, severe toxic, obscene, threat, insult, identity attack	312,735	168	7
Abusive and Hateful tweets	Twitter	hateful, abusive	99,996	51	9
SBIC	Twitter, Reddit, Stormfront, Gab, microaggressions	offensive	44,875	68	60
Unhealthy Comments	news site comments	unhealthy	44,355	81	3
Hate Speech and Offensive tweets	Twitter	hate speech, offensive	24,783	16	13
CAD	Reddit	identity-directed abuse, affiliation-directed abuse, person-directed abuse	23,417	84	17
OLID	Twitter	offensive	14,100	16	3
HASOC-2019	Twitter, Facebook	hate speech, offensive, profanity	7,005	19	6

Table 3: Number of instances containing the query terms for the group 'poor' in nine toxic language datasets. Train/dev/test splits for each dataset were merged.

9. HASOC-2019 (Mandl et al., 2019): a dataset of tweets and Facebook posts annotated by its creators for hate speech, offensive content, and profanity, and whether the offense is targeted or untargeted. We considered a tweet 'toxic' if it was labeled as 'hate speech', 'offensive', or 'profanity'.

(More details on the datasets are provided in Appendix A.) We did not consider datasets annotated exclusively for hate speech since socio-economic status is not considered an attribute that defines a protected group in legal terms and, therefore, none of the existing hate speech datasets include the group 'poor' as a target in their definitions of hate speech.

We used the same query terms for the group 'poor' that we used in Sec. 3. Table 3 shows the number of instances containing these terms in the selected datasets.[3] While the sizes of the datasets vary from a few thousand to two million, most contain only a few dozen instances mentioning the group 'poor', and only a handful of these instances are labeled as toxic/offensive.[4] These datasets tend to be collected using query terms that frequently occur in toxic content targeting groups based on gender, ethnicity, or religion, and thus may not capture toxic content about poor people. The only noticeable exception is the Civil Comments dataset that includes over 19K instances mentioning the group 'poor'. This is due to its size and to the fact that it comprises *all* online news comments collected through the Civil Comments platform, without any filtering. Notice, however, that the overwhelming majority of the messages mentioning the group 'poor' (over 95%) are labeled as non-toxic. This further demonstrates that topics related to poor people are frequently discussed online, but this group is rarely a target of NLP studies on toxicity.

In the Civil Comments dataset, toxicity was defined as 'general incivility that would likely prompt users to leave the discussion.' Not all instances mentioning the group 'poor' and originally labeled as 'toxic' are aporophobic as they can target other entities. We manually examined the Civil Comments test set for aporophobia, which we defined as 'explicit or implicit expressions of rejection, aversion, or contempt towards poor or homeless people'. First, we looked at the instances originally labeled as 'toxic'. Among 11,701 such instances in the test set, only 93 instances mention the group 'poor', and only 21 of them are instances of aporophobia. This clearly demonstrates that existing datasets do not contain a sufficient sample of aporophobia for classifiers to effectively learn the concept.

[3]Since SBIC has the targeted group explicitly labeled, we searched for words *poor*, *poverty*, and *homeless* in the targeted group description.

[4]Most instances mentioning the group 'poor' in SBIC are labeled 'toxic' as the majority of these instances are jokes collected from intentionally offensive subReddits.

Next, we examined instances of the Civil Comments test set originally labeled as 'non-toxic' by all of the annotators (i.e., with score of zero for all seven toxic categories). We manually annotated a random sample of 300 instances mentioning the group 'poor' and originally labeled 'non-toxic', and found 54 (18%) instances of aporophobia.[5] This indicates that aporophobic views can be expressed very subtly and are deeply rooted in our society so that none of the annotators considered these texts toxic.

To further demonstrate the unsuitability of the existing toxic language datasets for modeling aporophobia, we evaluated the performance of three publicly available, high-quality pre-trained RoBERTa-based toxicity prediction models on these aporophobic instances:

1. Detoxify[6] (Hanu and Unitary team, 2020): an open-source multi-class model fine-tuned on the Civil Comments dataset;
2. Wiki+Civil[7]: a binary toxicity model fine-tuned on the combination of the Wiki Toxicity and Civil Comments datasets;
3. TweetEval[8] (Barbieri et al., 2020): a RoBERTa-based model trained on 58M English tweets and fine-tuned on the OLID dataset.

Table 4 shows the recall these models achieve on the aporophobic instances originally labeled as either 'toxic' or 'non-toxic', i.e., the percentage of the aporophobic instances for which the models predicted the toxicity score > 0.5. For comparison, we also show precision and recall for the Toxic class these models achieve on the full Civil Comments test set. Observe that while the models demonstrate good overall performance on the test set and moderate to high recall on aporophobic instances originally labeled as 'toxic', they all fail to recognize aporophobia in more implicit instances that also proved challenging for human annotators. Overall, we conclude that the existing toxic language datasets are ill-suited for training effective models for aporophobia detection, and new datasets specifically targeting this phenomenon are urgently needed.

Model	Full test set		Recall on aporophobia	
	Prec.	Recall	'toxic'	'non-toxic'
Detoxify	0.57	0.83	0.57	0
Wiki+Civil	0.58	0.86	0.67	0.02
TweetEval	0.31	0.85	0.86	0.07

Table 4: Performance of three classification models on the Civil Comments test set (194,641 instances) and aporophobic instances originally labeled as 'toxic' (21 instances) or 'non-toxic' (54 instances) in the test set.

5 Discussion

Our exploratory analysis of tweets revealed a significant presence of aporophobic views expressed or confronted by the users. Since only a small percentage of people with low income use Twitter (at least in the U.S., the country with the highest number of Twitter users),[9] the views and opinions about this group come mostly from the out-group. Many users felt the need to dispute stereotypical beliefs and discriminatory actions against the poor and the homeless populations, indicating that such views are prevalent in social media and offline. Since aporophobia has not received the same attention as other types of discrimination (e.g., based on race or gender), and since it often manifests in subtle and implicit rejection or contempt, aporophobic language may not be perceived as hateful or threatening. Nevertheless, it can cause human suffering and jeopardize initiatives to fight poverty, since poverty reduction policies may not be supported when the persons in need are being blamed for their situation (Arneson, 1997).

In a context where the United Nations is calling for urgent action to end poverty, NLP techniques allow for a novel view to inform poverty reduction policies by measuring and tracking the various manifestations of aporophobia. Such instances can be organized according to the levels of negative action associated with prejudices, documented in cognitive science as avoidance, antilocution, discrimination and physical attack (Allport, 1954), at micro (individual), meso (institutional), and macro (national) levels (Comim et al., 2020). Furthermore, bias and discrimination have traditionally been studied for individual dimensions (e.g., gen-

[5]Similarly, we found instances originally labeled 'non-toxic' that contain aporophobic views in the CAD (6 out of 65) and Unhealthy Comments (11 out of 78 instances).

[6]https://huggingface.co/unitary/unbiased-toxic-roberta

[7]https://huggingface.co/SkolkovoInstitute/roberta_toxicity_classifier

[8]https://huggingface.co/cardiffnlp/twitter-roberta-base-offensive

[9]https://www.pewresearch.org/internet/2021/04/07/social-media-use-in-2021/

der, race, etc.) (Hoffmann, 2019). Yet, different types of biases are often intertwined and aggravate one another (Lalor et al., 2022). Aporophobia can be incorporated in the intersectional view of bias and discrimination, with complex interrelations with racism, sexism, and xenophobia.

But while NLP techniques may be valuable in measuring aporophobic attitudes in written communications—such as news articles, social media, and educational material—current models, lexicons, and datasets are inadequate to effectively address this problem. In addition, expressions of aporophobia cannot simply be banned from public view. Alternative strategies for countering aporophobia and mitigating its harms need to be developed. Counter-speech and public awareness, as well as institutional and government policies, are some of the tools to reduce prejudice and discrimination against the poor. The NLP community can play a major role in developing such mechanisms in collaboration with social scientists and policy makers.

6 Conclusion and Future Work

Aporophobia is pervasive and entrenched in society, yet so far has been overlooked in NLP research on toxic language. This preliminary study indicates that existing toxic language datasets do not support the development of models for detecting and countering this type of societal bias, and new resources and methods need to be designed and built. However, since toxic and abusive language (including aporophobia) is a relatively rare phenomenon in online communications, random data sampling might be inefficient to collect appropriate amounts of aporophobic statements to characterize the phenomenon in language (Schmidt and Wiegand, 2017; Founta et al., 2018). Yet, other sampling techniques (e.g., keyword-based, content written by specific users) aiming at increasing the proportion of toxic messages can result in biased data distributions and learnt spurious correlations (Wiegand et al., 2019). Future work should address the problem of collecting data that adequately represents the phenomenon of aporophobia. Further, practical annotation guidelines and annotator training programs need to be developed to ensure that annotators have a proper understanding of aporophobia as a concept and can effectively recognize its explicit and implicit manifestations.

An aporophobia index (Comim et al., 2020), built and updated by tracking aporophobic views and actions reported or confronted on social media, can help government and non-governmental organizations analyze the trends of this phenomenon and correlate them with economic indicators on poverty and inequality. Such an aporophobia index, offering regular updates on aporophobia levels for different geographic locations, would provide valuable insights to tackle poverty as a societal problem, as opposed to a problem of the poor, and define alternative poverty reduction strategies that act on public awareness.

Research in this field is therefore critical for instrumental reasons: currently 685M people (10% of the total world population) still live in extreme poverty and the COVID-19 pandemic could make poverty levels increase by up to 8.3% (United Nations, 2022). Poverty is a worldwide problem that affects not only developing countries, but also a significant percentage of the population in thriving economies: for example, in the US, 37.9 million people live in poverty (Creamer et al., 2022). But fighting aporophobia is also essential because of intrinsic reasons: "Recognition of equal dignity and compassion is the key to an ethics of cordial reason and is indispensable to the overcoming of inhumane discrimination" (Cortina, 2022).

7 Limitations

In this exploratory study, we focused on English-language resources. Further, we examined only one social media platform, Twitter. As any other platform, Twitter has a biased demographic representation of users in terms of language, location, ethnicity, gender, age, socio-economic status, and other characteristics. In particular, Twitter is predominantly used in the United States.[10] As a result, user attitudes examined in this study primarily represent Western views and may differ significantly from views common in other regions of the world. Future studies on aporophobia need to include other languages and world regions and consider cultural differences while measuring and mitigating this type of social bias.

When searching for aporophobia-related texts, we excluded derogatory terms and slurs associated with the group 'poor' as such explicit forms of online abuse tend to be easier to detect by human

[10] https://www.statista.com/statistics/242606/number-of-active-twitter-users-in-selected-countries/

annotators and NLP models. Nevertheless, when designing tools for measuring and mitigating aporophobia such explicit expressions need to be taken into account. Furthermore, there is a wide variety of linguistic expressions referring to poor and homeless people, and sometimes this target group is not even mentioned at all, but could be inferred from the context (e.g., contexts referring to hunger, food stamps and/or other benefits, ghettos, etc.). To effectively confront aporophobia, NLP resources (lexicons, datasets, classification models) need to have a wide coverage of explicit and implicit linguistic expressions of the phenomenon.

Finally, we targeted only textual data. However, many social media posts combine text with other types of data, such as images and videos. Recent techniques for modeling multi-modal data can be employed to ensure a better coverage of various types of social media posts.

Ethics Statement

Confronting aporophobia, as an application similar to addressing other types of abusive and toxic language, poses a number of risks and ethical issues, including tension between freedom of speech and respect for equality and dignity, biased data sampling and data annotation, dual use, and many others, discussed in previous works by Hovy and Spruit (2016); Vidgen et al. (2019); Leins et al. (2020); Vidgen and Derczynski (2020); Cortiz and Zubiaga (2020); Kiritchenko et al. (2021); Salminen et al. (2021). Future research on this topic should comply with trustworthy AI principles of transparency, justice and fairness, non-maleficence, responsibility, and privacy (Jobin et al., 2019). Special attention should be paid to involving all legitimate stakeholders in the identification and definition of actions to counteract aporophobia, including the affected communities, non-governmental organizations (NGOs) and government officials working on poverty mitigation. In particular, the views and needs of the communities from both the Global North and the Global South should be included.

References

Alberto Alesina, Stefanie Stantcheva, and Edoardo Teso. 2018. Intergenerational Mobility and Preferences for Redistribution. *American Economic Review*, 108(2):521–54.

Gordon W Allport. 1954. *The Nature of Prejudice*. Basic Books.

Lauren D Applebaum. 2001. The influence of perceived deservingness on policy decisions regarding aid to the poor. *Political Psychology*, 22(3):419–442.

Richard J Arneson. 1997. Egalitarianism and the undeserving poor. *Journal of Political Philosophy*, 5(4):327–350.

Francesco Barbieri, Jose Camacho-Collados, Luis Espinosa Anke, and Leonardo Neves. 2020. TweetEval: Unified benchmark and comparative evaluation for tweet classification. In *Findings of the Association for Computational Linguistics: EMNLP 2020*, pages 1644–1650, Online. Association for Computational Linguistics.

Camiel J Beukeboom and Christian Burgers. 2019. How stereotypes are shared through language: A review and introduction of the social categories and stereotypes communication (SCSC) framework. *Review of Communication Research*, 7:1–37.

Daniel Borkan, Lucas Dixon, Jeffrey Sorensen, Nithum Thain, and Lucy Vasserman. 2019. Nuanced metrics for measuring unintended bias with real data for text classification. In *Companion Proceedings of The 2019 World Wide Web Conference*, pages 491—500.

Luke Breitfeller, Emily Ahn, David Jurgens, and Yulia Tsvetkov. 2019. Finding microaggressions in the wild: A case for locating elusive phenomena in social media posts. In *Proceedings of the 2019 Conference on Empirical Methods in Natural Language Processing and the 9th International Joint Conference on Natural Language Processing (EMNLP-IJCNLP)*, pages 1664–1674, Hong Kong, China. Association for Computational Linguistics.

Ricardo JGB Campello, Davoud Moulavi, and Jörg Sander. 2013. Density-based clustering based on hierarchical density estimates. In *Proceedings of the Pacific–Asia Conference on Knowledge Discovery and Data Mining*, pages 160–172. Springer.

Lucas Chancel and Thomas Piketty. 2021. Global income inequality, 1820-2020: The persistence and mutation of extreme inequality. *Journal of the European Economic Association*.

Raj Chetty, Nathaniel Hendren, Patrick Kline, Emmanuel Saez, and Nicholas Turner. 2014. Is the United States Still a Land of Opportunity? Recent Trends in Intergenerational Mobility. *American Economic Review*, 104(5):141–47.

Flavio Comim, Mihály Tamás Borsi, and Octasiano Valerio Mendoza. 2020. The multi-dimensions of aporophobia.

Adela Cortina. 2022. *Aporophobia: Why We Reject the Poor Instead of Helping Them*. Princeton University Press.

Diogo Cortiz and Arkaitz Zubiaga. 2020. Ethical and technical challenges of AI in tackling hate speech. *The International Review of Information Ethics*, 29.

John Creamer, Emily A Shrider, Kalee Burns, and Frances Chen. 2022. Poverty in the United States: 2021. *US Census Bureau*.

Georgina Curto, Mario Fernando Jojoa Acosta, Flavio Comim, and Begoña Garcia-Zapirain. 2022. Are AI systems biased against the poor? a machine learning analysis using Word2Vec and GloVe embeddings. *AI & Society*, pages 1–16.

Thomas Davidson, Dana Warmsley, Michael Macy, and Ingmar Weber. 2017. Automated hate speech detection and the problem of offensive language. In *Proceedings of the International AAAI Conference on Web and Social Media*, pages 512–515.

David Everatt. 2008. The undeserving poor: poverty and the politics of service delivery in the poorest nodes of South Africa. *Politikon*, 35(3):293–319.

Joseph Fishkin. 2014. *Bottlenecks: A New Theory of Equal Opportunity*. Oxford University Press, USA.

Paula Fortuna and Sérgio Nunes. 2018. A survey on automatic detection of hate speech in text. *ACM Computing Surveys (CSUR)*, 51(4):1–30.

Antigoni Maria Founta, Constantinos Djouvas, Despoina Chatzakou, Ilias Leontiadis, Jeremy Blackburn, Gianluca Stringhini, Athena Vakali, Michael Sirivianos, and Nicolas Kourtellis. 2018. Large scale crowdsourcing and characterization of Twitter abusive behavior. In *Proceedings of the 12th International AAAI Conference on Web and Social Media*.

Nancy Fraser and Axel Honneth. 2003. *Redistribution or recognition? A political–philosophical exchange*. Verso Books.

Maarten Grootendorst. 2022. BERTopic: Neural topic modeling with a class-based TF-IDF procedure. *arXiv preprint arXiv:2203.05794*.

Jürgen Habermas. 1990. *Moral consciousness and communicative action*. MIT press.

Laura Hanu and Unitary team. 2020. Detoxify. Github. https://github.com/unitaryai/detoxify.

Zenia Hellgren and Lorenzo Gabrielli. 2021. Racialization and aporophobia: Intersecting discriminations in the experiences of non-western migrants and Spanish Roma. *Social Sciences*, 10(5):163.

Anna Lauren Hoffmann. 2019. Where fairness fails: Data, algorithms, and the limits of antidiscrimination discourse. *Information, Communication & Society*, 22(7):900–915.

Axel Honneth. 1996. *The struggle for recognition: The moral grammar of social conflicts*. MIT press.

Dirk Hovy and Shannon L. Spruit. 2016. The social impact of natural language processing. In *Proceedings of the 54th Annual Meeting of the Association for Computational Linguistics (Volume 2: Short Papers)*, pages 591–598, Berlin, Germany. Association for Computational Linguistics.

Anna Jobin, Marcello Ienca, and Effy Vayena. 2019. The global landscape of AI ethics guidelines. *Nature Machine Intelligence*, 1:389–399.

Svetlana Kiritchenko, Isar Nejadgholi, and Kathleen C Fraser. 2021. Confronting abusive language online: A survey from the ethical and human rights perspective. *Journal of Artificial Intelligence Research*, 71:431–478.

Varada Kolhatkar, Hanhan Wu, Luca Cavasso, Emilie Francis, Kavan Shukla, and Maite Taboada. 2020. The SFU opinion and comments corpus: A corpus for the analysis of online news comments. *Corpus Pragmatics*, 4(2):155–190.

Austin C Kozlowski, Matt Taddy, and James A Evans. 2019. The geometry of culture: Analyzing the meanings of class through word embeddings. *American Sociological Review*, 84(5):905–949.

John P. Lalor, Yi Yang, Kendall Smith, Nicole Forsgren, and Ahmed Abbasi. 2022. Benchmarking Intersectional Biases in NLP. *Proceedings of the 2022 Conference of the North American Chapter of the Association for Computational Linguistics: Human Language Technologies*, pages 3598–3609.

Kobi Leins, Jey Han Lau, and Timothy Baldwin. 2020. Give me convenience and give her death: Who should decide what uses of NLP are appropriate, and on what basis? In *Proceedings of the 58th Annual Meeting of the Association for Computational Linguistics*, pages 2908–2913, Online. Association for Computational Linguistics.

Thomas Mandl, Sandip Modha, Prasenjit Majumder, Daksh Patel, Mohana Dave, Chintak Mandlia, and Aditya Patel. 2019. Overview of the HASOC track at FIRE 2019: Hate speech and offensive content identification in Indo-European languages. In *Proceedings of the 11th Forum for Information Retrieval Evaluation*, pages 14–17.

Yascha Mounk. 2017. *The Age of Responsibility: Luck, Choice, and the Welfare State*. Harvard University Press.

Deepa Narayan and Patti Petesch. 2002. *Voices of the poor: From many lands*. Washington, DC: World Bank and Oxford University Press.

Isar Nejadgholi, Kathleen Fraser, and Svetlana Kiritchenko. 2022. Improving generalizability in implicitly abusive language detection with concept activation vectors. In *Proceedings of the 60th Annual Meeting of the Association for Computational Linguistics (Volume 1: Long Papers)*, pages 5517–5529, Dublin, Ireland. Association for Computational Linguistics.

Gandalf Nicolas, Xuechunzi Bai, and Susan T. Fiske. 2021. Comprehensive stereotype content dictionaries using a semi-automated method. *European Journal of Social Psychology*, 51(1):178–196.

Heather Nunn and Anita Biressi. 2009. The undeserving poor. *Soundings*, (41):107.

OECD. 2018. A Broken Social Elevator? How to Promote Social Mobility. Technical report.

Carla Perez Almendros, Luis Espinosa Anke, and Steven Schockaert. 2020. Don't patronize me! an annotated dataset with patronizing and condescending language towards vulnerable communities. In *Proceedings of the 28th International Conference on Computational Linguistics*, pages 5891–5902, Barcelona, Spain (Online). International Committee on Computational Linguistics.

Ilan Price, Jordan Gifford-Moore, Jory Flemming, Saul Musker, Maayan Roichman, Guillaume Sylvain, Nithum Thain, Lucas Dixon, and Jeffrey Sorensen. 2020. Six attributes of unhealthy conversations. In *Proceedings of the Fourth Workshop on Online Abuse and Harms*, pages 114–124, Online. Association for Computational Linguistics.

Elisa Reis, Mick Moore, Juliana Martínez Franzoni, and Thomas Pogge. 2005. *Elite perceptions of poverty and inequality*. Zed Books.

Joni Salminen, Maria Jose Linarez, Soon-gyo Jung, and Bernard J Jansen. 2021. Online hate detection systems: Challenges and action points for developers, data scientists, and researchers. In *Proceedings of the 8th International Conference on Behavioral and Social Computing (BESC)*, pages 1–7. IEEE.

Michael J Sandel. 2020. *The Tyranny of Merit: What's Become of the Common Good?* Penguin UK.

Maarten Sap, Saadia Gabriel, Lianhui Qin, Dan Jurafsky, Noah A. Smith, and Yejin Choi. 2020. Social bias frames: Reasoning about social and power implications of language. In *Proceedings of the 58th Annual Meeting of the Association for Computational Linguistics*, pages 5477–5490, Online. Association for Computational Linguistics.

Anna Schmidt and Michael Wiegand. 2017. A survey on hate speech detection using natural language processing. In *Proceedings of the Fifth International Workshop on Natural Language Processing for Social Media*, pages 1–10.

Eric Michael Smith, Melissa Hall, Melanie Kambadur, Eleonora Presani, and Adina Williams. 2022. "I'm sorry to hear that": Finding New Biases in Language Models with a Holistic Descriptor Dataset. In *Proceedings of the 2022 Conference on Empirical Methods in Natural Language Processing*, pages 9180—-9211, Abu Dhabi, United Arab Emirates.

United Nations. 2018. Report of the special rapporteur on extreme poverty and human rights on his mission to the United States of America.

United Nations. 2022. The sustainable development goals report 2022.

Bertie Vidgen and Leon Derczynski. 2020. Directions in abusive language training data, a systematic review: Garbage in, garbage out. *Plos One*, 15(12):e0243300.

Bertie Vidgen, Alex Harris, Dong Nguyen, Rebekah Tromble, Scott Hale, and Helen Margetts. 2019. Challenges and frontiers in abusive content detection. In *Proceedings of the Third Workshop on Abusive Language Online*, pages 80–93, Florence, Italy. Association for Computational Linguistics.

Bertie Vidgen, Dong Nguyen, Helen Margetts, Patricia Rossini, and Rebekah Tromble. 2021. Introducing CAD: the contextual abuse dataset. In *Proceedings of the 2021 Conference of the North American Chapter of the Association for Computational Linguistics: Human Language Technologies*, pages 2289–2303, Online. Association for Computational Linguistics.

Zeerak Waseem and Dirk Hovy. 2016. Hateful symbols or hateful people? predictive features for hate speech detection on Twitter. In *Proceedings of the NAACL Student Research Workshop*, pages 88–93, San Diego, California. Association for Computational Linguistics.

Michael Wiegand, Josef Ruppenhofer, and Thomas Kleinbauer. 2019. Detection of Abusive Language: the Problem of Biased Datasets. In *Proceedings of the 2019 Conference of the North American Chapter of the Association for Computational Linguistics: Human Language Technologies, Volume 1 (Long and Short Papers)*, pages 602–608, Minneapolis, Minnesota. Association for Computational Linguistics.

Ellery Wulczyn, Nithum Thain, and Lucas Dixon. 2017. Ex machina: Personal attacks seen at scale. In *Proceedings of the 26th International Conference on World Wide Web*, WWW '17, pages 1391–1399, Republic and Canton of Geneva, CHE. International World Wide Web Conferences Steering Committee.

Lakshman Yapa. 2002. How the discipline of geography exacerbates poverty in the third world. *Futures*, 34(1):33–46.

Marcos Zampieri, Shervin Malmasi, Preslav Nakov, Sara Rosenthal, Noura Farra, and Ritesh Kumar. 2019a. Predicting the type and target of offensive posts in social media. In *Proceedings of the 2019 Conference of the North American Chapter of the Association for Computational Linguistics: Human Language Technologies, Volume 1 (Long and Short Papers)*, pages 1415–1420, Minneapolis, Minnesota. Association for Computational Linguistics.

Marcos Zampieri, Shervin Malmasi, Preslav Nakov, Sara Rosenthal, Noura Farra, and Ritesh Kumar. 2019b. SemEval-2019 task 6: Identifying and categorizing offensive language in social media (OffensEval). In *Proceedings of the 13th International Workshop on Semantic Evaluation*, pages 75–86, Minneapolis, Minnesota, USA. Association for Computational Linguistics.

A Existing Toxicity Datasets

We used nine large, English-language, toxicity datasets:

- **Civil Comments Dataset**[11] (Borkan et al., 2019): The dataset includes public comments from about 50 English-language news sites across the world posted in 2015-2017 via the Civil Comments platform. The comments were annotated for toxicity and six toxicity subtypes (severe toxicity, obscene, threat, insult, identity attack, and sexual explicit) through crowd-sourcing. Each toxicity and toxicity subtype score is a real value which represents the fraction of annotators who believed the category applied to the given comment. The dataset is released under CC0, as is the underlying comment text, and was used in the Jigsaw Unintended Bias in Toxicity Classification Kaggle challenge.

- **Wiki Toxicity**[12] (Wulczyn et al., 2017): The dataset consists of comments from Wikipedia's talk page edits. The comments were annotated through crowd-sourcing for six categories of toxicity: toxic, severe toxic, obscene, threat, insult, and identity attack. The dataset is released under CC0, with the underlying comment text being governed by Wikipedia's CC-SA-3.0. It was used in the Jigsaw Toxic Comment Classification Kaggle challenge.

- **Abusive and Hateful Tweet Corpus by Founta et al. (2018)**[13]: This is a large corpus of tweets annotated through crowd-sourcing for hateful, abusive, spam, and normal language. The tweets were selected using a boosted random sampling technique where a random sample was complemented with tweets that showed strong negative polarity and that contained at least one offensive word. This boosting procedure helped improve the coverage of the minority (non-normal) classes since hateful and abusive tweets tend to appear quite rarely in the Twitter stream. We used an updated version of the dataset with 100K annotated tweets. The dataset is available by requesting access from the authors.

- **Social Bias Inference Corpus (SBIC)**[14] (Sap et al., 2020): The dataset contains textual instances collected from various sources: posts from three intentionally offensive subReddits (r/darkJokes, r/meanJokes, r/offensiveJokes), posts from two English subreddits that were banned for inciting violence against women (r/Incels and r/MensRights), posts from known English hate communities Stormfront and Gab, posts from a corpus of microaggressions (Breitfeller et al., 2019), and a sample of tweets from three existing English Twitter datasets created by Founta et al. (2018); Waseem and Hovy (2016); Davidson et al. (2017). Each instance was annotated via crowd-sourcing for offensiveness, intent to offend, sexual content, target group, whether the speaker is part of the target group, and the implied statement. The dataset is publicly available. We used version 2.

- **Unhealthy Comments Corpus**[15] (Price et al., 2020): The dataset includes public comments from the Globe and Mail (a large Canadian newspaper) news website randomly sampled from the SFU Opinion and Comment Corpus dataset (Kolhatkar et al., 2020). Only comments with 250 characters or less were included in the sample. The comments were annotated through crowd-sourcing for the binary category 'healthy' vs. 'unhealthy' and for the presence of six potentially 'unhealthy' categories: (1) hostile; (2) antagonistic, insulting, provocative or trolling; (3) dismissive; (4) condescending or patronising; (5) sarcastic; and (6) an unfair generalisation. All labels are binary and include confidence scores. The labels and confidence scores were obtained as aggregated answers of multiple annotators taking into account the annotators' 'trustworthiness' scores. The dataset is released under CC BY-NC-SA 4.0.

- **Hate Speech and Offensive Language Tweet Corpus by Davidson et al. (2017)**[16]: The dataset consists of tweets collected using hateful words and phrases compiled by Hatebase.org. The tweets were annotated through crowd-sourcing for three categories: (1) hate speech, (2) offensive language but not hate speech, and (3)

[11] https://www.kaggle.com/competitions/jigsaw-unintended-bias-in-toxicity-classification/data

[12] https://www.kaggle.com/competitions/jigsaw-toxic-comment-classification-challenge/data

[13] https://github.com/ENCASEH2020/hatespeech-twitter

[14] https://maartensap.com/social-bias-frames/

[15] https://github.com/conversationai/unhealthy-conversations

[16] https://github.com/t-davidson/hate-speech-and-offensive-language

neither hate speech, nor offensive. The dataset is publicly available.

- **Contextual Abuse Dataset (CAD)**[17] (Vidgen et al., 2021): The dataset contains a stratified sample of posts and comments from 16 subReddits, which were identified as likely to contain higher-than-average levels of abuse. The messages were collected over 6 months from 1st February 2019 to 31st July 2019. All posts and comments were manually annotated within the context of conversational threads for six primary categories: identity-directed abuse, affiliation-directed abuse, person-directed abuse, counter-speech, non-hateful slurs, and neutral. Each instance was assigned to one or more of the six categories. The annotations were done by two annotators, and the disagreements were resolved through an expert-driven group-adjudication process. The dataset is released under CC Attribution 4.0 International. We used version 1.1.

- **Offensive Language Identification Dataset (OLID)**[18] (Zampieri et al., 2019a): The dataset consists of tweets collected using query terms and constructions that are often included in offensive messages, such as 'you are', 'she is', 'gun control', 'MAGA', etc. The tweets were annotated via crowd-sourcing for offensiveness (offensive or not), type of offense (targeted insult or untargeted), and target of offense (individual, group, or other). The dataset is publicly available. It was used in the shared task SemEval 2019 Task 6: Identifying and Categorizing Offensive Language in Social Media (OffensEval) (Zampieri et al., 2019b), and is part of the evaluation benchmark TweetEval (Barbieri et al., 2020).

- **Hate Speech and Offensive Content Identification in Indo-European Languages (HASOC-2019)**[19] (Mandl et al., 2019): The dataset consists of Twitter and Facebook posts collected using hashtags and keywords that contained offensive content. The posts were manually annotated by the creators of the dataset for hate speech, offensive content, and profanity, and whether the offense is targeted or untargeted. The dataset is publicly available and was used in the first edition of the HASOC track at FIRE 2019. We used only the English portion of the dataset.

[17] https://zenodo.org/record/4881008#.Y6dTinbMIuU

[18] https://github.com/cardiffnlp/tweeteval

[19] https://hasocfire.github.io/hasoc/2019/dataset.html

Problematic Webpage Identification: A Trilogy of Hatespeech, Search Engines and GPT

Warning: The paper contains examples which the reader might find offensive.

Ojasvin Sood **Sandipan Dandapat**
Microsoft Corporation
{ojsood,sadandap}@microsoft.com

Abstract

In this paper, we introduce a fine-tuned transformer-based model focused on problematic webpage classification to identify webpages promoting hate and violence of various forms. Due to the unavailability of labelled problematic webpage data, first we propose a novel webpage data collection strategy which leverages well-studied short-text hate speech datasets. We have introduced a custom GPT-4 few-shot prompt annotation scheme taking various webpage features to label the prohibitively expensive webpage annotation task. The resulting annotated data is used to build our problematic webpage classification model. We report the accuracy (87.6% F1-score) of our webpage classification model and conduct a detailed comparison of it against other state-of-the-art hate speech classification model on problematic webpage identification task. Finally, we have showcased the importance of various webpage features in identifying a problematic webpage.

1 Introduction

Since the advent of the Internet, there has been a rapid rise of content being generated by both users and organisations, which has also expedited the rise of hateful and violent content. In this paper, we focus on the identification of such content within webpages on the internet. We define webpages promoting hate and violence against individuals and communities as *Problematic* webpages. These problematic webpages often affect various Search Engines, which index such webpages resulting in them showing up in the search results. Problematic webpages can be indexed by the search engine crawlers when crawling the web. The ranking models executing at the back-end of these search engines can end up showing these problematic webpages, when a user queries for something similar. This is not just limited to user queries, which are themselves having a problematic intent. Such problematic webpages can also show up in information seeking innocuous queries on sensitive topics as well. For example, there is a possibility that a hateful webpage towards black community ends up as a search result for a query: *data on black population in US*. This can lead to a bad experience for the end user, as well as spread of targeted hate against certain individuals and communities. Thus, problematic webpage classification has its applications in search engine indexing, and ranking to filter out such webpages in search engine results and stop spread of such problematic content on the internet. Problematic webpages also contribute to hate speech texts in social media as part of a post, comment. Aljebreen et al. (2021) have estimated that 21% of tweets in general have URLs shared within them. Hence, problematic webpage classification can also be additionally applied to improve hate speech detection as the URLs shared within the tweet can be an important feature to classify the underlying text.

A lot of research has happened on automatic hate speech detection, with several hate speech datasets (Mollas et al., 2022; Mathew et al., 2021; ElSherief et al., 2021; Ousidhoum et al., 2019; de Gibert et al., 2018), and models (Kim et al., 2022; Caselli et al., 2021a; Sarkar et al., 2021; Rajput et al., 2021). These data sets and models primarily focus on identifying hate and violence in short-text data in the form of posts, comments on various social media platforms. The existing hate speech models can be leveraged to identify user queries which might lead to problematic webpages showing up in the top results of a search engine. However, these model cannot be used to identify problematic webpages and remove them from the top results for such queries. Many hate speech detection models (Caselli et al., 2021b; Sarkar et al., 2021; Ousidhoum et al., 2019) replace URLs with a placeholder *URL* from the short-text before conducting hate speech detection. This indicates that the underlying information in the URL shared along with the corresponding piece

The 7th Workshop on Online Abuse and Harms (WOAH), pages 126–137
July 13, 2023

of text is lost when classifying that speech as hateful. Hence the current hate speech detection techniques are focused on a part of the boarder scope of online hate and abuse. These hate speech models do not focus on classifying webpages which are prominent in spreading hate and violence in two main forms. Firstly, problematic webpages can show up as results in search engine queries, and secondly, as part of posts, comments in popular user generated content sharing platforms. Therefore, identifying a problematic webpage is very much crucial to stop online hate. To the best of our knowledge, there has been little to no research in identifying webpages which promote hate and violence of various forms.

A webpage is a very complex object as compared to short-texts and contains a variety of associated features which includes URL, Title, Body, Links, Ads. Existing state-of-the-art hate speech detection models often are limited towards detecting shorter text-based hateful content (e.g. tweets, social media posts, reviews etc.). In this paper, we show that these existing SOTA hate speech detection models are not effective in solving the problem from the perspective of detecting problematic webpages. This is due to complex structures of webpages, large amount of context present within them, and the nature of the data used to train these hate speech models. Some of these issues can be addressed with a new classification model dedicated to identifying problematic webpages. We show that such a model trained on data created from webpages containing important features, and annotated with GPT-4 does much better than state-of-the-art hate speech detection models.

There exist a lot of challenges to build such a dataset of webpages, both collecting and annotating. Hateful, violent Webpages cannot be easily discovered and mined. Webpage is also not something that can be generated synthetically, rather can only be mined from the World Wide Web. A lot of work has happened in website classification with respect to phishing, e-commerce website classification such as (Yang et al., 2019; Bruni and Bianchi, 2019). These works primarily focus on the developing classification models and often ignore the process of mining candidate webpages to build such classifiers. This calls for a strategy to discover and mine webpages on the internet to build a comprehensive data set, and eventually build a classification model.

Annotating webpages is also a very challenging problem which requires to consider various webpage features such as URL, Title, Headings, SubHeadings, Body, Links, Ads. The problematic webpages are ever-evolving, and are very subtle while promoting hate. To address these issues, sometimes it is required to look at the entire page content which can be very long. In the webpages curated as part of this work, we observed that the webpage body contains a large number of tokens (5350 ± 205). Some webpages discussing sensitive topics in the form of news and information can be misinterpreted as problematic. Similarly, some webpages which are very subtle when promoting problematic content such as political propaganda and spreading hate against a community can be misinterpreted as non-problematic. Hence, it is a complex task that requires a lot of time and attention for a human judge to annotate these webpages. This is a major challenge making it very difficult to build a large scale annotated problematic webpage data set. Therefore, we plan to use GPT-4 (OpenAI, 2023) to annotate these webpages at larger scale, as it has been observed that it exhibits strikingly close to human-level performance on complex benchmark tasks (Bubeck et al., 2023). It is difficult to use GPT-4 as a classifier on its own due the scalability issue towards annotating billions of webpages. Thus, we use GPT-4 to annotate a significant amount of data to train a reasonably accurate classifier which further can be used in scale for labelling large volume of webpages.

Therefore in this paper, we focus on creating a fine-tuned Transformer-based (Vaswani et al., 2017) webpage classification model focused on webpage text features: *URL*, *Title*, *Headings* and *Paragraph Texts* to identify problematic webpages promoting harmful content. We present a novel webpage data collection and annotation strategy, and use that to create the training, validation, and measurement set which can help future research in this area. We will release all the data publicly upon the acceptance of the paper.

The main contribution of the paper are as follows:

- We propose a novel strategy to create dataset in any webpage classification tasks using short-text dataset available (often easily) for the similar tasks and search engines.

- We also developed a precise few shot GPT-4

prompt to annotate harmful webpages using various features from the webpage.

- We have created a comprehensive and diverse data set which will be useful in future research in problematic webpage classification.
- We have fine-tuned a Transformer-based model for classifying problematic webpages with a reasonably good quality with F1-score of 87.6%.

2 Data Collection and Annotation Process

As mentioned in the previous section, there are many challenges in creating an annotated problematic webpages dataset. Some such problems include: discovering potential candidate webpages from the internet, annotating webpages which are often comprised of large volume of text and has rich meta information, and feature extraction to appropriately represent the webpage. We propose a novel solution to discover candidate webpages by leveraging popular search engines. For feature extractions, we have used popular web scraping tools, and also processed the input data to create important features (cf. Section 2.1). The webpage annotation (cf. Section 2.2) using GPT-4 takes care of the complex structure and longer token sequence. Algorithm 1 illustrates the data curation and annotation process. The details of the steps are described in the following subsections.

Algorithm 1 Webpage Data Collection & Annotation

Input:

$HSData = \{ H_1, H_2, \ldots \}$

$SearchEngines = \{ Google, Bing \}$

Output:

$W = \{ (U_1, T_1, B_1), (U_2, T_2, B_2), \ldots \}$ //W indicates set of webpages, U indicates URL, T indicates Title, B indicates BodyText,

$O = \{ (W_1, L_1), (W_2, L_2), \ldots \}$ //L indicates Label, 0 indicates Output

1: **for** H_i in $HSData$ **do**
2:     **for** S_j in $SearchEngines$ **do**
3:         $H_i \leftarrow$ Preprocess(H_i)
4:         $U_{i,j} \leftarrow S_j(H_i)$
5:         U.Add($U_{i,j}$)
6:     **end for**
7: **end for**
8: $U \leftarrow$ Unique(U)
9: $W \leftarrow$ Scraping(U)
10: $O_D \leftarrow$ DomainLabelling(W)
11: $O_G \leftarrow$ GPT(W)
12: $O \leftarrow \{O_D, O_G\}$

2.1 Webpage Data Curation

Webpage data curation starts with collecting existing hate speech short-text data sets (refereed as *HSData* in step 1 of the algorithm) dealing with different forms of hate and violence. We curated multiple data sets published in this field such as those described in (Mollas et al., 2022; de Gibert et al., 2018; ElSherief et al., 2021; Davidson et al., 2017; Kennedy et al., 2020). Each of these public data can be consider as one data point H_i. In the step 3, we therefore pre-process the data to remove unnecessary spaces, non-ASCII characters and stop words in *Preprocess*() function.

We use popular search engines to mine webpages using the short-text hate speech data. The intuition behind using search engine comes from the sophisticated indexing, ranking which often helps in retrieving relevant webpages Das and Jain (2012). This makes search engines well suited to mine relevant webpages given some related short-text data. In Step 4, the pre-processed short-text hatespeech data (H_i) is queried against popular web search engines (S_j) by leveraging their APIs from Google,[1] and Bing,[2] to mine the top 10 webpages $U_{i,j}$ for these pre-processed queries(H_i) using search engine S_j. The URLs $U_{i,j}$ mined in the above steps (step 1 to 7) are then de-duplicated in Step 8. The number of unique URLs mined from these search engines for each of the short-text datasets are shown in Table 1.

Dataset	#Texts	#Webpages
Davidson et al. (2017)	20620	80342
Mollas et al. (2022)	433	2145
de Gibert et al. (2018)	1196	6783
ElSherief et al. (2021)	8188	45321
Kennedy et al. (2020)	14170	64765

Table 1: Distribution of Curated & Annotated Webpages

We extract webpage features in Step 9 using *Scraping*(), to accurately represent a webpage. The

[1] https://developers.google.com/custom-search

[2] https://www.microsoft.com/en-us/bing/apis/bing-web-search-api

extracted features included in our work are *URL, Title, Headings, SubHeadings, Paragraph Texts*. We have leveraged open source python libraries such as Selenium,[3] Beautiful Soup,[4] to scrape these URLs. The extracted *Headings, Subheadings, Paragraph Texts* are appended together to create a feature called *BodyText*. Thus, the final data set consists of 150k unique webpage objects, *W* contains three features: *URL* (U), *Title*(T), *BodyText*(B) which have been represented in the output $W = (U, T, B)$. Note that the count of webpages mentioned in Table 1 do not sum up to 150k, many webpages appear as search engine results for more than one hate speech short-text datasets.

Manually inspecting the data W, we observed that $\sim 42\%$ of non-problematic data come from the domain of sports, and e-commerce. These webpages are not related to any potentially sensitive hate or violence topics, hence its safe to annotate them as non-problematic page directly. On manually spot checking sports, and e-commerce websites, we have not seen any problematic content. However, it may be the case that some hateful, violent content may appear in these sports and e-commerce websites. In step 10, we labelled 50k webpages directly by applying a simple domain-level labelling using *DomainLabelling*(). We extract the domain name for the website and match it with a curated list of domains focused on sports [5] and e-commerce.[6] This helped to reduce the GPT-4 labelling time and cost. The remaining 90k webpages are annotated using GPT-4 in step 11.

2.2 GPT Prompt Creation, Validation, and Annotation

The first step towards the annotation process was deciding upon the various categories of problematic content that we will be targeting with our annotation process. Similar to various categories of hate speech as described in (Mollas et al., 2022), we decided to go with similar categories i.e. problematic content promoting hate based on race, religion, gender, sexual orientation and violence. The data that we have curated with our strategy will be annotated in the following classes.

- Race
- Gender Identiy
- Religion
- Sexual Orientation
- Violence
- Non-Problematic

A webpage belonging to either one or more of the first five classes is labelled as Problematic.

To develop the GPT-4 based annotation process, the foremost step is creating a gold standard annotated set of webpages, which will be leveraged to measure the accuracy of various iterations and variations of prompts. We randomly sampled a set of 1000 webpages from the set of collected data which was manually labelled by 2 in-house experts[7]. We duplicate some of the dataset among annotators to measure the inter annotator agreement. We have got a pairwise $\kappa = 0.87$ using Cohen's kappa (Cohen, 1960) indicating high quality reliable annotation.

The GPT-4 prompt needs detailed context to be able to accurately distinguish between problematic and non-problematic webpages. Hence, we make use of different webpage features (*URL, Title, BodyText*) extracted in the previous step and include them in the prompt as part of the input section. This along with detailed instructions gives the required context to GPT-4 to label a webpage.

2.2.1 Prompt Development

Our prompt is comprised of multiple sections which includes *Task Description, Instructions, Input, Examples* as shown in Figure 1. During the prompt development cycle, we tried multiple strategies of prompting with different combinations of the aforementioned sections. Following are the different prompting strategies we have explored in this work.

Basic Instructions: Figure 1 (a) shows the basic version of the prompt. Here we have a simple prompt with *Task Description*, basic *Instructions*, *Input* and ask the GPT-4 model to annotate the webpage. In the basic instructions GPT-4 is expected to give a binary label for each of the five classes of hate and violence. This means any candidate webpage is either problematic or non-problematic in each of 5 sub classes of hate and violence.

Precise Instructions: In this version of the prompt, we have a more complex prompt where

[3]https://pypi.org/project/selenium/
[4]https://pypi.org/project/beautifulsoup4/
[5]https://www.similarweb.com/top-websites/sports/sports/
[6]https://www.kaggle.com/datasets/wiredwith/websites-list

[7]The annotators are very proficient in english and have done all their formal education in english, and have been doing these kind of annotations for last 4 years

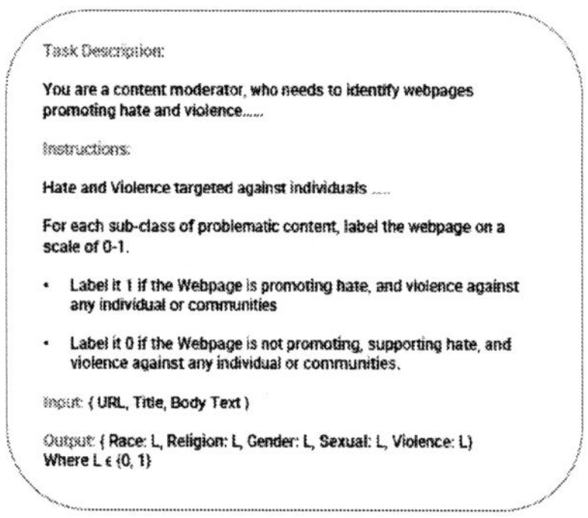

(a) Basic Prompt

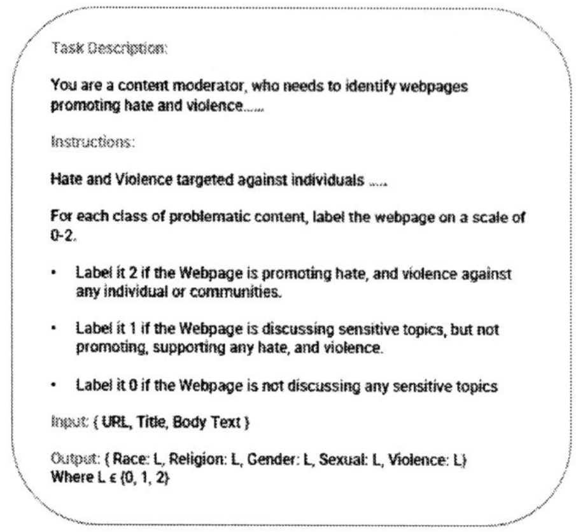

(b) Precise Prompt

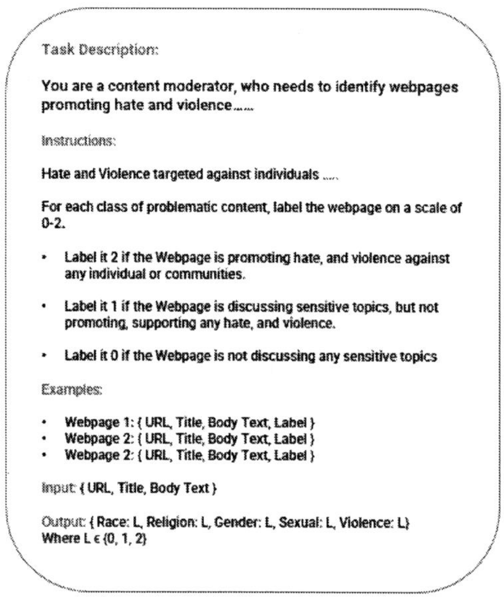

(c) Few-shot Prompt

Figure 1: Different GPT-4 prompts used for webpage annotation. For all the actual prompts, please refer to Figure 2 in Appendix

the basic *Instructions* are modified to the version that can be seen in Figure 1 (b). Instead of a binary label, we have asked GPT-4 to label each webpage on a three point label for each subclass of hate and violence. This helps GPT-4 model make more precise annotations, and better understand the decision boundary between problematic and non-problematic webpages. In the domain of hateful and violent content, it can be misleading for models to understand content which is discussing sensitive topics but not promoting any problematic intent. Introducing a three point labelling mechanism removes this confusion and clarifies the decision boundary. This enables GPT-4 make more precise judgements.

Precise Instructions with Few-shot Examples: In the final version of the prompt as seen in 1 (c), we add the *Examples* section to help GPT-4 identify problematic webpage content (Liu et al., 2021; Brown et al., 2020). Giving examples in case of webpage annotation with GPT-4 can be challenging. The Body Text feature as observed in our dataset is very long (5350 $\pm$ 205 tokens). In such a scenario, including the entire *BodyText* feature will make the final prompt too long. This can lead to recency bias, and loosing the entire context for the GPT-4 annotation model. We propose to leverage text summarisation technique to create a summarised body text feature to be included in few shot examples. We have leveraged GPT-4 model (Please refer to Figure 2 in Appendix for Webpage Content Summarisation prompt) itself to summarise few chosen examples from the gold set. These are leveraged as few shot examples in this prompt version.

2.3 Prompt Performance

The detailed results of GPT-based annotation on the 1000 webpages using different prompts is reported in Table 2. The results observed on identifying problematic webpages in each hate sub-class are inline with general observations reported in (Chiu et al., 2022; Mollas et al., 2022) that addition of detailed instruction and few-shot examples generally yield better classification results for hate speech detection. We find that adding precise instructions increase the F1-Score by 5.7 absolute points compared to the Basic prompt. points overall. Furthermore, adding few-shot examples to the Precise prompt increase the F1-score by 10.6 absolute points compared the the Basic prompt. We found higher F1-score for sexual harm and violence compared to other 3 sub classes. This can be explained by the fact that often explicit words (profane, adult words, harmful words) are available in the surface form for sexual and violence categories. Our observations suggests that these sub classes of problematic content tend to be promoting more explicit form of hate with language which is not very subtle. In contrast, webpages promoting Gender, Race and Religion hate are more implicit in nature with subtle tonality.

In Step 11 of Algorithm 1, we use the best performing prompt (precise instructions with few-shot examples) to annotate the 90k webpages with *GPT*(). GPT-4 labelling identifies 21k problematic webpages. The class wise distribution of the final dataset with the following prompt strategy is given in Table 3. Note that a webpage can belong to multiple hate categories. For example, a webpage which is problematic in gender hate class might be problematic in sexual hate class too. The aggregated label after GPT annotation for a webpage is: *Problematic, Topically Sensitive, Clean* The aggregated labelling strategy is as follows:

- Webpage is **Problematic**, if it is labelled as problematic in terms of any one of the the hate classes.
- Webpage is **Topically Sensitive** if its aggregated label is not problematic, and is labelled as topically sensitive in at least one hate class.
- Webpage is **Clean** if its aggregated label is neither problematic nor of sensitive topic.

2.4 Data set Description

The final annotated data consists of three broader labels: *Problematic, Topically Sensitive, Clean*. Annotating the 90k domain filtered webpages, we have 21k problematic, 44k non-problematic and topically sensitive, 25k clean webpages. To prepare the final data set, we decided to maintain a rough ratio of 1:2:2 for problematic, topically sensitive and clean classes, respectively. This was to ensure that the final model should be robust and does not have any bias to a particular class due to the data distribution. Hence, we randomly sampled some more clean webpages (17k) from previous domain-level filtered data. Our final data set comprised of 21k Problematic, 44k Topically Sensitive, and 42k Clean webpages. Note, that the *Topically Sensitive* data can be effective use as counterfactual data to make the model more robust (Wu et al., 2021). Each webpage is represented by three features – *URL, Title, BodyText*.

3 Experiments & Results

As mentioned in Section 1, latency and cost are the major challenges to leverage GPT-4 to annotate webpages at scale. This is important point to consider during our experimentation as there are billions of webpages in a search engine index, and millions of webpages embedded in social media posts and comments. Thus, to solve the problem of identifying problematic webpage classification, we need a lighter model.

3.1 Model Training

We build the problematic webpage classifier using Transformer-based (Vaswani et al., 2017) models and fine tune the same using our labelled dataset. We have experimented with various pre-trained transformer base models such as BERT (Devlin et al., 2019), HateBERT(Caselli et al., 2021a), Longformer(Beltagy et al., 2020), and compared the results. Longformer models have been included in our experiment specially because we observed that the input sequence can be very long in a webpage (5350 ± 205 tokens). BERT and HateBERT limit the maximum input sequence length to 512

Class	Basic			Precise			Few-shot		
	P	R	F1	P	R	F1	P	R	F1
Race	71.3	75.6	73.4	83.9	80.2	82.0	89.4	87.6	**88.5**
Gender	72.5	74.1	73.3	80.6	79.9	80.2	87.0	87.4	**87.2**
Religion	66.6	72.3	69.3	78.5	75.1	76.8	86.9	81.4	**84.1**
Sexual	79.4	82.5	80.9	87.5	88.3	87.9	93.5	87.6	**90.5**
Violence	78.7	83.5	81.0	89.2	84.4	86.7	92.7	89.3	**91.0**
Overall	76.3	79.9	78.1	85.3	82.3	83.8	90.1	87.3	**88.7**

Table 2: Prompt Accuracy per Hate sub-classes (P: Precision, R: Recall, F1: F1-Score)

Class	#Problematic	#Sensitive Topic
Race	5312	11512
Gender	3414	7631
Religion	3451	5904
Sexual	4513	10467
Violence	6718	14871
Overall	**21712**	**44512**

Table 3: Distribution of labelled webpages. Note that one instance may occur in multiple classes thus the overall number may not be equal to the sum of the individual classes.

Class	Model	F1
Race	BERT	80.8 ± 0.7
	HateBERT	81.9 ± 0.1
	Longformer	**87.6 ± 0.4**
Gender	BERT	76.9 ± 0.2
	HateBERT	78.7 ± 0.3
	Longformer	**83.1 ± 0.9**
Religious	BERT	75.3 ± 0.9
	HateBERT	75.6 ± 0.5
	Longformer	**78.0 ± 0.2**
Sexual	BERT	83.5 ± 0.2
	HateBERT	85.7 ± 0.9
	Longformer	**89.1 ± 0.4**
Violence	BERT	84.7 ± 0.2
	HateBERT	84.3 ± 0.4
	Longformer	**88.7 ± 0.9**
Overall	BERT	82.9 ± 0.8
	HateBERT	83.6 ± 0.9
	Longformer	**87.6 ± 0.4**

Table 4: Webpage Classification Performance

tokens. Longformer on the other hand has a maximum limit of 4096 tokens which can fit our webpage data without much truncation.

To create the input text for the tokenizers, we have leveraged the same three features (*URL, Title, Body Text*) as was previously used in GPT-4 prompt. These text features were appended together, separated by corresponding separator tokens. The maximum input sequence length limitations require us to choose and send the most relevant context to the model. Pre-processing of the input text was done to ensure that only relevant tokens are used to fine-tune and infer the model. Basic pre-processing steps involves the removal of (i) unnecessary spaces, non-ASCII characters, numbers (except the number *18* due to its frequent occurrence in the adult pages) (ii) common Webpage related tokens like "www", "https", "php" and (iii) tokens which either contain greater than 15 characters, or only a single character. We train a binary classification model with two classes: Problematic, Non-Problematic. Here, Non-Problematic includes both *Sensitive Topic* and *Clean*.

We have considered 80% of the data set as training data in fine-tuning the pre-trained models, 10% as validation data to measure the out-of-sample performance of the model during training, and hyper-parameter tuning, and 10% as test data to measure the out-of-sample performance after training. To prevent over-fitting, we have used stratified sampling to select 0.8, 0.1, and 0.1 portions of the data from each class (Race/Gender/Religion/Sexual/Violence) while creating train, validation, and test set.

To understand the importance of different features, we have experimented with three models trained on increasing level of contexts – *URL*, (*URL + Title*), (*URL + Title + BodyText*). We have also trained a HateBERT-based classification model fine-tuned on baseline short-text hate speech

Feature	F1
URL	51.7
Title	58.1
BodyText	76.9
URL + Title	71.8
URL + Title + BodyText	**87.6**

Table 5: Webpage Feature Importance

datasets in Table 1. This is to show the importance of webpage specific data collection instead of solely using short-text hate speech data.

3.2 Model Performance & Results

Table 4 presents the details of our experimental results across all categories using 3 SOTA models tuned and tested on our GPT-4 annotated dataset. Longformer based webpage classification model outperforms and reaches an overall F1-score of 87.6%. We find that Longformer models have much better accuracy in all 5 categories and have 4.7 and 4 absolute point improvement in F1-score compared to BERT and HateBERT models, respectively. HateBERT model performs slightly better than BERT with an overall F1-score of 83.6% and 82.9%, respectively.

Furthermore, we evaluated the best performing Longformer-based webpage classification model with different combinations of features to understand the importance of the features. Table 5 details the results, which show that all the three features are very important to provide detailed context to the model to classify a webpage. Each feature on its own has much lower performance compared to the combined feature. *BodyText* on its own has the highest accuracy compared to the other two features (*URL* and *Title*). This essentially indicates that a lot of useful information is there in the Body Text for webpage classification but the URL and Title also provides additional information to improve the overall performance.

Finally, in Table 6, we present the comparison of best performing Longformer based problematic webpage classification model (L-PWC) against the Hate speech classification model trained using only short-text data (S-HSC). L-PWC model outperforms the S-HSC model in all classes and has an overall gain of 13.7% compared to the S-HSC model.

Class	Model	F1
Race	S-HSC	72.9 ± 0.2
	L-PWC	$\mathbf{87.6 \pm 0.4}$
Gender	S-HSC	69.2 ± 0.8
	L-PWC	$\mathbf{83.1 \pm 0.9}$
Religious	S-HSC	66.7 ± 0.4
	L-PWC	$\mathbf{78.0 \pm 0.2}$
Sexual	S-HSC	75.4 ± 0.5
	L-PWC	$\mathbf{89.1 \pm 0.4}$
Violence	S-HSC	74.1 ± 0.6
	L-PWC	$\mathbf{88.7 \pm 0.9}$
Overall	S-HSC	72.9 ± 0.9
	L-PWC	$\mathbf{87.6 \pm 0.4}$

Table 6: Performance comparison between L-PWC and S-HSC models. L-PWC: Longformer based Problematic Webpage Classification, S-HSC: Hate Speech Classification trained on Short-Text data

4 Conclusion

This paper presents a novel way of collecting and annotating problematic webpages which is important for building a problematic webpage classification model. We have shown that easily available short-text data along with the knowledge of SOTA generative models (GPT-4) can help in building annotated datasets for a complex task such as problematic webpage classification. We also report and re-establish the fact that writing precise prompt along with a few examples is effective and achieve very high quality annotation. We compare different pre-trained models and fine-tune them with our dataset and report comparative results. We also report an ablation study and show that the different features used in our experiment are together effective for webpage classification. Finally, we show empirically that our data set is effective for building a problematic webpage classifier.

The work can be further extended by leveraging additional features for webpage classification such as Ads, Link Connections to other webpages, Authority of the domain. The work can also be extended towards creating multilingual dataset for problematic webpage classification and subsequently build a model for the same.

5 Limitations

The dataset created as part of our contribution leverages hate speech datasets focusing on the English language. Therefore, the model has neither seen, nor been evaluated in other languages.

References

Abdullah Aljebreen, Weiyi Meng, and Eduard Dragut. 2021. Segmentation of tweets with urls and its applications to sentiment analysis. *Proceedings of the AAAI Conference on Artificial Intelligence*, 35(14):12480–12488.

Iz Beltagy, Matthew E. Peters, and Arman Cohan. 2020. Longformer: The long-document transformer.

Tom Brown, Benjamin Mann, Nick Ryder, Melanie Subbiah, Jared D Kaplan, Prafulla Dhariwal, Arvind Neelakantan, Pranav Shyam, Girish Sastry, Amanda Askell, et al. 2020. Language models are few-shot learners. *Advances in neural information processing systems*, 33:1877–1901.

Renato Bruni and Gianpiero Bianchi. 2019. Website categorization: a formal approach and robustness analysis in the case of e-commerce detection. *Expert Systems with Applications*, 142:113001.

Sébastien Bubeck, Varun Chandrasekaran, Ronen Eldan, Johannes Gehrke, Eric Horvitz, Ece Kamar, Peter Lee, Yin Tat Lee, Yuanzhi Li, Scott Lundberg, Harsha Nori, Hamid Palangi, Marco Tulio Ribeiro, and Yi Zhang. 2023. Sparks of artificial general intelligence: Early experiments with gpt-4.

Tommaso Caselli, Valerio Basile, Jelena Mitrović, and Michael Granitzer. 2021a. HateBERT: Retraining BERT for abusive language detection in English. In *Proceedings of the 5th Workshop on Online Abuse and Harms (WOAH 2021)*, pages 17–25, Online. Association for Computational Linguistics.

Tommaso Caselli, Valerio Basile, Jelena Mitrović, and Michael Granitzer. 2021b. Hatebert: Retraining bert for abusive language detection in english.

Ke-Li Chiu, Annie Collins, and Rohan Alexander. 2022. Detecting hate speech with gpt-3.

Jacob Cohen. 1960. A coefficient of agreement for nominal scales. *Educational and psychological measurement*, 20(1):37–46.

Abhishek Das and Ankit Jain. 2012. Indexing the world wide web: The journey so far. In *Next Generation Search Engines: Advanced Models for Information Retrieval*, pages 1–28. IGI Global.

Thomas Davidson, Dana Warmsley, Michael Macy, and Ingmar Weber. 2017. Automated hate speech detection and the problem of offensive language.

Ona de Gibert, Naiara Perez, Aitor García-Pablos, and Montse Cuadros. 2018. Hate speech dataset from a white supremacy forum.

Jacob Devlin, Ming-Wei Chang, Kenton Lee, and Kristina Toutanova. 2019. Bert: Pre-training of deep bidirectional transformers for language understanding.

Mai ElSherief, Caleb Ziems, David Muchlinski, Vaishnavi Anupindi, Jordyn Seybolt, Munmun De Choudhury, and Diyi Yang. 2021. Latent hatred: A benchmark for understanding implicit hate speech. In *Proceedings of the 2021 Conference on Empirical Methods in Natural Language Processing*, pages 345–363, Online and Punta Cana, Dominican Republic. Association for Computational Linguistics.

Lei Gao, Alexis Kuppersmith, and Ruihong Huang. 2018. Recognizing explicit and implicit hate speech using a weakly supervised two-path bootstrapping approach.

Chris J Kennedy, Geoff Bacon, Alexander Sahn, and Claudia von Vacano. 2020. Constructing interval variables via faceted rasch measurement and multitask deep learning: a hate speech application. *arXiv preprint arXiv:2009.10277*.

Jiyun Kim, Byounghan Lee, and Kyung-Ah Sohn. 2022. Why is it hate speech? masked rationale prediction for explainable hate speech detection.

Jiachang Liu, Dinghan Shen, Yizhe Zhang, Bill Dolan, Lawrence Carin, and Weizhu Chen. 2021. What makes good in-context examples for gpt-3? *arXiv preprint arXiv:2101.06804*.

Binny Mathew, Punyajoy Saha, Seid Muhie Yimam, Chris Biemann, Pawan Goyal, and Animesh Mukherjee. 2021. Hatexplain: A benchmark dataset for explainable hate speech detection. *Proceedings of the AAAI Conference on Artificial Intelligence*, 35(17):14867–14875.

Ioannis Mollas, Zoe Chrysopoulou, Stamatis Karlos, and Grigorios Tsoumakas. 2022. ETHOS: a multilabel hate speech detection dataset. *Complex &amp Intelligent Systems*, 8(6):4663–4678.

OpenAI. 2023. Gpt-4 technical report.

Nedjma Ousidhoum, Zizheng Lin, Hongming Zhang, Yangqiu Song, and Dit-Yan Yeung. 2019. Multilingual and multi-aspect hate speech analysis. In *Proceedings of EMNLP*. Association for Computational Linguistics.

Gaurav Rajput, Narinder Singh Punn, Sanjay Kumar Sonbhadra, and Sonali Agarwal. 2021. Hate speech detection using static BERT embeddings. In *Big Data Analytics*, pages 67–77. Springer International Publishing.

Diptanu Sarkar, Marcos Zampieri, Tharindu Ranasinghe, and Alexander Ororbia. 2021. fBERT: A neural transformer for identifying offensive content. In *Findings of the Association for Computational Linguistics: EMNLP 2021*, pages 1792–1798, Punta Cana, Dominican Republic. Association for Computational Linguistics.

Ashish Vaswani, Noam Shazeer, Niki Parmar, Jakob Uszkoreit, Llion Jones, Aidan N. Gomez, Lukasz Kaiser, and Illia Polosukhin. 2017. Attention is all you need.

Tongshuang Wu, Marco Tulio Ribeiro, Jeffrey Heer, and Daniel S Weld. 2021. Polyjuice: Generating counterfactuals for explaining, evaluating, and improving models. *arXiv preprint arXiv:2101.00288*.

Peng Yang, Guangzhen Zhao, and Peng Zeng. 2019. Phishing website detection based on multidimensional features driven by deep learning. *IEEE Access*, 7:15196–15209.

A Appendix

Problematic webpage classification is even more skewed as compared to classification of hate speech. Prominent search engines have already developed certain filtering mechanisms to remove problematic webpages from their search engine results. Therefore, we also sampled data from the given hate speech data sets to pick short text which are more problematic in nature in terms of hate, violence and hence, more likely to yield a problematic webpage when queried in these search engines. Hence, with each data set we have chosen a threshold to get the most problematic phrases.

The datasets that have been used for mining short text data corresponding to hate speech are:

(Davidson et al., 2017): A crowd-sourced hate speech lexicon to collect tweets containing hate speech keywords, which contains data labelled into three classes hate, offensive, neither. For our dataset preparation, we have filtered out short text data belonging to hate and offensive classes, which is roughly $\sim$ 20k in quantity.

(de Gibert et al., 2018): These files contain text extracted from Stormfront, a white supremacist forum. A random set of forums posts have been sampled from several sub-forums and split into sentences. Those sentences have been manually labelled as containing hate speech or not, according to certain annotation guidelines. We have filtered the dataset and used $\sim$ 1k posts labelled as hateful.

(Mollas et al., 2022): ETHOS is a textual dataset based on YouTube, Reddit comments validated using a crowd-sourcing platform with two variants: binary and multi-label. We have sampled data from this dataset where the binary label for that instance is hate speech. This helped us get 433 short-text hate speech.

(ElSherief et al., 2021): This dataset focuses on presenting a benchmark for implicit hate speech data. While other datasets focus on explicit hate, abuse towards a individual or community, this specially focuses on implicit hate or indirect hate, which helps in the mining of diverse webpages promoting subtle hate or opinionated content. We have filtered the dataset and only taken the implicit & explicit hate posts which is $\sim$ 8k posts.

(Kennedy et al., 2020): The dataset released in their work is mined using comments from various social media platforms. Originally containing 39k comments, it also presents a continuous hate speech score for the data. To mine relevant webpages for our use case, we have filtered it and taken only those comments where the hate speech score value is greater than 0.5. This leaves us with $\sim$ 14k social media comments.

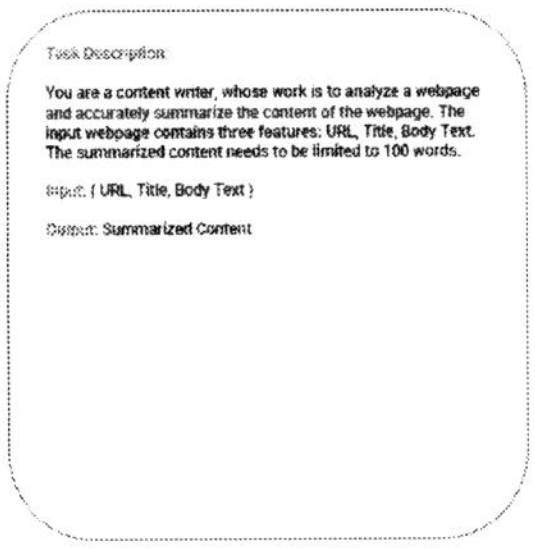

(a) Webpage Summarization Prompt

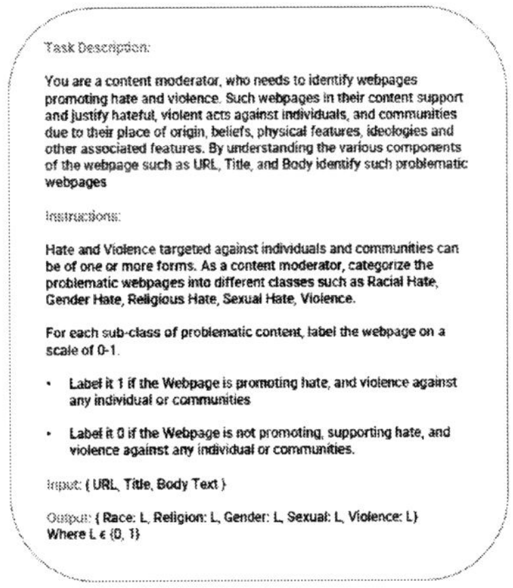

(b) Basic Prompt

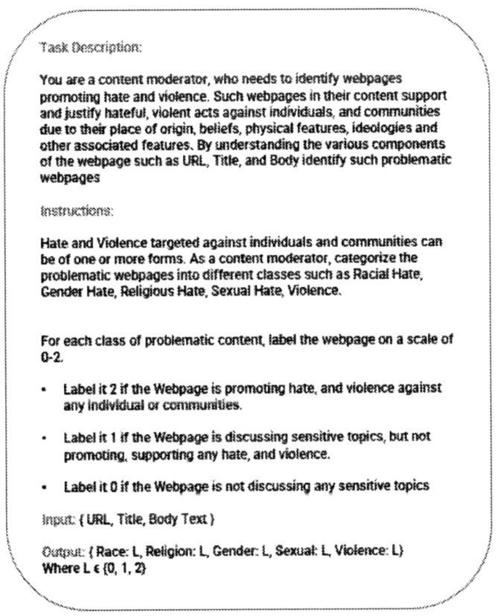

(c) Precise Prompt

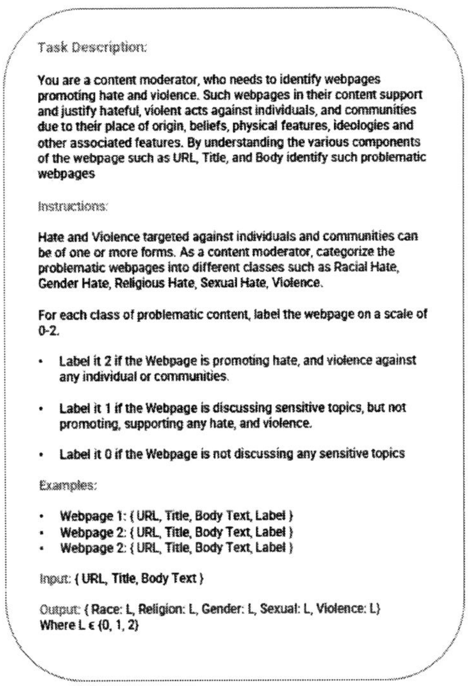

(d) Few-shot Prompt

Figure 2: Actual Webpage Annotation Prompt

Concept-Based Explanations to Test for False Causal Relationships Learned by Abusive Language Classifiers

Isar Nejadgholi, Svetlana Kiritchenko, Kathleen C. Fraser, and Esma Balkır
National Research Council Canada
Ottawa, Canada
{Isar.Nejadgholi,Svetlana.Kiritchenko,Kathleen.Fraser,Esma.Balkir}@nrc-cnrc.gc.ca

Abstract

Classifiers tend to learn a false causal relationship between an over-represented concept and a label, which can result in over-reliance on the concept and compromised classification accuracy. It is imperative to have methods in place that can compare different models and identify over-reliances on specific concepts. We consider three well-known abusive language classifiers trained on large English datasets and focus on the concept of *negative emotions*, which is an important signal but should not be learned as a sufficient feature for the label of abuse. Motivated by the definition of *global sufficiency*, we first examine the unwanted dependencies learned by the classifiers by assessing their accuracy on a challenge set across all decision thresholds. Further, recognizing that a challenge set might not always be available, we introduce concept-based explanation metrics to assess the influence of the concept on the labels. These explanations allow us to compare classifiers regarding the degree of false global sufficiency they have learned between a concept and a label.

Content Warning: *This paper presents examples that may be offensive or upsetting.*

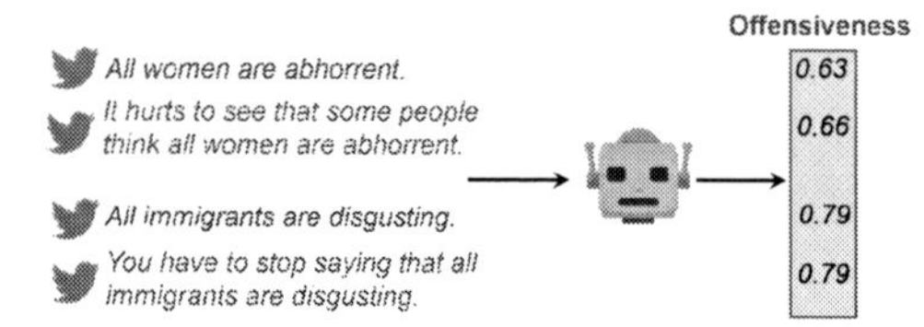

Figure 1: Probability of offensiveness generated by the TweetEval Classifier (Barbieri et al., 2020). The classifier has learned a false global sufficiency between negative emotions and the label of offense. It over-relies on this concept and ignores the broader context.

1 Introduction

In various natural language classification tasks, particularly in abusive language detection, certain concepts are known to be strong signals for the label of interest. These concepts are often over-represented in the respective class of the training set, making them susceptible to being learned as potential causes for the label. Consequently, the classifier over-relies on these concepts and ignores the broader context, leading to reduced generalizability (Yin and Zubiaga, 2021). Hence, to ensure models are robust and reliable, it is crucial to develop methods that can detect these over-reliances in various natural language classification tasks.

In the context of abusive language detection, we consider the concept of *negative emotions*. The presence of an expression associated with *negative emotion* is an important signal for detecting abusive language and has been used in feature-based systems before (Chiril et al., 2022; Fortuna and Nunes, 2018). Crucially, in some examples, negative emotion words might be the cause for the abusive label, i.e., the sentence might not be abusive if the negative emotion word is replaced with other words (e.g., *I know these people. They are **disgusting***). However, at the global level, the relationship between negative emotion and abusive language is a strong correlation, not causation, as it is neither globally necessary nor globally sufficient for the label of abuse.[1] Negative emotions are not globally necessary for the label of abuse because there are abusive sentences that do not contain any negative emotion words (e.g., offensive jokes, stereotyping and microaggressions). Also, words evoking negative emotions are not globally sufficient for a sentence to be abusive when interpreted in a broader context (e.g., *We should admit that in our society, they are **oppressed**.*). But, an end-to-end model might learn that negative emotion in a sentence is globally sufficient for that sentence to be abusive. Such a classifier will struggle in classifying non-abusive sentences that contain negative emotion

[1] Phenomenon P is globally sufficient for the Phenomenon Q, if whenever P happens, Q happens too. P is globally necessary for Q if whenever Q happens, P happens, too (Zaeem and Komeili, 2021).

The 7th Workshop on Online Abuse and Harms (WOAH), pages 138–149
July 13, 2023 ©2023 Association for Computational Linguistics

words leading to a lack of generalizability. An example of such a case is shown in Figure 1. Specifically, classifiers' over-reliance on the negative emotion signal can inadvertently discriminate against marginalized groups since their communications (e.g., discussing their experiences of discrimination and marginalization) can contain negative emotion words and, therefore can be wrongly considered abusive.

We explore a scenario where a user, aware of the importance of negative emotions for their use case, wants to evaluate and compare a set of trained models. Their goal is to identify and eliminate those models that are more prone to generating inaccurate results due to an overemphasis on negative emotions as primary indicators. For that, we use concept-based explanations to test if a model has learned a false global causal relationship between a user-identified concept and a label where the true relationship is a correlation. Note that global causal relationships explain the model's output across an entire dataset, as opposed to local causal explanations, which concern the dependency of an individual prediction on a specific input feature.

Concept-based explanations are a class of explainability methods that provide global explanations at the level of human-understandable concepts (Yeh et al., 2022). While local explanations help the users understand the model's reasoning for an individual decision with respect to the input features, global explanations are critical in comparing the processes learned by models and selecting the one that best suits the needs of a use case (Balkir et al., 2022; Burkart and Huber, 2021). Global explanations might be obtained at the level of input features through aggregating local explanations (Lundberg et al., 2020). Alternatively, global-by-design methods (e.g., probing classifiers (Conneau et al., 2018)) can be used to gain insights at higher levels of abstractions, such as linguistic properties or human-defined concepts.[2]

Similar to most feature importance explainability methods (e.g, Ribeiro et al. (2016); Lundberg and Lee (2017a)), concept-based explanations are originally designed to measure the *importance* of a concept. The intuitive meaning of *importance* usually refers to correlation, and it can be interpreted differently based on two notions of causality: necessity and sufficiency (Galhotra et al., 2021). Local explainability methods usually focus on features that are of high local necessity or high local sufficiency for the label (Watson et al., 2021; Balkır et al., 2022; Joshi et al., 2022), thus considered important by human users. However, at the global level, all features must be interpreted in a larger context for accurate decision-making. We aim to determine if concept-based explanations can be utilized to evaluate whether a trained binary classifier for abusive language detection has learned a false global sufficiency relationship between the label and the concept of negative emotion. Our code and data are available at `https://github.com/IsarNejad/Global-Sufficiency/tree/main`. Our main contributions are:

- We formalize the issue of over-reliance on a concept as falsely learned global sufficiency. For the task of an abusive language classifier, we consider concepts related to *negative emotion* as being important but not globally sufficient for the label of abuse. We discuss how learning these concepts as globally sufficient results in compromised classification accuracies.

- Based on our formalization of false global sufficiency, as a baseline method, we measure the over-reliance of models on a human-defined concept using an unseen challenge set that contains the concept in both classes. Recognizing that various classifiers may have a distinct range of optimal decision thresholds, we assess the over-reliance on a concept across all possible decision thresholds and show that one of the classifiers over-relies on emotion-related concepts significantly more than the other two classifiers.

- Taking the challenge set approach as a baseline for comparison, we propose novel concept-based explanation metrics, demonstrating that similar conclusions about the degree of false global sufficiency can be drawn using these metrics. Building on previous work, we modify the TCAV procedure to measure not only the feature's importance but also the extent of its impact on the label. We conclude that a concept-based method is preferable as it eliminates the need for manual data curation.

2 Concept-Based Explanations

Concept-based explanations evaluate the model's decision-making mechanism at the level of a

[2]Here, we use the term "feature" to refer to the latent representations of a semantic concept learned by a classifier.

human-defined concept expected to be important for the task (Koh et al., 2020). Specifically, we use the Testing Concept Activation Vectors (TCAV) method to measure the influence of a human-defined concept on the model's predictions (Kim et al., 2018). The idea of TCAV is based on the observation that human-understandable concepts can be encoded as meaningful and insightful information in the linear vector space of trained neural networks (Mikolov et al., 2013). A Concept Activation Vector (CAV), which represents the concept in the embedding space, is a vector normal to a hyperplane that separates concept and non-concept examples. Such a hyperplane is obtained by training a linear binary classifier to separate the representations of concept and non-concept examples in the embedding space.

Although TCAV can be applied to all neural network classifiers, for simplicity we limit our experiments to binary RoBERTa-based abusive language classifiers. We choose the RoBerta-based models for their superior performance in processing social media data compared to other base language models (Liu et al., 2019). The concept, C, is defined by N_C concept examples. Also, N_R random examples are used to define non-concept examples. The RoBERTa representations for all these examples are calculated using f_{emb}, which maps an input text to its [CLS] token representation. Then, P number of CAVs, v_C^p, are generated, each through training a linear classifier that separates a sub-sample (with size N_c) of concept examples from a sub-sample of random examples (with size N_r) in the RoBERTa embedding space. The *conceptual sensitivity* of a label to the CAV, v_C^p, at input x can be computed as the directional derivative $S_{C,p}(x)$:

$$S_{C,p}(x) = \lim_{\epsilon \to 0} \frac{h(f_{emb}(x)+\epsilon v_C^p)-h(f_{emb}(x))}{\epsilon} = \nabla h(f_{emb}(x)).v_C^p \quad (1)$$

where h maps the RoBERTa representation to the logit value of the class of interest.

In this work, we use two metrics to specify the influence of the concept on the model's prediction. First, we calculate $TCAV_{dir}$, the fraction of inputs in a set of input examples X, for which the directional derivative $S_{C,p}(x)$ is positive, i.e.:

$$TCAV_{dir}^{C,p} = \frac{|x \in X : S_{C,p}(x) > 0|}{|X|} \quad (2)$$

$TCAV_{dir}$ indicates the fraction of input examples for which the prediction scores of the model increase if the input representation is infinitesimally moved towards the concept representation. This metric has been widely used to identify if the label has learned the concept as an important signal for the label (Yeh et al., 2020).

Besides the widely used metric of $TCAV_{dir}$ (referred to as $TCAV$ score in previous work), we introduce a new metric, $TCAV_{mag}$, which considers the size of the directional derivatives, and measures the magnitude of the influence of the concept on the label for the positive directional derivatives:

$$TCAV_{mag}^{C,p} = \frac{\sum_{x \in X, S_{C,p}(x)>0} S_{C,p}(x)}{|X|} \quad (3)$$

We demonstrate in our results that $TCAV_{mag}$ can be an indicator of the over-reliance of the label on the concept. When calculated for all CAVs, Equations 2 and 3 generate two distributions of scores with size P for the concept C. Using a t-test, these distributions are compared with the distributions of $TCAV_{dir}$ and $TCAV_{mag}$ calculated for random examples to check for statistical significance (Kim et al., 2018).

3 False Global Sufficiency

Phenomenon P is considered globally sufficient for phenomenon Q ($P \Rightarrow Q$) if, whenever P occurs, Q also occurs (Zaeem and Komeili, 2021). In other words, global sufficiency refers to the extent to which a concept can explain the model's output across all instances in a held-out dataset, as opposed to the more studied topic of local sufficiency, which concerns the stability of an individual prediction for a given feature in perturbed contexts (Balkır et al., 2022).

In a real-world setting, it is very unlikely that any single concept is truly sufficient for the label at a global level. In a binary classifier, a concept C is falsely learned as sufficient for the positive label if all inputs containing C are classified as positive by the classifier, regardless of context. This undesired dependency of the label on the concept suggests that the model has failed to learn how the concept interacts with context to influence the label. While this issue is closely related to spurious correlation, we use the term *false global sufficiency* because spurious correlation typically implies that the feature is irrelevant to the label, and a correlation is learned due to a confounding factor. In contrast, we consider the cases where the feature is relevant and important but not globally sufficient.

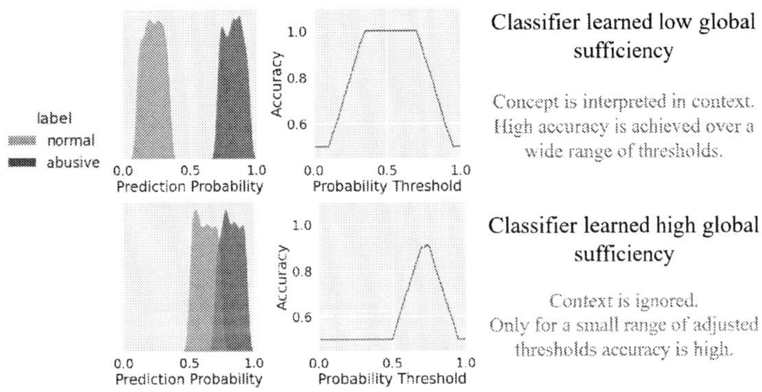

Figure 2: Illustration of the potential distribution of probabilities generated by a trained binary classifier for a challenge set that represents an important concept, along with accuracy versus threshold curves.

To make this clearer, consider the case of abusive language detection and the concept of negative emotions; if the mere presence of negative emotions in a sentence always guarantees the prediction of the positive label (abuse), then the model has learned a false sufficiency relation between the concept and the label. It over-relies on this feature and ignores the context.

To quantify falsely learned global sufficiency, we consider two scenarios: 1) where a balanced challenge set is available, which contains C in all of its examples (both classes), and 2) where no challenge set is available. For the first scenario we use the traditional approach of assessing accuracy of the classifier on a held-out test set. This approach provides a baseline in our evaluations. For the second scenario, we propose concept-based explanation metrics and compare them with the baselines obtained with the challenge sets.

3.1 Quantifying the Falsely Learned Global Sufficiency with a Challenge Set

Based on our definition of global sufficiency, one way to assess a model's over-reliance on a concept is to evaluate its performance on a held-out challenge set, $\mathbb{F}$, containing both positive and negative examples of the concept of interest (Yin and Zubiaga, 2021). For simplicity, we assume that this challenge set consists of equal numbers of positive and negative examples. If a model learns a high global sufficiency between the concept C and the label of abuse, all examples in both positive and negative classes of a challenge set $\mathbb{F}$ will be labeled as abusive. However, if the model interprets the concept in context, only the positive examples of $\mathbb{F}$ will receive the abusive label. This indicates that in cases where the decision threshold of the classifier clearly separates the probability distributions of the two classes, the model has learned a low global sufficiency between the concept and the label.

However, when comparing different classifiers, it is important to note that a reliable classifier should perform well (high precision and high recall) over a broad range of decision thresholds. This is because different applications may require different thresholds depending on the desired trade-off between precision and recall. For example, a classifier used to moderate social media content may need to prioritize precision over recall, which could mean using a high threshold to avoid false positives. On the other hand, a classifier used to detect all instances of abusive language may need to prioritize recall over precision, which would mean using a lower threshold to catch as many instances of abuse as possible, even if it means tolerating more false positives. Therefore, a classifier that is reliable over a wide range of decision thresholds can be more effective in different use cases, making it more practical and adaptable.

Figure 2 demonstrates two hypothetical cases for the distribution of probabilities that the classifiers might generate for the challenge set $\mathbb{F}$. A classifier that learned low global sufficiency between C and the positive label generates easily separable distributions of probabilities for the positive and negative examples of $\mathbb{F}$. In other words, for a large range of decision thresholds, the two classes of $\mathbb{F}$ are separable, and high accuracy is achieved. Conversely, the classifier that has learned high global sufficiency between C and the positive label assigns a similar distribution of probabilities to both negative and positive examples. The two classes of $\mathbb{F}$ are hardly separable, and for a wide range of thresholds, the accuracy is low. Note that in order for this classifier to be accurate, it requires a careful adjustment of the decision threshold with a labeled dataset. However, this process can be very costly.

Based on this discussion, we argue that $AUC\_Challenge$, the area under the curve of accuracy vs threshold, is a quantitative indicator of the separability of two classes of $\mathbb{F}$ for all decision thresholds. According to our definition above, global sufficiency is negatively correlated with the separability of these classes. Therefore, $False\_Suff$, described in Equation 4, is a quantitative metric that can be used to compare the degree of sufficiency learned by the classifiers based on $\mathbb{F}$:

$$False\_Suff = 1 - AUC\_Challenge \quad (4)$$

3.2 Quantifying the Falsely Learned Global Sufficiency with Concept-Based Explanations

The practical application of the method detailed in Section 3.1 can be limited due to the necessity of creating a custom challenge set. In this section, we use concept-based explanation to measure the falsely learned global sufficiency in a scenario where a challenge set is not available, but a lexicon representing the concept of interest exists. Following the approach of Nejadgholi et al. (2022a), we employ short templates and the concept lexicon to generate unlabeled concept examples. Then, we utilize the method described in Section 2 to compute two metrics: $TCAV_{dir}$ and $TCAV_{mag}$. If the $TCAV_{dir}$ value for the concept significantly deviates from that of random concepts, it indicates that the classifier has learned an association between the label and the concept. A significant difference in $TCAV_{mag}$ compared to random concepts suggests a strong influence of the concept on the label, potentially causing the classifier to disregard the context when the concept is present. While the absolute values of these metrics might not be definitive, we show that they can be used to compare various classifiers in terms of the degree of global sufficiency they have learned for a concept.

4 Sufficiency of the Concept of *Describing Protected Groups with Negative Emotion*

In this section, we evaluate the metrics introduced in Section 3 in explaining the extent of the falsely learned sufficiency between a human-defined concept and the positive label of the classifiers. We

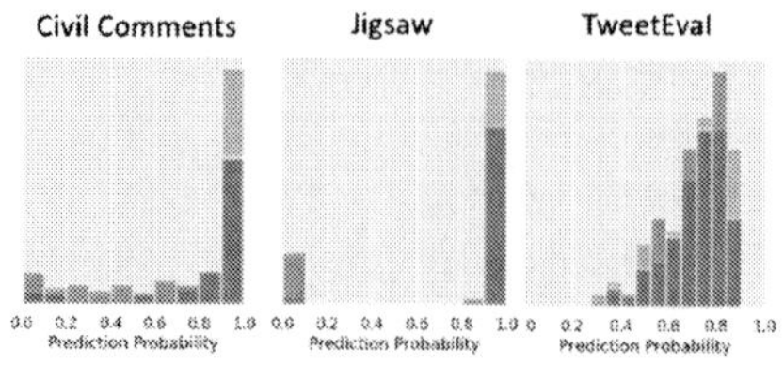

Figure 3: Probability distributions generated by the classifiers for a challenge set (F2 and F21 of HateCheck).

specifically consider the concept of *describing a protected group with negative emotion words* and refer to it as *DesNegEm* for brevity. We chose this concept because it is tightly related to hate speech and is expected to be important for more general definitions of harmful language, such as toxic, abusive or offensive. Still, it is not a sufficient concept for these labels and has to be interpreted in the broader context (as shown by examples in Table 1).

We consider three RoBERTa-based binary classifiers, publically available and trained with large English datasets. The models are trained for general definitions of abusive language, toxicity or offensive language. We refer to these classifiers by their training datasets: Jigsaw, Civil Comments (or Civil for brevity) and TweetEval. These models are described in detail in Appendix A

Quantifying Sufficiency with a Challenge Set: To calculate the metric described in Section 3.1, we first use the HateCheck (Röttger et al., 2021) test cases to build a challenge set for the concept of *DesNegEm*. For that, we use the F2 and F21 functionalities of HateCheck, i.e., the hateful and non-hateful examples that include this concept (Table 1). Figure 3 shows the distribution of probabilities that the three classifiers generate for this challenge set. We observe that, for a large range of decision thresholds, all three classifiers label the majority of the examples of both classes of the challenge set with a positive label. In other words, all three classifiers have learned a high sufficiency between *DesNegEm* and the label of abuse. However, the extent of the learned sufficiency is different among the classifiers. The TweetEval classifier makes the least differentiation between the two classes and generates similar distributions of probabilities for negative and positive examples with the *DesNegEm* concept. Because of this overlap between probability distributions of positive and negative classes, the accuracy of this classifier is low over all ranges of thresholds, as shown in Fig-

Functionality	Example Test Case	Gold Label	n
F2: Description using very negative attributes	"[IDENTITY] are disgusting." "All [IDENTITY] like them are vile."	hateful	140
F21: Denouncement of hate that make direct reference to it	"You have to stop calling [IDENTITY] disgusting."	non-hate	140

Table 1: Used test cases from HateCheck (Röttger et al., 2021).

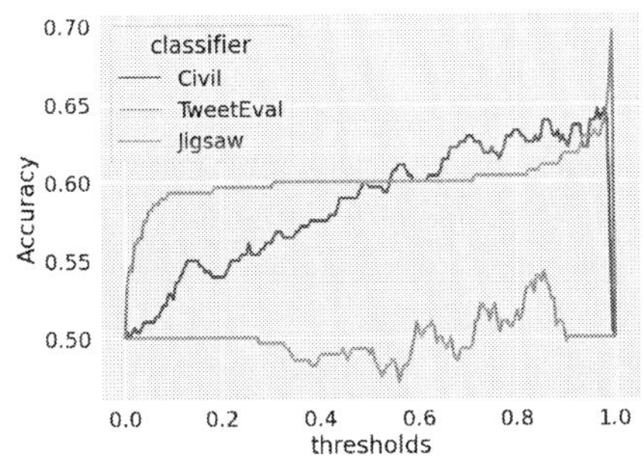

Figure 4: Accuracy vs threshold curve for the challenge set (F2 and F21 of HateCheck).

ure 4. The false sufficiency learned by the Jigsaw and the Civil Comments classifiers is less extreme, and Jigsaw makes the most differentiation between the two classes.

This observation can be quantified with the $False\_Suff$ metric (Equation 4) using the area under the curves in Figure 4. We obtain $False\_Suff$ of 0.41, 0.40, and 0.50 for Civil, Jigsaw and TweetEval, respectively. This metric shows a higher falsely learned sufficiency score for TweetEval than the two other classifiers, as expected. Based on these observations, we expect TCAV metrics to show lower scores for Civil and Jigsaw than the TweetEval classifier.

Global Sufficiency with Concept-Based Explanations: Here, we use the results obtained with the challenge set as a baseline to evaluate the TCAV-based metrics. Concept examples are generated using the template '*<protected_group> are <emotion_word>*.', where *<protected_group>* is one of the protected groups *women*, *trans people*, *gay people*, *black people*, *disabled people*, *Muslims* and *immigrants* as identified by Röttger et al. (2021). For *<emotion_word>*, we use the *disgust* and *anger* categories of the NRC Emotion Intensity Lexicon (NRC-EIL) (Mohammad, 2018). We use the NLTK package[3] to filter out words other than adjectives, past tense verbs and past participles, and also remove the words with emotion intensity lower than 0.5. After these steps, we are left with 368 concept words. We calculate the $TCAV_{dir}$ and $TCAV_{mag}$ scores for the concept of *DesNegEm* and compare those to the metrics calculated for random concepts with t-test for statistical significance. For random concepts, the concept examples are random tweets collected with stop words. In our implementation of the TCAV procedure, $N_R = 1000$, $N_c = 50$, $N_r = 200$ and $N_C = 386$ (number of filtered lexicon words). For input examples, X, we use 2000 tweets collected with stop words.

[3]https://www.nltk.org/

As presented in Table 2, for the Civil classifier, $TCAV_{dir}$ is not significantly different from the random concept, indicating that the concept information might not always be encoded as a coherent concept in the embedding space of this classifier. However, $TCAV_{mag}$ is significantly higher than random, indicating that when the information is encoded well, the presence of this concept has a significant influence on the label of abuse. The other two classifiers have learned a strong association between the concept and the label, i.e., when the concept is added to a neutral context, the likelihood of the positive label increases. However, only in the case of the TweetEval classifier, $TCAV_{mag}$ is significantly different from the random concepts, indicating a strong influence of the concept on the label, which might override the context. Therefore, for TweetEval the distribution of generated probabilities is mostly determined by the concept, not the context (similar distributions are obtained for the positive and negative examples of the challenge set). The other two classifiers consider the context to some extent and generate relatively different distributions of probabilities for the two classes.

Discussion: For all classifiers, the presence of the concept *describing a protected group with negative emotion words* is a strong signal for the label of abuse. All classifiers struggle in considering the broader contexts in sentences such as '*It is not acceptable to say <protected_group> are disgusting.*' Among the three classifiers, TweetEval has learned a higher degree of sufficiency, leading to its worse performance on a challenge set containing this con-

	$TCAV_{dir}$		$TCAV_{mag}$	
classifier	DesNegEm	random	DesNegEm	random
Civil	0.67(0.05)	0.5(0.4)	**0.05(0.03)**	0.00(0.01)
Jigsaw	**1(0)**	0.7(0.4)	0.04(0.01)	0.05(0.05)
TweetEval	**1(0)**	0.7(0.4)	**0.15(0.03)**	0.01(0.01)

Table 2: Mean and standard deviation of the TCAV score for explaining the sufficiency of *Describing Protected Groups with Negative Emotion* (DesNegEm) for the three classifiers. All scores statistically significantly different from random concepts are in boldface.

cept. The TCAV metrics can be used to compare the classifiers regarding the false sufficiency relationships they have learned. These metrics provide similar insights to what is learned from assessing global sufficiency with a challenge set.

5 Global Sufficiency of Fine-Grained Negative Emotions Concepts

In the previous section, we considered the concept of *describing protected groups with negative emotions*, which is tightly related to hate speech, and thus prone to be mistakenly learned as sufficient for the label of abuse. In this section, we test our proposed method for a less obvious case by disentangling the concept of emotions and hate speech. We focus on the concept of *describing a (non-protected) group of people with negative emotions*, which differs from the previous section in 1) removing the protected groups and replacing them with unprotected groups and 2) breaking down the emotion concept to more fine-grained levels.

For fine-grained emotion concepts, we first develop a compact challenge set, examples of which are presented in Table 3. Since we consider non-protected groups in this challenge set, the examples are labeled as abusive/non-abusive as opposed to hateful/non-hateful in HateCheck (shown in Table 1). We assess the sufficiency of these concepts with the challenge set first and then compare the results to those of the proposed concept-based explanation metrics. Our goal is to investigate if the findings for the broad concept of describing protected groups with negative emotions can also be replicated at a more nuanced level of emotional granularity. We analyze the models for fine-grained categories of negative emotions, identified by Mohammad (2018), namely *disgust*, *anger*, *sadness*, and *fear*. Similar pre-processing steps to what was described in Section 4 were performed to filter the lexicon in each category of emotions.

For the challenge set, we write five abusive and five non-abusive example templates for each emotion. Then we generate 40 abusive and 40 non-abusive examples by replacing <group> with one of the terms *Canadians, Chinese people, doctors, teachers, school children, football players, my neighbours, and men* to represent non-protected groups.[4] Full list of examples of this challenge set is available in our GitHub repository mentioned in Section 1. Equivalently, for the TCAV procedure for concept templates, we use '*They are <emotion_word>*', instead of '*<protected_group> are <emotion word>*', which we used in Section 4.

5.1 Results

We first compare the three classifiers in handling negative emotions by investigating the results they produce for the challenge set. The $False_{suff}$ scores in Table 5 show that TweetEval has learned the highest sufficiency between these concepts and the label of abuse and therefore achieves the lowest separability between the positive and negative classes of the challenge set. To further clarify this we show the accuracy vs threshold curve for the *disgust* category of the challenge set in Figure 5. We observe that TweetEval only reaches high accuracies for a small range of thresholds, i.e, it generates a similar distribution of probabilities for the positive and negative classes that contain the emotion of *disgust*. On the other hand, Jigsaw has learned the least global sufficiency and reaches high accuracy over a wide range of thresholds.

Then we turn to the TCAV scores shown in Table 4. First, $TCAV_{dir}$ shows that the Civil Comments classifier is not significantly sensitive to negative emotions, i.e., the feature of negative emotions is not fully learned as a coherent feature by this classifier. TweetEval, on the other hand, shows significant $TCAV_{dir}$ and $TCAV_{mag}$ scores, indicating that this classifier is not only sensitive to these concepts but the influence of the concept on

[4]Though nationality may be considered a protected characteristic in some contexts, we include "Canadian" and "Chinese" here since nationality was not included in HateCheck and therefore not covered in the previous section.

Emotion	Example	Gold Label
disgust	"<group> are known for being **trash**."	abusive
	"It's reasonable that <group> are feeling **vindictive**."	non-abusive
anger	"All <group> are **abhorrent**."	abusive
	"<group> were **infuriated** by the injustice. "	non-abusive
sadness	"<group> are known for being **pathetic**."	abusive
	"<group> were **crushed** by the injustice."	non-abusive
fear	"<group> are just so **scary**."	abusive
	"<group> are **threatened** by these policies."	non-abusive

Table 3: Challenge set created for emotion categories. In each sentence, we use a word from the corresponding category of the NRC Emotion Intensity Lexicon (NRC-EIL) (Mohammad, 2018), shown in bolded font.

	$TCAV_{dir}$				$TCAV_{mag}$			
classifier	disgust	anger	sadness	fear	disgust	anger	sadness	fear
Civil	0.48(0.37)	0.26(0.27)	0.31(0.31)	0.19(0.27)	0.05(0.06)	0.02(0.03)	0.02(0.03)	0.01(0.03)
Jigsaw	**0.98(0.09)**	**0.93(0.2)**	0.91(0.2)	**0.95(0.18)**	0.08(0.03)	0.05(0.03)	0.03(0.02)	0.05(0.03)
TweetEval	**1(0)**	**1(0)**	**1(0)**	**1(0)**	**0.20(0.04)**	**0.17(0.04)**	**0.11(0.03)**	**0.13(0.03)**

Table 4: Mean and standard deviation of concept-based metrics for four negative emotion concepts. Scores that are significantly different from random concepts are in boldface.

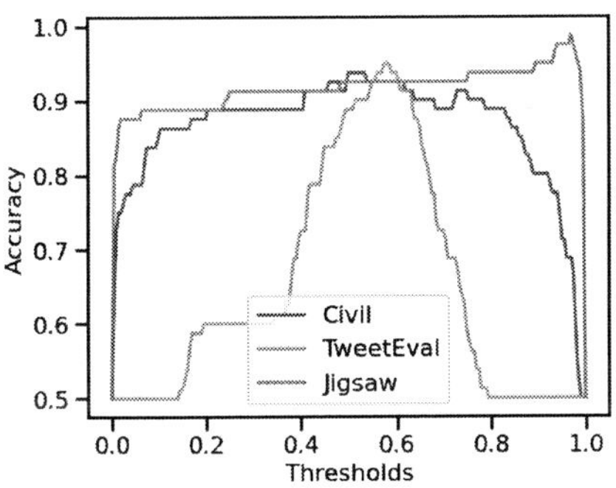

Figure 5: Accuracy vs threshold for the disgust category of the challenge set.

the label is also significantly high. Jigsaw is the classifier that has learned the dependency between negative emotions and the label of abuse and therefore is sensitive to it (as indicated by $TCAV_{dir}$), but the magnitude of the influence of concept on the label is not significantly high, and the concept is interpreted in the larger context. Interestingly, the magnitude of the influence of *disgust* and *anger* is higher than *fear* and *sadness* for all classifiers, stating a higher association of *disgust* and *anger* with abusive language. These results are in line with conclusions drawn from assessing global sufficiency with a challenge set.

6 Related Works

Most of the explainability works in NLP focus on feature importance methods to measure the importance of an input feature for the prediction at the local level (Bahdanau et al., 2015; Sundararajan et al., 2017; Ribeiro et al., 2016; Lundberg and Lee, 2017b). However, recent works highlight that models should be assessed beyond feature importance criteria and that the reasoning behind the model's decisions should be investigated through explainability methods. Some examples of such explainability methods include counterfactual reasoning (Wu et al., 2021; Kaushik et al., 2021; Ribeiro et al., 2020; Ross et al., 2020) or necessity and sufficiency metrics (Balkır et al., 2022; Joshi et al., 2022). Also, there is a need to compare various classifiers at the global level. Although local explanations can be aggregated to generate global explanations, they are usually obtained through costly interventions and are not practical to be applied on a large scale. For global explanations, a popular approach is to train probing classifiers (Conneau et al., 2018). However, probes only identify whether a classifier has learned a feature but stay silent about whether the feature is used in predictions (Belinkov, 2022; Tenney et al., 2019; Rogers et al., 2020). Amnesic probing is an extension of probing classifiers that identifies whether removing a feature influences the model's predictions, which relates to the notion of the global necessity of a human-understandable concept for a prediction (Ravfogel et al., 2020; Elazar et al., 2021). Our work, on the other hand, focuses on the global sufficiency of concepts. While probing classifiers are applied to linguistic properties such as POS

	False_Suff			
classifier	disgust	anger	sadness	fear
Civil	0.13	0.35	0.19	0.25
Jigsaw	0.08	0.28	0.14	0.22
TweetEval	0.36	0.36	0.35	0.35

Table 5: The global sufficiency of emotion categories learned by classifiers with respect to the challenge set described in Table 3.

tagging, which are necessary for accurate language processing, we focus on human-defined semantic concepts that are known to be important for the label and test if they have been falsely learned as a sufficient cause for the label.

Concept-based explanations have been introduced in computer vision and are mostly used to explain image classification models (Graziani et al., 2018; Ghorbani et al., 2019; Yeh et al., 2020). In NLP, concept-based explanations were used to measure the sensitivity of an abusive language classifier to the emerging concept of *COVID-related anti-Asian hate speech* (Nejadgholi et al., 2022b), to assess the fairness of abusive language classifiers in using the concept of sentiment (Nejadgholi et al., 2022a), and to explain a text classifier with reference to the concepts identified through topic modelling (Yeh et al., 2020). To the best of our knowledge, our work is the first that uses concept-based explanations to assess the sufficiency of human-defined concepts in text classification.

7 Conclusion

Concept-based explanations can assess the influence of a concept on a model's predictions. We used two metrics based on the TCAV method: the TCAV *direction* score identifies whether the classifier has learned an association between a concept and a label, and the TCAV *magnitude* score measures the extent of the influence of the concept on the label. We showed that the best-performing abusive language classifiers learned that negative emotion is associated with abuse (positive direction) but did not over-rely on this concept (low magnitude); that is, they did not overestimate the global sufficiency of that concept.

Our method can potentially be used for other NLP classification tasks. This approach is suitable for tasks where certain concepts are closely related to the label, but not enough to make a definitive determination. For example, in sentiment analysis, the price of products may have a strong connection to negative sentiment, but is insufficient to determine it. Further research should explore how concept-based explanations can help identify cases where certain concepts are relied upon too heavily in abusive language detection or other NLP classification tasks.

8 Limitations

Our work has limitations. First, we use the TCAV framework, which assumes that concepts are encoded in the linear space of semantic representations. However, recent works show that in some cases, linear discriminants are not enough to define the semantic representations of concepts in the embedding spaces (Koh et al., 2020). Future work should consider nonlinear discriminants to accurately represent concepts in the hidden layers of NLP neural networks.

In this study, we used simple challenge sets to obtain a baseline for assessing the effectiveness of concept-based explanations in measuring false global sufficiency. Future work should focus on curating challenge sets by annotating user-generated data for the label and the concepts, in order to achieve a stronger baseline.

Our work is limited to pre-defined concepts and requires human input to define the concepts with examples. However, defining concepts in TCAV is less restrictive than pre-defining features in other explainability methods, in that concepts are abstract ideas that can be defined without requiring in-depth knowledge of the model's inner workings or the specific features it is using. This allows for a more flexible approach where users can test the model regarding their concept of interest.

Our method can only be applied to concepts that are known to be important for the classifier and are prone to being over-represented in training sets. It's important to check this condition independently before using our metrics. In cases where this condition does not hold true, the metrics we use in our work may be interpreted differently and may not be reliable indicators of global sufficiency. Also, we only considered two variations of emotion-related concepts. Other variations such as *expression of negative emotions by the writer of the post* should be investigated in future work.

Further, our metrics are limited to cases where different classifiers are being compared since the most important information is in the relative value of the metrics. Our metrics should not be used as absolute scores for testing a classifier.

Testing a classifier for false causal relationships is most valuable for detecting the potential flaws of the models. If our metrics do not reveal a false relationship between the concept and the label, that should not be interpreted as an indicator of a flawless model.

Ethical Statement

As with most AI technology, this approach can be used adversely to exploit the system's vulnerabilities and produce toxic texts that would be undetectable by the studied classifier. Specifically, for methods that require access to the model's inner layers, care should be taken so that only trusted parties could gain such access. The obtained knowledge should only be used for model transparency purposes, and the security concerns should be adequately addressed.

Regarding environmental concerns, contemporary NLP systems based on pre-trained large language models, such as RoBERTa, require significant computational resources to train and fine-tune. Larger training datasets, used for fine-tuning, usually result in better classification performance but also an even higher computational cost. To lower the cost of this study and its negative impact on the environment, we chose to use existing, publicly available classification models.

References

Dzmitry Bahdanau, Kyung Hyun Cho, and Yoshua Bengio. 2015. Neural machine translation by jointly learning to align and translate. In *Proceedings of the 3rd International Conference on Learning Representations*.

Esma Balkir, Svetlana Kiritchenko, Isar Nejadgholi, and Kathleen Fraser. 2022. Challenges in applying explainability methods to improve the fairness of NLP models. In *Proceedings of the 2nd Workshop on Trustworthy Natural Language Processing (TrustNLP 2022)*, pages 80–92, Seattle, U.S.A. Association for Computational Linguistics.

Esma Balkır, Isar Nejadgholi, Kathleen Fraser, and Svetlana Kiritchenko. 2022. Necessity and sufficiency for explaining text classifiers: A case study in hate speech detection. In *Proceedings of the 2022 Conference of the North American Chapter of the Association for Computational Linguistics: Human Language Technologies*, pages 2672–2686, Seattle, United States. Association for Computational Linguistics.

Francesco Barbieri, Jose Camacho-Collados, Luis Espinosa Anke, and Leonardo Neves. 2020. TweetEval: Unified benchmark and comparative evaluation for tweet classification. In *Findings of the Association for Computational Linguistics: EMNLP 2020*, pages 1644–1650, Online. Association for Computational Linguistics.

Yonatan Belinkov. 2022. Probing classifiers: Promises, shortcomings, and advances. *Computational Linguistics*, 48(1):207–219.

Daniel Borkan, Lucas Dixon, Jeffrey Sorensen, Nithum Thain, and Lucy Vasserman. 2019. Nuanced metrics for measuring unintended bias with real data for text classification. In *Companion Proceedings of The 2019 World Wide Web Conference*, pages 491—500.

Nadia Burkart and Marco F Huber. 2021. A survey on the explainability of supervised machine learning. *Journal of Artificial Intelligence Research*, 70:245–317.

Patricia Chiril, Endang Wahyu Pamungkas, Farah Benamara, Véronique Moriceau, and Viviana Patti. 2022. Emotionally informed hate speech detection: a multi-target perspective. *Cognitive Computation*, 14(1):322–352.

Alexis Conneau, German Kruszewski, Guillaume Lample, Loïc Barrault, and Marco Baroni. 2018. What you can cram into a single vector: Probing sentence embeddings for linguistic properties. *arXiv preprint arXiv:1805.01070*.

Yanai Elazar, Shauli Ravfogel, Alon Jacovi, and Yoav Goldberg. 2021. Amnesic probing: Behavioral explanation with amnesic counterfactuals. *Transactions of the Association for Computational Linguistics*, 9:160–175.

Paula Fortuna and Sérgio Nunes. 2018. A survey on automatic detection of hate speech in text. *ACM Computing Surveys (CSUR)*, 51(4):1–30.

Sainyam Galhotra, Romila Pradhan, and Babak Salimi. 2021. Explaining black-box algorithms using probabilistic contrastive counterfactuals. In *Proceedings of the 2021 International Conference on Management of Data*, pages 577–590.

Amirata Ghorbani, James Wexler, James Y Zou, and Been Kim. 2019. Towards automatic concept-based explanations. *Advances in Neural Information Processing Systems*, 32.

Mara Graziani, Vincent Andrearczyk, and Henning Müller. 2018. Regression concept vectors for bidirectional explanations in histopathology. In *Understanding and Interpreting Machine Learning in Medical Image Computing Applications*, pages 124–132. Springer.

Laura Hanu. 2020. How well can we detoxify comments online? Unitary, accessed on 15 June, 2022.

Laura Hanu and Unitary team. 2020. Detoxify. Github. https://github.com/unitaryai/detoxify.

Nitish Joshi, Xiang Pan, and He He. 2022. Are all spurious features in natural language alike? an analysis through a causal lens. *arXiv preprint arXiv:2210.14011*.

Divyansh Kaushik, Amrith Setlur, Eduard H Hovy, and Zachary Chase Lipton. 2021. Explaining the efficacy of counterfactually augmented data. In *Proceedings of the International Conference on Learning Representations*.

Been Kim, Martin Wattenberg, Justin Gilmer, Carrie Cai, James Wexler, Fernanda Viegas, et al. 2018. Interpretability beyond feature attribution: Quantitative testing with concept activation vectors (tcav). In *Proceedings of the International Conference on Machine Learning*, pages 2668–2677. PMLR.

Pang Wei Koh, Thao Nguyen, Yew Siang Tang, Stephen Mussmann, Emma Pierson, Been Kim, and Percy Liang. 2020. Concept bottleneck models. In *Proceedings of the International Conference on Machine Learning*, pages 5338–5348. PMLR.

Yinhan Liu, Myle Ott, Naman Goyal, Jingfei Du, Mandar Joshi, Danqi Chen, Omer Levy, Mike Lewis, Luke Zettlemoyer, and Veselin Stoyanov. 2019. Roberta: A robustly optimized bert pretraining approach. *arXiv preprint arXiv:1907.11692*.

Scott M Lundberg, Gabriel Erion, Hugh Chen, Alex DeGrave, Jordan M Prutkin, Bala Nair, Ronit Katz, Jonathan Himmelfarb, Nisha Bansal, and Su-In Lee. 2020. From local explanations to global understanding with explainable AI for trees. *Nature Machine Intelligence*, 2(1):56–67.

Scott M Lundberg and Su-In Lee. 2017a. A unified approach to interpreting model predictions. In I. Guyon, U. V. Luxburg, S. Bengio, H. Wallach, R. Fergus, S. Vishwanathan, and R. Garnett, editors, *Advances in Neural Information Processing Systems 30*, pages 4765–4774. Curran Associates, Inc.

Scott M Lundberg and Su-In Lee. 2017b. A unified approach to interpreting model predictions. *Advances in Neural Information Processing Systems*, 30.

Tomas Mikolov, Kai Chen, Greg Corrado, and Jeffrey Dean. 2013. Efficient estimation of word representations in vector space. *arXiv preprint arXiv:1301.3781*.

Saif M. Mohammad. 2018. Word affect intensities. In *Proceedings of the 11th Edition of the Language Resources and Evaluation Conference (LREC-2018)*, Miyazaki, Japan.

Isar Nejadgholi, Esma Balkır, Kathleen C Fraser, and Svetlana Kiritchenko. 2022a. Towards procedural fairness: Uncovering biases in how a toxic language classifier uses sentiment information. In *Proceedings of the Workshop on Analyzing and Interpreting Neural Networks for NLP (BlackboxNLP)*.

Isar Nejadgholi, Kathleen Fraser, and Svetlana Kiritchenko. 2022b. Improving generalizability in implicitly abusive language detection with concept activation vectors. In *Proceedings of the 60th Annual Meeting of the Association for Computational Linguistics (Volume 1: Long Papers)*, pages 5517–5529, Dublin, Ireland. Association for Computational Linguistics.

Shauli Ravfogel, Yanai Elazar, Hila Gonen, Michael Twiton, and Yoav Goldberg. 2020. Null it out: Guarding protected attributes by iterative nullspace projection. In *Proceedings of the 58th Annual Meeting of the Association for Computational Linguistics*, pages 7237–7256.

Marco Tulio Ribeiro, Sameer Singh, and Carlos Guestrin. 2016. "Why should i trust you?" Explaining the predictions of any classifier. In *Proceedings of the 22nd ACM SIGKDD International Conference on Knowledge Discovery and Data Mining*, pages 1135–1144.

Marco Tulio Ribeiro, Tongshuang Wu, Carlos Guestrin, and Sameer Singh. 2020. Beyond accuracy: Behavioral testing of NLP models with CheckList. In *Proceedings of the 58th Annual Meeting of the Association for Computational Linguistics*, pages 4902–4912, Online. Association for Computational Linguistics.

Anna Rogers, Olga Kovaleva, and Anna Rumshisky. 2020. A primer in bertology: What we know about how bert works. *Transactions of the Association for Computational Linguistics*, 8:842–866.

Alexis Ross, Ana Marasović, and Matthew E Peters. 2020. Explaining NLP models via minimal contrastive editing (MiCE). *arXiv preprint arXiv:2012.13985*.

Paul Röttger, Bertie Vidgen, Dong Nguyen, Zeerak Waseem, Helen Margetts, and Janet Pierrehumbert. 2021. HateCheck: Functional tests for hate speech detection models. In *Proceedings of the 59th Annual Meeting of the Association for Computational Linguistics and the 11th International Joint Conference on Natural Language Processing (Volume 1: Long Papers)*, pages 41–58, Online. Association for Computational Linguistics.

Mukund Sundararajan, Ankur Taly, and Qiqi Yan. 2017. Axiomatic attribution for deep networks. In *Proceedings of the International Conference on Machine Learning*, pages 3319–3328.

Ian Tenney, Patrick Xia, Berlin Chen, Alex Wang, Adam Poliak, R Thomas McCoy, Najoung Kim, Benjamin Van Durme, Samuel R Bowman, Dipanjan Das, et al. 2019. What do you learn from context? probing for sentence structure in contextualized word representations. *arXiv preprint arXiv:1905.06316*.

David S Watson, Limor Gultchin, Ankur Taly, and Luciano Floridi. 2021. Local explanations via necessity and sufficiency: Unifying theory and practice. In *Uncertainty in Artificial Intelligence*, pages 1382–1392. PMLR.

Tongshuang Wu, Marco Tulio Ribeiro, Jeffrey Heer, and Daniel Weld. 2021. Polyjuice: Generating counterfactuals for explaining, evaluating, and improving models. In *Proceedings of the 59th Annual Meeting of the Association for Computational Linguistics and the 11th International Joint Conference on Natural Language Processing (Volume 1: Long Papers)*, pages 6707–6723, Online. Association for Computational Linguistics.

Ellery Wulczyn, Nithum Thain, and Lucas Dixon. 2017. Ex machina: Personal attacks seen at scale. In *Proceedings of the 26th International Conference on World Wide Web*, WWW '17, pages 1391–1399, Republic and Canton of Geneva, CHE. International World Wide Web Conferences Steering Committee.

Chih-Kuan Yeh, Been Kim, Sercan Arik, Chun-Liang Li, Tomas Pfister, and Pradeep Ravikumar. 2020. On completeness-aware concept-based explanations in deep neural networks. *Advances in Neural Information Processing Systems*, 33:20554–20565.

Chih-Kuan Yeh, Been Kim, and Pradeep Ravikumar. 2022. Human-centered concept explanations for neural networks. In P. Hitzler and M. K. Sarker, editors, *Neuro-Symbolic Artificial Intelligence: The State of the Art*, volume 342, page 2. IOS Press.

Wenjie Yin and Arkaitz Zubiaga. 2021. Towards generalisable hate speech detection: a review on obstacles and solutions. *PeerJ Computer Science*, 7:e598.

Mohammad Nokhbeh Zaeem and Majid Komeili. 2021. Cause and effect: Concept-based explanation of neural networks. In *2021 IEEE International Conference on Systems, Man, and Cybernetics (SMC)*, pages 2730–2736. IEEE.

Marcos Zampieri, Shervin Malmasi, Preslav Nakov, Sara Rosenthal, Noura Farra, and Ritesh Kumar. 2019. Predicting the type and target of offensive posts in social media. In *Proceedings of the 2019 Conference of the North American Chapter of the Association for Computational Linguistics: Human Language Technologies, Volume 1 (Long and Short Papers)*, pages 1415–1420, Minneapolis, Minnesota. Association for Computational Linguistics.

A Models

We include the following publicly available abusive language classification models in this study:

- **Jigsaw**[5]: a RoBERTa-based binary toxicity classifier fine-tuned on the combination of two datasets created by Jigsaw and used in Kaggle competitions on toxicity prediction in 2018-2020. The first dataset, Wikipedia Toxic Comments (Wulczyn et al., 2017), includes 160K comments from Wikipedia talk pages. The second dataset, Civil Comments (Borkan et al., 2019), comprises over 1.8M online comments from news websites. Both datasets are annotated for toxicity (and its subtypes) by crowd-sourcing. The model creators report the AUC of 0.98 and F1-score of 0.76 on the Wikipedia Toxic Comments test set. The model is released under CC BY-NC-SA 4.0.

- **Civil Comments**[6] (Hanu and Unitary team, 2020): a multi-class RoBERTa-based model fine-tuned on the Civil Comments dataset to predict toxicity and six toxicity subtypes (severe toxicity, obscene, threat, insult, identity attack, and sexual explicit). A part of the dataset is annotated for identity groups targeted in toxic comments. The prediction model is trained to optimize the outcome fairness for the groups in addition to the overall accuracy. This is achieved through the loss function that combines the weighted loss functions for two tasks, toxicity prediction and identity prediction (Hanu, 2020).

- **TweetEval**[7] (Barbieri et al., 2020): a RoBERTa-based binary classifier to detect offensive language, released as part of the TweetEval evaluation benchmark. The model was trained on 58M tweets and then fine-tuned on the Offensive Language Identification Dataset (OLID) (Zampieri et al., 2019). The OLID training set comprises about 12K tweets. The model achieved the macro-averaged F1-score of 77.1 on the OLID test set.

[5] https://huggingface.co/SkolkovoInstitute/roberta_toxicity_classifier/tree/main

[6] https://huggingface.co/unitary/unbiased-toxic-roberta

[7] https://huggingface.co/cardiffnlp/twitter-roberta-base-offensive

“Female Astronaut: Because sandwiches won’t make themselves up there!": Towards multi-modal misogyny detection in memes

Smriti Singh* Dept. of Computer Science UT Austin

Amritha Haridasan* Dept. of Computer Science UT Austin

Raymond Mooney Dept. of Computer Science UT Austin

Abstract

A rise in the circulation of memes has led to the spread of a new form of multimodal hateful content. Unfortunately, the degree of hate women receive on the internet is disproportionately skewed against them. This, combined with the fact that multimodal misogyny is more challenging to detect as opposed to traditional text-based misogyny, signifies that the task of identifying misogynistic memes online is one of utmost importance. To this end, the MAMI dataset was released, consisting of 12000 memes annotated for misogyny and four sub-classes of misogyny - shame, objectification, violence and stereotype. While this balanced dataset is widely cited, we find that the task itself remains largely unsolved. Thus, in our work, we[1] investigate the performance of multiple models in an effort to analyse whether domain specific pretraining helps model performance. We also investigate why even state of the art models find this task so challenging, and whether domain-specific pretraining can help. Our results show that pretraining BERT on hateful memes and leveraging an attention-based approach with ViT outperforms state of the art models by more than 10%. Further, we provide insight into why these models may be struggling with this task with an extensive qualitative analysis of random samples from the test set.

1 Introduction

With a rise in social media usage, memes have become an important part of expression, and communication today. Multiple research studies have found that memes play a role in shaping a wide range of beliefs, such as climate change, use as bonding icons, political discussion, and social development. This new form of media, however, is still host to old-school offensive content that was previously seen in non-multimodal settings. This includes hate speech of different forms, such as sexism and racism. The emergence of this popular media format has brought along the need to detect hateful content in multimodal formats, to ensure that the internet remains a safe space for all groups. Further, there has been evidence to show that women are disproportionately targeted on the internet. For example, 33% of women under 35 say they have been sexually harassed online, while 11% of men under 35 say the same[2]. It has also been shown through many psychological and social science-based studies that the effects of online hate speech are observed well beyond the boundaries of the cyber world (Pluta et al., 2023). Yet, traditional, language-based misogyny detection techniques are no longer fully effective when it comes to multimodal misogyny. This is because, unlike text-based misogyny, identifying multimodal misogyny involves picking up on visual cues combined with sarcasm and linguistic nuances.

To try and bridge this challenge, Fersini et al. (2022) developed, licensed, and released MAMI: Multimedia automatic misogyny detection, a dataset of 12000 memes, labeled for misogyny and four subclasses – shaming, objectification, violence, and stereotypes. The dataset is balanced across all classes and was released as a part of the SemEval Task in 2022. While this dataset is widely cited, and there have been multiple approaches developed to leverage this dataset for misogyny detection, we find that this challenging task remains unsolved to a large extent. To the best of our knowledge, no research aims to understand exactly why even the best models are unable to succeed at this task. Moreover, there is no research (to the best of our knowledge) that showcases the potential benefit (or lack thereof) of using models pre-trained on other hate-speech data. Therefore, the focus of our work is two-fold: Thus, in our work, instead of

[1] /* denotes equal contribution

[2] https://www.forbes.com/sites/ewelinaochab/2023/03/08/when-the-harassment-of-women-moves-online/?sh=3a9d64223f29

The 7th Workshop on Online Abuse and Harms (WOAH), pages 150–159

solely focusing on developing a model that outperforms the current state-of-the-art architectures, we focus on the following broader research questions:

- Do multimodal models understand misogyny in memes better than language-only or vision-only models?
- Do these models benefit from pre-training on text hate-speech datasets?
- What can't these models do? What mistakes do they make? Is there a pattern that can be observed in their mistakes?

Our contributions, per the aforementioned research questions, are as follows:

- We present a multimodal model, BERT*+VIT, that is pre-trained on hate-speech text data, finetuned on the MAMI dataset.
- An extensive quantitative analysis of the performance of various state-of-the-art models when fine-tuned on the MAMI dataset – text only, language only, and multimodal.
- A qualitative analysis of the mistakes made by different models.

The rest of this paper is organized as follows: Section 2 describes the related work, Section 3 elaborates on the experiments we conduct as a part of our methodology and Section 4 summarizes the results obtained.

2 Related Work

One of the first large-scale challenges that involved detecting hateful memes is the 'Hateful memes challenge' organized by Facebook AI (Kiela et al., 2020). To quote the authors, "Memes pose an interesting multimodal fusion problem: Consider a sentence like "love the way you smell today" or "look how many people love you". Unimodally, these sentences are harmless, but combine them with an equally harmless image of a skunk or a tumbleweed, and suddenly they become mean." They release the hateful memes dataset, consisting of 10,000 memes annotated for unimodal hate, multimodal hate, benign text, benign image, and random non-hateful examples.

This was followed by many research efforts to categorize memes beyond hateful, such as Zia et al. (2021), who looked at classifying memes as racist and/or sexist, Nafiah and Prasetyo (2021) who focused on analyzing and identifying sexist memes during the COVID-19 pandemic, and Suryawanshi et al. (2020) who used the presidential election to develop a dataset of memes consisting of racism, sexism and homophobia.

The MAMI dataset (Fersini et al., 2022) was the first of its kind to motivate the sub-classification of misogynistic memes. This task, as a part of the SemEval 2022 contest, showcased many noteworthy methodologies for the proposed problem. For example, Sharma et al. (2022b) proposed an R2D2 architecture that used pre-trained models as feature extractors for text and images. They used these features to learn multimodal representation using methods like concatenation and scaled dot product attention. This methodology achieved an F1 score of 0.757 and was ranked 3rd in Subtask, and 10th on Subtask B, with an F1 score of 0.690. In another study, Mahadevan et al. (2022) develop an ensemble model consisting of XLM-RoBERTa, DistilBERT, ResNext, and Data-efficient Image Transformer to achieve an average F1 of 0.71 on Task A and 0.69 on Task B. However, these authors established an SVM as their baseline. Our goal is to explore a wider range of similar models, using such models as a baseline, and hopefully develop a better one. For now, we plan to use precision, recall, and F1 score as our evaluation metrics, along with a manual qualitative analysis that can provide insight into how to better direct future model improvements.

Another interesting approach is that proposed by Muti et al. (2022), which combines BERT and CLIP, achieving an F1 of 0.727 on sub Task A, and an F1 of 0.710 on sub Task B. Kalkenings and Mandl (2022) extends a similar approach by using BERT and FCNN, and testing it on the aforementioned Facebook AI's hateful meme challenge dataset for generalisability. An approach that is similar to ours to an extent is that of Sharma et al. (2022a), who test a variety of language models on the text part of the MAMI dataset. Our approach involves using such models to establish a comparative baseline of language-only models and combine them with vision-based models to analyze how that affects model performance. Finally, in another noteworthy experiment, Hakimov et al. (2022) proposes a CLIP text encoder and an LSTM for the text encoding part of the model. This model attains an F1 score of 0.834 on subtask A and an F1 score of

0.731 on subtask B.

In our work, we want to look beyond merely training a classifier that outperforms these methods. We are more interested in analyzing the finer details, and understanding *what* these models are doing wrong. Further, we are interested in establishing comparison baselines through text models and vision models to gain insight into which feature is more important, and to what extent. To the best of our knowledge, prior to this, there has been no experimentation to show the benefits of using pretrained models for multimodal misogyny detection.

3 Methodology

As discussed in Section 2, following the SemEval Task itself, we will refer to Task A as the classification of a meme as misogynistic and Task B as the subclassification of a misogynistic meme. Further, all models are finetuned on this dataset. As described later in the paper, BERT* benefits from pretraining on the hateful meme dataset.

3.1 MAMI: Dataset description

Although the MAMI dataset has been well described in the original paper (Fersini et al., 2022), we provide a summary of it here, for a holistic understanding of the experiments conducted in this study.

This dataset consists of 12,000 memes. The breakdown of these memes for train-test-dev is 10,000 - 1,000- 1,000 respectively. Further, the misogynistic memes are classified into four subclasses as mentioned above. The distribution across subclasses is shown below in Table 1.

The process of gathering pertinent memes for analysis involved searching popular social media platforms like Twitter and Reddit, as well as accessing dedicated meme creation and sharing websites such as 9GAG, Knowyourmeme, and Imgur. To ensure an adequate number of misogynous memes, the researchers undertook activities such as searching for meme threads focused on women, exploring discussions by individuals with anti-women or anti-feminist sentiments, investigating recent events. By employing these methods, a diverse dataset of relevant memes was successfully compiled for further examination in their study.

The authors found a coefficient of 0.5767 for agreement on misogynous vs. not misogynous annotations, and a coefficient of 0.3373 for the type of misogyny labeling. The dataset details are presented in Table 2. The Fleiss-k measure indicated moderate agreement for misogynous labeling, indicating a relatively straightforward task for humans. However, the agreement for the type of misogyny annotation was fair, suggesting a more challenging task.

Subclass	Train	Test
Shaming	1274	126
Stereotype	2810	350
Objectification	2202	348
Violence	953	153

Table 1: Distribution of misogynistic memes across subclasses

The dataset is evenly split between misogynistic and non-misogynistic memes with 5000 samples in the train and test set each,

3.2 Unimodal models

To establish baseline models, we experiment with a variety of language and vision models. For language models, we use the text from the memes and finetune the following models:

- BERT
- DeBERTa
- RoBERTa
- Hateful memes pre-trained BERT

Here, the last model is a model hosted on HuggingFace that has been pre-trained on the text from the hateful memes dataset released by Facebook AI [3]. Similarly, we train the following vision models on the memes to establish vision-only baselines:

- CNN
- Inception
- ViT

We showcase the performance of these models in Section 4.

[3]https://huggingface.co/am4nsolanki/autonlp-text-hateful-memes-36789092

	Misogyny Labelling (Sub-task A)			Type of Misogyny Labelling (Sub-task B)				
	Misogynous	Not Misogynous	Fleiss-k Agreement	Shaming	Stereotype	Objectification	Violence	Fleiss-k Agreement
Training Set	5000(50%)	5000(50%)	0.5767	1274(25.48%)	2810(56.20%)	2202(44.04%)	953(19.06%)	0.3373
Test Set	500(50%)	500(50%)	0.5767	146(29.20%)	350(70.00%)	348(69.60%)	153(30.60%)	0.3373

Table 2: Dataset Characteristics (Fersini et al., 2022)

3.3 Multimodal models

3.3.1 CLIP

CLIP (Contrastive Language-Image Pre-training) (Radford et al., 2021) is a state-of-the-art language and vision model developed by OpenAI. It is capable of understanding images and natural language text and can perform a range of tasks such as image classification, object detection, and captioning. The model has been trained on a large dataset of image-text pairs, allowing it to learn the correlations between visual and textual features. One of the unique features of CLIP is that it uses a contrastive learning approach, which means that it learns by comparing and contrasting similar and dissimilar image-text pairs.

The CLIP model consists of two parts: a vision encoder and a language encoder. The vision encoder is a convolutional neural network (CNN) that takes in an image and outputs a vector representation of the image. The language encoder is a transformer-based model that takes in natural language text and outputs a vector representation of the text. For our research, we finetuned the model with the Adam optimizer with a learning rate of 1e-4, weight decay of 0.01, and a batch size of 16. The maximum number of epochs is limited to 20, and early stopping is implemented with a patience of 3 epochs.

3.3.2 BERT + Inception

The BERT + Inception model (Guda et al., 2020) is a deep learning model that combines two different neural networks, BERT and Inception, to achieve better performance on image-text matching tasks. BERT, or Bidirectional Encoder Representations from Transformers (Devlin et al., 2018), is a pre-trained language model that excels at natural language processing (NLP) tasks, such as sentiment analysis and text classification. On the other hand, Inception is a convolutional neural network (CNN) (Szegedy et al., 2016) that is well-suited for image recognition and classification tasks. By combining these two models, the BERT + Inception model can effectively encode both text and image inputs and map them to a common latent space for matching.

The text encoder uses the BERT architecture, which is pre-trained on a large corpus of text data. The BERT model is used to encode textual descriptions into a fixed-size vector. The image encoder uses the InceptionV3 architecture, with the weights pre-trained on the ImageNet dataset. The InceptionV3 model is modified to remove the top classification layer and replace it with a global average pooling layer to generate a fixed-size feature vector for each input image. The sequence and pooled outputs from the text input are concatenated with the processed image input and passed through three dense layers with ReLU activation and dropout layers. The purpose of these dense layers is to combine the information from both the image and text encoders and generate a more informative representation for the final classification. The model is trained using a contrastive loss function (Alluri and Krishna, 2021) that encourages the image and text representations to be similar for positive pairs, and dissimilar for negative pairs. The batch size used in the training loop is 256. The model is trained for 10 epochs in each iteration of the training loop, and early stopping is implemented with a patience of 5 epochs, with a learning rate of 1e-4.

3.3.3 BERT + ViT

BERT is designed for processing text data and does not take into account the visual information present in many modern datasets. The Vision Transformer (Dosovitskiy et al., 2020) is a neural network architecture that has been specifically designed for processing visual information, such as images or videos. It uses a self-attention mechanism to analyze and process visual information, allowing it to learn complex patterns and relationships between different elements in an image. By combining BERT with the Vision Transformer (Velioglu and Rose, 2020), we can create a powerful hybrid architecture that can process both text and visual information simultaneously.

The model has three input layers – one for the image input, one for the text input, and one for the input masks. The text input is processed using the BERT model to encode the input text into contextualized embeddings, and the image input is processed using the Vision Transformer (ViT) model to flatten images into patches to linearly project and combine with position encoding. The output features of the two models are combined using an attention mechanism and then passed through a 1D convolutional layer and a flatten layer to create joint features. The final output of the model is a probability distribution over the possible classes, which is obtained by passing the joint text and image embedding features through one or more fully connected layers with sigmoid activation. During training, the model is optimized using backpropagation and stochastic gradient descent with cross-entropy loss. The model was trained using Adam optimizer with a learning rate of 4e-5 for 5 epochs and a batch size of 16 was used.

3.3.4 VisualBERT

VisualBERT (Li et al., 2019)is a pre-trained model that combines the power of the BERT architecture with visual features to understand language in the context of images. The architecture of VisualBERT consists of two separate encoders, one for the visual modality and one for the textual modality. The visual encoder processes the image and extracts visual features, which are then combined with the textual features extracted by the textual encoder. These features are then fed into the BERT model for further processing, allowing the model to understand the relationship between the image and the text. VisualBERT uses a hierarchical approach to process the visual information, starting with low-level visual features and gradually moving up to more abstract concepts.

In VisualBERT, (Muennighoff, 2020) the image features extracted from pre-trained object proposal systems, such as Faster-RCNN, are treated as input tokens, just like words in a text. These image features are unordered, meaning they are not processed in any particular sequence or order. Along with the text, the image features are fed into the multi-layer Transformer architecture of VisualBERT, where they are processed and used to build a joint representation of the text and image. This allows the model to capture the intricate associations between text and image and enables it to perform tasks that require understanding the semantics of both modalities. The model was fine-tuned using an Adam optimizer with a learning rate of 2e-5, training for 10 epochs with a batch size of 32.

3.3.5 BERT* + ViT

Here, BERT* refers to a BERT model which is pre-trained on the hateful memes dataset released by Facebook AI. We propose using the model, BERT* + ViT which is a model that combines two powerful neural networks, a domain-specific pre-trained BERT model and ViT (Sohn and Lee, 2019). The image is passed through the Vision Transformer (ViT), while the text is passed through the BERT model. The text sequence embedding and image embedding are then combined using an attention mechanism, which attends to the relevant parts of the image based on the text input.

The model has achieved state-of-the-art performance on several benchmark datasets for hate speech detection (d'Sa et al., 2020). The use of both text and image information improves the model's ability to detect subtle nuances in hate speech and non-hate speech messages. The attention mechanism allows the model to attend to the most relevant features in both modalities and combine them to make a prediction. The convolutional layer further refines the joint features obtained from the two models, and the final dense layer predicts the probability of hate speech. The model has been pre-trained on a large corpus of hate speech data, making it highly effective at detecting hate speech in real-world scenarios. The training process utilized the Adam optimizer with a learning rate of 4e-5 for a duration of 5 epochs, and the training data were processed in batches of 16.

4 Results

4.1 Comparison of Baseline Models and Multimodal Models

Tables 3 and 4 answer our first two research questions about how each baseline compares to multimodal models, and how domain-specific pretraining may be useful to the model.

Model	Precision	Recall	F1	Modality
BERT	0.662	0.650	0.643	Lang
DeBERTa	0.684	0.682	0.681	Lang
RoBERTa	0.632	0.628	0.620	Lang
BERT*	0.685	0.695	0.690	Lang
CNN	0.571	0.782	0.616	Vision
ViT	0.611	0.659	0.632	Vision
Inception	0.511	0.672	0.623	Vision
BERT + Inception	0.623	0.778	0.694	Both
BERT + ViT	0.624	0.890	0.734	Both
BERT* +ViT	**0.862**	**0.881**	**0.874**	**Both**
CLIP	0.655	0.782	0.652	Both
VisualBERT	0.623	0.687	0.666	Both

Table 3: Performance of various finetuned models on subtask A. BERT* denotes the BERT model that has been pretrained on the hateful memes dataset.

Here, we find that BERT*+VIT outperforms even the top-ranking models described in Section 2 by a considerable margin. This indicates that domain-specific pretraining is indeed, quite useful in boosting model performance.

We also observe that apart from the model that has the advantage of domain-specific pretraining, the other models don't have a very large difference in terms of F1 scores. However, as one would expect, we see that the vision-only baselines are a bit lower than the text-only baselines. Multimodality can help significantly, for example, adding ViT improves the F1 score of BERT by 9 points. However, we find that some multimodal models actually perform worse than unimodal models (for instance, CLIP and DeBERTa). This implies a need for investigation as to what may be confounding the multimodal models, which we present our analysis for in Section 4.2.

Table 4 shows the performance of these models on subtask B. For this subtask, we record the F1 score for each class to ensure readability. Here, we see that the pre-trained multimodal model outperforms the others by a small margin. The table indicates that memes containing violence and objectification are easier to detect compared to the other classes, regardless of the model used. This is probably due to the fact that these are the most non-ambiguous memes, i.e., the classes where the memes (especially likely the text) often have only one meaning. This is discussed further below.

4.2 Qualitative Analysis

To answer our last research question, we present an extensive qualitative analysis of 200 randomly sampled memes from the test set. Our goal is to find potential patterns in errors made by the best-performing model. This is, to the best of our knowledge, the first time an error analysis is being performed for any model finetuned on the MAMI dataset. Our observations are as follows:

4.2.1 Visual Grounding in itself is not enough

For around 80 memes (out of the 200 randomly sampled ones), we find that the incorrect prediction might be owing to the fact that even visual grounding is not enough. This is particularly true for memes belonging to the stereotype class, but can occasionally apply to the shaming class too. We show an example in Figure 1. The idea here is that the model needs to be able to understand the stereotype behind the image/text combination, and simply looking at the memes may not provide that.

4.2.2 Lack of Context

Some memes (around 15) lack context in terms of exactly how they are offensive. These are memes that might prove challenging to classify even for humans. One such example is shown in Figure 2.

4.2.3 Lack of understanding of subtle objectification

Most of the memes that were randomly sampled from the objectification class are quite explicit in nature. However, the ones that have a lower degree of objectification/sexuality often go undetected by the model. For example, in Figure 3, it is not

Model	Stereotype	Shaming	Objectification	Violence
BERT	0.633	0.612	0.688	0.689
DeBERTa	0.651	0.627	0.655	0.678
RoBERTa	0.624	0.618	0.677	0.682
Pretrained BERT	0.644	0.683	0.685	0.691
CNN	0.551	0.582	0.577	0.613
ViT	0.541	0.608	0.591	0.612
Inception	0.595	0.605	0.613	0.599
BERT + Inception	0.644	0.621	0.685	0.690
BERT + ViT	0.653	0.631	0.695	0.710
BERT*+ViT	**0.697**	**0.695**	**0.693**	**0.721**
CLIP	0.648	0.628	0.655	0.684
VisualBERT	0.647	0.623	0.676	0.683

Table 4: Performance of various finetuned models on subtask B. BERT* denotes the BERT model that has been pretrained on the hateful memes dataset.

Figure 1: An example where it is necessary to understand the stereotype that "women belong in the kitchen" is misogynistic. The model misclassifies this as neutral.

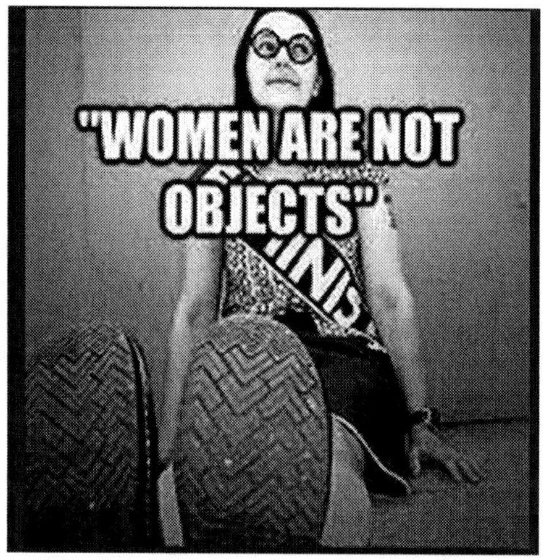

Figure 2: An example where context is unclear. The model marks this as violent.

enough to look at the image in itself, because all that is visible is a woman posing for the camera. It is also not enough to read the text. Some social context is needed to interpret that this meme could be hinting toward sex trafficking or other illicit similarities.

4.3 Analysis of benefits of pre-training

In this part of the paper, we provide examples of where pre-training helps BERT* classify complicated memes that require an understanding of visuolinguistic cues.

4.3.1 Understanding complex objectification

We find that by pre-training on hateful memes, the model is able to identify memes that objectify us-

Figure 3: An example where objectification is subtle. The model misclassified this as shaming.

ing a combination of visual cues and complicated linguistic cues. Figure 4 shows an example of this phenomenon.

Figure 4: An example where the objectification is through a combination of visuo-linguistic cues. BERT* correctly classifies this as objectification.

4.3.2 Understanding lewd complex linguistic cues

Our results indicate that pretraining helps BERT* pick up on some complex linguistic innuendos that are offensive. The reason for this is somewhat unclear, but we hypothesize that the model benefits from a larger exposure to multimodal hateful content. For example, consider the meme shown in Figure 5. The model correctly identifies it as shaming, This means that it understands that losing a shoe in this case is suggestive of provocative shaming. This example doesn't rely on any visual cues, but the model is still able to classify it correctly.

Figure 5: An example of BERT* correctly identifying complex linguistic cues

4.3.3 Connecting seemingly harmless text with objectifying images

While identifying misogynistic memes that are hateful through subtle visual cues and otherwise seemingly harmless text is still a challenge in this area, we find that BERT* benefits from pretraining to at least identify these memes correctly, if not subclassify them properly. For example, BERT* marks the meme shown in Figure 6 correctly as misogynistic in subtask A, but makes an error in classifying it as shaming instead of objectification, our hypothesis is that the model may further benefit from pretraining/finetuning on larger datasets that contain more examples of misogyny.

5 Conclusion

In this research, we have delved into the challenging task of identifying misogynistic memes online. By utilizing the MAMI dataset with 12,000 annotated memes, we have established baselines and conducted experiments with various models, including text-only, vision-only, and multimodal models. Our findings indicate that pretraining BERT on hateful memes and utilizing an attention-based approach with ViT performs better than the state-of-the-art models by more than 10% for subtask A, and by 2% on subtask B. This highlights the importance of domain-specific pretraining in identifying multimodal misogyny. Further, we have

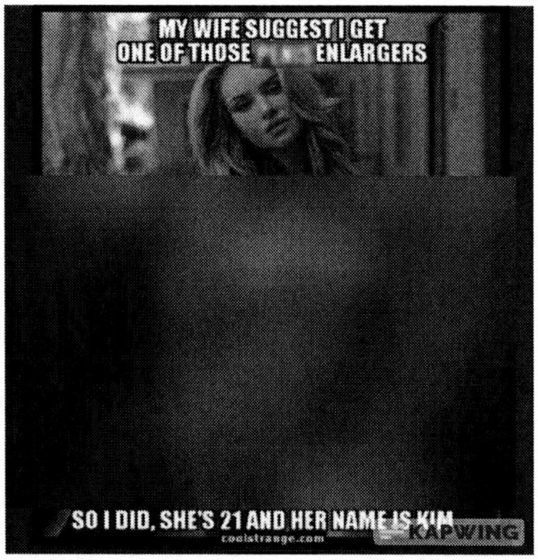

Figure 6: An example where BERT* benefits from pretraining is being able to identify this meme as misogynistic, but fails to subclassify it correctly.

provided a comprehensive qualitative analysis of random samples from the test set, which provided insight into the challenges of detecting multimodal misogyny. Our research emphasizes that identifying misogynistic memes online is a complex task that necessitates a thorough consideration of both visual and linguistic cues, and the significance of domain-specific pretraining in this area. Future work includes extending the dataset to multiple languages to evaluate the generalizability of the proposed approach beyond English. Additionally, a similar analysis could be performed on multimodal media such as reels and TikToks to assess the effectiveness of the proposed approach on these platforms. Further research is also needed to reduce the computational complexity of training and deploying these models for downstream tasks. Finally, investigating the interpretability of the proposed approach could shed light on which multimodal cues are most indicative of misogyny, thereby helping to better understand the underlying mechanisms of this phenomenon.

References

Nayan Varma Alluri and Neeli Dheeraj Krishna. 2021. Multi modal analysis of memes for sentiment extraction. In *2021 Sixth International Conference on Image Information Processing (ICIIP)*, volume 6, pages 213–217. IEEE.

Jacob Devlin, Ming-Wei Chang, Kenton Lee, and Kristina Toutanova. 2018. Bert: Pre-training of deep bidirectional transformers for language understanding. *arXiv preprint arXiv:1810.04805*.

Alexey Dosovitskiy, Lucas Beyer, Alexander Kolesnikov, Dirk Weissenborn, Xiaohua Zhai, Thomas Unterthiner, Mostafa Dehghani, Matthias Minderer, Georg Heigold, Sylvain Gelly, et al. 2020. An image is worth 16x16 words: Transformers for image recognition at scale. *arXiv preprint arXiv:2010.11929*.

Ashwin Geet d'Sa, Irina Illina, and Dominique Fohr. 2020. Bert and fasttext embeddings for automatic detection of toxic speech. In *2020 International Multi-Conference on: "Organization of Knowledge and Advanced Technologies"(OCTA)*, pages 1–5. IEEE.

Elisabetta Fersini, Francesca Gasparini, Giulia Rizzi, Aurora Saibene, Berta Chulvi, Paolo Rosso, Alyssa Lees, and Jeffrey Sorensen. 2022. SemEval-2022 task 5: Multimedia automatic misogyny identification. In *Proceedings of the 16th International Workshop on Semantic Evaluation (SemEval-2022)*, pages 533–549, Seattle, United States. Association for Computational Linguistics.

Bhanu Prakash Reddy Guda, Sasi Bhushan Seelaboyina, Soumya Sarkar, and Animesh Mukherjee. 2020. Nwqm: A neural quality assessment framework for wikipedia. In *Proceedings of the 2020 Conference on Empirical Methods in Natural Language Processing (EMNLP)*, pages 8396–8406.

Sherzod Hakimov, Gullal S Cheema, and Ralph Ewerth. 2022. Tib-va at semeval-2022 task 5: A multimodal architecture for the detection and classification of misogynous memes. *arXiv preprint arXiv:2204.06299*.

Milan Kalkenings and Thomas Mandl. 2022. University of Hildesheim at SemEval-2022 task 5: Combining deep text and image models for multimedia misogyny detection. In *Proceedings of the 16th International Workshop on Semantic Evaluation (SemEval-2022)*, pages 718–723, Seattle, United States. Association for Computational Linguistics.

Douwe Kiela, Hamed Firooz, Aravind Mohan, Vedanuj Goswami, Amanpreet Singh, Pratik Ringshia, and Davide Testuggine. 2020. The hateful memes challenge: Detecting hate speech in multimodal memes. *Advances in Neural Information Processing Systems*, 33:2611–2624.

Liunian Harold Li, Mark Yatskar, Da Yin, Cho-Jui Hsieh, and Kai-Wei Chang. 2019. Visualbert: A simple and performant baseline for vision and language. *arXiv preprint arXiv:1908.03557*.

Shankar Mahadevan, Sean Benhur, Roshan Nayak, Malliga Subramanian, Kogilavani Shanmugavadivel, Kanchana Sivanraju, and Bharathi Raja Chakravarthi. 2022. Transformers at semeval-2022 task 5: A feature extraction based approach for misogynous meme detection. In *Proceedings of the 16th International*

Workshop on Semantic Evaluation (SemEval-2022), pages 550–554.

Niklas Muennighoff. 2020. Vilio: State-of-the-art visio-linguistic models applied to hateful memes. *arXiv preprint arXiv:2012.07788*.

Arianna Muti, Katerina Korre, and Alberto Barrón-Cedeño. 2022. UniBO at SemEval-2022 task 5: A multimodal bi-transformer approach to the binary and fine-grained identification of misogyny in memes. In *Proceedings of the 16th International Workshop on Semantic Evaluation (SemEval-2022)*, pages 663–672, Seattle, United States. Association for Computational Linguistics.

Asriatun Nafiah and Dimas Teguh Prasetyo. 2021. Sexist memes related to covid-19 pandemic in social media, is it matter? In *Proceeding Conference on Genuine Psychology*, volume 1, pages 82–94.

Agnieszka Pluta, Joanna Mazurek, Jakub Wojciechowski, Tomasz Wolak, Wiktor Soral, and Michał Bilewicz. 2023. Exposure to hate speech deteriorates neurocognitive mechanisms of the ability to understand others' pain. *Scientific Reports*, 13(1):4127.

Alec Radford, Jong Wook Kim, Chris Hallacy, Aditya Ramesh, Gabriel Goh, Sandhini Agarwal, Girish Sastry, Amanda Askell, Pamela Mishkin, Jack Clark, et al. 2021. Learning transferable visual models from natural language supervision. In *International conference on machine learning*, pages 8748–8763. PMLR.

Gagan Sharma, Gajanan Sunil Gitte, Shlok Goyal, and Raksha Sharma. 2022a. IITR CodeBusters at SemEval-2022 task 5: Misogyny identification using transformers. In *Proceedings of the 16th International Workshop on Semantic Evaluation (SemEval-2022)*, pages 728–732, Seattle, United States. Association for Computational Linguistics.

Mayukh Sharma, Ilanthenral Kandasamy, and Vasantha W B. 2022b. R2D2 at SemEval-2022 task 5: Attention is only as good as its values! a multimodal system for identifying misogynist memes. In *Proceedings of the 16th International Workshop on Semantic Evaluation (SemEval-2022)*, pages 761–770, Seattle, United States. Association for Computational Linguistics.

Hajung Sohn and Hyunju Lee. 2019. Mc-bert4hate: Hate speech detection using multi-channel bert for different languages and translations. In *2019 International Conference on Data Mining Workshops (ICDMW)*, pages 551–559. IEEE.

Shardul Suryawanshi, Bharathi Raja Chakravarthi, Mihael Arcan, and Paul Buitelaar. 2020. Multimodal meme dataset (multioff) for identifying offensive content in image and text. In *Proceedings of the second workshop on trolling, aggression and cyberbullying*, pages 32–41.

Christian Szegedy, Vincent Vanhoucke, Sergey Ioffe, Jon Shlens, and Zbigniew Wojna. 2016. Rethinking the inception architecture for computer vision. In *Proceedings of the IEEE conference on computer vision and pattern recognition*, pages 2818–2826.

Riza Velioglu and Jewgeni Rose. 2020. Detecting hate speech in memes using multimodal deep learning approaches: Prize-winning solution to hateful memes challenge. *arXiv preprint arXiv:2012.12975*.

Haris Bin Zia, Ignacio Castro, and Gareth Tyson. 2021. Racist or sexist meme? classifying memes beyond hateful. In *Proceedings of the 5th Workshop on Online Abuse and Harms (WOAH 2021)*, pages 215–219.

Conversation Derailment Forecasting with Graph Convolutional Networks

Enas Altarawneh
York University
enas@eecs.yorku.ca

Ameeta Agrawal
Portland State University
ameeta@pdx.edu

Michael Jenkin
York University
jenkin@eecs.yorku.ca

Manos Papagelis
York University
papaggel@eecs.yorku.ca

Abstract

Online conversations are particularly susceptible to derailment, which can manifest itself in the form of toxic communication patterns like disrespectful comments or verbal abuse. Forecasting conversation derailment predicts signs of derailment in advance enabling proactive moderation of conversations. Current state-of-the-art approaches to address this problem rely on sequence models that treat dialogues as text streams. We propose a novel model based on a graph convolutional neural network that considers dialogue user dynamics and the influence of public perception on conversation utterances. Through empirical evaluation, we show that our model effectively captures conversation dynamics and outperforms the state-of-the-art models on the CGA and CMV benchmark datasets by 1.5% and 1.7%, respectively.

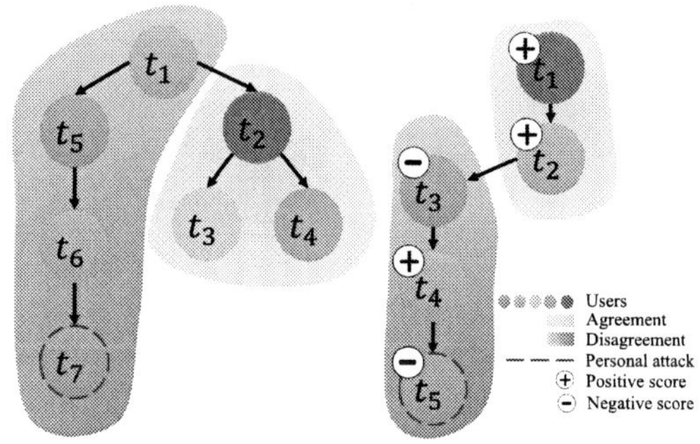

(a) Conversation C_{CGA} (b) Conversation C_{CMV}

Figure 1: Conversation derailment examples coming from two benchmark datasets, CGA and CMV; (a) illustrates graph dynamics in a conversation, and (b) illustrates public perception through votes in a conversation. Our FGCN model exploits these features to improve the accuracy of conversation derailment forecasting.

1 Introduction

The widespread availability of chat or messaging platforms, social media, forums and other online communities has led to an increase in the number of online conversations between individuals and groups. In contrast to offline or face-to-face communication, online conversations require moderation to maintain the integrity of the platform and protect users' privacy and safety (Kilvington, 2021). Moderation can help to prevent harassment, trolling, hate speech, and other forms of abusive behavior (Tontodimamma et al., 2021). It can also help to prevent and address conversation derailment.

Conversation derailment refers to the process by which a conversation or discussion is redirected away from its original topic or purpose, typically as a result of inappropriate or off-topic comments or actions by one or more participants. In online conversations, derailment can be exacerbated by the lack of nonverbal cues and the perceived anonymity that can be provided by the internet. Conversation derailment can lead to confusion, frustration, and a lack of productivity or progress in the conversation. Table 1 shows an example conversation taken from the popular CGA benchmark dataset (Zhang et al., 2018). One can observe that there is offensive language used by one of the participants that leads the conversation to derail. The severity of the verbal attack may indicate a prior history between the two participants in previous conversations.

In this research, we examine the problem of *forecasting conversation derailment*. The ability to predict conversation derailment early has multifold benefits: (i) it is *more timely*, as it allows for proactive moderation of conversations (before they cause any harm) due to early warning, (ii) it is *more scalable*, as it allows to automatically monitor large active online communities, a task that is otherwise time-consuming, (iii) it is *more cost-effective*, as it may provide enough aid to limit the number of human moderators needed, and (iv) it may identify upsetting content early and prevent human moderators from being exposed to it.

Early efforts towards automatic moderation fo-

The 7th Workshop on Online Abuse and Harms (WOAH), pages 160–169
July 13, 2023 ©2023 Association for Computational Linguistics

Turn	User	Text	Label
$N-3$	$\mathcal{A}$	*"Proper use of an editor's history includes fixing errors or violations of Wikipedia policy or correcting related problems on multiple articles."*	
$N-2$	$\mathcal{B}$	*"It's very clear that you just go to my contributions list and look to see what biography articles I've worked on, then you go and look to see if you can find something wrong with them. "*	
$N-1$	$\mathcal{A}$	*"So, what is wrong with fixing things? At the top of my talk page, it says to keep it on your watchlist. "*	
N	$\mathcal{B}$	*"You cannot possibly be too stupid to understand the warning I'm giving you. I'm not going to repeat it."*	?

Table 1: A sample conversation from the Conversation Gone Awry (CGA) dataset showing a sequence of text utterances that end with a verbal abuse. Given the conversation context up to $N-1$ turns, the task is to predict whether turn N will be a respectful or offensive statement prior to it being presented leading to derailment (**it is offensive**, in this case).

cused on detecting inappropriate comments once they have occurred. But the utility of such an approach is limited as participants have already been exposed to an abusive behavior and any potential harm has already been caused. The current state-of-the-art approach to predict conversation derailment relies on sequence models that treat dialogues as text streams (Chang et al., 2022; Kementchedjhieva and Søgaard, 2021). However, this approach has limitations, as it ignores the semantics and dynamicity of a multi-party dialogue involving individuals' intrinsic tendencies and the history of interactions with other individuals.

Based on these observations, we propose a graph-based model to capture multi-party multi-turn dialogue dynamics. In addition, we leverage information associated with conversation utterances that provide public perception on whether an utterance is perceived as positive or negative.

There exist two popular benchmark datasets typically employed for the problem of interest: Conversations Gone Awry (CGA) (Zhang et al., 2018) and Reddit ChangeMyView (CMV) (Chang and Danescu-Niculescu-Mizil, 2019). Both datasets contain multi-party conversations, including the text and an anonymous user ID of each utterance, along with a label annotation on whether the conversation will derail or not. CMV also includes a public vote on each of the utterances that provides the public perception of individuals towards it.

Figure 1a shows an example multi-party conversation from CGA that is not sequential in nature. Note as well that some participants are in either agreement or disagreement of a heated argument. Graph models are more accustomed to represent such dialogue dynamics. Figure 1b shows an example conversation from CMV that shows sample voting scores on each utterance in the conversation that could be related to derailment.

Graph neural networks have been successfully used to model conversations for downstream classification tasks. For example, they have shown promise in forecasting the next emotion in a conversation (Li et al., 2021), a problem similar to that of interest in this work. This motivated us to explore this line of research and make the following contributions:

- We propose a novel model based on a graph convolutional neural network, *the Forecasting Graph Convolutional Network (FGCN)*, that captures dialogue user dynamics and public perception of conversation utterances.
- We perform an extensive empirical evaluation of FGCN that shows it outperforms the state-of-the-art models on the GCA and CMV benchmark datasets by 1.5% and 1.7%, respectively.

The remainder of the paper is organized as follows. Section 2 reviews related work. The technical problem of interest is presented in Section 3. Section 4 presents the proposed models. Section 5 presents the experimental setup, and Section 6 presents the results and a discussion. We conclude in Section 7.

2 Related Work

There has been considerable research attention on the problem of detecting various forms of toxicity in text data. There are methods for identifying cyberbullying (Wiegand et al., 2019), hate speech (Davidson et al., 2017), or negative sentiment (Agrawal and An, 2014; Wang and Cardie, 2016) or lowering the intensity of emotions (Ziems et al., 2022; Xie and Agrawal, 2023). These methods are useful in filtering unacceptable content. However, the focus of these models is on mostly analyzing or classifying already posted harmful texts.

The CRAFT models introduced by Chang et al. (2022) are the first models to go beyond classification of hate speech to addressing the problem of forecasting conversation derailment. The CRAFT models integrate two components: (a) a generative dialog model that learns to represent conversational dynamics in an unsupervised fashion, and (b) a supervised component that fine-tunes this representation to forecast future events. As a proof of concept, a mixed methods approach combining surveys with randomized controlled experiments investigated how conversation forecasting using the CRAFT model can help users (Chang et al., 2022) and moderators (Schluger et al., 2022) to proactively assess and deescalate tension in online discussions.

Extending the hierarchical recurrent neural network architecture with three task-specific loss functions proposed by Janiszewski et al. (2021) was shown to improve the CRAFT models. After pretrained transformer language encoders such as BERT (Devlin et al., 2018) proved to be successful at various NLP tasks, Kementchedjhieva and Søgaard (2021) explored how they can be used for forecasting derailment. The model in this work consists of a BERT checkpoint with a sequence classification (SC) head. Similarly, De Kock and Vlachos (2021) evaluated feature-based and neural models to predict whether disagreements in Wikipedia Talk page conversations will be escalated to mediation by a moderator.

Saveski et al. (2021) studied the relationship between structure and toxicity in conversations on Twitter at individual, dyad, and group level, and found that social relationships among users influence their behaviors. Salehabadi et al. (2022) also studied the differences between toxic and non-toxic conversations on Twitter, highlighting important differences between user engagement and toxicity. While these recent works stress the importance of user characteristics in conversation modeling, to our knowledge, models that incorporate such signals for the task of predicting derailment have remained unexplored.

Here we propose graph-based models for leveraging user-specific information. Graph convolutional neural networks have been used for conversation classification. In one popular application, emotion estimation, the graph model is used to account for speaker related information (Ghosal et al., 2019; Sun et al., 2021). Other work have used similar graph neural networks to forecast emotions (Zhong et al., 2019; Lubis et al., 2019; Liang et al., 2022; Li et al., 2021).

3 Problem Definition

In this section, we formally define the problem of *forecasting conversation derailment.* For a conversation $C = \{\{t_1, t_2, ..., t_N\}, \{u_1, u_2, ..., u_N\}, \{s_1, s_2, ..., s_N\}\}$ consisting of N turns, the last turn (i.e., the N'th turn) is the potential site of derailment where $l = \{civil, personal\ attack\}$ denotes the label of this turn.

For the ith turn, t_i denotes its text, u_i denotes its user, and s_i denotes an optional score, e.g., number of votes (up-vote/down-vote). An up-vote is a positive impression and a down-vote is a negative impression on the turn utterance. The goal is to forecast the derailment label l of the N'th turn given a conversation C up to $N - 1$ turns (i.e., without any information about the Nth turn).

4 Model for Forecasting Conversation Derailment

In this section, we describe our proposed Forecasting Graph Convolutional neural Network model, (FGCN), visualized in Figure 2.

4.1 Sequential encoding

The input to the model consists of the text t_i, user ID u_i and/or the public perception score s_i for each turn in the conversation $i \in [1, 2, ..., N - 1]$, as described below:

Textual input — the input consists of an encoding of the turn text t_i using BERT embeddings extracted after fine tuning as described in Kementchedjhieva and Søgaard (2021), resulting in the sequential encoding of the text as vector $t_i^{'}$.

User ID input — the input consists of an encoding of the user ID as a randomly initialized vector u_i, where each user has a unique vector; we use BiLSTM sequential encoding to obtain the utterance user ID vectors $u_i^{'}$. We use unique randomly initialized vectors to avoid privacy issues that may arise using actual IDs.

Public perception input — the input consists of a popularity score where the up-votes on a turn is subtracted by the down-votes on the same. To obtain the score vector s_i we use equal depth binning to capture three levels of popularity for positive

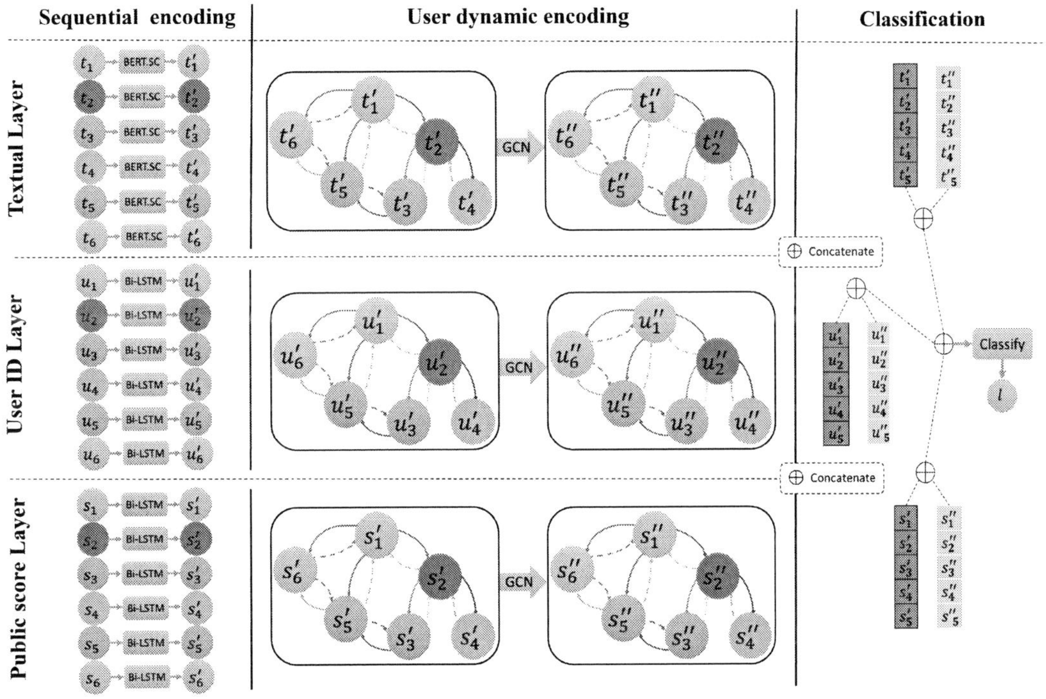

Figure 2: The FGCN model architecture.

scores and three levels of unpopularity for negative scores. We use a BiLSTM sequential encoder on s_i resulting in utterance public perception vectors $s_i^{'}$.

4.2 Graph Construction

For a given conversation, the output of the sequential encoder for each one of these input types $t_i^{'}$, $u_i^{'}$ and $s_i^{'}$ is used to initialize the vertices in the homogeneous graphs shown in Figure 2. The vertices in the graphs represent the turns in the conversation. Each graph $G_x = (V, E, R, W)$, for each type of input $x \in \{t, u, s\}$, is constructed with vertices $v_i \in V$, $r_{ij} \in E$ is the labeled edges between v_i and v_j, the edge labels (relations) $\in R$ and α_{ij} is the weight of the labeled edge r_{ij}, with $0 \leq \alpha_{ij} \leq 1$, where $\alpha_{ij} \in W, i \in [1, 2, ..., N-1]$ and $j \in$ the set of all neighboring vertices to v_i.

For each conversation we construct three types of graphs; a text-based G_t, a user-based G_u and a public perception score-based G_s. In G_t, each conversation turn is represented as a vertex $v_i \in V$ and is initialized with the textual sequentially encoded feature vector $t_i^{'}$, for all $i \in [1, 2, ..., N-1]$. In G_u each vertex is initialized with a utterance user ID vector $u_i^{'}$, for all $i \in [1, 2, ..., N-1]$ provided by the sequential encoder. Similarly, in G_s each vertex is initialized with a utterance public score vector $s_i^{'}$, for all $i \in [1, 2, ..., N-1]$ provided by the sequential encoder.

User to user relationship edge construction. We establish the direct user to user relationship in a conversation through the edge construction of each graph. This results in efficient graph modeling with less complexity compared to complete graphs. Figure 3 shows an example graph edge construction for a given conversation. In user-to-user relationship edge construction, each vertex v_i representing a turn in the conversation has directed edges connecting it to its preceding (parent) and succeeding comments/turns (children). Same user comments (turns) are also connected through directed edges. The user-to-user relation $\in R$ of an edge r_{ij} is set based on the user-to-user dependency between user u_i (of turn v_i) and user u_j (of turn v_j).

For example, in Figure 3, there are four users, so the set of edge labels R has the relation types shown under user-to-user dependency. Furthermore, as the graph is directed, two vertices can have edges in both directions with different relations. We use this to represent the past (backward) and future (forward) temporal dependency between the vertices, shown as temporal user dependency. The edge weights are set using a similarity based attention module. The attention function is computed such

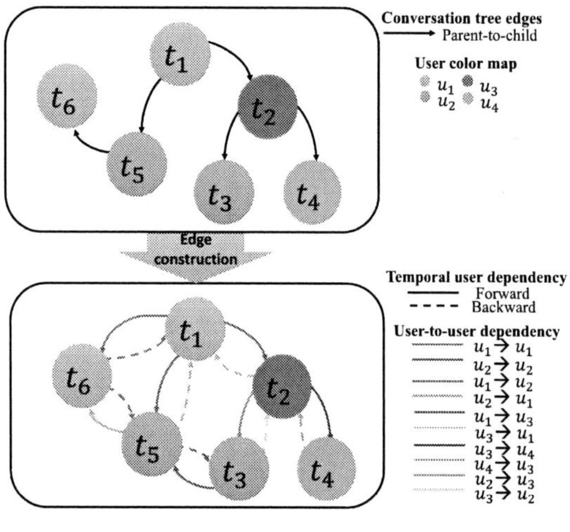

Figure 3: An example graph edge construction for the given conversation with user-to-user and temporal dependency.

that, for each vertex, the incoming set of edges has a sum total weight of 1. The weights are calculated as, $\alpha_{ij} = softmax(v_i^T W_e[v_{j1}, ..., v_{jm}])$, for j_k, where $k = 1, 2, .., m$, for the m vertices connected to v_i, ensuring the vertex v_i receives a total weight contribution of 1.

4.3 Feature Transformation

The sequentially encoded text features $t_i^{'}$, the user features $u_i^{'}$, and the public perception features $s_i^{'}$ of the graph network are transformed from user dynamic independent into user dynamic dependent feature vectors using a two-step graph convolution process employed by Ghosal et al. (2019). In the first step, a new feature vector is computed for each vertex in all three graphs by aggregating local neighbourhood information:

$$u_i^{''} = \sigma(\sum_{r \in R} \sum_{j \in N_i^r} \frac{\alpha_{ij}}{c_{i,r}} W_r u_j^{'} + \alpha_{ii} W_0 u_i^{'}),$$

$$t_i^{''} = \sigma(\sum_{r \in R} \sum_{j \in N_i^r} \frac{\alpha_{ij}}{c_{i,r}} W_r t_j^{'} + \alpha_{ii} W_0 t_i^{'})$$

$$s_i^{''} = \sigma(\sum_{r \in R} \sum_{j \in N_i^r} \frac{\alpha_{ij}}{c_{i,r}} W_r s_j^{'} + \alpha_{ii} W_0 s_i^{'})$$

for $i = 1, 2, ..., N-1$, where, α_{ii} and α_{ij} are the edge weights, and N_i^r is the neighbouring indices of vertex i under relation $r \in R$. $c_{i,r}$ is a problem specific normalization constant automatically learned in a gradient based learning setup. Σ is an activation function such as ReLU, and W_r and W_0 are learnable parameters of the transformation. In the second step, another local neighbourhood based transformation is applied over the outputs of the first step, as follows:

$$u_i^{''} = \sigma(\sum_{j \in N_i^r} W u_j^{''} + \alpha_{ii} W_0 u_i^{''}),$$

$$t_i^{''} = \sigma(\sum_{j \in N_i^r} W t_j^{''} + \alpha_{ii} W_0 t_i^{''})$$

$$s_i^{''} = \sigma(\sum_{j \in N_i^r} W s_j^{''} + \alpha_{ii} W_0 s_i^{''})$$

for $i = 1, 2, ..., N-1$, where, W and W_0 are transformation parameters, and σ is the activation function. This two step transformation accumulates the normalized sum of the local neighbourhood.

4.4 Forecasting Derailment

To form the final turn representation, the sequential encoded vectors $t_i^{'}$, $u_i^{'}$ and $s_i^{'}$, and the user dynamic encoded vectors $t_i^{''}$, $u_i^{''}$ and $s_i^{''}$ are concatenated for each turn i in a conversation to form:

$$g_i = [t_i^{'}, u_i^{'}, s_i^{'}, t_i^{''}, u_i^{''}, s_i^{''}]$$

Then, each g_i, $i \in \{1, 2...., N-1\}$ is concatenated to form a representation of the conversation C:

$$C^{'} = [g_1, g_2..., g_{N-1}]$$

Finally, $C^{'}$ is fed to a classifier with a linear layer, a full connected network and a sigmoid activation function, as described by Ghosal et al. (2019), to obtain the label $\hat{l}$ of each conversation C.

4.5 Model variants

To understand the effect of each type of input on forecasting derailment, we create variants of our model where the types of input are gradually included. The following is a more detailed description of the models used in this work.

FGCN-T — this variant of the model constructs one graph using the output of the sequential encoder on the textual data $t_i^{'}$. It is created for both CGA and CMV, as both contain the textual data. FGCN-T uses only the textual layer shown in Figure 2. At classification it concatenates $t_i^{'}$ with the result of the GCN feature transformation $t_i^{''}$ during user dynamic encoding.

Dataset	Input			Train	Val	Test
	t	u	s			
CGA	✓	✓	✓	2508	840	840
CMV	✓	✓	×	4106	1368	1368

Table 2: Statistics of the datasets. t denotes text input, u denotes user ID input and s denotes public perception score input. All splits are balanced between the two classes.

FCGN-TU — this variant of the model constructs two graphs using the output of the sequential encoder, one for the textual output $t_i^{'}$ and the other for the user ID output $u_i^{'}$. It is created for both CGA and CMV, as both contain the textual and user ID data. FGCN-TU uses the textual and user ID layer shown in Figure 2. At classification it concatenates $t_i^{'}$ and $u_i^{'}$ with the result of the GCN feature transformation $t_i^{''}$ and $u_i^{''}$ during user dynamic encoding.

FGCN-TS — this variant of the model constructs two graphs using the output of the sequential encoder, one for the textual output $t_i^{'}$ and the other for the public perception score output $s_i^{'}$. It is created for CMV, as only CMV contains the public perception data. FGCN-TS uses the textual and public score layer shown in Figure 2. At classification it concatenates $t_i^{'}$ and $s_i^{'}$ with the result of the GCN feature transformation $t_i^{''}$ and $s_i^{''}$ during user dynamic encoding.

FGCN-TSU — this variant of the model constructs three graphs using the output of the sequential encoder, one for the textual output $t_i^{'}$, the user ID output $u_i^{'}$ and the public perception score output $s_i^{'}$. It is created for CMV, as only CMV contains the public perception data. FGCN-TSU uses all layers shown in Figure 2. At classification it concatenates $t_i^{'}$, $u_i^{'}$ and $s_i^{'}$ with the result of the GCN feature transformation $s_i^{''}$ and $s_i^{''}$ during user dynamic encoding.

5 Experimental Setup

5.1 Datasets

We use two datasets for the task of forecasting derailment in conversations. Some statistics of the datasets are summarized in Table 2.

Conversations Gone Awry (CGA) dataset (Zhang et al., 2018) was extracted from Wikipedia Talk Page conversations. The conversations were sampled from WikiConv (Hua et al., 2018) based on an automatic measure of toxicity that ranges from 0 (not toxic) to 1 (is toxic). A conversation is extracted as a sample of derailment if the Nth comment in it has a toxicity score higher than 0.6 and all the preceding comments have a score lower than 0.4. Conversations having all comments with a toxicity score below 0.4 are extracted as samples of non-derailment. This set of conversations is further filtered through manual annotation to determine whether after an initial civil exchange a personal attack occurs from one user towards another. The conversations include the turn with the personal attack. This means all $N-1$ turns in a conversation are civil and the N'th one is either civil or contains a personal attack. The dataset also contains additional information about each comment in the conversation such as the user posting the comment and the ID of the parent comment that this comment was a reply to.

Reddit ChangeMyView (CMV) dataset (Chang and Danescu-Niculescu-Mizil, 2019) was extracted from Reddit conversations held under the ChangeMyView subreddit. Conversations were identified as derailed if there was a deletion of a turn by the platform moderators. This could have been done under Reddit's Rule: "Don't be rude or hostile to other users." Unlike CGA, there is no control to ensure that all the preceding comments to the last one would be civil, resulting in some noise in the data. The dataset also contains additional information about each comment in the conversation such as the user posting the comment, the ID of the parent comment that this comment was a reply to, and a votes score (i.e., the number of up-votes minus the number of down-votes).

5.2 Evaluation Metrics

Following prior work, we report the performance of the models in terms of accuracy (Acc), precision (P), recall (R), and F1-score. We also report the forecast horizon H introduced by Kementchedjhieva and Søgaard (2021), which is the mean of the turns in which the first detection of derailment occurred for the set of conversations that derail.

5.3 Baselines

Our FGCN model and its variants are evaluated against the state-of-the-art methods below.

CRAFT (Chang and Danescu-Niculescu-Mizil, 2019) is a model with a hierarchical recurrent neural network architecture, which integrates a generative dialog model that learns to represent conver-

TRANING	MODEL	CGA Acc	CGA P	CGA R	CGA F1	CMV Acc	CMV P	CMV R	CMV F1
STATIC	CRAFT	64.4	62.7	71.7	66.9	60.5	57.5	81.3	67.3
	BERT·SC	64.7	61.5	79.4	69.3	62.0	58.6	82.8	68.5
	FGCN-T	66.4	63.0	79.5	70.3	62.9	59.2	83.0	69.1
	FGCN-TU	66.9	63.3	80.2	**70.8**	63.2	59.5	83.0	69.3
	FGCN-TS	-	-	-	-	64.2	60.3	83.2	69.9
	FGCN-TSU	-	-	-	-	64.7	60.7	83.3	**70.2**
DYNAMIC	BERT·SC+	64.3	61.2	78.9	68.8	56.5	56.0	73.2	61.7
	FGCN-T+	65.7	62.2	79.7	69.9	62.1	58.5	82.0	68.3
	FGCN-TU+	65.9	62.4	80.2	**70.2**	62.7	58.8	82.7	68.8
	FGCN-TS+	-	-	-	-	62.9	59.2	82.9	69.1
	FGCN-TSU+	-	-	-	-	63.5	59.7	83.1	**69.5**

Table 3: Experimental results for forecasting conversation derailment. Best F1-score are in bold.

sational dynamics in an unsupervised fashion, and a supervised component that fine-tunes this representation to forecast future events. This model is trained statically. Static training entails that all $N-1$ turns $\{t_1, ..., t_{N-1}\}$ of a conversation of N turns are used as one input instance.

BERT·SC (Kementchedjhieva and Søgaard, 2021) is a model consisting of the BERT checkpoint with a sequence classification (SC) head, trained statically, i.e. in the same manner as CRAFT.

BERT·SC+ (Kementchedjhieva and Søgaard, 2021) similar to BERT·SC consists of the BERT checkpoint with a sequence classification (SC) head, but is instead trained *dynamically*. Dynamic training entails that a conversation of N turns $\{t_1, ..., t_{N-1}\}$ with label l is mapped to multiple training samples, each representing a different phase of the conversation unfolding, but all labeled with the same label l. So a conversation of N turns is converted into $N-1$ training instances samples $\{t_1\}, \{t_1, t_2\}, ..., \{t_1, ..., t_{N-1}\}$ instead of just the one $\{t_1, ..., t_{N-1}\}$.

5.4 Implementation

We use two training paradigms, static and dynamic: In **static training**, for each conversation we use one training instance with all turns $\{\{t_1, ..., t_{N-1}\}$, $\{u_1, ..., u_{N-1}\}$ and/or $\{s_1, ..., s_{N-1}\}\}$ as input. In **dynamic training**, we use multiple instances of each conversation, by varying the last turn used in each training instance. So, we use $\{t_1$, u_1 and/or $s_1\}$ as an instance, $\{\{t_1, t_2\}$, $\{u_1, u_2\}$, and/or $\{s_1, s_2\}\}$ as another instance, and so on until the last instance $\{\{t_1, ..., t_{N-1}\}$, $\{u_1, ..., u_{N-1}\}$ and/or $\{s_1, ..., s_{N-1}\}\}$. So we have $N-1$ instances of each conversation. We denote all dynamically trained models with an added "+" at the end of the model name.

At inference time, the model is tested dynamically, i.e., by using turn $\{t_1$, u_1 and/or $s_1\}$ as input, and making a prediction $\hat{l_1}$, then using turns $\{\{t_1, t_2\}$, $\{u_1, u_2\}$, and/or $\{s_1, s_2\}\}$, and making a prediction $\hat{l_2}$, and so on until $N-1$ predictions have been accumulated. The overall predicted label for a given conversation is then obtained as $\hat{l} = \max_{i=1}^{N-1} \hat{l_i}$.

Our models used the same BERT implementation (i.e., `bert-base-uncased`) as in the baseline models (Kementchedjhieva and Søgaard, 2021), for our textual sequential encoding, to ensure a comparable evaluation setting. However, it is worth mentioning that any pretrained language model can be used. The graph neural network component described in this work is implemented with settings similar to that reported by Ghosal et al. (2019). The results are reported as an average over 10 different runs with random initialization, to account for variance in model performance.

6 Results and Discussion

In the forecasting conversation derailment experiment we report the results of the static and dynamic training of our model and its variants and compare with baselines. In the analyzing mean forecast horizon experiment we show how early each model can forecast derailment.

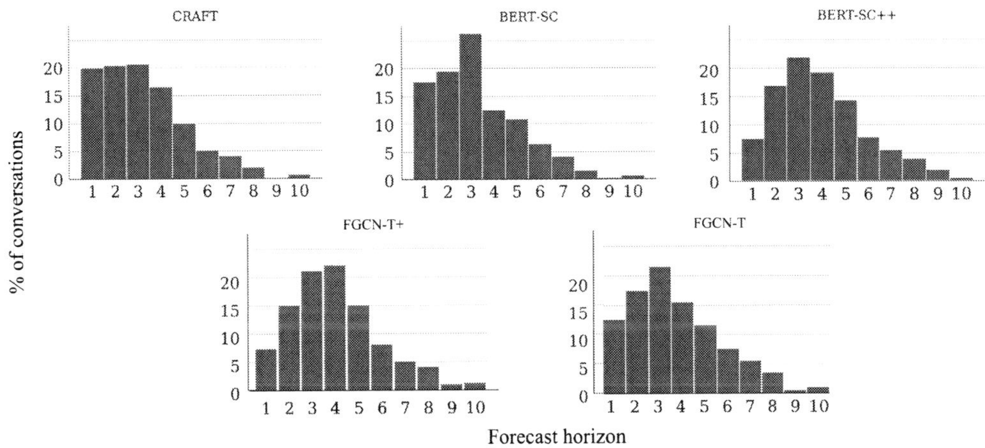

Figure 4: Forecast horizon on the CGA dataset with a model drawn at random from among the 10 available ones. A horizon of 1 means that an upcoming derailment was only predicted on the last turn before it occurred.

6.1 Forecasting Conversation Derailment

The results in Table 3 show that across both the datasets, FGCN-T, our text based graph neural network model, outperforms baseline models when given similar text input. FGCN-TU, which explicitly uses user ID's in addition to text data, further improves the results for both the datasets. FGCN-TS, which uses text and public perception data in the CMV dataset, brings similar improvements. Furthermore, the results of the FGCN-TSU model, which uses text, user and public perception data, indicate that incorporating all three features when available can be beneficial. Note that CGA does not provide any public perception data and was excluded from this experiment.

Statically trained models outperform their corresponding dynamically trained models. However, our dynamically trained models outperform both statically and dynamically trained baselines.

Taken together, these results indicate that modeling conversations using a graph neural network improves the models' forecasting F1-score. They also demonstrate that this modeling framework is flexible and allows for incorporating more types of data that may be beneficial. For instance, future work could investigate the potential benefit of integrating explicit emotion or sentiment values (Babanejad et al., 2019; Agrawal et al., 2016) into derailment forecasting models.

6.2 Analyzing Mean Forecast Horizon

How early can the model forecast the derailment? To answer this question we calculate the forecast horizon H, the mean of the turn in which the first detection of derailment occurred for the set of conversations that derail. A forecast horizon H of 1 means that a derailment coming up on turn N was first detected on turn $N-1$. A longer forecast horizon (i.e., a higher H) allows for earlier interventions and potentially allows moderators to delete the upcoming personal attack as soon as it appears on their platform to avoid any form of escalation. Models that are able to detect a potential intervention earlier have a clear advantage.

	CGA	**CMV**
CRAFT	2.36	4.01
BERT·SC	2.60	3.90
BERT·SC+	<u>2.85</u>	<u>4.06</u>
FGCN-T	2.73	4.03
FGCN-T+	**2.96**	**4.12**

Table 4: Experimental results of mean forecast horizon (H).The best result is shown in bold whereas the second best result has been underlined.

In Table 4 we report the results of the mean forecast horizon H. The results show that our model FGCN-T+ with its dynamic training provides the earliest overall forecasting of derailment with a mean H of 4.12 for CMV, and 2.95 for CGA. Followed by another dynamically trained model BERT.SC+. For the statically trained models (CRAFT, BERT.SC, and FGCN-T), FGCN-T has the best performance as it seems to be able to better model the dynamic relationships between the users of the turns with its graph model, obtaining a mean H of 4.03 for CMV and, 2.73 for CGA.

We perform further analysis of the forecast horizon results for CGA. Figure 4 illustrates the forecast horizon of the different models. In earlier work, both CRAFT and BERT·SC, the models make a prediction with a forecast horizon $H > 1$ turn at a high rate. Only 20% of CRAFT's forecasts and 17.5% of BERT·SC's forecasts came on the last turn before the derailment. Turning to BERT·SC+, we see that dynamic training has helped in shifting a lot of the density from $H <= 3$ towards $H > 3$. The last-minute forecasts for BERT·SC+ model come at a rate of only 7.5%. FGCN-T and FGCN-T+ uses BERT.SC in its sequential textual component and combines it with a graph component. FGCN-T was also able to shift density from $H <= 3$ towards $H > 3$ even though it was trained statically, indicating that the result was due to the graph modeling. The dynamiclly trained FGCN-T+ outperforms all by shifting even more density towards $H > 3$ and a last minute forecast at a rate of only 7%.

7 Conclusion

Unlike previous models which were based on simpler sequence models, FGCN is built on a graph convolutional neural network and is able to capture the dynamics of multi-party dialogue, including user relationships and public perception of conversation statements. FGCN performed significantly better than state-of-the-art models on two widely used benchmark datasets, CGA and CMV. Conversation derailment is a significant issue that frequently and severely impacts our online social interactions, whether in casual settings or more formal contexts such as online learning or remote work. The ability to accurately predict derailment has the potential to enhance the effectiveness of moderation and thus protect individuals who are vulnerable to emotional abuse or harm and improve the overall quality of online interactions.

Limitations

Graph models require four or more utterances to form meaningful conversation connections and model their dynamics. In some cases, conversations that derail are not sufficiently long and may be best modeled by simpler sequential models. Any of these models will work best with asynchronous conversations where there is a time lag between the turns to allow for moderation after forecasting.

Ethics Statement

In our paper, we focus on the problem of forecasting conversation derailment. The practical employment of any such system on online platforms has potential positive impact, but several things would be important to first consider, including whether forecasting is fair (Williamson and Menon, 2019), how to inform users about the forecasting (in advance, and when the forecasting affects users), and finally what other action is taken when derailment is forecast. Please refer to (Kiritchenko et al., 2020) for a related overview of such considerations, in the context of abusive language detection.

Acknowledgments

We are grateful to the anonymous reviewers for their insightful feedback. The financial support of NSERC, the NCRN, VISTA and the IDEaS network is gratefully acknowledged.

References

Ameeta Agrawal and Aijun An. 2014. Kea: Sentiment analysis of phrases within short texts. In *Proceedings of the 8th International Workshop on Semantic Evaluation (SemEval 2014)*.

Ameeta Agrawal, Raghavender Sahdev, Heidar Davoudi, Forouq Khonsari, Aijun An, and Susan McGrath. 2016. Detecting the magnitude of events from news articles. In *2016 IEEE/WIC/ACM International Conference on Web Intelligence (WI)*. IEEE.

Nastaran Babanejad, Ameeta Agrawal, Heidar Davoudi, Aijun An, and Manos Papagelis. 2019. Leveraging emotion features in news recommendations. In *Proceedings of the 7th International Workshop on News Recommendation and Analytics (INRA)*.

Jonathan P. Chang and Cristian Danescu-Niculescu-Mizil. 2019. Trouble on the horizon: Forecasting the derailment of online conversations as they develop. In *Proceedings of the 2019 Conference on Empirical Methods in Natural Language Processing and the 9th International Joint Conference on Natural Language Processing (EMNLP-IJCNLP)*, pages 4743–4754, Hong Kong, China. Association for Computational Linguistics.

Jonathan P Chang, Charlotte Schluger, and Cristian Danescu-Niculescu-Mizil. 2022. Thread with caution: Proactively helping users assess and deescalate tension in their online discussions. *Proceedings of the ACM on Human-Computer Interaction*, 6(CSCW2):1–37.

Thomas Davidson, Dana Warmsley, Michael W. Macy, and Ingmar Weber. 2017. Automated hate speech detection and the problem of offensive language. *CoRR*, abs/1703.04009.

Christine De Kock and Andreas Vlachos. 2021. I beg to differ: A study of constructive disagreement in online conversations. *arXiv preprint arXiv:2101.10917*.

Jacob Devlin, Ming-Wei Chang, Kenton Lee, and Kristina Toutanova. 2018. BERT: pre-training of deep bidirectional transformers for language understanding. *CoRR*, abs/1810.04805.

Deepanway Ghosal, Navonil Majumder, Soujanya Poria, Niyati Chhaya, and Alexander F. Gelbukh. 2019. Dialoguegcn: A graph convolutional neural network for emotion recognition in conversation. *CoRR*, abs/1908.11540.

Yiqing Hua, Cristian Danescu-Niculescu-Mizil, Dario Taraborelli, Nithum Thain, Jeffery Sorensen, and Lucas Dixon. 2018. WikiConv: A corpus of the complete conversational history of a large online collaborative community. In *Proceedings of the 2018 Conference on Empirical Methods in Natural Language Processing*, pages 2818–2823, Brussels, Belgium. Association for Computational Linguistics.

Piotr Janiszewski, Mateusz Lango, and Jerzy Stefanowski. 2021. Time aspect in making an actionable prediction of a conversation breakdown. In *Machine Learning and Knowledge Discovery in Databases. Applied Data Science Track*, pages 351–364, Cham. Springer International Publishing.

Yova Kementchedjhieva and Anders Søgaard. 2021. Dynamic forecasting of conversation derailment. In *Proceedings of the 2021 Conference on Empirical Methods in Natural Language Processing*, pages 7915–7919, Online and Punta Cana, Dominican Republic. Association for Computational Linguistics.

Daniel Kilvington. 2021. The virtual stages of hate: Using goffman's work to conceptualise the motivations for online hate. *Media, Culture & Society*, 43(2).

Svetlana Kiritchenko, Isar Nejadgholi, and Kathleen C. Fraser. 2020. Confronting abusive language online: A survey from the ethical and human rights perspective. *CoRR*, abs/2012.12305.

Dayu Li, Xiaodan Zhu, Yang Li, Suge Wang, Deyu Li, Jian Liao, and Jianxing Zheng. 2021. Emotion inference in multi-turn conversations with addressee-aware module and ensemble strategy. In *Proceedings of the 2021 Conference on Empirical Methods in Natural Language Processing*, pages 3935–3941.

Yunlong Liang, Fandong Meng, Ying Zhang, Yufeng Chen, Jinan Xu, and Jie Zhou. 2022. Emotional conversation generation with heterogeneous graph neural network. *Artificial Intelligence*, 308:103714.

Nurul Lubis, Sakriani Sakti, Koichiro Yoshino, and Satoshi Nakamura. 2019. Positive emotion elicitation in chat-based dialogue systems. *IEEE/ACM Transactions on Audio, Speech, and Language Processing*, 27:866–877.

Nazanin Salehabadi, Anne Groggel, Mohit Singhal, Sayak Saha Roy, and Shirin Nilizadeh. 2022. User engagement and the toxicity of tweets. *arXiv preprint arXiv:2211.03856*.

Martin Saveski, Brandon Roy, and Deb Roy. 2021. The structure of toxic conversations on twitter. In *Proceedings of the Web Conference*.

Charlotte Schluger, Jonathan P Chang, Cristian Danescu-Niculescu-Mizil, and Karen Levy. 2022. Proactive moderation of online discussions: Existing practices and the potential for algorithmic support. *Proceedings of the ACM on Human-Computer Interaction*, 6(CSCW2):1–27.

Yang Sun, Nan Yu, and Guohong Fu. 2021. A discourse-aware graph neural network for emotion recognition in multi-party conversation. pages 2949–2958.

Alice Tontodimamma, Eugenia Nissi, Annalina Sarra, and Lara Fontanella. 2021. Thirty years of research into hate speech: topics of interest and their evolution. *Scientometrics*, 126(1):157–179.

Lu Wang and Claire Cardie. 2016. A piece of my mind: A sentiment analysis approach for online dispute detection. *CoRR*, abs/1606.05704.

Michael Wiegand, Josef Ruppenhofer, and Thomas Kleinbauer. 2019. Detection of Abusive Language: the Problem of Biased Datasets. In *Proceedings of the 2019 Conference of the North American Chapter of the Association for Computational Linguistics: Human Language Technologies, Volume 1 (Long and Short Papers)*, pages 602–608, Minneapolis, Minnesota. Association for Computational Linguistics.

Robert Williamson and Aditya Menon. 2019. Fairness risk measures. In *Proceedings of the 36th International Conference on Machine Learning*, volume 97 of *Proceedings of Machine Learning Research*, pages 6786–6797. PMLR.

Justin Xie and Ameeta Agrawal. 2023. Emotion and sentiment guided paraphrasing. In *Proceedings of the 13th Workshop on Computational Approaches to Subjectivity, Sentiment and Social Media Analysis*.

Justine Zhang, Jonathan P. Chang, Cristian Danescu-Niculescu-Mizil, Lucas Dixon, Dario Taraborelli, Nithum Thain, and Dario Taraborelli. 2018. Conversations gone awry: Detecting warning signs of conversational failure. In *Proceedings of ACL*.

Peixiang Zhong, Di Wang, and Chunyan Miao. 2019. An affect-rich neural conversational model with biased attention and weighted cross-entropy loss.

Caleb Ziems, Minzhi Li, Anthony Zhang, and Diyi Yang. 2022. Inducing positive perspectives with text reframing. *arXiv preprint arXiv:2204.02952*.

Resources for Automated Identification of Online Gender-Based Violence: A Systematic Review

Gavin Abercrombie[1] and **Aiqi Jiang**[1,3] and **Poppy Gerrard-Abbott**[4,5]
and **Ioannis Konstas**[1,2] and **Verena Rieser**[1*]
[1]The Interaction Lab, Heriot-Watt University [2]Alana AI
[3]Computational Linguistics Lab, Queen Mary University of London
[4]School of Social and Political Science, University of Edinburgh [5]EmilyTest
{g.abercrombie, a.jiang, i.konstas, v.t.rieser}@hw.ac.uk
pgerrard@ed.ac.uk

Abstract

Online Gender-Based Violence (GBV), such as misogynistic abuse, is an increasingly prevalent problem that technological approaches have struggled to address. Through the lens of the GBV framework, which is rooted in social science and policy, we systematically review 63 available resources for automated identification of such language. We find the datasets are limited in a number of important ways, such as their lack of theoretical grounding and stakeholder input, static nature, and focus on certain media platforms. Based on this review, we recommend development of future resources rooted in sociological expertise and centering stakeholder voices, namely GBV experts and people with lived experience of GBV.

1 Introduction

We are in the midst of an 'epidemic of online abuse', which disproportionately affects women and minoritised groups and has worsened during and after the COVID-19 pandemic: 46% of women and marginalised gender identities such as transgender users experience gender-based online abuse, with non-binary people and Black and minority ethnic women at 50% (Glitch UK and EVAW, 2020).

In recent years, technology companies and computer science researchers have made efforts to automate the identification of hate speech and other toxic or abusive language, and have released datasets and resources for training machine classification systems (see e.g. Poletto et al., 2021; Vidgen and Derczynski, 2021). While some of these have focused on sexist and misogynistic abuse (e.g. Jiang et al., 2022; Zeinert et al., 2021), overall, systems still perform worse at detecting such instances, with high failure rates (Nozza et al., 2019).

In this review, we examine efforts at producing resources for automated content moderation through the lens of Gender-Based Violence (GBV). We particularly focus on the extent to which stakeholders, namely GBV experts and people with lived experience of GBV have been included in the design and production of these resources.

The GBV framework While there is a growing body of natural language processing (NLP) work purporting to address *sexism* and *misogyny*, these terms are often used imprecisely in the literature and dataset taxonomies. We advocate for the use of the term 'gender-based violence', which was first used by the United Nations to promote a comprehensive, umbrella theorisation of endemic violence and abuse (United Nations, 2021) arising from a gender stereotypic society of unequal gender orders and gender stratification (UN General Assembly, 1993). GBV is often non-linear[1] and overlapping, entailing hybrid behaviours of physical, digital, verbal, psychological, and sexual violence; implicit and explicit forms; and spanning multiple spaces, actors, and events–inclusive of numerous types of abuse and specialist focuses, such as coercive control, domestic violence, intimate partner violence, sexual harassment and stalking.

The concept has been broadened by the European Union to include online abuse (Dominique, 2021; Lomba et al., 2021) as GBV has come to be understood as affecting both online and offline life, manifesting in victims/survivors' communities, domestic, and occupational lives. Conceptualising GBV in a modern context shows how the framework has adapted to a digitised and globalised world, expanding and diversifying to contemporary types. Online forms of GBV, with a particular focus on 'cybersexism' and 'cybermisogny' include taking photographs and

*Now at Google DeepMind.

[1]'Non-linearity' refers to how the realities of GBV do not follow isolated incident trajectories of 'not victim'/victim/recovery. Victimisation is episodic, always mixing different forms, and happens multiple times across lifespans (it cross-cuts 'time and space') (Lindgren and Renck, 2008; Mouffe, 2013).

The 7th Workshop on Online Abuse and Harms (WOAH), pages 170–186
July 13, 2023 ©2023 Association for Computational Linguistics

videos without consent, so-called 'revenge pornography' (or 'image-based abuse'), deepfakes, rape-supportive jokes and memes, cyberflashing, cyberstalking (including 'creeping'), cyberbullying, trolling, anti-feminist forums and bots targeting feminist content, social media-based harassment, grooming, threatening private messages, the dissemination of private information, catfishing and doxing (Get Safe Online, 2023; Glitch, 2022). As phenomena that are morphing, multi-pronged, and crossing the boundaries of multiple social worlds, modern GBV is more complex than ever and more challenging to regulate. Online GBV is of specific interest because it has distinct characteristics, namely that it is rising sharply and is mostly perpetrated by strangers (Amnesty International, 2017).

The GBV concept recognises that people of all genders are victimised by, perpetrate, uphold, and enable (gender) stereotypes and the systematic violence and abuse arising from them, occurring at the point(s) of situational power differentials and axes of difference. Spectrum-based and pluralistic, GBV is perpetrated by numerous people across boundaries of time and cultural sites, experienced in every level of social life, combining macro factors, such as patriarchal belief systems, meso factors such as institutional dismissal, and micro factors such as interpersonal relations (Public Health Scotland, 2021). The GBV framework has been recognised and strategically adopted by organisations such as the World Bank (2019), the World Health Organization (2020), and the Scottish Government (2016), among others. Its increasing take-up in policy-making at both supranational and national levels relates to the framework's exhaustive and inclusive approach, considering age, class, disability, geography, history, race, and socioeconomics.

Terminology As the framework is widely encompassing, GBV accounts for terms that are often used loosely and interchangeably in NLP literature, annotation schema and guidelines, which we clarify here. According to Manne (2017), **Sexism** 'consists in ideology that has the overall function of rationalising and justifying patriarchal social relations'. Sexism provides the underlying assumptions, beliefs, and stereotypes, as well as theories and narratives concerning gender differences that cause people to 'support and participate in patriarchal social arrangements'—and engage in misogynistic behaviour. **Misogyny**, on the other hand, consists of actions that serve to police and enforce those sexist norms and assumptions. As Manne (2017) puts it, misogyny is the "'law enforcement" branch of a patriarchal order'.

Our contributions In this paper, we reassess resources for automated abusive language identification through the GBV framework, paying particular attention to the conceptual strand dedicated to violence against women and girls (VAWG) in the form of (online) sexism and misogyny. We conduct a systematic review considering factors that are pertinent to stakeholders (i.e. people with lived experience of GBV and organisations that support them), such as stakeholder representation and data selection. We highlight gaps in currently available resources, and make recommendations for future dataset creation. Specifically, we address the following **Research questions**:

R1. How is GBV characterised?

R2. Who is represented in annotation of the data?

R3. From which platforms have the data been sourced?

R4. How has the data been sampled?

R5. Which languages are represented?

R6. During which time periods were the data created?

For motivation of these questions and analysis of the findings, see section 4. We create a new repository of resources for computational identification of GBV structured around the issues highlighted here. This is available at `https://github.com/HWU-NLP/GBV-Resources`.

2 Related work

In addition to the sociological and policy literature outlined in section 1, our methodology and research aims are informed by work from NLP and human-computer interaction in a number of areas.

GBV online A number of studies address computational analysis of aspects of GBV, such as the tone of news reports on incidents of rape and femicide (De La Paz et al., 2017; Minnema et al., 2022) and user engagement with GBV stories on social media (ElSherief et al., 2017; Purohit et al., 2016). However, we are not aware of prior work applying the framework to abusive language detection.

Abusive, hateful, and toxic language detection There are several reviews summarising work on detection of related but broader phenomena such as hate speech (e.g. Vidgen et al., 2019). In a survey of ethical issues surrounding automated content moderation, Kiritchenko et al. (2021) highlight the importance of engaging with stakeholders, considering annotator welfare and labelling disagreement—factors we also analyse in this online GBV review.

For hate speech detection resources, Poletto et al. (2021) present a systematic review of hate speech benchmark datasets, finding that the field lacks a common framework, that annotation schema and taxonomies are not systematically described, and that targeted sampling methodologies result in neglect of prevalent forms of abuse—issues we further examine and make recommendations on.

We draw heavily on Vidgen and Derczynski (2021), who systematically reviewed abusive language datasets and provide the hatespeechdata.com repository. While this comprehensive resource provides one of our search sources and many of the resources we review, we examine a number of factors it does not touch upon, such as the correspondence of annotation schemes to the GBV framework, and the levels of stakeholder participation.

Sexism and misogyny detection In recent years, there has been growing interest in developing datasets for the identification of phenomena related to sexism and misogyny as a separate task from more general abusive, hateful, offensive, or toxic language detection. This has included a number of shared tasks, such as EXIST (Rodríguez-Sánchez et al., 2021, 2022; Plaza et al., 2023), AMI (Fersini et al., 2018, 2022), SemEval-2019 Task 5 (Basile et al., 2019), and EDOS (Kirk et al., 2023).

For an earlier overview, Shushkevich and Cardiff (2019) surveyed the detection of misogynistic text, primarily on Twitter. They focus on approaches to technical aspects of automatic classification and performance measured on benchmark datasets. We are not aware of prior work that situates computational resources within a cohesive framework rooted in social science and policy, as we provide.

Stakeholder participation In this review, we focus on the extent to which stakeholders such as experts in and victims of GBV are included and consulted in the production of resources for its identification. Participatory design has a long history of being incorporated into projects in the field of human-computer interaction (e.g Muller and Kuhn, 1993). However, despite a handful of successful projects (e.g Birhane et al., 2022), the inclusion of stakeholders in NLP and AI design tends to remain superficial at best (Delgado et al., 2021).

3 Review methodology

In order to form a comprehensive picture of the available resources and to conduct a replicable and transparent review, we follow the systematic methodology of Moher et al. (2009). The search protocol is shown in Figure 1, and outlined below.

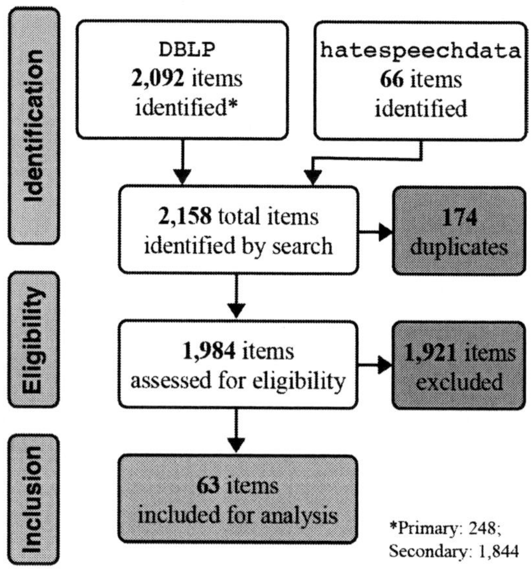

Figure 1: Flow diagram showing the phases of the selection of research items analysed in this review.

Databases Following a scoping study to establish coverage of GBV-related publications and datasets, we searched two databases: the DBLP Computer Science Bibliography[2] and hatespeechdata.com.[3] We found that these were sufficient to cover all papers published at typical NLP venues such as the ACL Anthology.[4]

Keyword selection We used the primary search keywords *misogyn**, *sexis**, and *"gender based violence"*. For DBLP, to capture publications that concern hate speech and abusive language more generally, but that include categories relevant to GBV, we also search using the secondary keywords *hate speech* | *detection* | *rhetoric*, *abuse*,

[2]https://dblp.org/

[3]https://hatespeechdata.com/

[4]https://aclanthology.org/

and *abusive* | *offensive* | *toxic language* | *speech*, which we developed from the results of our scoping study. Search using secondary terms is unnecessary in hatespeechdata.com, where all included entries concern hate speech and abusive language. To filter out irrelevant publications, we then search within the whole text results for our primary keywords. We also perform a manual search of hatespeechdata.com, adding items that describe general hate speech and abusive or toxic language datasets which include sexism, misogyny, or gender-based abuse as categories in their taxonomies. We conducted all searches on April 21st 2023.

Eligibility criteria Table 1 shows the inclusion and exclusion criteria we applied. Two authors of this paper read the identified items applying the criteria, and cross checking agreement.

Include	Exclude
Describes a dataset designed and manually annotated for text classification of toxic language, hate speech, or related phenomena.	Describes a previously released dataset with no modifications (e.g. shared task system paper).
Data is from online sources such as social media and website comments.	Data is from other sources such as scripted TV shows.
GBV specified as target phenomena (e.g. 'misogyny', 'sexism').	Describes general toxic language dataset without fine-grained GBV concepts.

Table 1: Inclusion/exclusion criteria.

For items found in hatespeechdata.com, we directly apply the inclusion/exclusion criteria. For items retrieved from the DBLP, we first automatically select two groups of items for the first round of eligibility assessment: i) dataset description papers with keywords '*dataset*' / '*corpus*' in the title; ii) GBV-related papers with primary keywords mentioned in the whole text content. We then apply the criteria to manually check the remaining items.

Summary of included resources Following the systematic search process, we eventually include 63 relevant items for analysis in the review. These are shown in Table 2 along with summary statistics describing the resources. Of these, all but eight of the described datasets are currently available to download, while those described by Fersini et al. (2022) and Zeinert et al. (2021) require sign-up or email request to obtain access. Due to licensing and privacy issues, the majority of the resources sourced from Twitter include only the ID numbers of posts, which is likely to result in difficulties in retrieving their contents given elapsed time and changes in the accessibility of the platform's API.

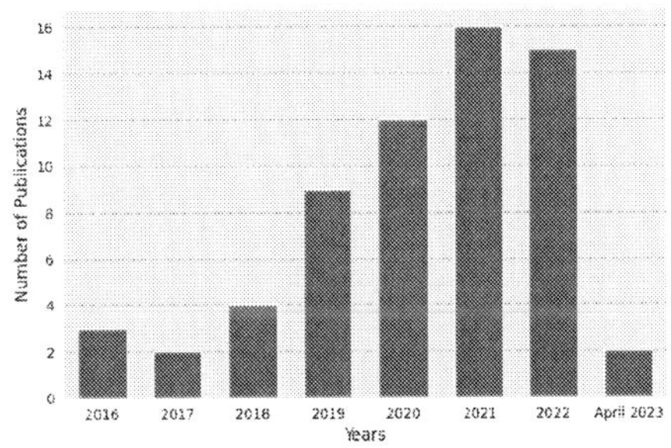

Figure 2: Publications per year up to April 2023.

Figure 2 shows the number of GBV detection resources over time, with relevant work first appearing in 2016 and increasing in number until 2022.[5]

4 Research questions and analysis

With this review, we synthesise information on the following aspects of the available resources:[6]

Characterisation of GBV Given the framework outlined in section 1, we investigate how GBV is characterised in the resources: what terminology is used to describe GBV (e.g. 'sexism', 'misogyny'), how these concepts are theorised, and how GBV fits into the datasets' taxonomies. Overall, we find that use of terminology is confused, and limited engagement with sociological theory.

We find that a large number of resources (28, 41.8%) name '*sexism*' as their target phenomena of interest. The majority of these describe this only superficially as, for example 'hate against women' (Guellil et al., 2021b) or 'hate speech including sexism' (Yadav et al., 2023). However, several 'sexism' resources are grounded—to greater or lesser extents—in sociological theory. Sharifirad and Jacovi (2019) cite Mills (2008)' definitions of sexism, concluding that 'sexism seems to be a relatively complex concept which is [not] easy to define', while Jha and Mamidi (2017) contrasts 'benevolent' and 'hostile' forms of sexism as described by Glick and Fiske (1997). The most comprehensive grounding of sexism in theory is provided by Samory et al. (2021), who compile a 'sexism codebook' based on nearly 30 psychological

[5]For further statistics and visualisations, see Appendix A.

[6]Detailed notes on the resources with respect to these dimensions are provided in the repository at https://github.com/HWU-NLP/GBV-Resources.git.

Publication/source reference	Conceptualisation of target phenomena	Media platform	Level of analysis	Language	Size	Avail-ability
Al-Hassan and Al-Dossari (2022)	*Sexism* as category	Twitter	Post	Arabic	11,000	✗
Almanea and Poesio (2022)	*Misogyny, Sexism*	Twitter	Post	Arabic	964	✓
Alsafari et al. (2020)	*Gender-based hate* as category	Twitter	Post	Arabic	5361	✓
Anzovino et al. (2018)	*Misogyny*	Twitter	Post	English	4,454	✓
Assenmacher et al. (2021)	*Sexism*	Rheinische Post	Post	German	85,000	✓
Basile et al. (2019)	*Women* as target	Twitter	Post	English, Spanish	19,600	✓
Bhattacharya et al. (2020)	*Misogyny*	Facebook, Twitter, YouTube	Post	Bangla, English, Hindi	25,000+	✓
Borkan et al. (2019)	*Gender identity (female, male, transgender, non-binary)*	Online comment forums	Comment	English	450,000	✓
Bosco et al. (2018)	*Gender issues* as category	Facebook, Twitter	Post	Italian	8,000	✓
Cercas Curry et al. (2021)	*Sexism, Sexual harassment*	Dialogue systems, Facebook	Conversation	English	4,185	✓
Chiril et al. (2021)	*Sexism*	Twitter	Post	French	9,282	✓
Chiril et al. (2019)	*Sexism*	Twitter	Post	French	3,085	✗
Chiril et al. (2020)	*Sexism*	Twitter	Post	French	12,000	✓
Chung and Lin (2021)	*Sex (gender, sexual orientation, or gender identity)* as category	PTT (Taiwanese bulletin board)	Post, comment	Chinese	1000 posts, 121,344 com.	✓
Das et al. (2022)	*Gender as target*	Twitter	Post	Bengali	10,178	✓
El Ansari et al. (2020)	*Discrimination and Violence Against Women*	Twitter	Post	Arabic	1,690	✗
Fanton et al. (2021)	*Women* as target	Semi-synthetic text	Post	English	5,003	✓
Fersini et al. (2018)	*Misogyny*	Twitter	Post	English, Spanish	8,115	✓
Fersini et al. (2020)	*Misogyny*	Twitter	Post	Italian	7,961	✓
Fersini et al. (2022)	*Misogyny*	9GaG, Imgur, Knowyourmeme, Reddit, Twitter	Meme	English	15,000	✓
García-Díaz et al. (2021)	*Misogyny, Violence against Women*	Twitter	Post	Speanish	7,682	✓
Gomez et al. (2020)	*Sexism*	Twitter	Post	English	149,823	✓
Gong et al. (2021)	*Gender* as target	YouTube	Comment, sentence	English	11,540	✗
Grosz and Conde-Cespedes (2020)	*Sexism*	Twitter, related quotes collection	Post, quote	English	1,100+	✓
Guellil et al. (2021a)	*Sexism*	YouTube	Comment, reply	Arabic	3,798	✗
Guest et al. (2021)	*Misogyny*	Reddit	Post (header and body)	English	6,567	✓
Hewitt et al. (2016)	*Misogyny*	Twitter	Post	English	5,500	✗
Hoefels et al. (2022)	*Sexism*	Twitter		Romanian	39,245	✓
Ibrohim and Budi (2019)	*Gender* as category	Twitter	Post	Indonesian	13,169	✓
Jha and Mamidi (2017)	*Sexism (benevolent vs hostile)*	Twitter	Post	English	712	✓
Jiang et al. (2022)	*Sexism*	Sina Weibo	Post, comment	Chinese	8,969	✓
Jeong et al. (2022)	*Gender & sexual orientation* as target	NAVER news, YouTube	Post	Korean	40,429	✓
Kennedy et al. (2020)	*Gender identity* as target, *Sexist speech*	Twitter, Reddit, YouTube	Comment	English	39,565	✓
Kennedy et al. (2022)	*Gender identity* as target	Gab	Post	English	27,665	✓
Kirk et al. (2023)	*Sexism*	Gab; Reddit	Post, comment	English	20,000	✓
Kumar et al. (2018)	*Gendered Aggression*	Facebook, Twitter	Post, comment	Hindi-English	39,000	✓
Kwarteng et al. (2022)	*Misogyny (misogynoir)*	Twitter	Post	English	4,532	✓
Lee et al. (2022)	*Gender* as category	Korean news site	Comment	Korean	109,692	✓
Leite et al. (2020)	*Misogyny*	Twitter	Post	(Brazilian) Portuguese	21,000	✓
Lynn et al. (2019)	*Misogyny*	Urban Dictionary	Post	English	2,285	✓
Mathew et al. (2021)	*Women* as target	Twitter, Gab	Words, phrases, posts	English	20,148	✓
Mulki and Ghanem (2021)	*Misogyny*	Twitter	Post	Arabic (Levantine)	6,550	✓
Mollas et al. (2022)	*Gender* as category	Reddit, Youtube	Post, comment	English	1,072	✓
Moon et al. (2020)	*Gender bias* as category	NAVER entertainment news	Comment	Korean	9,381	✓
Ousidhoum et al. (2019)	*Gender* as target	Twitter	Post	Arabic, English, French	13,000	✓
Petrak and Krenn (2022)	*Misogyny*	Austrian news	Comment	German	6,600	✗
Plaza et al. (2023)	*Sexism*	Twitter, Gab,	Post	English, spanish	9,400	✓
de Pelle and Moreira (2017)	*Sexism*	Globo (news)	Post	(Brazilian) Portuguese	1,250	✓
Rizwan et al. (2020)	*Sexism*	Twitter	Post	Roman Urdu	10,041	✓
Rodríguez-Sánchez et al. (2020)	*Sexism*	Twitter	Post	Spanish	3,600	✓
Rodríguez-Sánchez et al. (2021)	*Sexism*	Gab, Twitter	Post	English, Spanish	11,345	✓
Rodríguez-Sánchez et al. (2022)	*Sexism*	Gab, Twitter	Post	English, Spanish	12,403	✓
Romim et al. (2022)	*Gender* as category	Facebook, TikTok, YouTube	Post, comment	Bangla	50,281	✓
Samory et al. (2021)	*Sexism*	Twitter	Post	English	91	✓
Sharifirad and Jacovi (2019)	*Sexism*	Twitter	Post	English	3,240	✓
Sharifirad and Matwin (2019)	*Sexism*	Twitter	Post	English		✓
Strathern and Pfeffer (2022)	*Misogyny*	Twitter	Post	English	266,579	✓
Talat (2016)	*Sexism*	Twitter	Post	English	4,033	✓
Talat and Hovy (2016)	*Sexism*	Twitter	Post	English	16,000	✓
Toosi (2019)	*Sexism*	Twitter	Post	English	31,961	✓
Vidgen et al. (2021)	*Gender: women & Gender: minorities* as targets	Synthetic text	Post	English	41,255	✓
Yadav et al. (2023)	*Sexism* as a category	Twitter	Post	Arabic, English, French, German, Hindi, Spanish	497,660	✗
Zeinert et al. (2021)	*Misogyny*	Twitter, Facebook, Reddit	Post	Danish	279,000	✓

Table 2: Summary of included resources for automated identification of GBV-related phenomena.

scales including *Attitudes toward Women* (Spence and Helmreich, 1972), *Neosexism* (Tougas et al., 1995), and *Gender-Roles Attitudes* (García-Cueto et al., 2015). They also bemoan the 'lack of definitional clarity' in prior work on automated sexism detection.

19 (28.4%) of the resources are constructed with *gender*-based abuse as one of several *categories* or *targets* of more general hate speech. These are variously described as 'gender bias' (Moon et al., 2020), 'gender issues' (Bosco et al., 2018), or to include female, male, transgender, and non-binary genders (Borkan et al., 2019). The latter is similar in approach to the eight resources in which gender is conceived as one of various *targets*. Inclusion in gender as a target ranges from 'women' (Basile et al., 2019; Fanton et al., 2021; Mathew et al., 2021); to separation of 'gender: women' from 'gender: minorities' (Vidgen et al., 2021); to 'women, men, non-binary or third gender, transgender women, transgender men, transgender (unspecified)' (Kennedy et al., 2020), the latter identifying these groups as those protected in U.S. law.

16 (23.9%) of the resources characterise the target phenomenon as '*misogyny*'. Almanea and Poesio (2022) ground this only in prior computer science literature, describing misogynistic language as 'a category which overlap[s] with sexism towards women'. Petrak and Krenn (2022) explicitly conflate sexism and misogyny, but provide the disclaimer that their guidelines 'are not meant as an accurate abstract definition', but rather to assist annotators in making judgements. García-Díaz et al. (2021) delineate online misogyny into several categories including 'violence against relevant women', where 'relevant' signifies known targets of abuse. Anzovino et al. (2018) and Mulki and Ghanem (2021) consider language used in 'cybermisogyny', as outlined by Poland (2016). The latter also characterises misogyny as 'hatred of or contempt for women', citing feminist sociology and media studies (Moloney and Love, 2018) and the U.S. Constitution (Nockleby, 2000). Strathern and Pfeffer (2022) provide the most comprehensive overview of misogyny, comparing, among other sources, definitions from feminist philosophy (Allen, 2022), digital media studies (Ostini and Hopkins, 2015), and gender studies (Megarry, 2014), and devise a taxonomy based on these as well as computer science resources.

Despite its widespread adoption in policymaking (see section 1), we do not find any existing resources rooted in the GBV framework.

Annotators Most datasets for supervised machine learning are annotated by small numbers of anonymous crowdworkers (Vidgen and Derczynski, 2021), biasing the labelled data towards the opinions, world views, and lived experiences of those people who happen to work on the crowdsourcing platforms. Rottger et al. (2022) describe a scale of annotation scenarios ranging from highly *prescriptive* to *descriptive*, where the former attempts to induce annotators to follow a defined schema, while the latter seeks to elicit their individual and potentially conflicting points of view. There is a growing movement to recognise, that for many tasks, there may be no single 'ground truth', different judgements may be equally valid, or preservation of minority perspectives should be facilitated (Abercrombie et al., 2022; Aroyo and Welty, 2015; Plank, 2022). In the following, We report on who and how many annotators are represented, their expert or stakeholder knowledge, the level of training and/or supervision, and the guidelines and instructions with which they work. We examine these resources through the lenses of data *perspectivism* (Cabitza et al., 2023),[7] *participatory design* (Delgado et al., 2021; Muller et al., 2021) and *design justice* (Costanza-Chock, 2020), reporting on the extent to which different points of view are represented and the levels at which stakeholders are included as participants in decision making.

Due to the psychological harm working with abusive language can cause and its potential to traumatise victims (Kirk et al., 2022; Shmueli et al., 2021), we also assess the annotator welfare measures reportedly taken in constructing these resources.

Overall, we find that engagement with stakeholders is limited, minority annotator perspectives are usually not preserved, and comprehensive annotator welfare measures are unusual.

Representation: Reporting of *who* undertook dataset annotation is patchy, with only nine resources accompanied by a full data statement or annotator information to a similar degree of detail (Assenmacher et al., 2021; Cercas Curry et al., 2021; Das et al., 2022; Guest et al., 2021; Ibrohim and Budi, 2019; Leite et al., 2020; Kirk et al., 2023;

[7] See also the Perspectivist Data Manifesto: `https://pdai.info/`

Zeinert et al., 2021). From the information that *is* provided, we find that 16 (25%) of the datasets were annotated by crowdworkers, and 19 (30%) by people at various levels of academia ranging from the authors and other researchers to undergraduate students. The term 'expert' is used loosely, and refers variously to Gender Studies students (Cercas Curry et al., 2021; Chiril et al., 2020, 2021), people the authors provided some form of training to (Guest et al., 2021), 'experienced moderators' (Petrak and Krenn, 2022), or is not explicitly defined at all (Rodríguez-Sánchez et al., 2022; Vidgen et al., 2021). Where we understand the 'experts' in question to potentially be stakeholders, they are described as 'non-activist feminists' (Jha and Mamidi, 2017), 'feminist and anti-racism activists' Talat (2016), or Gender Studies students. Only Vidgen et al. (2021) report on whether their annotators have themselves been victims of online abuse, and we do not find evidence of the authors engaging with GBV-focused organisations to ensure victims are represented.

Data perspectivism: We find only six datasets (10%) released with multiple labels preserved (Cercas Curry et al., 2021; Hoefels et al., 2022; Kennedy et al., 2020; Kirk et al., 2023; Leite et al., 2020; Talat, 2016), with the others providing only aggregated labels, hence losing any potentially informative minority judgements.

Annotator welfare: Very few publications report any measures taken to ensure annotator welfare. Those that do follow welfare guidelines by Kennedy et al. (2020) (Strathern and Pfeffer, 2022); Vidgen et al. (2019) (Vidgen et al., 2021); the ACL Code of Ethics (Lee et al., 2022); Kirk et al. (2022) (Kirk et al., 2023); and Rivers and Lewis (2014) (Das et al., 2022). Despite the fact that any research with human subjects (including annotators) requires approval by an Institutional Review Board (IRB) (particularly when dealing with potentially upsetting material) (Shmueli et al., 2021), only two papers reports their studies having passed ethical review (Cercas Curry et al., 2021; Jeong et al., 2022).

Platforms While GBV is prevalent in all online spaces, most NLP research tends to collect data from freely accessible social media sources such as Twitter and Facebook. We ask: for which platforms are datasets available, and what is the modality of the data (i.e. text or multi-modal)? We find that the resources are very heavily skewed towards textual data from Twitter.

The majority of GBV resources are sourced from social media such as Twitter, Reddit, and Gab (a platform known for its right-wing user base). Twitter is by far the most accessible platform that provides an API and more lenient policies for gathering and disseminating data, with almost half of the available datasets (51.8%) being obtained exclusively or in combination with other sources from it. Reddit (7.1%) and Gab (7.1%) are also widely sourced with relatively lax moderation policies for user-generated content. Other popular platforms for procuring GBV datasets include Youtube (8.2%), Facebook (5.9%), and news website (7.1%) And around 34.9% of resources collect data from mixed sources.

Almost all the resources directly collect user-generated content online, except for Vidgen et al. (2021)'s set of human-generated synthetic data that mimics real-world social media posts, and another employing a semi-synthetic collection approach by iteratively refining a generative language model to create new samples that experts review and/or post-edit (Fanton et al., 2021). The only multi-modal datasets are those of Fersini et al. (2022), who released a set of misogynistic memes, and Gomez et al. (2020), who collected and labelled tweets that include text and images for attacks on different communities including the label '*sexist*'.

Overall, we find no evidence that researchers' choices of which media platforms to target are driven by stakeholders' requirements.

Data sampling A strong motivation for engaging stakeholders in annotation is that, following *standpoint theory* (Harding, 1991), in many cases, those with relevant lived experience are the only people capable of recognising subtle, implicit abuse such as stereotypes and micro-aggressions. However, it is recognised that commonly used data sampling techniques do not account for this type of language, meaning that it is sparsely represented in datasets (Vidgen and Derczynski, 2021).

Indeed, we find that, where reported, nearly all the resources (20) have been sampled using keyword search. Those that have not, were generally gathered from specific sources known to consist predominantly of text espousing hateful ideologies such as Gab (Kennedy et al., 2022; Mathew et al., 2021; Plaza et al., 2023; Rodríguez-Sánchez et al., 2022) or particular forums on Reddit (Fersini et al.,

2022; Guest et al., 2021; Kennedy et al., 2020; Kirk et al., 2023; Mollas et al., 2022). Alternative strategies are to collect items on topics that attract toxic comments (Bhattacharya et al., 2020), items already flagged by community moderators (Assenmacher et al., 2021), or those addressed to people known to be victims of online abuse (Basile et al., 2019; Fersini et al., 2022; García-Díaz et al., 2021; Mulki and Ghanem, 2021; Strathern and Pfeffer, 2022; Yadav et al., 2023). Only Lee et al. (2022) rely on random selection to produce a more realistic but sparse data representation, while Zeinert et al. (2021) explore a range of sampling techniques in an effort to obtain a balanced representation of positively labelled (i.e. misogynistic) examples.

Languages As NLP research is heavily skewed towards English (Bender, 2009; Hovy and Prabhumoye, 2021), negatively affecting its ability to benefit diverse communities, we report on the languages represented in the available resources.

The resources cover a total of 16 languages, the vast majority of which are Indo-European (49 datasets, 77.8%). Specifically, most available resources are exclusively in English (26, 41.3%), followed by Spanish (8, 12.7%), Arabic (8, 12.7%), and French (5, 7.9%). There are also nine multilingual datasets covering a variety of languages including Arabic, French, German, Hindi, Italian, and Spanish, all of which include English as one of the languages. Overall, coverage of non-English languages is poor, with only one dataset even for a language as widely spoken as Chinese (Jiang et al., 2022).

Temporality While language use evolves, new societal events occur, and abusers use creative ways to circumvent content moderation (Talat et al., 2017), NLP datasets are usually collected over a specific time frame, limiting the ability of systems to make correct predictions on new instances (Kiela et al., 2021). We report on the time frames and scales over which the datasets were collected and whether they are static or dynamic.

25 (39.7%) of the datasets do not report collection dates. Time spans of those that do are presented in Figure 3[8]. The majority were collected in the past five years. The variation in the time frames covered by GBV datasets could be due to a variety of factors, such as the release of new platforms

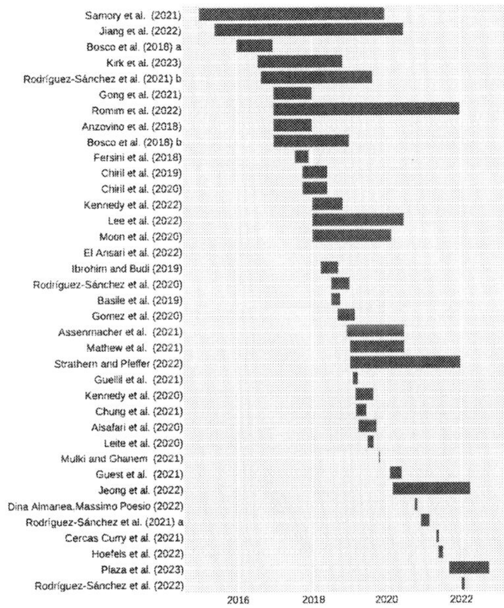

Figure 3: Data time spans. Those labeled *a*/*b* are data subsets from the same resource but different platforms and periods.

or tools for data collection, the emergence of new GBV-related topics, and changes in the policy or accessibility of social media platforms. The fact that Twitter is the most commonly used platform for data collection, as previously mentioned in the analysis of platforms, could be one factor in the time spans distribution. Twitter's popularity, user activity, and high volume of user-generated content may make it easier for researchers to collect data over shorter time frames. And the distribution of time frames is also likely influenced by factors such as the scope of GBV data and the size of the datasets.

All but one of the resources are collected on a static time scale, with only one gathered dynamically in a human-in-the-loop setting (Vidgen et al., 2021). Current classification systems are commonly trained on these static datasets over fixed time frames, which has negative implications for their effectiveness, generalisability, and robustness in identifying instances of GBV in real-time.

5 Discussion and recommendations

This review has uncovered several limitations in the available resources and the approaches of NLP researchers towards constructing them. We summarise these and make future recommendations.

[8]For space, we exclude Lynn et al. (2019) (collected 1999-2006) and show Samory et al. (2021) (2008-2019) from 2015.

Conceptualisation With a couple of exceptions (e.g. Samory et al., 2021; Strathern and Pfeffer, 2022), the phenomena targeted in the reviewed resources are not clearly defined or strongly rooted in theory or expertise from outside computer science. Similar observations have been made for operationalisation of related concepts, such as bias and stereotypes (Blodgett et al., 2021), and value alignment (Irving and Askell, 2019).
Recommendation: Resource creators should collaborate with social scientists to ground them in expert knowledge of the target phenomena. We advocate for the use of GBV as a framework, which encompasses several facets currently operationalised in different ways by computer science researchers. It recognises how all forms of online abuse affect people of every gender both online and off, and has been widely adopted by policymakers.

Stakeholder participation Parker and Ruths (2023) propose that computer scientists should:

> *stop thinking about online hate speech as something requiring methods, and start thinking about it as something that demands solutions. This change — treating hate speech less like a task and more like the real-world problem it is — would orient CS research towards the concerns of other stakeholders, and thus begin the collaborative pursuit toward a safe Internet.*

However, we find little evidence of such a paradigm shift having occurred when it comes to designing these resources, with stakeholder participation limited to the recruitment of loosely defined 'expert' annotators—where it occurs at all.
Recommendations: Resource development projects should, as far as possible, strive to include stakeholders from the outset by including representatives in research teams. Stakeholder participation should be integrated throughout development, and is especially important in the design of taxonomies, guidelines, and at annotation, when judgements about what constitutes GBV are made. Due to the risks involved, annotator welfare should be prioritised by following guidelines such as those of Kirk et al. (2022), and IRB approval sought before any data collection. In documenting resources, authors should provide full data statements or similar (e.g. Bender and Friedman, 2018; Díaz et al., 2022), and, to preserve minority voices, dataset releases should includenon-aggregated labels (Prabhakaran et al., 2021).

Data collection Media data for these resources is not sourced from diverse sources, with the majority from Twitter, the choice of which does not appear to be driven by stakeholders. Furthermore, as the datasets are static in nature, their relevance as reference sources for automated classification decays over time; and, due to data sampling methods, positively labelled (i.e. abusive) examples are skewed towards the more explicit forms of online GBV.
Recommendation: There is a great need for the development of new methods to surface the diversity of GBV found online. One solution is to create platforms to which victims of abuse and bystanders can submit examples. This could facilitate creation of improved resources on many of the limiting dimensions we outline in this review: dynamic datasets to which new examples are regularly added; stakeholder participation in data and platform selection and labelling; and inclusion of implicit and subtle examples of GBV, as well as multimedia data.

Limitations and ethical considerations

We use a systematic review methodology in order to provide a reproducible and objective snapshot of the current research situation. However, we acknowledge that the choices made (such as search repositories and eligibility criteria) may not have captured every existing relevant resource. We aim to regularly update the repository of GBV resources at `https://github.com/HWU-NLP/GBV-Resources` and open it to submissions via push requests in order to provide a dynamic and comprehensive record.

Following D'Ignazio and Klein (2020), we acknowledge that this research is influenced by the positionalities of its authors. To situate our perspective, we are four Computer Science and one Social Science academic researchers working in public institutions in Europe. Three of us identify as women and two as men, and we are of European and Asian nationalities. This work forms part of a project conducted in partnership with charitable organisations that work on combating GBV and supporting its victims.

In this paper, we make a number of recommendations that complicate typical NLP resource creation workflows, and could have the unintended consequence of dissuading researchers from working on these problems. However, we appreciate that interdisciplinary work is difficult to instigate, organise, and carry out, and that it is not usually motivated by typical academic or industry reward structures. Our intention is to point out practical ways in which resource development can be improved and to encourage researchers to move towards more participatory solutions.

Acknowledgements

We would like to thank the anonymous reviewers for all their valuable comments and suggestions. Gavin Abercrombie, Aiqi Jiang, Poppy Gerrard-Abbott, Ioannis Konstas, and Verena Rieser were supported by the EPSRC project 'Equally Safe Online' (EP/W025272/1 and EP/W025493/1), and Gavin Abercrombie and Verena Rieser were also supported by the EPSRC project 'Gender Bias in Conversational AI' (EP/T023767/1). Verena Rieser was also supported by a Leverhulme Trust Senior Research Fellowship (SRF/R1/201100). Aiqi Jiang was supported by China Scholarship Council (CSC Funding, No. 201908510140).

References

Gavin Abercrombie, Valerio Basile, Sara Tonelli, Verena Rieser, and Alexandra Uma, editors. 2022. *Proceedings of the 1st Workshop on Perspectivist Approaches to NLP @LREC2022*. European Language Resources Association, Marseille, France.

Areej Al-Hassan and Hmood Al-Dossari. 2022. Detection of hate speech in Arabic tweets using deep learning. *Multimedia systems*, 28(6):1963–1974.

Amy Allen. 2022. Feminist Perspectives on Power. In Edward N. Zalta and Uri Nodelman, editors, *The Stanford Encyclopedia of Philosophy*, Fall 2022 edition. Metaphysics Research Lab, Stanford University.

Dina Almanea and Massimo Poesio. 2022. ArMIS - the Arabic misogyny and sexism corpus with annotator subjective disagreements. In *Proceedings of the Thirteenth Language Resources and Evaluation Conference*, pages 2282–2291, Marseille, France. European Language Resources Association.

Safa Alsafari, Samira Sadaoui, and Malek Mouhoub. 2020. Hate and offensive speech detection on Arabic social media. *Online Social Networks and Media*, 19:100096.

Amnesty International. 2017. Amnesty reveals alarming impact of online abuse against women. Accessed: 2023-05-09.

Maria Anzovino, Elisabetta Fersini, and Paolo Rosso. 2018. Automatic identification and classification of misogynistic language on Twitter. In *Natural Language Processing and Information Systems*, pages 57–64, Cham. Springer International Publishing.

Lora Aroyo and Chris Welty. 2015. Truth is a lie: Crowd truth and the seven myths of human annotation. *AI Magazine*, 36(1):15–24.

Dennis Assenmacher, Marco Niemann, Kilian Müller, Moritz Seiler, Dennis M Riehle, and Heike Trautmann. 2021. Rp-mod&RP-crowd: Moderator-and crowd-annotated German news comment datasets. In *NeurIPS Datasets and Benchmarks*.

Valerio Basile, Cristina Bosco, Elisabetta Fersini, Debora Nozza, Viviana Patti, Francisco Manuel Rangel Pardo, Paolo Rosso, and Manuela Sanguinetti. 2019. SemEval-2019 task 5: Multilingual detection of hate speech against immigrants and women in Twitter. In *Proceedings of the 13th International Workshop on Semantic Evaluation*, pages 54–63, Minneapolis, Minnesota, USA. Association for Computational Linguistics.

Emily M. Bender. 2009. Linguistically naïve != language independent: Why NLP needs linguistic typology. In *Proceedings of the EACL 2009 Workshop on the Interaction between Linguistics and Computational Linguistics: Virtuous, Vicious or Vacuous?*, pages 26–32, Athens, Greece. Association for Computational Linguistics.

Emily M. Bender and Batya Friedman. 2018. Data statements for natural language processing: Toward mitigating system bias and enabling better science. *Transactions of the Association for Computational Linguistics*, 6:587–604.

Shiladitya Bhattacharya, Siddharth Singh, Ritesh Kumar, Akanksha Bansal, Akash Bhagat, Yogesh Dawer, Bornini Lahiri, and Atul Kr. Ojha. 2020. Developing a multilingual annotated corpus of misogyny and aggression. In *Proceedings of the Second Workshop on Trolling, Aggression and Cyberbullying*, pages 158–168, Marseille, France. European Language Resources Association (ELRA).

Abeba Birhane, William Isaac, Vinodkumar Prabhakaran, Mark Diaz, Madeleine Clare Elish, Iason Gabriel, and Shakir Mohamed. 2022. Power to the people? Opportunities and challenges for participatory AI. In *Equity and Access in Algorithms, Mechanisms, and Optimization*, EAAMO '22, New York, NY, USA. Association for Computing Machinery.

Su Lin Blodgett, Gilsinia Lopez, Alexandra Olteanu, Robert Sim, and Hanna Wallach. 2021. Stereotyping Norwegian salmon: An inventory of pitfalls in fairness benchmark datasets. In *Proceedings of the 59th Annual Meeting of the Association for Computational Linguistics and the 11th International Joint Conference on Natural Language Processing (Volume 1: Long Papers)*, pages 1004–1015, Online. Association for Computational Linguistics.

Daniel Borkan, Lucas Dixon, Jeffrey Sorensen, Nithum Thain, and Lucy Vasserman. 2019. Nuanced metrics for measuring unintended bias with real data for text classification. In *Companion Proceedings of*

The 2019 World Wide Web Conference, WWW '19, page 491–500, New York, NY, USA. Association for Computing Machinery.

Cristina Bosco, Dell'Orletta Felice, Fabio Poletto, Manuela Sanguinetti, and Tesconi Maurizio. 2018. Overview of the EVALITA 2018 hate speech detection task. In *EVALITA 2018-Sixth Evaluation Campaign of Natural Language Processing and Speech Tools for Italian*, volume 2263, pages 1–9. CEUR.

Federico Cabitza, Andrea Campagner, and Valerio Basile. 2023. Toward a perspectivist turn in ground truthing for predictive computing. In *Proceedings of the AAAI Conference on Artificial Intelligence.*

Amanda Cercas Curry, Gavin Abercrombie, and Verena Rieser. 2021. ConvAbuse: Data, analysis, and benchmarks for nuanced abuse detection in conversational AI. In *Proceedings of the 2021 Conference on Empirical Methods in Natural Language Processing*, pages 7388–7403, Online and Punta Cana, Dominican Republic. Association for Computational Linguistics.

Patricia Chiril, Farah Benamara, and Véronique Moriceau. 2021. "be nice to your wife! the restaurants are closed": Can gender stereotype detection improve sexism classification? In *Findings of the Association for Computational Linguistics: EMNLP 2021*, pages 2833–2844, Punta Cana, Dominican Republic. Association for Computational Linguistics.

Patricia Chiril, Farah Benamara Zitoune, Véronique Moriceau, Marlène Coulomb-Gully, and Abhishek Kumar. 2019. Multilingual and multitarget hate speech detection in tweets. In *Actes de la Conférence sur le Traitement Automatique des Langues Naturelles (TALN) PFIA 2019. Volume II : Articles courts*, pages 351–360, Toulouse, France. ATALA.

Patricia Chiril, Véronique Moriceau, Farah Benamara, Alda Mari, Gloria Origgi, and Marlène Coulomb-Gully. 2020. An annotated corpus for sexism detection in French tweets. In *Proceedings of the 12th Language Resources and Evaluation Conference*, pages 1397–1403, Marseille, France. European Language Resources Association.

I Chung and Chuan-Jie Lin. 2021. TOCAB: A dataset for Chinese abusive language processing. In *2021 IEEE 22nd International Conference on Information Reuse and Integration for Data Science (IRI)*, pages 445–452.

Sasha Costanza-Chock. 2020. *Design Justice: Community-Led Practices to Build the Worlds We Need.* MIT Press.

Mithun Das, Somnath Banerjee, Punyajoy Saha, and Animesh Mukherjee. 2022. Hate speech and offensive language detection in Bengali. In *Proceedings of the 2nd Conference of the Asia-Pacific Chapter of the Association for Computational Linguistics and the 12th International Joint Conference on Natural Language Processing (Volume 1: Long Papers)*, pages 286–296, Online only. Association for Computational Linguistics.

Meliza De La Paz, Maria Regina Estuar, and John Noel Victorino. 2017. Discovering conversation spaces in the public discourse of gender violence: a comparative between two different contexts. In *Proceedings of the 31st Pacific Asia Conference on Language, Information and Computation*, pages 376–383. The National University (Phillippines).

Rogers Prates de Pelle and Viviane P Moreira. 2017. Offensive comments in the Brazilian web: A dataset and baseline results. In *Anais do VI Brazilian Workshop on Social Network Analysis and Mining*. SBC.

Fernando Delgado, Stephen Yang, Michael Madaio, and Qian Yang. 2021. Stakeholder participation in AI: Beyond "add diverse stakeholders and stir". In *Proceedings of the Human-Centered AI workshop at NeurIPS 2021.*

Mark Díaz, Ian Kivlichan, Rachel Rosen, Dylan Baker, Razvan Amironesei, Vinodkumar Prabhakaran, and Emily Denton. 2022. Crowdworksheets: Accounting for individual and collective identities underlying crowdsourced dataset annotation. In *2022 ACM Conference on Fairness, Accountability, and Transparency*, FAccT '22, page 2342–2351, New York, NY, USA. Association for Computing Machinery.

Catherine D'Ignazio and Lauren Klein. 2020. *Data Feminism.* The MIT Press.

Fontaine-Lepage Dominique. 2021. Combating Gender-Based Violence: Cyber violence. European added value assessment study, EESC: European Economic and Social Committee.

Oumayma El Ansari, Zahir Jihad, and Mousannif Hajar. 2020. A dataset to support sexist content detection in Arabic text. In *Image and Signal Processing*, pages 130–137, Cham. Springer International Publishing.

Mai ElSherief, Elizabeth Belding, and Dana Nguyen. 2017. #NotOkay: Understanding Gender-Based Violence in social media. *Proceedings of the International AAAI Conference on Web and Social Media*, 11(1):52–61.

Margherita Fanton, Helena Bonaldi, Serra Sinem Tekiroğlu, and Marco Guerini. 2021. Human-in-the-loop for data collection: a multi-target counter narrative dataset to fight online hate speech. In *Proceedings of the 59th Annual Meeting of the Association for Computational Linguistics and the 11th International Joint Conference on Natural Language Processing (Volume 1: Long Papers)*, pages 3226–3240, Online. Association for Computational Linguistics.

Elisabetta Fersini, Francesca Gasparini, Giulia Rizzi, Aurora Saibene, Berta Chulvi, Paolo Rosso, Alyssa Lees, and Jeffrey Sorensen. 2022. SemEval-2022 task 5: Multimedia automatic misogyny identification. In *Proceedings of the 16th International Workshop on Semantic Evaluation (SemEval-2022)*, pages 533–549, Seattle, United States. Association for Computational Linguistics.

Elisabetta Fersini, Debora Nozza, and Paolo Rosso. 2020. AMI@ EVALITA2020: Automatic misogyny identification. In *EVALITA*.

Elisabetta Fersini, Paolo Rosso, and Maria Anzovino. 2018. Overview of the task on automatic misogyny identification at IberEval 2018. *Ibereval@ sepln*, 2150:214–228.

Eduardo García-Cueto, Francisco Javier Rodríguez-Díaz, Carolina Bringas-Molleda, Javier López-Cepero, Susana Paíno-Quesada, and Luis Rodríguez-Franco. 2015. Development of the gender role attitudes scale (GRAS) amongst young Spanish people. *International Journal of Clinical and Health Psychology*, 15(1):61–68.

José Antonio García-Díaz, Mar Cánovas-García, Ricardo Colomo-Palacios, and Rafael Valencia-García. 2021. Detecting misogyny in Spanish tweets. An approach based on linguistics features and word embeddings. *Future Generation Computer Systems*, 114:506–518.

Get Safe Online. 2023. Online abuse. https://www.getsafeonline.org/personal/articles/online-abuse/. Accessed 2023-05-07.

Peter Glick and Susan T. Fiske. 1997. Hostile and benevolent sexism. *Psychology of Women Quarterly*, 21(1):119–135.

Glitch. 2022. Violence Against Women & Girls code of practice. Accessed: 2023-05-09.

Glitch UK and EVAW. 2020. The ripple effect: COVID-19 and the epidemic of online abuse.

Raul Gomez, Jaume Gibert, Lluis Gomez, and Dimosthenis Karatzas. 2020. Exploring hate speech detection in multimodal publications. In *Proceedings of the IEEE/CVF Winter Conference on Applications of Computer Vision (WACV)*.

Hongyu Gong, Alberto Valido, Katherine M. Ingram, Giulia Fanti, Suma Bhat, and Dorothy L. Espelage. 2021. Abusive language detection in heterogeneous contexts: Dataset collection and the role of supervised attention. *Proceedings of the AAAI Conference on Artificial Intelligence*, 35(17):14804–14812.

Dylan Grosz and Patricia Conde-Cespedes. 2020. Automatic detection of sexist statements commonly used at the workplace. In *Pacific Asian Conference on Knowledge Discovery and Data Mining (PAKDD), Wokshop (Learning Data Representation for Clustering) LDRC*, Singapour, Singapore.

Imane Guellil, Ahsan Adeel, Faiçal Azouaou, Mohamed Boubred, Yousra Houichi, and Akram Abdelhaq Moumna. 2021a. Sexism detection: The first corpus in Algerian dialect with a code-switching in Arabic/ French and English. *CoRR*, abs/2104.01443.

Imane Guellil, Faical Azouaou, Fodil Benali, and Hachani Ala-Eddine. 2021b. ONE: Toward ONE model, ONE algorithm, ONE corpus dedicated to sentiment analysis of Arabic/Arabizi and its dialects. In *Proceedings of the Eleventh Workshop on Computational Approaches to Subjectivity, Sentiment and Social Media Analysis*, pages 236–249, Online. Association for Computational Linguistics.

Ella Guest, Bertie Vidgen, Alexandros Mittos, Nishanth Sastry, Gareth Tyson, and Helen Margetts. 2021. An expert annotated dataset for the detection of online misogyny. In *Proceedings of the 16th Conference of the European Chapter of the Association for Computational Linguistics: Main Volume*, pages 1336–1350, Online. Association for Computational Linguistics.

Sandra Harding. 1991. *Whose science? Whose knowledge?: Thinking from women's lives.* Cornell University Press.

Sarah Hewitt, T. Tiropanis, and C. Bokhove. 2016. The problem of identifying misogynist language on Twitter (and other online social spaces). In *Proceedings of the 8th ACM Conference on Web Science*, WebSci '16, page 333–335, New York, NY, USA. Association for Computing Machinery.

Diana Constantina Hoefels, Çağrı Çöltekin, and Irina Diana Mădroane. 2022. CoRoSeOf - an annotated corpus of Romanian sexist and offensive tweets. In *Proceedings of the Thirteenth Language Resources and Evaluation Conference*, pages 2269–2281, Marseille, France. European Language Resources Association.

Dirk Hovy and Shrimai Prabhumoye. 2021. Five sources of bias in natural language processing. *Language and Linguistics Compass*, 15(8):e12432.

Muhammad Okky Ibrohim and Indra Budi. 2019. Multi-label hate speech and abusive language detection in Indonesian Twitter. In *Proceedings of the Third Workshop on Abusive Language Online*, pages 46–57, Florence, Italy. Association for Computational Linguistics.

Geoffrey Irving and Amanda Askell. 2019. AI safety needs social scientists. *Distill*.

Younghoon Jeong, Juhyun Oh, Jongwon Lee, Jaimeen Ahn, Jihyung Moon, Sungjoon Park, and Alice Oh. 2022. KOLD: Korean offensive language dataset. In *Proceedings of the 2022 Conference on Empirical Methods in Natural Language Processing*, pages 10818–10833, Abu Dhabi, United Arab Emirates. Association for Computational Linguistics.

Akshita Jha and Radhika Mamidi. 2017. When does a compliment become sexist? analysis and classification of ambivalent sexism using twitter data. In *Proceedings of the Second Workshop on NLP and Computational Social Science*, pages 7–16, Vancouver, Canada. Association for Computational Linguistics.

Aiqi Jiang, Xiaohan Yang, Yang Liu, and Arkaitz Zubiaga. 2022. SWSR: A Chinese dataset and lexicon for online sexism detection. *Online Social Networks and Media*, 27.

Brendan Kennedy, Mohammad Atari, Aida Mostafazadeh Davani, Leigh Yeh, Ali Omrani, Yehsong Kim, Kris Coombs Jr., Shreya Havaldar, Gwenyth Portillo-Wightman, Elaine Gonzalez, Joe Hoover, Aida Azatian, Alyzeh Hussain, Austin Lara, Gabriel Cardenas, Adam Omary, Christina Park, Xin Wang, Clarisa Wijaya, Yong Zhang, Beth Meyerowitz, and Morteza Dehghani. 2022. Introducing the Gab hate corpus: Defining and applying hate-based rhetoric to social media posts at scale. *Language Resources & Evaluation*, 56:79–108.

Chris J. Kennedy, Geoff Bacon, Alexander Sahn, and Claudia von Vacano. 2020. Constructing interval variables via faceted Rasch measurement and multitask deep learning: A hate speech application.

Douwe Kiela, Max Bartolo, Yixin Nie, Divyansh Kaushik, Atticus Geiger, Zhengxuan Wu, Bertie Vidgen, Grusha Prasad, Amanpreet Singh, Pratik Ringshia, Zhiyi Ma, Tristan Thrush, Sebastian Riedel, Zeerak Waseem, Pontus Stenetorp, Robin Jia, Mohit Bansal, Christopher Potts, and Adina Williams. 2021. Dynabench: Rethinking benchmarking in NLP. In *Proceedings of the 2021 Conference of the North American Chapter of the Association for Computational Linguistics: Human Language Technologies*, pages 4110–4124, Online. Association for Computational Linguistics.

Svetlana Kiritchenko, Isar Nejadgholi, and Kathleen C. Fraser. 2021. Confronting abusive language online: A survey from the ethical and human rights perspective. *Journal of Artificial Intelligence Research*, 71.

Hannah Kirk, Abeba Birhane, Bertie Vidgen, and Leon Derczynski. 2022. Handling and presenting harmful text in NLP research. In *Findings of the Association for Computational Linguistics: EMNLP 2022*, pages 497–510, Abu Dhabi, United Arab Emirates. Association for Computational Linguistics.

Hannah Rose Kirk, Wenjie Yin, Bertie Vidgen, and Paul Röttger. 2023. SemEval-2023 Task 10: Explainable Detection of Online Sexism. In *Proceedings of the 17th International Workshop on Semantic Evaluation (SemEval-2023)*. Association for Computational Linguistics.

Ritesh Kumar, Aishwarya N. Reganti, Akshit Bhatia, and Tushar Maheshwari. 2018. Aggression-annotated corpus of Hindi-English code-mixed data. In *Proceedings of the Eleventh International Conference on Language Resources and Evaluation (LREC 2018)*, Miyazaki, Japan. European Language Resources Association (ELRA).

Joseph Kwarteng, Serena Coppolino Perfumi, Tracie Farrell, Aisling Third, and Miriam Fernandez. 2022. Misogynoir: Challenges in detecting intersectional hate. *Social Network Analysis and Mining*, 12(1):166.

Jean Lee, Taejun Lim, Heejun Lee, Bogeun Jo, Yangsok Kim, Heegeun Yoon, and Soyeon Caren Han. 2022. K-MHaS: A multi-label hate speech detection dataset in Korean online news comment. In *Proceedings of the 29th International Conference on Computational Linguistics*, pages 3530–3538, Gyeongju, Republic of Korea. International Committee on Computational Linguistics.

João Augusto Leite, Diego Silva, Kalina Bontcheva, and Carolina Scarton. 2020. Toxic language detection in social media for Brazilian Portuguese: New dataset and multilingual analysis. In *Proceedings of the 1st Conference of the Asia-Pacific Chapter of the Association for Computational Linguistics and the 10th International Joint Conference on Natural Language Processing*, pages 914–924, Suzhou, China. Association for Computational Linguistics.

Maria Scheffer Lindgren and Barbro Renck. 2008. Intimate partner violence and the leaving process: Interviews with abused women. *International Journal of Qualitative Studies on Health and Well-being*, 3(2):113–124.

N. Lomba, C. Navarra, and M. Fernandes. 2021. Combating Gender–Based Violence: Cyber violence. European added value assessment study, European Parliament.

Theo Lynn, Patricia Takako Endo, Pierangelo Rosati, Ivanovitch Silva, Guto Leoni Santos, and Debbie Ging. 2019. Urban dictionary definitions dataset for misogyny speech detection.

Kate Manne. 2017. *Down Girl: The Logic of Misogyny*. Oxford University Press.

Binny Mathew, Punyajoy Saha, Seid Muhie Yimam, Chris Biemann, Pawan Goyal, and Animesh Mukherjee. 2021. HateXplain: A benchmark dataset for explainable hate speech detection. *Proceedings of the AAAI Conference on Artificial Intelligence*, 35(17):14867–14875.

Jessica Megarry. 2014. Online incivility or sexual harassment? Conceptualising women's experiences in the digital age. *Women's Studies International Forum*, 47:46–55.

Sara Mills. 2008. *Language and Sexism*. Cambridge University Press.

Gosse Minnema, Sara Gemelli, Chiara Zanchi, Tommaso Caselli, and Malvina Nissim. 2022. Dead or murdered? predicting responsibility perception in femicide news reports. In *Proceedings of the 2nd Conference of the Asia-Pacific Chapter of the Association for Computational Linguistics and the 12th International Joint Conference on Natural Language Processing (Volume 1: Long Papers)*, pages 1078–1090, Online only. Association for Computational Linguistics.

David Moher, Alessandro Liberati, Jennifer Tetzlaff, and Douglas G. Altman. 2009. Preferred reporting items for systematic reviews and meta-analyses: The PRISMA statement. *Annals of Internal Medicine*, 151(4):264–269. PMID: 19622511.

Ioannis Mollas, Zoe Chrysopoulou, Stamatis Karlos, and Grigorios Tsoumakas. 2022. ETHOS: a multi-label hate speech detection dataset. *Complex & Intelligent Systems*.

Mairead Eastin Moloney and Tony P. Love. 2018. Assessing online misogyny: Perspectives from sociology and feminist media studies. *Sociology Compass*, 12(5):e12577. E12577 SOCO-1299.R2.

Jihyung Moon, Won Ik Cho, and Junbum Lee. 2020. BEEP! Korean corpus of online news comments for toxic speech detection. In *Proceedings of the Eighth International Workshop on Natural Language Processing for Social Media*, pages 25–31, Online. Association for Computational Linguistics.

Chantal Mouffe. 2013. Feminism, citizenship, and radical democratic politics. In *Feminists Theorize the Political*, pages 387–402. Routledge.

Hala Mulki and Bilal Ghanem. 2021. Let-mi: An Arabic Levantine Twitter dataset for misogynistic language. In *Proceedings of the Sixth Arabic Natural Language Processing Workshop*, pages 154–163, Kyiv, Ukraine (Virtual). Association for Computational Linguistics.

Michael Muller, Christine T. Wolf, Josh Andres, Michael Desmond, Narendra Nath Joshi, Zahra Ashktorab, Aabhas Sharma, Kristina Brimijoin, Qian Pan, Evelyn Duesterwald, and Casey Dugan. 2021. Designing ground truth and the social life of labels. In *Proceedings of the 2021 CHI Conference on Human Factors in Computing Systems*, CHI '21, New York, NY, USA. Association for Computing Machinery.

Michael J Muller and Sarah Kuhn. 1993. Participatory design. *Communications of the ACM*, 36(6):24–28.

John T. Nockleby. 2000. Hate speech, volume 1. In Leonard W. Levy and Kenneth L. Karst, editors, *Encyclopedia of the American Constitution (2nd ed.)*. Macmillan.

Debora Nozza, Claudia Volpetti, and Elisabetta Fersini. 2019. Unintended bias in misogyny detection. In *IEEE/WIC/ACM International Conference on Web Intelligence*, WI '19, page 149–155, New York, NY, USA. Association for Computing Machinery.

Jenny Ostini and Susan Hopkins. 2015. Online harassment is a form of violence. *The Conversation*, 8:1–4.

Nedjma Ousidhoum, Zizheng Lin, Hongming Zhang, Yangqiu Song, and Dit-Yan Yeung. 2019. Multilingual and multi-aspect hate speech analysis. In *Proceedings of the 2019 Conference on Empirical Methods in Natural Language Processing and the 9th International Joint Conference on Natural Language Processing (EMNLP-IJCNLP)*, pages 4675–4684, Hong Kong, China. Association for Computational Linguistics.

Sara Parker and Derek Ruths. 2023. Is hate speech detection the solution the world wants? *Proceedings of the National Academy of Sciences*, 120(10):e2209384120.

Johann Petrak and Brigitte Krenn. 2022. Misogyny classification of German newspaper forum comments.

Barbara Plank. 2022. The "problem" of human label variation: On ground truth in data, modeling and evaluation. In *Proceedings of the 2022 Conference on Empirical Methods in Natural Language Processing*, pages 10671–10682, Abu Dhabi, United Arab Emirates. Association for Computational Linguistics.

Laura Plaza, Jorge Carrillo-de Albornoz, Roser Morante, Enrique Amigó, Julio Gonzalo, Damiano Spina, and Paolo Rosso. 2023. Overview of EXIST 2023: sEXism Identification in Social NeTworks. In *Advances in Information Retrieval: 45th European Conference on Information Retrieval, ECIR 2023, Dublin, Ireland, April 2–6, 2023, Proceedings, Part III*, pages 593–599. Springer.

Bailey Poland. 2016. *Haters: Harassment, abuse, and violence online*. University of Nebraska Press.

Fabio Poletto, Valerio Basile, Manuela Sanguinetti, Cristina Bosco, and Viviana Patti. 2021. Resources and benchmark corpora for hate speech detection: A systematic review. *Language Resources and Evaluation*, 55.

Vinodkumar Prabhakaran, Aida Mostafazadeh Davani, and Mark Diaz. 2021. On releasing annotator-level labels and information in datasets. In *Proceedings of The Joint 15th Linguistic Annotation Workshop (LAW) and 3rd Designing Meaning Representations (DMR) Workshop*, pages 133–138, Punta Cana, Dominican Republic. Association for Computational Linguistics.

Public Health Scotland. 2021. Public Health Scotland.

Hemant Purohit, Tanvi Banerjee, Andrew Hampton, Valerie L. Shalin, Nayanesh Bhandutia, and Amit Sheth. 2016. Gender-based violence in 140 characters or fewer: A #BigData case study of Twitter. *First Monday*, 21(1).

Caitlin M. Rivers and Bryan L. Lewis. 2014. Ethical research standards in a world of big data. *F1000Research*, 3:38.

Hammad Rizwan, Muhammad Haroon Shakeel, and Asim Karim. 2020. Hate-speech and offensive language detection in Roman Urdu. In *Proceedings of the 2020 Conference on Empirical Methods in Natural Language Processing (EMNLP)*, pages 2512–2522, Online. Association for Computational Linguistics.

Francisco Rodríguez-Sánchez, Jorge Carrillo-de Albornoz, and Laura Plaza. 2020. Automatic classification of sexism in social networks: An empirical study on Twitter data. *IEEE Access*, 8:219563–219576.

Francisco Rodríguez-Sánchez, Jorge Carrillo-de Albornoz, Laura Plaza, Julio Gonzalo, Paolo Rosso, Miriam Comet, and Trinidad Donoso. 2021. Overview of EXIST 2021: sEXism Identification in Social NeTworks. *Procesamiento del Lenguaje Natural*, 67:195–207.

Francisco Rodríguez-Sánchez, Jorge Carrillo-de Albornoz, Laura Plaza, Adrián Mendieta-Aragón, Guillermo Marco-Remón, Maryna Makeienko, María Plaza, Julio Gonzalo, Damiano Spina, and Paolo Rosso. 2022. Overview of EXIST 2022: sEXism Identification in Social NeTworks. *Procesamiento del Lenguaje Natural*, 69:229–240.

Nauros Romim, Mosahed Ahmed, Md Saiful Islam, Arnab Sen Sharma, Hriteshwar Talukder, and Mohammad Ruhul Amin. 2022. BD-SHS: A benchmark dataset for learning to detect online Bangla hate speech in different social contexts. In *Proceedings of the Thirteenth Language Resources and Evaluation Conference*, pages 5153–5162, Marseille, France. European Language Resources Association.

Paul Rottger, Bertie Vidgen, Dirk Hovy, and Janet Pierrehumbert. 2022. Two contrasting data annotation paradigms for subjective NLP tasks. In *Proceedings of the 2022 Conference of the North American Chapter of the Association for Computational Linguistics: Human Language Technologies*, pages 175–190, Seattle, United States. Association for Computational Linguistics.

Mattia Samory, Indira Sen, Julian Kohne, Fabian Flöck, and Claudia Wagner. 2021. "Call me sexist, but...": Revisiting sexism detection using psychological scales and adversarial samples. In *ICWSM*, pages 573–584.

Scottish Government. 2016. Equally Safe: Scotland's strategy for preventing and eradicating violence against women and girls. Strategy plan, Scottish Government.

Sima Sharifirad and Alon Jacovi. 2019. Learning and understanding different categories of sexism using convolutional neural network's filters. In *Proceedings of the 2019 Workshop on Widening NLP*, pages 21–23, Florence, Italy. Association for Computational Linguistics.

Sima Sharifirad and Stan Matwin. 2019. When a tweet is actually sexist. A more comprehensive classification of different online harassment categories and the challenges in NLP. *arXiv preprint arXiv:1902.10584*.

Boaz Shmueli, Jan Fell, Soumya Ray, and Lun-Wei Ku. 2021. Beyond fair pay: Ethical implications of NLP crowdsourcing. In *Proceedings of the 2021 Conference of the North American Chapter of the Association for Computational Linguistics: Human Language Technologies*, pages 3758–3769, Online. Association for Computational Linguistics.

Elena Shushkevich and John Cardiff. 2019. Automatic misogyny detection in social media: A survey. *Computación y Sistemas*.

Janet T. Spence and Robert Helmreich. 1972. The attitudes toward women scale: An objective instrument to measure attitudes toward the rights and roles of women in contemporary society. *Catalog of Selected Documents in Psychology*, 2.

Wienke Strathern and Juergen Pfeffer. 2022. Identifying different layers of online misogyny.

Zeerak Talat. 2016. Are you a racist or am I seeing things? Annotator influence on hate speech detection on Twitter. In *Proceedings of the First Workshop on NLP and Computational Social Science*, pages 138–142, Austin, Texas. Association for Computational Linguistics.

Zeerak Talat, Thomas Davidson, Dana Warmsley, and Ingmar Weber. 2017. Understanding abuse: A typology of abusive language detection subtasks. In *Proceedings of the First Workshop on Abusive Language Online*, pages 78–84, Vancouver, BC, Canada. Association for Computational Linguistics.

Zeerak Talat and Dirk Hovy. 2016. Hateful symbols or hateful people? Predictive features for hate speech detection on Twitter. In *Proceedings of the NAACL Student Research Workshop*, pages 88–93, San Diego, California. Association for Computational Linguistics.

Ali Toosi. 2019. Twitter sentiment analysis. https://www.kaggle.com/datasets/arkhoshghalb/twitter-sentiment-analysis-hatred-speech. Accessed: 2023-04-28.

Francine Tougas, Rupert Brown, Ann M Beaton, and Stéphane Joly. 1995. Neosexism: Plus ça change, plus c'est pareil. *Personality and social psychology bulletin*, 21(8):842–849.

UN General Assembly. 1993. Declaration on the elimination of violence against women. un general assembly resolution 48/104 assembly. Resolution, United Nations.

United Nations. 2021. 'endemic violence against women cannot be stopped with a vaccine' says who chief. `https://news.un.org/en/story/2021/03/1086812`. Accessed: 2023-06-07.

Bertie Vidgen and Leon Derczynski. 2021. Directions in abusive language training data, a systematic review: Garbage in, garbage out. *PLOS ONE*, 15:1–32.

Bertie Vidgen, Alex Harris, Dong Nguyen, Rebekah Tromble, Scott Hale, and Helen Margetts. 2019.

Challenges and frontiers in abusive content detection. In *Proceedings of the Third Workshop on Abusive Language Online*, pages 80–93, Florence, Italy. Association for Computational Linguistics.

Bertie Vidgen, Tristan Thrush, Zeerak Waseem, and Douwe Kiela. 2021. Learning from the worst: Dynamically generated datasets to improve online hate detection. In *Proceedings of the 59th Annual Meeting of the Association for Computational Linguistics and the 11th International Joint Conference on Natural Language Processing (Volume 1: Long Papers)*, pages 1667–1682, Online. Association for Computational Linguistics.

World Bank. 2019. Gender-Based Violence (Violence Against Women and Girls). Accessed: 2023-05-09.

World Health Organization. 2020. WHO announced as a global leader of the generation equality action coalition on ending gender-based violence. https://www.who.int/news/item/01-07-2020-Equality-Action-Coalition-endinggender-based-violence.

Ankit Yadav, Shubham Chandel, Sushant Chatufale, and Anil Bandhakavi. 2023. LAHM : Large annotated dataset for multi-domain and multilingual hate speech identification.

Philine Zeinert, Nanna Inie, and Leon Derczynski. 2021. Annotating online misogyny. In *Proceedings of the 59th Annual Meeting of the Association for Computational Linguistics and the 11th International Joint Conference on Natural Language Processing (Volume 1: Long Papers)*, pages 3181–3197, Online. Association for Computational Linguistics.

A Figures of Analysis

We present visualisations of resource statistics in Figures 4, 5, 6, 7, and 8.

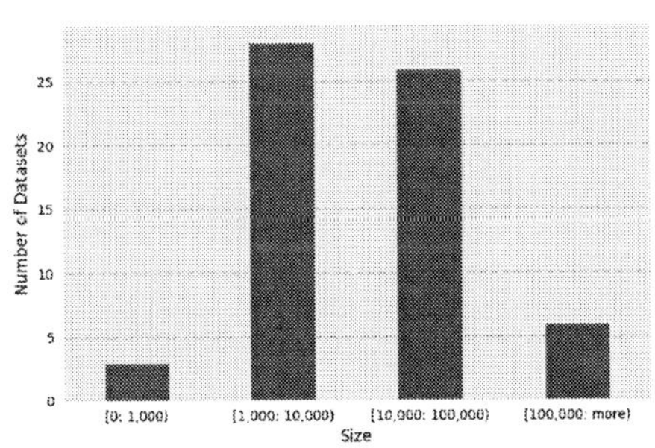

Figure 4: The distribution of GBV dataset sizes.

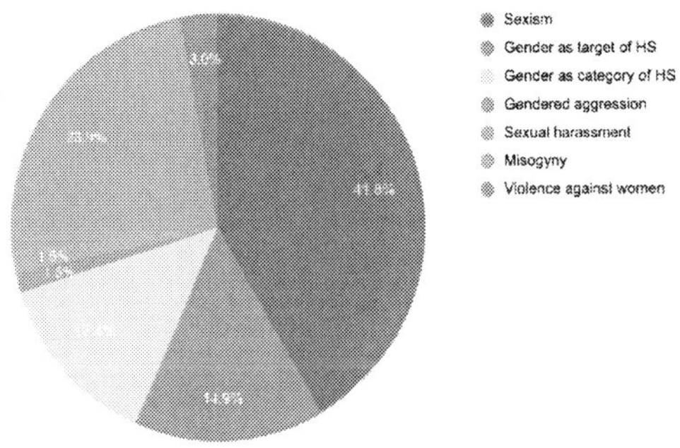

Figure 5: The distribution of characterisation of GBV.

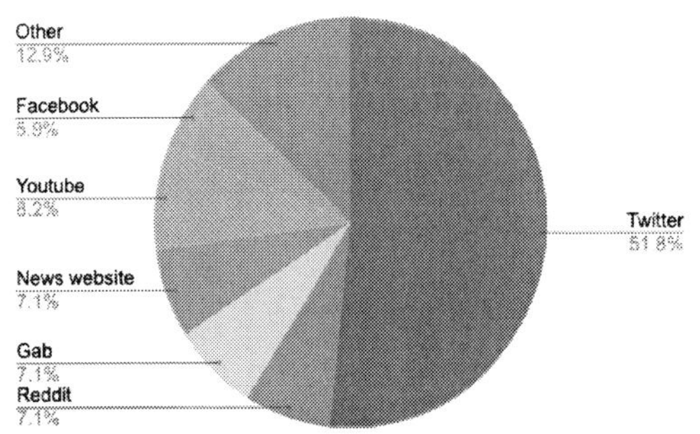

Figure 6: The distribution of platforms for GBV data collection.

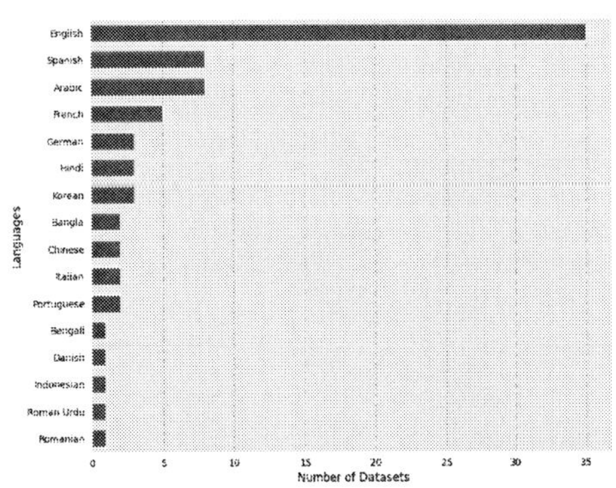

Figure 7: Number of GBV datasets across languages, including numbers if the language in multilingual datasets.

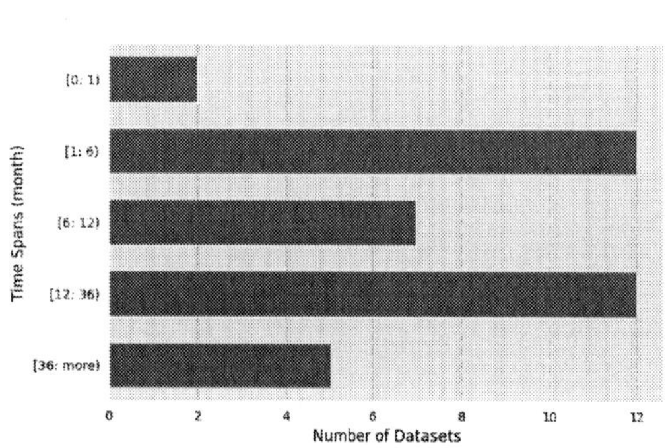

Figure 8: The distribution of time spans in GBV resources, excluding resources that are not reported collection time.

Evaluating the Effectiveness of Natural Language Inference for Hate Speech Detection in Languages with Limited Labeled Data

Janis Goldzycher **Moritz Preisig** **Chantal Amrhein** **Gerold Schneider**
Department of Computational Linguistics
University of Zurich
{goldzycher,amrhein,gschneid}@cl.uzh.ch, moritz.preisig@uzh.ch

Abstract

Most research on hate speech detection has focused on English where a sizeable amount of labeled training data is available. However, to expand hate speech detection into more languages, approaches that require minimal training data are needed. In this paper, we test whether natural language inference (NLI) models which perform well in zero- and few-shot settings can benefit hate speech detection performance in scenarios where only a limited amount of labeled data is available in the target language. Our evaluation on five languages demonstrates large performance improvements of NLI fine-tuning over direct fine-tuning in the target language. However, the effectiveness of previous work that proposed intermediate fine-tuning on English data is hard to match. Only in settings where the English training data does not match the test domain, can our customised NLI-formulation outperform intermediate fine-tuning on English. Based on our extensive experiments, we propose a set of recommendations for hate speech detection in languages where minimal labeled training data is available. [1]

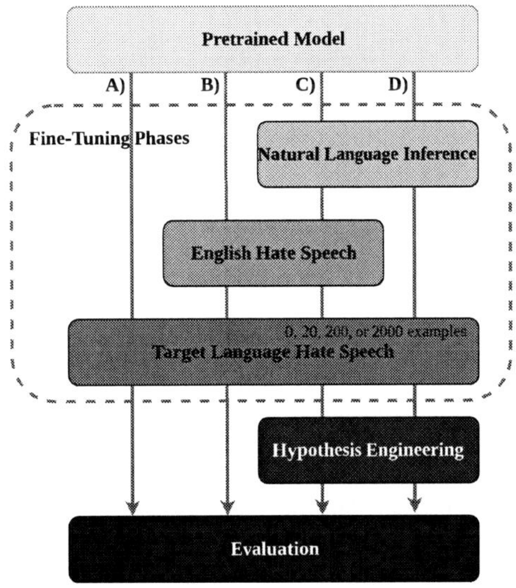

Figure 1: Approaches evaluated in this paper: A) Standard fine-tuning. B) Intermediate fine-tuning on English hate speech as proposed by Röttger et al. (2022a). Via C) and D), we explore natural language inference as an additional intermediate fine-tuning step. The natural language inference formulation further allows hypothesis engineering (Goldzycher and Schneider, 2022).

1 Introduction

Hate speech is a global issue that transcends linguistic boundaries, but the majority of available datasets for hate speech detection are in English (Poletto et al., 2021; Yin and Zubiaga, 2021). This limits the capabilities of automatic content moderation and leaves most language communities around the world underserved. Creating labeled datasets is not only slow and expensive but also risks psychological impacts on the annotators (Kirk et al., 2022a). Although the number of non-English datasets is increasing, most languages still have limited or no datasets available (Poletto et al., 2021).

Consequently, there is a pressing need to develop methods that can efficiently expand hate speech detection into languages with less labeled data. Repurposing natural language inference models for text classification leads to well-performing zero-shot and few-shot classifiers (Yin et al., 2019). Recently, Goldzycher and Schneider (2022) showed that zero-shot NLI-based setups can outperform standard few-shot finetuning for English hate speech detection. This raises the question of whether natural language inference can be used to expand hate speech detection into more languages in a data-efficient manner.

In this paper, we aim to systematically evaluate the effectiveness of NLI fine-tuning for languages beyond English where we do not have an abun-

[1] We make our code publically available at https://github.com/jagol/xnli4xhsd.

The 7th Workshop on Online Abuse and Harms (WOAH), pages 187–201
July 13, 2023 ©2023 Association for Computational Linguistics

dance of labeled training data. We give an overview of the experiment setup and compared approaches in Figure 1. Unlike Goldzycher and Schneider (2022), and inspired by Röttger et al. (2022a), we do not restrict ourselves to a zero-shot setup but further analyse the usefulness of an NLI-formulation when we have access to a limited amount of labeled examples in the target language as well as additional English data for intermediate fine-tuning. We believe that this mirrors a more realistic setup and allows us to offer clear recommendations for best practices for hate speech detection in languages with limited labeled data.

Our experiments with 0 up to 2000 labeled examples across five target languages (Arabic, Hindi, Italian, Portuguese, and Spanish) demonstrate clear benefits of an NLI-based formulation in zero-shot and few-shot settings compared to standard few-shot fine-tuning in the target language. While Röttger et al.'s (2022a) approach of fine-tuning on English data before standard few-shot learning on the target language proves to be a strong baseline, we reach similar performance when fine-tuning NLI-based models on intermediate English data. Building on the results by Goldzycher and Schneider (2022), who showed that targeted hypothesis engineering can help avoid common classification errors with NLI-based models, we find that such strategies offer an advantage in scenarios where we have expert knowledge about the domain but no in-domain English data for intermediate fine-tuning.

Overall, our contributions are the following:

1. We are able to reproduce the results of Röttger et al. (2022a), demonstrating the validity of their approach.
2. We evaluate NLI fine-tuning for expanding hate speech detection into more languages and find it to be beneficial if no English labeled data is available for intermediate fine-tuning.
3. We evaluate NLI-based models paired with hypothesis engineering and show that we can outperform previous work in settings where we have knowledge about the target domain but no domain-specific labeled English data.

2 Related Work

Hate speech is commonly defined as attacking, abusive or discriminatory language that targets protected groups or an individual for being a member of a protected group. A protected group is defined by characteristics such as gender, sexual orientation, disability, race, religion, national origin or similar (Fortuna and Nunes, 2018; Poletto et al., 2021; Vidgen et al., 2021; Yin and Zubiaga, 2021). The automatic detection of hate speech is typically formulated as a binary text classification task with short texts, usually social media posts and comments, as input (Founta et al., 2018). Despite most work being focused on English (Founta et al., 2018), in the last years there has been a growing trend to expand into more languages (Mandl et al., 2019, 2020; Röttger et al., 2022b; Yadav et al., 2023).

In what follows, we first review the relevant literature for multi- and cross-lingual hate speech detection, and then move on to the previous work in zero-shot and few-shot text classification with a specific focus on NLI-based methods, and finally focus on hypothesis engineering (Goldzycher and Schneider, 2022).

2.1 Multi- and Cross-lingual Hate Speech Detection

The scarcity of labeled datasets for hate speech detection in non-English languages has led to multiple approaches addressing this problem using meta-learning (Mozafari et al., 2022), active learning (Kirk et al., 2022b), label-bootstrapping (Bigoulaeva et al., 2023), pseudo-label fine-tuning (Zia et al., 2022), and multi-task learning using multilingual auxiliary tasks such as dependency parsing, named entity recognition and sentiment analysis (Montariol et al., 2022).

The most important research for our investigation is the study conducted by Röttger et al. (2022a). In their work, the authors train and evaluate models across five distinct languages: Arabic, Hindi, Italian, Portuguese, and Spanish. Their findings reveal that by initially fine-tuning multilingual models on English hate speech and subsequently fine-tuning them with labeled data in the target language, they achieve significant performance improvements in low-resource settings compared to only fine-tuning a monolingual model in the target language. In this study, we adopt their evaluation setup, reproduce their results and compare our results directly to their approach. For this reason, we will elaborate on and reference the specifics of their experimental setup throughout Section 3.

2.2 Zero-Shot and Few-Shot Classification

The development of language models which serve as a foundation for fine-tuning rather than training from scratch, has facilitated the implementation of zero-shot and few-shot text classification approaches, such as prompting (Liu et al., 2021) and task descriptions (Raffel et al., 2020). These techniques transform the target task into a format similar to the pre-training task and are typically employed in conjunction with large language models. Following this scheme, Chiu and Alexander (2021) leverage GPT-3 to detect hate speech with the prompts "Is this text racist?" and "Is this text sexist?".

In contrast to prompting, NLI-based prediction refers to reformulating the target task into an NLI task and thus into a (previous) fine-tuning task. In this setup, a model receives a premise and a hypothesis and is tasked with predicting whether the premise entails the hypothesis, contradicts it, or is neutral towards it. Yin et al. (2019) were the first to demonstrate the effectiveness of such an approach. They used an NLI model for zero-shot topic classification by inputting the text to be classified as the premise and constructing a hypothesis for each topic in the form of "This text is about <topic>". A prediction of *entailment* is to be interpreted as the input text belonging to the topic in the given hypothesis. Wang et al. (2021) demonstrated that this task reformulation benefits few-shot learning scenarios for various tasks, including offensive language identification.

2.3 Hypothesis Engineering

Goldzycher and Schneider (2022) pair an input text with multiple hypotheses in order to let an NLI model predict different aspects of the input text. They then use a rule-based approach to combine these predicted aspects into a final prediction for the hate speech label. More specifically, they distinguish between a main hypothesis and auxiliary hypotheses. The main hypothesis claims that the input text contains hate speech. The auxiliary hypotheses claim various relevant aspects such as that the input text is about a protected group in order to correct mispredictions of the main hypothesis. To find effective hypothesis combinations they conduct an error analysis on the English HateCheck (Röttger et al., 2021) dataset and propose four *strategies* based on this error analysis:

Filtering by target: Avoid false positives by predicting if any protected group is targeted in the input text.

Filtering reclaimed slurs: Avoid false positives by predicting indicators that a slur is used in a reclaimed fashion. Indicators used are: the speaker talks about themself or positive sentiment.

Filtering counterspeech: Avoid false positives by recognizing when another speech act is referenced, predicting if that speech act is hate speech and predicting the stance towards the referenced speech.

Catching dehumanizing comparisons: Avoid false negatives by checking if a protected group and negatively associcated animals appear together in a sentence with a negative sentiment.

In our experiments, we will evaluate the effectiveness of the first three strategies for NLI-based hate speech detection. However, we will exclude the fourth strategy due to its lack of clear benefits in Goldzycher and Schneider (2022). More implementation details are provided in Section 3.3 and Appendix B.

3 Experiment Setup

Our experiment setup is largely based on the one created by Röttger et al. (2022a) and can be seen in Figure 2. In what follows, we first describe their setup, which we replicated as a baseline for our results. We then describe how we expanded their setup for the NLI-based experiments.

3.1 Reproducing Röttger et al. (2022a)

Data The authors use three English hate speech datasets (Founta et al., 2018; Kennedy et al., 2020; Vidgen et al., 2021, abbreviated as **FEN**, **KEN**, and **DEN**, respectively) which are all downsampled to 20,000 examples. **FEN** and **KEN** are sourced from Twitter and **DEN** consists of human-created adversarial examples. They further make use of five Twitter datasets in the respective target languages: Basile et al. (2019) for Spanish (**BAS19_ES**), Fortuna et al. (2019) for Portuguese (**FOR19_PT**), Modha et al. (2022) for Hindi (**HAS21_HI**), Ousidhoum et al. (2019) for Arabic (**OUS19_AR**), and Manuela et al. (2020) for Italian (**SAN20_IT**). The Multilingual HateCheck (MHC) (Röttger et al., 2022b) is used for additional, complementary evaluation. This suite of synthetic, evaluation-only

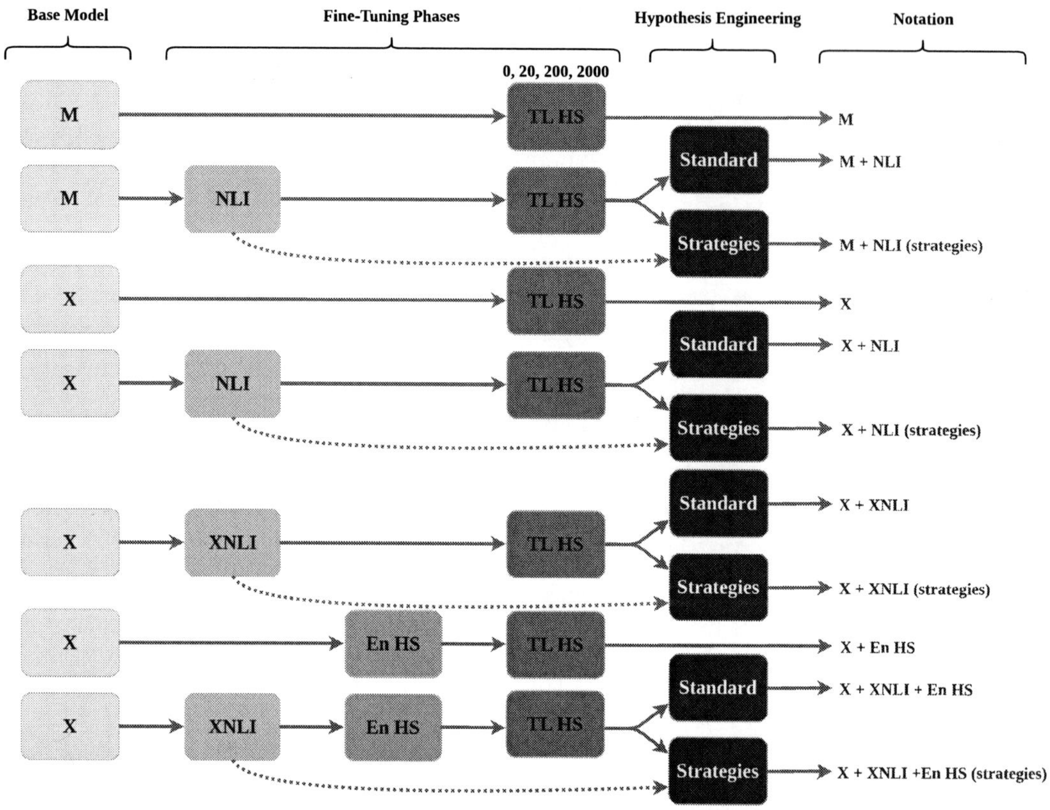

Figure 2: Experiment Setup. The base model is either monolingual **M** or multilingual **X**. In a first optional training phase, the model is fine-tuned either on the full XNLI dataset (**XNLI**) or on the subset of XNLI that is in the target language (**NLI**). A second optional training phase follows, in which a model is fine-tuned on an English hate speech dataset (**En HS**). Note that **En HS** is a stand-in for the specific English dataset the model is fine-tuned on, i.e. either **DEN**, if it is fine-tuned on Vidgen et al. (2021) or **FEN**, if it is fine-tuned on Founta et al. (2018). Finally, each model is fine-tuned on 0, 20, 200, or 2000 examples of a hate speech dataset in the target language (**TL HS**). If the model was fine-tuned on NLI, we either evaluate in a standard fashion with one hypothesis (**Standard**), or with hypothesis engineering strategies (**Strategies**). The dotted arrows show that for auxiliary hypotheses of the strategies a model version that was only fine-tuned on NLI is used. Further explanations of the dataset and model notation are provided in Section 3.

datasets, that covers a range of typical, but hard to classify, cases for hate speech detection is available in all five target languages. The datasets are further described in Appendix C.

Preprocessing All datasets are cleaned with the same preprocessing steps that have been used for training of XLM-T Barbieri et al. (2022). These consist of replacing all URLs with "https" and all usernames (strings starting with an "@") with "@user". Further, the authors downsampled the non-hate speech class in **FEN** and **KEN** such that the relative frequency of hate speech increased from 5.0% to 22% and from 29.3% to 50% respectively.

Models Röttger et al. (2022a) use Twitter-XLM-RoBERTa-base (Barbieri et al., 2022), typically abbreviated to XLM-T, as a multi-lingual base model. This model is derived from XLM-R (Conneau et al., 2020) and has been further pre-trained on a multilingual Twitter corpus. Further they use the following mono-lingual base-models: AraBERT-v2 (Antoun et al., 2020) for Arabic, Hindi BERT for Hindi, UmBERTo (Parisi et al., 2020) for Italian, BERTimbau (Souza et al., 2020) for Portuguese, and RoBERTuito (Pérez et al., 2022) for Spanish.

Training The training procedure consists of two fine-tuning phases: In the optional first phase, specifically proposed by Röttger et al. (2022a), a model is fine-tuned on English

	BAS19_ES			FOR19_PT			HAS21_HI			OUS19_AR			SAN20_IT			Avg. Diff.
N	20	200	2000	20	200	2000	20	200	2000	20	200	2000	20	200	2000	
M	0.48	0.67	**0.84**	0.46	0.62	0.71	0.46	0.49	0.56	0.45	0.55	0.68	0.40	0.70	**0.78**	-0.03
X	0.40	0.61	0.82	0.45	0.52	0.71	0.46	0.46	**0.59**	0.45	0.55	**0.69**	0.40	0.66	0.76	-0.03
X + DEN	**0.66**	**0.75**	0.83	**0.63**	0.68	0.71	0.51	0.53	0.58	0.51	0.64	0.67	**0.64**	**0.71**	0.76	-0.01
X + FEN	0.54	0.70	0.82	**0.63**	**0.69**	**0.72**	**0.54**	**0.55**	**0.59**	**0.59**	**0.66**	0.68	**0.64**	**0.71**	0.75	-0.01
X + KEN	0.63	0.72	0.82	**0.63**	0.68	0.71	0.52	**0.55**	**0.59**	**0.59**	0.65	**0.69**	**0.64**	**0.71**	0.75	0.00
Avg. Diff.	-0.03	-0.02	0.02	-0.01	-0.05	-0.01	-0.01	-0.02	-0.01	-0.01	-0.06	-0.02	0.00	-0.02	-0.01	-0.02
	HateCheck_ES			HateCheck_PT			HateCheck_Hi			HateCheck_Ar			HateCheck_It			Avg. Diff.
N	20	200	2000	20	200	2000	20	200	2000	20	200	2000	20	200	2000	
M	0.44	0.48	0.59	0.35	0.50	0.62	0.23	0.23	0.23	0.26	0.23	0.24	0.28	0.39	0.54	0.01
X	0.40	0.31	0.60	0.31	0.32	0.64	0.34	0.23	0.24	0.30	0.23	0.24	0.36	0.42	0.59	0.00
X + DEN	**0.82**	**0.82**	**0.80**	**0.79**	**0.81**	**0.78**	**0.57**	**0.38**	**0.36**	**0.61**	**0.48**	**0.35**	**0.82**	**0.81**	**0.79**	0.01
X + FEN	0.57	0.60	0.64	0.56	0.59	0.62	0.34	0.30	0.34	0.35	0.34	0.29	0.54	0.55	0.58	-0.01
X + KEN	0.57	0.58	0.63	0.62	0.64	0.64	0.40	0.30	0.31	0.31	0.30	0.29	0.53	0.59	0.62	0.02
Avg. Diff.	0.02	0.00	-0.01	0.02	-0.04	0.02	0.02	-0.04	0.03	-0.02	0.00	0.02	0.02	-0.01	0.06	0.01

Table 1: Reproduction of results on held-out test sets and the Multilingual HateCheck. "Avg. Diff." contains the average difference to the original results by Röttger et al. (2022a) per row and column respectively.

hate speech (**En HS**). In the second phase, the model is fine-tuned on N target language hate speech examples (**TL HS**), where $N \in \{10, 20, 30, 40, 50, 100, 200, 300, 400, 500, 1000, 2000\}$.[2] The training setup and the corresponding model notation are included in Figure 2 as **X + En HS**. Note that **En HS** is a stand-in for the specific English dataset the model is fine-tuned on, i.e. either **FEN**, **KEN**, or **DEN**. Additionally, Röttger et al. (2022a) compare against the baselines of fine-tuning a monolingual model directly on the target language (**M**) and fine-tuning a multilingual model directly on the target language (**X**). Training specifics, including hyperparameters, are provided in Appendix A.

3.2 NLI Fine-Tuning

In order to test the effectiveness of NLI fine-tuning, we add to this setup an additional optional phase which is placed before **En HS**. This optional first phase has three variants:

M + NLI: A monolingual model in the target language is fine-tuned on the subset of XNLI (Conneau et al., 2018)[3] that is also in the target language.

X + NLI: The multilingual model is fine-tuned on the subset of XNLI that is in the target language.

X + XNLI: The multilingual model is fine-tuned on the entire XNLI dataset, concatenated with the MNLI dataset (Williams et al., 2018)[4]. To encourage cross-lingual transfer learning, the translations of premises and hyptheses are shuffled such that for a given example the premise might be in Spanish and the hypothesis in Arabic.[5]

If a model has been trained on NLI examples, we continue to train that model in an NLI formulation, even when fine-tuning on hate speech data. The model is then presented with the input text as the premise and "This text is hate speech." as the hypothesis. The label "hate speech" then corresponds to "entailment" and "not hate speech" to "contradiction".

3.3 Hypothesis Engineering

We employ the combination of the three strategies "Filtering by Target", "Filtering Counterspeech", and "Filtering Reclaimed Slurs" since they led to the best results in Goldzycher and Schneider (2022). Further implementation details are provided in Appendix B. We evaluate the strategies in combination with all models that have been fine-tuned on XNLI or a subset of it. All models that were fine-tuned on a hate speech dataset are specific to one hypothesis claiming that there is hate

[2] As explained later in Section 4, we only train and evaluate at $N \in \{0, 20, 200, 2000\}$.

[3] More information on the XNLI dataset is given in Appendix C.

[4] More information on MNLI is given in Appendix C.

[5] This method of shuffling translations such that the premise and hypothesis are presented in different languages to the model has been employed for popular models such as joeddav/xlm-roberta-large-xnli.

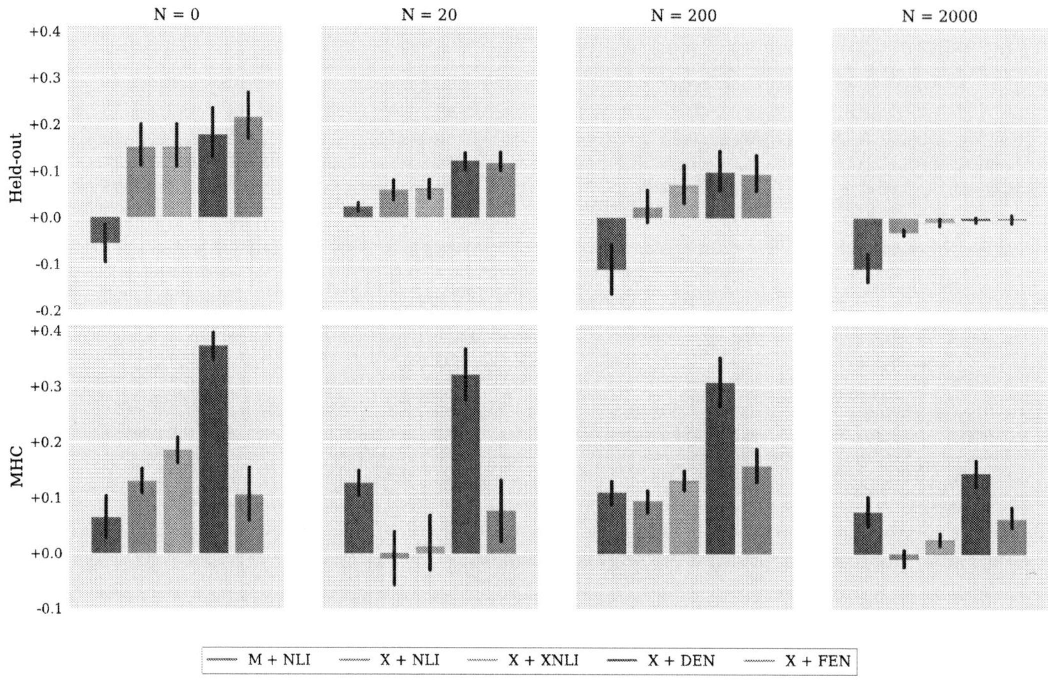

Figure 3: Evaluation of NLI fine-tuning on languages that are in XNLI, namely, Arabic, Hindi, and Spanish. The figure shows the absolute difference in macro-F_1 score when adding an intermediate fine-tuning step to fine-tuning in the target language (i.e. the difference to **M** and **X**, respectively).

speech in the input text. In such cases, we thus use the initial model, that has only been fine-tuned on an NLI dataset for all auxiliary hypothesis predictions.

4 Evaluation

Following Röttger et al. (2022a), we evaluate each setting displayed in Figure 2 on two test-sets: (1) the held-out test set in the target language and (2) the HateCheck dataset in the target language. But in contrast to their setup, we evaluate in $N \in \{0, 20, 200, 2000\}$ target language training examples. We thus evaluate at three scenarios (20, 200 and 2000) where our results are directly comparable to the results of Röttger et al. (2022a) and add a zero-shot scenario. The metric is macro-F_1 in order to account for imbalanced test sets. Like Röttger et al. (2022a), we train 10 models per setting, report the averaged results and the bootstrapped 95% confidence intervals, represented as errorbars in Figure 3 and shaded areas in Figures 4 to 7.

In what follows, we group the results according to research questions. The full results are given in Appendix D.

4.1 Can we Reproduce the Results of Röttger et al. (2022a)?

Table 1 contains the reproduction results and the average differences to the original results per language, number of examples N, and model. On average our results are lower by two percentage points on the held-out test sets and higher by one percentage point on the HateCheck test sets. We observe that: (1) Like Röttger et al. (2022a), our results follow a trend of diminishing returns. The larger performance increase often comes from increasing from 20 to 200 examples and not from increasing from 200 to 2000 examples, even though the absolute increase in examples is much larger in the second comparison. (2) Like Röttger et al. (2022a), we see that with an increasing number of examples, the benefit of fine-tuning on English hate speech decreases. At 2000 examples, the monolingual model that has directly been fine-tuned on target language examples has in most cases caught up with or even beats English fine-tuning.

Overall, we view our results as a confirmation of their findings. In order to simplify our evaluation, and since **X + FEN** and **X + KEN** have very similar results, we will only include **X + FEN** as a repre-

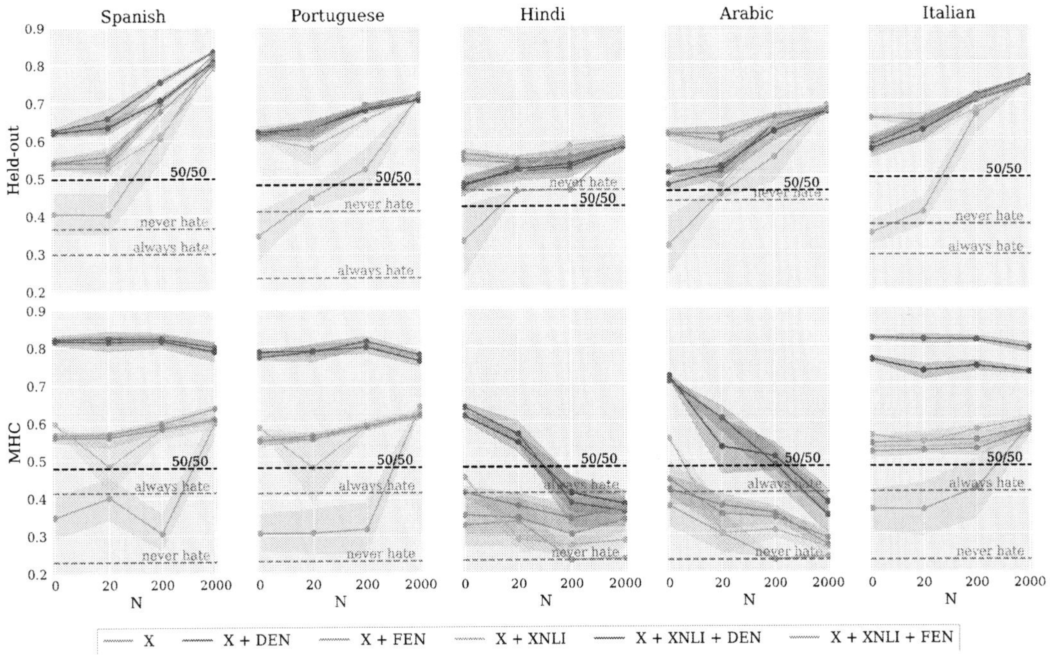

Figure 4: Evaluation of NLI fine-tuning on top of English hate speech fine-tuning. The results are given in macro-F_1.

sentative for natural data (as opposed to synthetic, adversarial data) in the following experiments.

4.2 How Does an NLI-Formulation Compare to Röttger et al. (2022a)?

We compare the baselines and settings proposed by Röttger et al. (2022a) with fine-tuning on monolingual NLI data in the target language (**M + NLI** and **X + NLI**) and fine-tuning on the entire XNLI dataset (**X + XNLI**). Only three languages (Arabic, Hindi, and Spanish) appear both in the evaluation setup and in XNLI. Since **M + NLI** and **X + NLI** training is only possible for languages in XNLI, we focus on the results in these three languages. The differences in performance averaged over the three languages are given in Figure 3.

Overall we see that introducing an intermediate fine-tuning step improves performance in most cases, but the benefits decrease with more target language examples available. While **X** is almost always improved by NLI fine-tuning, the stronger (recall from Table 1) baseline **M** only benefits from NLI fine-tuning on the HateCheck testset (second row of plots). When comparing **X + NLI** with **X + XNLI** we observe slightly more benefits from fine-tuning on the full XNLI dataset. Even though NLI-fine-tuning (orange) leads to clear benefits it is outperformed by fine-tuning on English hate speech on **X** (blue) as proposed by Röttger et al. (2022a) in all setups. This finding raises the question if training on additional English labeled data is also beneficial in an XNLI-based setup which we aim to answer in the next section.

4.3 Are there Benefits to NLI-Finetuning when Given English Hate Speech Data?

To answer this question we compare the performance of intermediate fine-tuning on English hate speech (Röttger et al., 2022a) to first fine-tuning on XNLI and then fine-tuning on English hate speech. The results are displayed in Figure 4.

We make the following observations: (1) Since we now evaluate on all five languages, it is interesting to see how an NLI formulation performs for Portuguese and Italian which are not part of the XNLI dataset. For both testsets, we observe that even for unseen languages an NLI formulation has clear benefits over standard finetuning on target language examples (orange vs. green). (2) On held-out test sets (first row of plots), fine-tuning on both XNLI and English hate speech (purple) improves zero-shot performance in Hindi, Arabic and Italian and matches zero-shot performance of only fine-tuning on English hate speech (blue) in Spanish and Portuguese. (3) The combination of the two approaches (purple) can also lead to im-

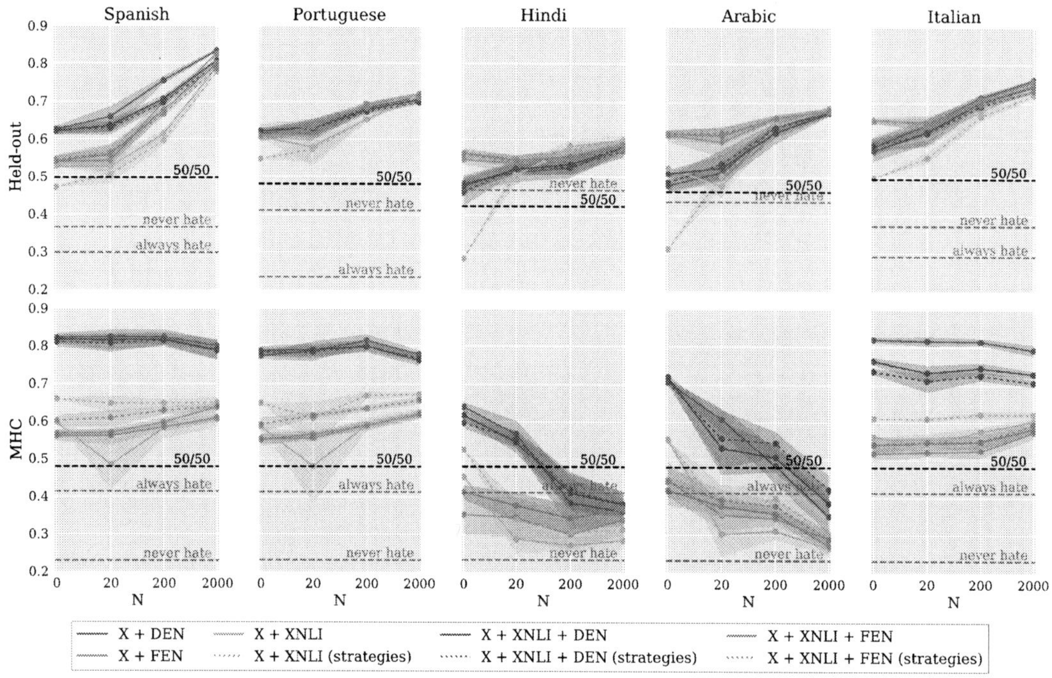

Figure 5: Evaluation of hypothesis engineering strategies.

proved few-shot results on Arabic and Hindi but reaches comparable performance or has a negative effect, when compared to only English hate speech fine-tuning (blue), in the other languages. (4) On Multilingual HateCheck (second row of plots) we observe mixed results, where additional intermediate XNLI fine-tuning tends to decrease results when fine-tuning on **DEN** but increase results when fine-tuning on **FEN**.

Overall, we find that performance improves more from intermediate fine-tuning on English (green vs. blue) than an NLI formulation (green vs. orange) and that there are negligible advantages to combining the two approaches (blue vs. purple). As discussed in the related work section, previous work by Goldzycher and Schneider (2022) showed that zero-shot hate speech detection for English could be improved with carefully engineered auxiliary hypotheses for an NLI setup. In the next section, we focus on the question whether hypothesis engineering is also beneficial for our zero-shot and few-shot setups with other languages.

4.4 Can Hypothesis Engineering further Improve Performance?

We evaluate if hypothesis engineering, specifically the three strategies proposed by Goldzycher and Schneider (2022) as described in Section 2.3, is able to improve results. We take all models that have been fine-tuned on the full XNLI dataset and compare their performance with and without such hypothesis engineering strategies. The results are given in Figure 5.

On the held-out test sets (first row of plots), the strategies (dotted lines) show only in a few cases small positive effects but mostly negative effects. However, on HateCheck (second row of plots), we see that the strategies lead to clear performance improvements of **X + XNLI** and **X + XNLI + FEN**. This finding is not surprising since Goldzycher and Schneider (2022) specifically developed their hypothesis engineering strategies based on an error analysis on the English HateCheck data. For many languages, hypothesis engineering without intermediate English fine-tuning (orange dotted) even performs better than hypothesis engineering with fine-tuning on **FEN** (light purple dotted) which consists of Twitter data. Fine-tuning on English adversarial **DEN** hate speech examples (dark blue) remains the strongest approach for HateCheck since this fine-tuning data matches the testset conditions. However, our results show that if we have knowledge about the data the model will see at inference time (e.g. adversarial examples) but do not have matching English fine-tuning data (e.g. if only **FEN** were available), hypothesis engineering geared towards the target domain (orange dotted line) is the best-performing approach.

5 Conclusion

In this work, we systematically evaluated the effectiveness of an NLI task formulation for hate speech detection in scenarios where only few labeled data in the target language are available. We were able to reproduce results by Röttger et al. (2022a), who showed that intermediate fine-tuning on English hate speech is beneficial in such scenarios.

Following their setup with our NLI-based experiments, we answered the following questions: (1) How does NLI fine-tuning compare to English hate speech fine-tuning? Our results showed that while NLI fine-tuning leads to strong improvements over only fine-tuning in the target language it is outperformed by English hate speech fine-tuning. (2) Are there benefits to combining NLI fine-tuning with English hate speech fine-tuning? We observed minor improvements when only 0 or 20 target language examples are available, but no benefits when more examples are available. (3) Can hypothesis engineering further improve performance on the previously best NLI-based setting? Our experiments demonstrated that hypothesis engineering can outperform other approaches only when the domain of the input data at inference time is known, but no matching training data is available.

Based on our results, we offer the following recommendations for hate speech detection in languages where little labeled data is available in the target language:

- **In general domain scenarios:** Follow Röttger et al. (2022a) and perform standard intermediate fine-tuning on English data before training on target language examples if any are available.

- **In scenarios where less English data is available, e.g. hate speech against a specific protected group:** An intermediate NLI fine-tuning step is likely to be strongly beneficial compared to only fine-tuning on limited English and target language examples.

- **In scenarios where we have knowledge about the target domain but no matching English fine-tuning data is available:** Here, we suggest experimenting with targeted hypothesis engineering to reach the best possible performance. One exciting future avenue for this strategy is to focus on variation of protected groups across languages. Such culture and language-specific shifts will be hard to capture with English fine-tuning data but hypothesis engineering strategies offer more flexibility.

Finally, we want to highlight two areas for future work that arise from our experiments:

- **Fine-tuning phases:** We believe that a crucial circumstance limiting the effectiveness of NLI models for hate speech detection is the fact that NLI training datasets are typically from different domains, thus creating a domain gap between NLI fine-tuning and other training phases. We hypothesize that by mixing the fine-tuning phases the negative effects of the domain gap might be avoided or, at least, reduced.

- **Hypothesis engineering and model capacity:** In contrast to Goldzycher and Schneider (2022), we only observed positive results for hypothesis engineering in a few specific scenarios. One difference between the experiments in this paper and the ones in Goldzycher and Schneider (2022) that might explain the disparity in results is the model size: we use a base-sized multilingual RoBERTa model while they used an English-only BART-large model (Lewis et al., 2020), which we assume is generally more accurate in its NLI predictions and thus producing more reliable predictions for auxiliary hypotheses. Future work could thus evaluate the effect of model capacity on hypothesis engineering.

Acknowledgments

We thank Amit Moryossef and the anonymous reviewers for their helpful feedback. Janis Goldzycher and Gerold Schneider were funded by the University of Zurich Research Priority Program (project "URPP Digital Religion(s)"[6]). Chantal Amrhein received funding from the Swiss National Science Foundation (project MUTAMUR; no. 176727).

[6] https://www.digitalreligions.uzh.ch/en.html

Limitations

Even though our findings are backed by a large number of settings and experiments, the conclusions that can be drawn from this setup are limited in the following ways:

Datasets We evaluated on five languages, a small fraction of the languages that could benefit from such models. Specifically, our results are limited to languages that appear in the pretraining dataset of XLM-T. Further, we showed that XNLI fine-tuning can lead to significant performance increases, even for languages that do not appear in XNLI. However, the two languages we tested on (Italian and Portuguese) are related to other languages in XNLI. There is a need for further research on how much of these benefits can be retained when the target language is less related to one of the languages in XNLI.

Models For consistency and efficiency, we used the same multilingual model in all experiments. This means that our results are dependent on the specifics of the model, specifically the domain it has been pre-trained on and its model size. As already mentioned in Section 5, the small model size likely has had a negative impact on the results for hypothesis engineering.

Hypothesis Engineering All results are limited to the specific strategies that we tested. Further, potential errors in the automatic translations of the hypotheses of the strategies might have impacted the results. A strength of the approach, that we did not evaluate, is that they can be adjusted to new languages and cultures simply by specifying e.g. a new set of protected groups or group characteristics via auxiliary hypotheses, thereby avoiding the criticism that zero-shot cross-lingual hate speech detection does not adjust to the specific circumstances of a language and culture (Nozza, 2022).

References

Wissam Antoun, Fady Baly, and Hazem Hajj. 2020. AraBERT: Transformer-based model for Arabic language understanding. In *Proceedings of the 4th Workshop on Open-Source Arabic Corpora and Processing Tools, with a Shared Task on Offensive Language Detection*, pages 9–15, Marseille, France. European Language Resource Association.

Francesco Barbieri, Luis Espinosa Anke, and Jose Camacho-Collados. 2022. XLM-T: Multilingual language models in Twitter for sentiment analysis and beyond. In *Proceedings of the Thirteenth Language Resources and Evaluation Conference*, pages 258–266, Marseille, France. European Language Resources Association.

Valerio Basile, Cristina Bosco, Elisabetta Fersini, Debora Nozza, Viviana Patti, Francisco Manuel Rangel Pardo, Paolo Rosso, and Manuela Sanguinetti. 2019. SemEval-2019 task 5: Multilingual detection of hate speech against immigrants and women in Twitter. In *Proceedings of the 13th International Workshop on Semantic Evaluation*, pages 54–63, Minneapolis, Minnesota, USA. Association for Computational Linguistics.

Irina Bigoulaeva, Viktor Hangya, Iryna Gurevych, and Alexander Fraser. 2023. Label modification and bootstrapping for zero-shot cross-lingual hate speech detection. *Language Resources and Evaluation (1574-0218)*.

Ke-Li Chiu and Rohan Alexander. 2021. Detecting hate speech with GPT-3. *arXiv:2103.12407 [cs]*. ArXiv: 2103.12407.

Alexis Conneau, Kartikay Khandelwal, Naman Goyal, Vishrav Chaudhary, Guillaume Wenzek, Francisco Guzmán, Edouard Grave, Myle Ott, Luke Zettlemoyer, and Veselin Stoyanov. 2020. Unsupervised cross-lingual representation learning at scale. In *Proceedings of the 58th Annual Meeting of the Association for Computational Linguistics*, pages 8440–8451, Online. Association for Computational Linguistics.

Alexis Conneau, Ruty Rinott, Guillaume Lample, Adina Williams, Samuel Bowman, Holger Schwenk, and Veselin Stoyanov. 2018. XNLI: Evaluating cross-lingual sentence representations. In *Proceedings of the 2018 Conference on Empirical Methods in Natural Language Processing*, pages 2475–2485, Brussels, Belgium. Association for Computational Linguistics.

Paula Fortuna and Sérgio Nunes. 2018. A survey on automatic detection of hate speech in Text. *ACM Computing Surveys*, 51(4):85:1–85:30.

Paula Fortuna, João Rocha da Silva, Juan Soler-Company, Leo Wanner, and Sérgio Nunes. 2019. A hierarchically-labeled Portuguese hate speech dataset. In *Proceedings of the Third Workshop on Abusive*

Language Online, pages 94–104, Florence, Italy. Association for Computational Linguistics.

Antigoni Founta, Constantinos Djouvas, Despoina Chatzakou, Ilias Leontiadis, Jeremy Blackburn, Gianluca Stringhini, Athena Vakali, Michael Sirivianos, and Nicolas Kourtellis. 2018. Large scale crowdsourcing and characterization of twitter abusive behavior. *Proceedings of the International AAAI Conference on Web and Social Media*, 12(1).

Janis Goldzycher and Gerold Schneider. 2022. Hypothesis engineering for zero-shot hate speech detection. In *Proceedings of the Third Workshop on Threat, Aggression and Cyberbullying (TRAC 2022)*, pages 75–90, Gyeongju, Republic of Korea. Association for Computational Linguistics.

Brendan Kennedy, Xisen Jin, Aida Mostafazadeh Davani, Morteza Dehghani, and Xiang Ren. 2020. Contextualizing hate speech classifiers with post-hoc explanation. In *Proceedings of the 58th Annual Meeting of the Association for Computational Linguistics*, pages 5435–5442, Online. Association for Computational Linguistics.

Hannah Kirk, Abeba Birhane, Bertie Vidgen, and Leon Derczynski. 2022a. Handling and presenting harmful text in NLP research. In *Findings of the Association for Computational Linguistics: EMNLP 2022*, pages 497–510, Abu Dhabi, United Arab Emirates. Association for Computational Linguistics.

Hannah Kirk, Bertie Vidgen, and Scott Hale. 2022b. Is more data better? re-thinking the importance of efficiency in abusive language detection with transformers-based active learning. In *Proceedings of the Third Workshop on Threat, Aggression and Cyberbullying (TRAC 2022)*, pages 52–61, Gyeongju, Republic of Korea. Association for Computational Linguistics.

Mike Lewis, Yinhan Liu, Naman Goyal, Marjan Ghazvininejad, Abdelrahman Mohamed, Omer Levy, Veselin Stoyanov, and Luke Zettlemoyer. 2020. BART: Denoising Sequence-to-Sequence Pre-training for Natural Language Generation, Translation, and Comprehension. In *Proceedings of the 58th Annual Meeting of the Association for Computational Linguistics*, pages 7871–7880, Online. Association for Computational Linguistics.

Pengfei Liu, Weizhe Yuan, Jinlan Fu, Zhengbao Jiang, Hiroaki Hayashi, and Graham Neubig. 2021. Pre-train, Prompt, and Predict: A systematic survey of prompting methods in natural language processing. *arXiv:2107.13586 [cs]*. ArXiv: 2107.13586.

Thomas Mandl, Sandip Modha, Anand Kumar M, and Bharathi Raja Chakravarthi. 2020. Overview of the HASOC Track at FIRE 2020: Hate Speech and Offensive Language Identification in Tamil, Malayalam, Hindi, English and German. In *Forum for Information Retrieval Evaluation*, pages 29–32, Hyderabad India. ACM.

Thomas Mandl, Sandip Modha, Prasenjit Majumder, Daksh Patel, Mohana Dave, Chintak Mandlia, and Aditya Patel. 2019. Overview of the HASOC Track at FIRE 2019: Hate Speech and Offensive Content Identification in Indo-European Languages. In *Proceedings of the 11th Forum for Information Retrieval Evaluation*, FIRE '19, pages 14–17, New York, NY, USA. Association for Computing Machinery. Event-place: Kolkata, India.

Sanguinetti Manuela, Comandini Gloria, Elisa Di Nuovo, Simona Frenda, MARCO ANTONIO Stranisci, Cristina Bosco, Caselli Tommaso, Viviana Patti, Russo Irene, et al. 2020. HaSpeeDe 2 @ EVALITA2020: Overview of the EVALITA 2020 hate speech detection task. In *Proceedings of the Seventh Evaluation Campaign of Natural Language Processing and Speech Tools for Italian. Final Workshop (EVALITA 2020)*, pages 1–9. CEUR.

Sandip Modha, Thomas Mandl, Gautam Kishore Shahi, Hiren Madhu, Shrey Satapara, Tharindu Ranasinghe, and Marcos Zampieri. 2022. Overview of the HASOC subtrack at FIRE 2021: Hate speech and offensive content identification in english and indo-aryan languages and conversational hate speech. In *Proceedings of the 13th Annual Meeting of the Forum for Information Retrieval Evaluation*, FIRE '21, page 1–3, New York, NY, USA. Association for Computing Machinery.

Syrielle Montariol, Arij Riabi, and Djamé Seddah. 2022. Multilingual auxiliary tasks training: Bridging the gap between languages for zero-shot transfer of hate speech detection models. In *Findings of the Association for Computational Linguistics: AACL-IJCNLP 2022*, pages 347–363, Online only. Association for Computational Linguistics.

Marzieh Mozafari, Reza Farahbakhsh, and Noel Crespi. 2022. Cross-Lingual Few-Shot Hate Speech and Offensive Language Detection Using Meta Learning. *IEEE Access*, 10:14880–14896. Conference Name: IEEE Access.

Debora Nozza. 2022. Nozza@LT-EDI-ACL2022: Ensemble modeling for homophobia and transphobia detection. In *Proceedings of the Second Workshop on Language Technology for Equality, Diversity and Inclusion*, pages 258–264, Dublin, Ireland. Association for Computational Linguistics.

Nedjma Ousidhoum, Zizheng Lin, Hongming Zhang, Yangqiu Song, and Dit-Yan Yeung. 2019. Multilingual and multi-aspect hate speech analysis. In *Proceedings of the 2019 Conference on Empirical Methods in Natural Language Processing and the 9th International Joint Conference on Natural Language Processing (EMNLP-IJCNLP)*, pages 4675–4684, Hong Kong, China. Association for Computational Linguistics.

Loreto Parisi, Simone Francia, and Paolo Magnani. 2020. UmBERTo: An italian language model trained with whole word masking. `https://github.com/musixmatchresearch/umberto`.

Juan Manuel Pérez, Damián Ariel Furman, Laura Alonso Alemany, and Franco M. Luque. 2022. RoBERTuito: A pre-trained language model for social media text in Spanish. In *Proceedings of the Thirteenth Language Resources and Evaluation Conference*, pages 7235–7243, Marseille, France. European Language Resources Association.

Fabio Poletto, Valerio Basile, Manuela Sanguinetti, Cristina Bosco, and Viviana Patti. 2021. Resources and benchmark corpora for hate speech detection: A systematic review. *Language Resources and Evaluation*, 55(2):477–523.

Colin Raffel, Noam Shazeer, Adam Roberts, Katherine Lee, Sharan Narang, Michael Matena, Yanqi Zhou, Wei Li, and Peter J. Liu. 2020. Exploring the Limits of Transfer Learning with a Unified Text-to-Text Transformer. *Journal of Machine Learning Research*, 21(140):1–67.

Paul Röttger, Debora Nozza, Federico Bianchi, and Dirk Hovy. 2022a. Data-efficient strategies for expanding hate speech detection into under-resourced languages. In *Proceedings of the 2022 Conference on Empirical Methods in Natural Language Processing*, pages 5674–5691, Abu Dhabi, United Arab Emirates. Association for Computational Linguistics.

Paul Röttger, Haitham Seelawi, Debora Nozza, Zeerak Talat, and Bertie Vidgen. 2022b. Multilingual HateCheck: Functional tests for multilingual hate speech detection models. In *Proceedings of the Sixth Workshop on Online Abuse and Harms (WOAH)*, pages 154–169, Seattle, Washington (Hybrid). Association for Computational Linguistics.

Paul Röttger, Bertie Vidgen, Dong Nguyen, Zeerak Waseem, Helen Margetts, and Janet Pierrehumbert. 2021. HateCheck: Functional tests for hate speech detection models. In *Proceedings of the 59th Annual Meeting of the Association for Computational Linguistics and the 11th International Joint Conference on Natural Language Processing (Volume 1: Long Papers)*, pages 41–58, Online. Association for Computational Linguistics.

Fábio Souza, Rodrigo Nogueira, and Roberto Lotufo. 2020. BERTimbau: Pretrained BERT models for Brazilian Portuguese. In *9th Brazilian Conference on Intelligent Systems, BRACIS, Rio Grande do Sul, Brazil, October 20-23 (to appear)*.

Bertie Vidgen, Tristan Thrush, Zeerak Waseem, and Douwe Kiela. 2021. Learning from the worst: Dynamically generated datasets to improve online hate detection. In *Proceedings of the 59th Annual Meeting of the Association for Computational Linguistics and the 11th International Joint Conference on Natural Language Processing (Volume 1: Long Papers)*, pages 1667–1682, Online. Association for Computational Linguistics.

Sinong Wang, Han Fang, Madian Khabsa, Hanzi Mao, and Hao Ma. 2021. Entailment as few-shot learner. *arXiv:2104.14690 [cs]*. ArXiv: 2104.14690.

Adina Williams, Nikita Nangia, and Samuel Bowman. 2018. A broad-coverage challenge corpus for sentence understanding through inference. In *Proceedings of the 2018 Conference of the North American Chapter of the Association for Computational Linguistics: Human Language Technologies, Volume 1 (Long Papers)*, pages 1112–1122, New Orleans, Louisiana. Association for Computational Linguistics.

Thomas Wolf, Lysandre Debut, Victor Sanh, Julien Chaumond, Clement Delangue, Anthony Moi, Pierric Cistac, Tim Rault, Remi Louf, Morgan Funtowicz, Joe Davison, Sam Shleifer, Patrick von Platen, Clara Ma, Yacine Jernite, Julien Plu, Canwen Xu, Teven Le Scao, Sylvain Gugger, Mariama Drame, Quentin Lhoest, and Alexander Rush. 2020. Transformers: State-of-the-Art natural language processing. In *Proceedings of the 2020 Conference on Empirical Methods in Natural Language Processing: System Demonstrations*, pages 38–45, Online. Association for Computational Linguistics.

Ankit Yadav, Shubham Chandel, Sushant Chatufale, and Anil Bandhakavi. 2023. LAHM : Large annotated dataset for multi-domain and multilingual hate speech identification. *CoRR*, abs/2304.00913.

Wenjie Yin and Arkaitz Zubiaga. 2021. Towards generalisable hate speech detection: A review on obstacles and solutions. *PeerJ Computer Science*, 7:e598. Publisher: PeerJ Inc.

Wenpeng Yin, Jamaal Hay, and Dan Roth. 2019. Benchmarking zero-shot text classification: Datasets, evaluation and entailment approach. In *Proceedings of the 2019 Conference on Empirical Methods in Natural Language Processing and the 9th International Joint Conference on Natural Language Processing (EMNLP-IJCNLP)*, pages 3914–3923, Hong Kong, China. Association for Computational Linguistics.

Haris Bin Zia, Ignacio Castro, Arkaitz Zubiaga, and Gareth Tyson. 2022. Improving zero-shot cross-lingual hate speech detection with pseudo-label fine-tuning of transformer language models. *Proceedings of the International AAAI Conference on Web and Social Media*, 16:1435–1439.

A Training Details

All models were trained and evaluated using the `transformers` library (Wolf et al., 2020), version `4.26.1`. The hyperparameters for the NLI-fine-tuning stage are provided in Table 2. We always chose the best performing checkpoint on the validation set out the five epochs.

parameter	value
epochs	5
learning rate	2e-05
batch size	32
max sequence length	128

Table 2: Hyperparameters of NLI fine-tuning.

For intermediate fine-tuning on English hate speech and fine-tuning on target language examples, we used the same hyperparameters as Röttger et al. (2022a). They are given in Table 3 and Table 4.

parameter	value
epochs	3
learning rate	5e-05
batch size	16
max sequence length	128

Table 3: Hyperparameters for fine-tuning on English hate speech datasets.

parameter	value
epochs	5
learning rate	5e-05
batch size	16
max sequence length	128

Table 4: Hyperparameters for fine-tuning on hate speech datasets in the target language.

All other hyperparameters were kept at the default values of the huggingface Trainer-class.

B Hypothesis Engineering Details

Since we worked with monolingual models in the target language and with multilingual models that have been fine-tuned on English and other languages first, this raises the question in which language the hypotheses should be expressed. For monolingual models, we automatically translated all hypotheses with Google Translate to the target language. The model thus received the premise and hypothesis in the same language as input. For multilingual models, we kept the original English hypotheses. Since we shuffled the languages of premise and hypothesis in the NLI training-regime the models should be able to handle the differing languages well. Keeping the hypotheses in multilingual models in English also means that the hypothesis remains in the same language over multiple fine-tuning phases like intermediate fine-tuning on English hate speech data and target language fine-tuning.

Goldzycher and Schneider (2022) proposed two versions of the strategy "Filtering by Target": In the first version the model predicts if protected groups are targeted (e.g. "This text is about Muslims."). In the second version the model predicts if protected group characteristics are targeted (e.g. "This text is about religion."). Even though the second version performed worse in their experiments, we use this second version for our experiments, because its predictions are more neutral with respect to specific languages and cultures. This enabled us to use exactly the same strategies for each language. In a more sophisticated setup one could implement the first version predicting protected groups and adjust these groups for each language.

C Datasets

The key characteristics of all datasets we used in the experiments are described in Table 5. To create the MultiNLI dataset, sentences from diverse genres were collected and used as premises. Annotators then were tasked with creating artificial hypotheses for these premises. For XNLI, the test set was translated by human translators and the training set was translated automatically.

D Full Results

In order to highlight specific aspects of our results, we split them up over several Figures in the paper. The full results of all settings that we evaluated are provided in Figures 6 and 7.

code	paper	train	validation	test	% hate	source
			(X)NLI datasets			
MNLI	Williams et al. (2018)	40000	19650	-	-	diverse
XNLI	Conneau et al. (2018)	393000	24900	-	-	translation of MNLI
			English hate speech datasets (En HS)			
FEN	Founta et al. (2018)	20068	500	-	22.0	Twitter
KEN	Kennedy et al. (2020)	20692	500	-	50.0	Youtube, Twitter, Reddit
DEN	Vidgen et al. (2021)	38644	500	-	53.9	annotators, adversarial
			Target Language Hate Speech Datasets (TL HS)			
BAS19_ES	Basile et al. (2019)	4100	500	2000	41.5	Twitter
FOR19_PT	Fortuna et al. (2019)	3170	500	2000	31.5	Twitter
HAS21_HI	Modha et al. (2022)	3794	300	500	12.3	Twitter
OUS19_AR	Ousidhoum et al. (2019)	2053	300	1000	22.5	Twitter
SAN20_IT	Manuela et al. (2020)	5600	500	2000	41.8	Twitter
			Multilingual HateCheck (MHC)			
HateCheck_ES	Röttger et al. (2022b)	-	-	3745	70.3	annotators
HateCheck_PT	Röttger et al. (2022b)	-	-	3691	69.9	annotators
HateCheck_HI	Röttger et al. (2022b)	-	-	3565	69.8	annotators
HateCheck_AR	Röttger et al. (2022b)	-	-	3570	69.9	annotators
HateCheck_IT	Röttger et al. (2022b)	-	-	3690	70.0	annotators

Table 5: Statistics of training and evaluation datasets. In the case of FEN and KEN, we applied downsampling to the non-hate speech class. The table reflects the state after downsampling.

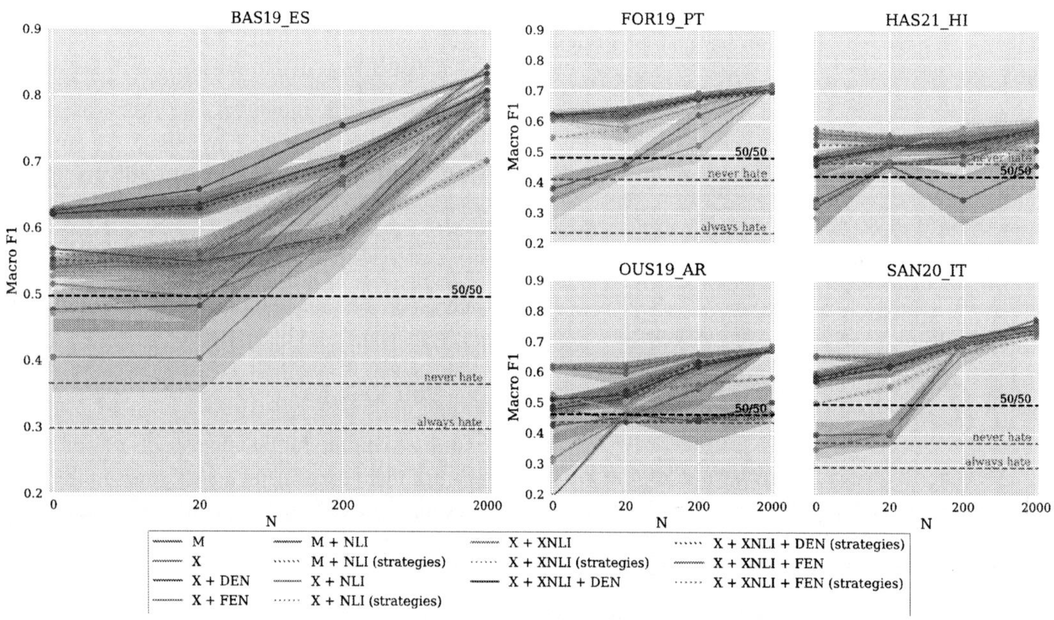

Figure 6: The full results on held-out test sets.

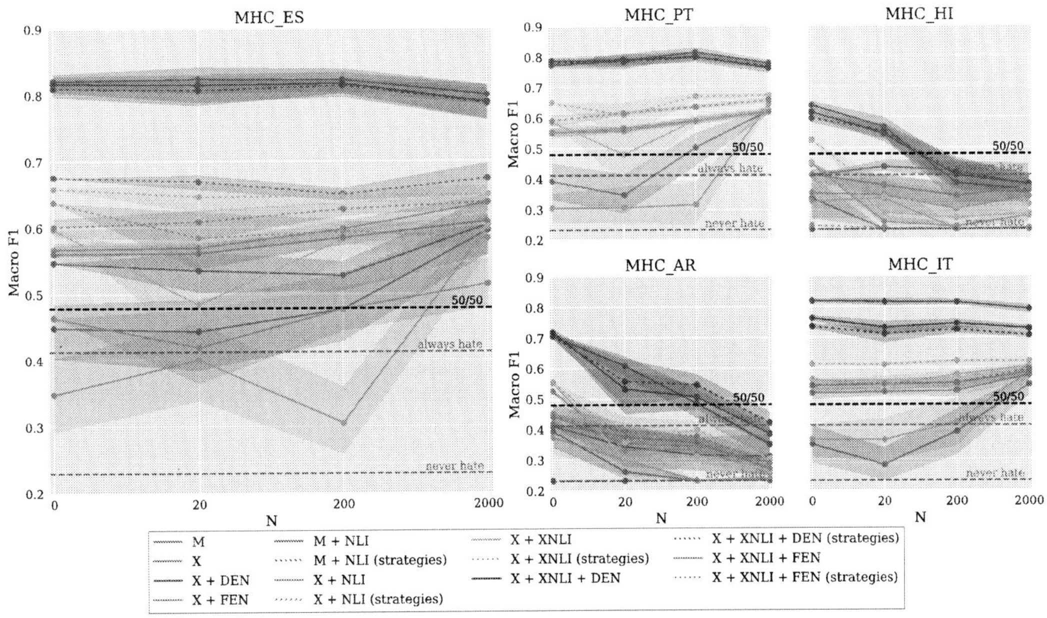

Figure 7: The full results on the multilingual HateCheck.

HOMO-MEX: A Mexican Spanish Annotated Corpus for LGBT+phobia Detection on Twitter

Juan Vásquez[1] and **Scott Thomas Andersen** [2]
Posgrado en Ciencia e Ingeniería de la Computación
Universidad Nacional Autónoma de México
juanmv@comunidad.unam.mx and stasen@comunidad.unam.mx

Gemma Bel-Enguix [3] and
Sergio-Luis Ojeda-Trueba [5]
Instituto de Ingeniería
Universidad Nacional
Autónoma de México
gbele@iingen.unam.mx and
sojedat@iingen.unam.mx

Helena Gómez-Adorno [4]
Instituto de Investigaciones en
Matemáticas Aplicadas y en Sistemas
Universidad Nacional
Autónoma de México
helena.gomez@iimas.unam.mx

Abstract

In the past few years, the NLP[1] community has actively worked on detecting LGBT+Phobia in online spaces, using textual data publicly available Most of these are for the English language and its variants since it is the most studied language by the NLP community. Nevertheless, efforts towards creating corpora in other languages are active worldwide. Despite this, the Spanish language is an understudied language regarding digital LGBT+Phobia. The only corpus we found in the literature was for the Peninsular Spanish dialects, which use LGBT+phobic terms different than those in the Mexican dialect. For this reason, we present Homo-MEX, a novel corpus for detecting LGBT+Phobia in Mexican Spanish. In this paper, we describe our data-gathering and annotation process. Also, we present a classification benchmark using various traditional machine learning algorithms and two pre-trained deep learning models to showcase our corpus classification potential.

1 Introduction

LGBT+Phobia[2] is a global problem (Arimoro, 2022). Among the consequences faced by the LGBT+ community are substance abuse disorders among its members (Wallace and Santacruz, 2017), (Burkhalter, 2015), disproportionate mental health problems (Lozano-Verduzco et al., 2017) (MONGeLLi et al., 2019), discrimination in the labor markets (Quintana, 2009) (Ng and Rumens, 2017), denial of access to education and health services (Hatzenbuehler et al., 2017) (Ayhan et al., 2020), and lack of human rights (López, 2017) (Ungar, 2000) (Peck, 2022).

In recent years, NLP has greatly advanced its methods for detecting hate speech in online communities (Poletto et al., 2021).

Therefore, in order to detect LGBT+Phobia in social networks, specifically on Twitter, we created a corpus designed for this task. To the best of our knowledge, no other corpora focused on LGBT+Phobia in Mexican Spanish have been created so far. This can be very useful for NLP purposes because it is well-known that Mexican Spanish has a specific lexicon and pragmatics. Because of this, it would be valuable to have NLP systems specializing in this Spanish variant.

The corpus we present includes public tweets scraped using Twitter's API that includes keywords that we expect will be used in LGBT+phobic contexts. We gathered a list of nouns used to refer to the LGBT+ community. Then, we scraped nearly ten thousand tweets that contained any of these nouns from the past two years. Thereafter, four annotators annotated each tweet as LGBT+phobic, not LGBT+phobic, or not related to the LGBT+ community. Finally, another group of four annotators identified the fine-grained LGBT+phobic type.

The main contributions of our work are the following:

1. We create and manually annotate a corpus of

[1]Natural Language Processing

[2]Any and all references to the LGBT+ community or LGBT+Phobia includes all members of the LGBTQIA+ community, that is, all sexual and gender minorities that deviate from the traditional gender-binary or the traditional heterosexual relationship and the discrimination they face for their identity.

The 7th Workshop on Online Abuse and Harms (WOAH), pages 202–214

tweets in Mexican Spanish based on a lexicon of LGBT+ terms[3].

2. We present various supervised classification models that could guide efforts towards the detection of online LGBT+Phobia; specifically, LGBT+Phobia in Mexican Spanish.

The rest of this paper is organized as follows. Section 2 surveys related literature and similar experiments. Section 3 describes the construction of our corpus. Section 4 details the methodology of the classification experiments. Section 5 discusses the results of the experiments. Finally, Section 6 describes experimental adjustments we would like to make in future experiments and closes the paper with conclusions. Appendix A provides a brief data statement to give insight into ethical considerations of the annotation process.

2 Related Work

Recent work explored using NLP to detect bullying, hate speech, violence, and aggressiveness. State-of-the-art models were developed for general-purpose hate detection and hateful content directed at a particular group. For these models to be developed, large quantities of data are essential. Recent data sets have emerged that seek to annotate hate towards marginalized groups, the majority being in English. Although multi-language models and data sets exist, having language-specific models and data (del Arco et al., 2021) is demonstrably helpful.

To the best of our knowledge, very few corpora have yet been developed to classify homophobic comments in Spanish in online communication. We seek to bridge this gap. First, we will describe relevant work in NLP, more specifically, models that are used for sentiment analysis, and identification of harassment and hate. Then, we present socially conscious work that seeks to be more inclusive and detect language discriminating against minority groups. Finally, we discuss works that include Spanish classification models.

2.1 NLP Models for general hate and abuse

Recent work in the NLP community seeks to detect harassment, bullying, and hate to improve the safety and quality of online spaces. In this section we present related work on sentiment analysis followed by hate detection.

2.1.1 Works for sentiment analysis

Models have been proposed to analyze sentiments in text for use in online platforms. For example, Demszky et al. (2020) includes a dataset of Reddit comments labeled with up to 27 emotions. Buechel et al. (2018) uses deep learning to learn emotion on data severely limited in size. They find that emotion can be successfully predicted even with models trained on very small data sets.

2.1.2 Works for hate detection

Plenty of work has come forth for the detection of hate speech and abusive language in Social Media (Lee et al., 2018; Kshirsagar et al., 2018; Jarquín-Vásquez et al., 2021).

Dinu et al. (2021) explores the use of pejorative language in Social Media, the context-dependent language used with a negative connotation. Similarly, discriminating language does not necessarily take the form of slurs but depends highly on the context of the comment.

Recent works like ElSherief et al. (2021) ElSherief et al. (2021) present a corpus of tweets as a benchmark for understand ing implicit rather than explicit hate speech.

Finally, HATECHECK (Röttger et al., 2021) provides functional tests for evaluating Hate speech detection models. These tests exposed key weaknesses and biases in state-of-the-art hate detection models.

2.2 Socially Conscious work in the NLP community

Socially conscious work has been made to detect racially, gender, or sexually inspired hate to make online spaces more inclusive. First, we will consider explicitly gender and racial bias, and following this, we will consider LGBT+-specific hate.

This is vital as Xu et al. (2021) demonstrates that standard detoxifying techniques can disproportionately affect generated text from minority communities. For example, by falsely flagging common identity mentions such as "gay" or "Muslim" because the model has learned to associate them with toxicity.

2.2.1 Hate and Bias

Hate and bias present in online spaces are harmful to minority and marginalized communities, but

[3]The link to the Github repository with the IDs and labels of the tweets will be available after the publication of this paper

recent efforts have been proposed to detect and address hateful and biased speech. Fraser et al. (2021) proposes the Stereotype Content Model in NLP adopted from social psychology to represent stereotypes along two axes, warmth, and competence. Their model takes words directed at a particular group and scores them on these dimensions. In addition, they discuss how to use this information to produce anti-stereotypes. Meanwhile, Sun and Peng (2021) creates an event-based dataset of gender bias from Wikipedia articles. They demonstrate that entries on females tend to include personal life events in career sections but not in the career sections for men. Meanwhile, more career-related achievements, such as awards, can be found in the personal life section for men but not for women. These subtle placements of events relevant to the person of interest are indicative of a gender bias in Wikipedia articles. Sheng et al. (2021) explores bias in Natural Language Generation tasks and provides a survey that explores how data and techniques can lead to bias in automatically generated text. They discuss how data, model architecture, methods for decoding, and even evaluation methods can produce a biased model.

An example of this bias, Excell and Moubayed (2021), demonstrates that using exclusively male annotators for a dataset of toxic comments yields weaker results than using exclusively female annotators. Combating this and keeping in mind that the scope of our work is LGBT+phobic content, we gathered annotators that identified as both male and female heterosexuals and members of the LGBT+ community. We also took special care to include annotators from various sexes so that each annotated subset of tweets with diverse representation of gender orientation and sexual identity (Section 3.2).

2.3 LGBT+ specific work

We wish to explore discrimination in natural language specific to the LGBT+ community. Several recent efforts have analyzed what kind of discrimination gender and sexual minorities face. For example, Gámez-Guadix and Incera (2021) addresses the sexual victimization of LGBT+ adolescents in online spaces, finding that many adolescents face gender and sexual-based victimization and receive unwanted sexual attention.

CH-Wang and Jurgens (2021) analyzes nearly 100 million tweets and Reddit comments to note the change of lexical variables indicative of support of gender and sexual minorities, finding that language use changes for community members who feel more accepted. They find that people shift from gender-neutral terms like "partner" to gender-specific terms like "husband" in places where marriage equality acts were enacted. Meanwhile, Khatua et al. (2019) analyzed tweets in India following the legalization of gay marriage. They found that tweets in support centered around justice and equality, while opposing tweets saw the decision as a threat to traditional Indian culture.

Hudhayri (2021) analyzes harassment toward Arab LGBTs in cyberspaces. They investigate semiotic harassment, which studies hidden connotations of harassment shared by language users.

Chakravarthi et al. (2021) generate a data set of multilingual transphobic and homophobic Youtube comments and use a diverse categorical labeling system to determine if the comment is homophobic or transphobic, specifying if it is derogatory or threatening, they even include labels for counterspeech and hope speech. Vargas et al. (2022) build a corpus of 7,000 Brazilian documents. Their corpus was annotated for a binary classification task (offensive versus non-offensive comments), and for a fine-grained classification task depending on the level of offensiveness found in the documents labeled as “offensive” (highly, moderately, and slightly offensive). Furthermore, the authors annotated the documents in nine classes, depending on the perpetrators of the hate speech found in their documents (xenophobia, racism, homophobia, sexism, religious intolerance, partyism, apology for the dictatorship, antisemitism, and fatphobia).

2.4 Hate Speech Identification in Spanish

On 2021, the PAN at CLEF Initiative organized the shared task *Profiling Hate Speech Spreaders on Twitter 2021*, which focused on identifying hate speech against people based on their race, color, ethnicity, gender, sexual orientation, nationality, religion, or another characteristic on Twitter (Bevendorff et al., 2021). The participants were given a dataset with tweets in English and Spanish and had to classify them into two classes. The highest accuracy obtained by the participants was 73.0% for tweets in English and 85.0% for tweets in Spanish (Rangel et al., 2021).

The IberLEF 2021 organized various shared tasks on *Harmful Information*. The first one, MeOffendEs@IBERLEF 2021, aimed at classifying offensive language and its categories in various Spanish dialects (Plaza-del Arco et al., 2021). Four subtasks were proposed in this shared task, all aimed at identifying *offensive language*. The organizers created a corpus made up of "multiple social networks and a diversity of variants of Spanish". The second shared task was EXIST (Rodríguez-Sánchez et al., 2021). Its goal was to identify online sexism. For this shared task, the participants were provided a dataset comprised of 6,977 tweets in English and Spanish. They had to perform two tasks: first, a binary classification of the tweets, then, a categorization of the type of sexism identified in the tweets. The highest accuracy obtained on the binary classification was 78.04%, while the classification among the types of sexism obtained an accuracy of 65.77%. The third shared task was DETOXIS (Taulé et al., 2021). This task aimed to "detect toxicity in comments posted in Spanish in response to different online news articles related to immigration". The highest F1 measure obtained in the first subtask, the toxicity detection task, aimed at performing a binary classification among the classes "toxic" and "non-toxic", was 85.16%. In contrast, the corresponding highest F1 for the second subtask, the toxicity level detection task, consisting of four labels, was 89.29%.

Similar efforts were the two shared tasks, Language Technology for Equality, Diversity, Inclusion (LT-EDI, ACL 2022); and SemEval-2019 Task 5: Multilingual Detection of Hate Speech Against Immigrants and Women in Twitter. The organizers of the first shared task focused on the automatic classification of Youtube comments in English and Tamil, labeled as transphobic and homophobic (García-Díaz et al., 2022), while the latter aimed at classifying hateful speech in a binary classification task and identifying if the targets of the hateful messages were single individuals or groups of people (Basile et al., 2019).

3 Corpus for LGBT+Phobia Detection in Mexican Spanish

This section describes the methodology for collecting data, our annotation process, and the challenges we faced. We also report the agreement between annotators.

3.1 Data Collection

Using Twitter's API, we collected publicly posted Spanish tweets originating from Mexico. The Twitter API supposedly collects public tweets randomly, and we can expect the grand majority of these tweets will be in Mexican Spanish by native speakers. However, speakers of other backgrounds speaking other languages or variants of the language may appear.

We annotated a large set of tweets that contained any noun indicative of the LGBT+ community. These terms were collected by linguistic students tasked with finding every noun used in Mexican Spanish about the LGBT+ community. These terms were collected from social networks like Twitter, Facebook, Instagram, and TikTok to study social media discourse. We selected the most representative lexicon. Also, we contemplate the variations each term could have; particularly in the Mexican LGBT+ community, these nouns have appreciative inflections or inflections related to gender. For example, for gender, the noun *joto* could inflect in *jote*, *jotx*, and *jota*. In the appreciative case, we could derive forms such as *jotito*, *jotón*, *jotite*, etc.

The lemmas of the selected terms, along with their translation and frequency of appearance, can be found in Table 1, and the full Table can be found in the Github repository [4].

Having defined these search terms and variations, we scrape tweets using the Twitter API and filter them depending on their geolocation metadata.

The tweets were scraped between the dates 01-01-2012 to 01-10-2022 (day-month-year format) to ensure that we had a vast and diverse corpus of tweets. We obtained 706,886 unique tweets and annotated 11,000 from the ten year span, half of them from verified accounts – before the monetization of account verification on the platform – and the half randomly selected from the tweets published by unverified accounts.

3.2 Annotation Process

Having gathered and filtered tweets, we sought annotators to begin the annotation process. We collected annotators that were both heterosexual and members of the LGBT+ community to ensure a diverse set of perspectives were used when labeling the tweets. Before the annotation process, we had a group meeting with the annotators, and we discussed various example tweets and how they interpreted them. Then we launched a practice run and discussed the results together. We added a simple tutorial to the platform that gave some of these

[4] https://github.com/juanmvsa/HOMO-MEX

Keyword	Translation	Count	Keyword	Translation	Count	Keyword	Translation	Count
Bi	Bi(sexual)	3330	Trans	Trans	3245	Gay	Gay	1811
Loca	Crazy (fem.)	1116	Puto	Whore	1102	Homosexual	Homosexual	1049
Joto	Faggot	1008	Lesbiana	Lesbian	827	Drag	Drag queen	597
Marica	Faggot	537	Vestida	Dressed Up	458	Bisexual	Bisexual	336
Maricón	Faggot	487	Transexual	Transexual	290	Transformer	A Trans person	279
Transgénero	Transgenedered	227	Travesti	Transvestite	226	Queer	Queer	202
Lencha	Lesbian	181	Mayate	Lesbian	179	Puñal	Gay man	114
Rarx	Strange	108	No binario	Non-binary	79	Clostera	Closeted person	75
Afeminado	An Effeminate	73	Intersexual	Intersexual	58	Pansexual	Pansexual	54
Asexual	Asexual	43	Machorra	Lesbian	40	Cuir	Queer	28
Femboy	Femboy	19	Tortilla	Tortilla	11	Trapito	Little rag	7
Crossdresser	Crossdresser	7	Sáfica	Safic	6	Muxhe	Muxhe	4
Género fluido	Gender Fluid	4	Arcoiris	Rainbow	4	Demisexual	Demisexual	3
Enby	Non-Binary	3	Hombre Con Falda	Man with a Skirt	2	Transformista	Trans person	2
Tijeras	Scissors	2	Panes	Pan	2	Mariposon	Faggot	1
Lechugona	Lesbian	1	Bigénero	Bigender	1			

Table 1: The following table contains slurs against the LGBT+ community and may be offensive to some readers. The number of times each keyword, or their inflections, appear in the corpus. We list the search term, the English translation, and the number of tweets they appear in. Some terms were removed because they were too saturated with their non-LGBT+ interpretation: bicicleta (bicycle), and tortilla. Tortilla, however, still appears in tweets that contain another search term.

examples and the labels the group created and clarified questions many annotators had. All annotators in this meeting had to go through this tutorial to refresh their memory before beginning the annotation. At some points, we had to add additional annotators to replace some who dropped out, and we required them to go through this tutorial as well and asked them to reach out with any questions or concerns; this is to ensure consistent understanding of the annotation process for those who could not attend the initial meetings. The tutorial also formally defined some terms such as *LGBT+phobia* and *Transphobia* and included some questions that they were required to answer to proceed to ensure that they were paying attention to the content. We include more information on the annotators in the Data Statement.

3.3 Annotation Schema

Here we explain the methodology for labeling the tweets and how we measured agreement between the annotators.

The annotators labeled the 11,000 tweets as "LGBT+phobic", "Not LGBT+phobic", and "irrelevant to the LGBT+ community". In this task, the annotators could only select one category. All tweets labeled as "LGBT+phobic" were later passed through an additional annotation process that identified the type of LGBT+phobia. In the second stage, the labels were "gayphobia", "lesbophobia", "biphobia", "transphobia", and "other lgbt+phobic content". Although *gay* is an umbrella term that encompasses much of the LGBT+ community, for the purposes of this annotation, we requested that the annotators only use this label if the tweet contained LGBT+phobic content towards homosexual cis-males to best contrast with the other labels. In this task, the annotators were allowed to annotate the tweets with all labels that applied because one tweet could have LGBT+phobic content towards multiple groups.

In the LGBT+phobia detection task, we requested that if a tweet could be seen as LGBT+phobic if the author does not belong to the community and not LGBT+phobic if the author is LGBT, the annotators give the benefit of the doubt to the author. Therefore, the dataset did not overuse the LGBT+phobic label when much of the discourse within the community can be seen as ironically LGBT+phobic without true intent of harm towards the LGBT+ community.

The annotators used a custom annotation platform that presented the tweets to them in random order and ensured that their responses were anonymized while verifying that each tweet is labeled by four annotators, two members of the LGBT community and two heterosexual, male, and female.

In the LGBT+phobia identification set, a label was selected if it had the majority of the votes. All tweets tied were presented to a different set of annotators to be re-annotated. Any tweets still presented a tie after this were assigned a final label based on a final specialized annotator's decision.

In the type of LGBT+phobia identification set, any label that had at least half of the annotators' votes was selected as a label for the tweet. In this task, the tweet can have multiple labels, such as "gayphobia", "lesbophobia" and "transphobia".

3.4 Annotation Results

After the annotation was completed, we examined the agreement of the annotators for each subset of the corpus, using Fleiss' Kappa. This information is available in Table 2.

For the detection subset we see a moderate agreement among all groups in the phobia detection task, and in the re-annotated tweets that had tied. We calculate the agreement among LGBT+ and Non-LGBT+ annotators, and compare it to the agreement among those of female or male sex, as well as among all annotators.

The fine-grained annotation agreements are not as consistent. We see that there is much more agreement among Non-LGBT+ annotators and Male annotators in every category of LGBT+phobia. LGBT+ annotators and Female annotators show the most disagreement in the annotation of gayphobia and Other types of LGBT+phobia. We hypothesize that this could be from inconsistent interpretations of language use in LGBT+ sub-communities that male and non-LGBT+ annotators may be less exposed to, keeping in mind that a group being in agreement does not necessarily mean they are correct.

3.4.1 Examples

With the tweets annotated, here we will provide a few examples of tweets and their labeling and a rough translation. Warning: these tweets could include distressing language and slurs against the LGBT+ community that may harm some readers.

LGBT+phobic Tweets Here are two examples of tweets that were labeled as LGBT+phobic. *"De que me sirve tener amigos gays si no me sirven para consejos de moda #badgayfriends"*, roughly translated to *"It is usless have gays friends if they dont give me fashion advice #badgayfriends"*. The author of this tweets assume that all the homosexuals know about fashion, a frequent stereotype that is also present in the hashtag. Another example is *"Lo siento, soy muy marica para el dolor)':"*, translated again roughly as *"Im sorry, Im such a fag when it comes to pain)':"*. Here the author relates weakness with the LGBT+ community.

Non LGBT+phobic Tweets Here we will include a few examples of tweets that were labeled as not having LGBT+phobic intent. *"Estados Unidos levanta la prohibición para que homosexuales donen sangre"*, translated to *"The United States lifts ban on homosexuals donating blood"*. Another example is *"Entonces lo que anda(mos) haciendo las viejas trans es crearnos mujeres COMO SE LE ENSEÑA AL NIÑO que es una mujer (objeto, sexuada, sumisa)"*, translated again roughly as *'So what we old trans are doing, We are making ourselves women as HOW BOYS ARE TAUGHT that a woman is (objectified, sexualized, submissive)'"*. Here the author employs *trans* to refer to themselves naturally.

Tweets with low agreement The following tweets had low agreement in the detection task. *"Ah verga es un duende? Yo pensaba era un alíen asexual"*, or in English, *"Ah fuck they're an elf? I thought they were an asexual alien."*, this tweet was labeled as LGBT+phobic. *"No, Sifo, no. O sea, no mames. No soy una puta. Qué te pasa. Si quieres que te la chupe, me vas a tener que pagar."*, which translates as *"No, Sifo, no. I mean, quit fucking with me. I'm not a whore. If you want me to suck it, you'll have to pay."* which was finally labeled as not relevant to the LGBT+ community.

3.5 Challenges to Annotation

One challenge we faced during the creation of Homo-MEX was the annotation process. Even though we had various annotators that were members of the LGBT+ community and/or were very aware of the issues faced by the LGBT+ Mexican community, the annotator inter-agreement was not very high. We attribute these results to the difficulty of differentiating between irony, resignification, appropriation of slurs, and humor inside the LGBT+ community, especially when the context may not be available. This limitation is important, however, because it best aligns with the circumstances of automatic LGBT+phobia detection based on just the tweets' textual content.

Another potential limitation could be the difficulty in counterbalancing the internalized stereotypes that the annotators might have. This has proven to influence the annotation behaviors (Davani et al., 2023).

The annotator agreement is especially low for the label "Other" in the fine-grained classification task. We suppose that the label may not be well

Detection Subset	Kappa				
	LGBT+	Non-LGBT+	Male	Female	All
Phobia Detection	0.449	0.371	0.392	0.474	0.430
Tie Break	0.517	0.369	0.416	0.409	0.465

Fine Grained Subset	Kappa				
	LGBT+	Non-LGBT+	Male	Female	All
Gayphobia	-0.055	0.732	0.789	-0.087	0.316
Lesbophobia	0.691	0.656	0.723	0.572	0.665
Biphobia	0.205	0.565	0.495	0.315	0.419
Transphobia	0.650	0.743	0.779	0.638	0.700
Other	-0.306	0.353	0.422	-0.322	-0.027

Table 2: We employ Fleiss' kappa to analyze the agreement among the annotators. More information can be found in Section 3.3. The group *Phobia Detection* refers to the annotation task identifying tweets that did or did not contain LGBT+phobia or were irrelevant to LGBT+ discourse. The group *Tie Break* is the agreement among the annotators who reclassified the tweets that tied in labels from the previous group. Finally, the second table represents the agreement for each LGBT+phobia category in the Fine Grained data set.

defined, or more nuanced types of LGBT+phobia may not be as easy to identify.

4 Experiments on the HOMO-MEX Corpus for LGBT+phobia Detection

To evaluate the performance of various classifiers on our corpus, we performed several experiments using two main approaches: traditional machine learning methods and deep learning architectures. We describe these experiments in this section.

The HOMO-MEX corpus consists of two overlapped subsets. The first subset is comprised of those tweets that can be either "LGBT+Phobic" (LP), "Not LGBT+Phobic" (NLP), and "irrelevant to the LGBT+ community" (I). On the other hand, the second subset contains the LGBT+Phobic tweets that were multi-labeled as "Lesbophobic" (L), "Gayphobic" (G), "Biphobic" (B), "Transphobic" (T), and "Other" (O). For conciseness, we will refer to the first subset as "LGBT+Phobia detection", and the second as "fine-grained classification". Both LGBT+Phobia detection and fine-grained classification subsets were split into train and test partitions. The resulting size and distribution of labels in each partition are shown in Tables 3 and 4. In table 4, the total of the train and test partitions is equal to 862 and 477, respectively, even though the addition of the tweets with every label (L, G, B, T, O) does not add to the counts since the tweets in this partition can have more than one label at a time. This allows the number of labels to be greater than the total size of the train and test partitions.

Partition	LP	NLP	I	Total
Train	862	4,360	1,778	7,000
Test	477	2,493	1,030	4,000
Total	1,339	6,853	2,808	11,000

Table 3: Size and label distribution for the LGBT+Phobia detection subset.

Partition	L	G	B	T	O	Total
Train	72	714	10	79	64	862
Test	34	414	3	38	32	477
Total	106	1,128	13	117	96	X

Table 4: Size and label distribution for the fine-grained classification subset.

4.1 Traditional Machine Learning Approach

Initially, we performed several pre-processing steps to the corpus. The first step in this process was the removal of stopwords using nltk's lexicon[5]. Then, we removed all diacritic characters, digits, and all other characters that were not a letter, or an underscore. Following, we tokenized the tweets using spaCy's small Spanish model, *es_news_core_sm*[6]. Finally, we generated the features for the different machine-learning algorithms. To achieve this, we made use of the bag-of-words algorithm and TF-IDF weighting scheme as implemented in scikit-learn (version 0.23.2) [7].

[5] https://github.com/xiamx/node-nltk-stopwords/blob/master/data/stopwords/spanish
[6] https://spacy.io/models/es
[7] https://scikit-learn.org/stable

4.2 Pre-trained Deep Learning Models Approach

Using both subsets (LGBT+Phobia detection and fine-grained classification), we fine-tuned various pre-trained large language models for classification. No pre-processing steps were performed in these experiments. The large language models that we used for these classification experiments were `bert-base-multilingual-cased` (Devlin et al., 2018), `bert-base-multilingual-uncased` (Devlin et al., 2018), `beto-cased` (Cañete et al., 2020), and `beto-uncased` (Cañete et al., 2020). We used hugging face's `transformers` (Wolf et al., 2019) library for their implementation[8].

5 Results and Discussion

We performed classification experiments using Naive Bayes, SVM, Logistic Regression, and Random Forest classifiers. Table 5 shows the metrics obtained using the LGBT+Phobia subset, and Table 6 shows the classification metrics obtained using the fine-grained subset. In addition, we used four BERT models to classify the tweets in both the LGBT+Phobia detection and fine-grained classification subsets. The results of these experiments can be observed in Table 7 for the LGBT+Phobia detection subset and in Table 8 for the fine-grained classification subset. We follow the PT1 method explained in Tsoumakas and Katakis (2007) to evaluate the fine-grained classification models. The PT1 method consists of splitting a classification problem (with $L = [A, B, C, D, E]$ labels) into a classification problem with $M = L \bigcup N$ labels, where $N = [\neg A, \neg B, \neg C, \neg D, \neg E]$. Then, the classification is treated as five binary subtasks, one for each label and its negation. For example, the first binary classification subtask would be with the labels $[A, \neg A]$, the second binary classification with the labels $[B, \neg B]$, and so on. Once the five metrics, one for each subset of labels, were generated, the average between them was computed. Those averages are reported in Tables 6 and 8.

Among the classical machine learning algorithms, SVM performs the best among almost all metrics in both partitions. Beto-cased produces the highest classification metrics in the LGBT+Phobia detection subset, while bert-base-multilingual-uncased outperforms the other bert-based models in the fine-grained classification subset. These results demonstrate that more work must be done on automatically classifying LGBT+phobic speech in Mexican Spanish.

6 Conclusion and future work

Detecting LGBT+Phobia using current NLP techniques is still an open task with much work left to do. The paper's contribution is twofold: first, we elaborate on a resource to study the topic in Mexican Spanish. Additionally, we test traditional ML methods, as well as BERT-based techniques, to identify LGBT+Phobia.

The corpus has been designed by filtering tweets with specific keywords related to the LGBT+ community in Mexico. Such tweets contain many references to LGBT+Phobia. However, surprisingly, there is more hateful speech when referring to the masculine gay community. Looking at the tweets with feminine terms, we see that many were written by women inside the community. This implies a different problem, the general invisibility of women, that should be tackled in the more general framework of sexism.

In the future, we hope to continue to expand the dataset to include more tweets with even more diverse terms to represent all members of the LGBT+ community. At present, many of the tweets marked as discriminatory only exhibit homophobia towards men.

A future dataset should include a more profound labeling procedure that can reduce ambiguity for the annotators and provide more information using a non-binary labeling system. Future approaches can include the categories of derogatory, threatening, humor remark and apparently neutral comment, among others.

Future papers should create a more representative dataset of Mexican Spanish tweets with a more thorough labeling system. Moreover, it will be interesting to the collection corpora in several variants of Spanish. With this, we plan to start a dialectal approach to the problem.

Furthermore, for automatic classification tasks, NLP practitioners should consider including lexicon-informed approaches for the generation of context-aware features for their classifiers, since this has proven its effectiveness in the case of hate speech detection from Brazil(Vargas et al., 2021). Finally, we wish to reiterate that further computational efforts against hate speech should always

[8] `https://huggingface.co/docs/transformers/v4.28.1/en/model_doc/bert#transformers.BertForTokenClassification`

Classification algorithm	Accuracy	Precision	Recall	F1-score
Naive Bayes	0.6885	0.8542	0.4244	0.4127
SVM	**0.8452**	0.7955	**0.7519**	**0.7670**
Logistic regression	0.8447	**0.8274**	0.7244	0.7592
Random forest	0.8302	0.7965	0. 7037	0.7349

Table 5: Classification results experiments using traditional ML algorithms on the LGBT+Phobia detection subset.

Classification algorithm	Accuracy	Precision	Recall	F1-score
Naive Bayes	0.9287	0.9643	0.5000	0.4813
SVM	**0.9589**	**0.9700**	**0.6558**	**0.6909**
Logistic regression	0.9312	0.9156	0.5122	0.5048
Random forest	0.9534	0.9648	0.6281	0.6622

Table 6: Classification results experiments on the fine-grained classification subset.

Classification algorithm	Accuracy	Precision	Recall	F1-score
bert-base-multilingual-uncased	0.8577	0.8558	0.8577	0.8566
bert-base-multilingual-cased	0.8492	0.8488	0.8485	0.8494
beto-cased	**0.8600**	**0.8592**	**0.8589**	**0.8600**
beto-uncased	0.8552	0.8554	0.8555	0.8552

Table 7: Classification results using BERT models on the LGBT+Phobia detection subset.

Classification algorithm	Accuracy	Precision	Recall	F1-score
bert-base-multilingual-uncased	**0.7815**	**0.9354**	**0.7815**	0.7396
bert-base-multilingual-cased	0.7614	0.8417	0.7614	**0.7422**
beto-uncased	0.7765	0.7713	0.7765	0.7403
beto-cased	0.7710	0.7879	0.7711	0.7416

Table 8: Classification results using BERT models on the fine-grained classification subset.

take into account LGBT people's experiences while designing their experiments. This, in recognition that hateful discourses against this population are often constructed by intersecting power structures –such as the symbolic discourses that produce the "immoral, defective, and inferior LGBT Individual" – which further limit the collaboration between the LGBT+ population and Academia in the battle against hate speech.

References

Augustine Edobor Arimoro. 2022. *Global Perspectives on the LGBT Community and Non-Discrimination.* IGI Global.

Cemile Hurrem Balik Ayhan, Hülya Bilgin, Ozgu Tekin Uluman, Ozge Sukut, Sevil Yilmaz, and Sevim Buzlu. 2020. A systematic review of the discrimination against sexual and gender minority in health care settings. *International Journal of Health Services*, 50(1):44–61.

Valerio Basile, Cristina Bosco, Elisabetta Fersini, Debora Nozza, Viviana Patti, Francisco Manuel Rangel Pardo, Paolo Rosso, and Manuela Sanguinetti. 2019. Semeval-2019 task 5: Multilingual detection of hate speech against immigrants and women in twitter. In *Proceedings of the 13th international workshop on semantic evaluation*, pages 54–63.

Emily M. Bender and Batya Friedman. 2018. Data Statements for Natural Language Processing: Toward Mitigating System Bias and Enabling Better Science. *Transactions of the Association for Computational Linguistics*, 6:587–604.

Janek Bevendorff, Berta Chulvi, Gretel Liz De La Peña Sarracén, Mike Kestemont, Enrique Manjavacas, Ilia Markov, Maximilian Mayerl, Martin Potthast, Francisco Rangel, Paolo Rosso, et al. 2021. Overview of pan 2021: authorship verification, profiling hate speech spreaders on twitter, and style change detection. In *International Conference of the Cross-Language Evaluation Forum for European Languages*, pages 419–431. Springer.

Sven Buechel, João Sedoc, H. Andrew Schwartz, and Lyle H. Ungar. 2018. Learning neural emotion analysis from 100 observations: The surprising effectiveness of pre-trained word representations. *CoRR*, abs/1810.10949.

Jack E Burkhalter. 2015. Smoking in the lgbt community. In *Cancer and the LGBT Community*, pages 63–80. Springer.

José Cañete, Gabriel Chaperon, Rodrigo Fuentes, Jou-Hui Ho, Hojin Kang, and Jorge Pérez. 2020. Spanish pre-trained bert model and evaluation data. *Pml4dc at iclr*, 2020(2020):1–10.

Sky CH-Wang and David Jurgens. 2021. Using sociolinguistic variables to reveal changing attitudes towards sexuality and gender. *CoRR*, abs/2109.11061.

Bharathi Raja Chakravarthi, Ruba Priyadharshini, Rahul Ponnusamy, Prasanna Kumar, Kayalvizhi Sampath, Durairaj Thenmozhi, Sathiyaraj Thangasamy, and John Phillip McCrae. 2021. Dataset for Identification of Homophobia and Transophobia in Multilingual YouTube Comments. *Natural Language Engineering*, page 44.

Aida Mostafazadeh Davani, Mohammad Atari, Brendan Kennedy, and Morteza Dehghani. 2023. Hate speech classifiers learn normative social stereotypes. *Transactions of the Association for Computational Linguistics*, 11:300–319.

Flor Miriam Plaza del Arco, M. Dolores Molina-González, L. Alfonso Ureña-López, and M. Teresa Martín-Valdivia. 2021. Comparing pre-trained language models for spanish hate speech detection. *Expert Systems with Applications*, 166:114120.

Dorottya Demszky, Dana Movshovitz-Attias, Jeongwoo Ko, Alan Cowen, Gaurav Nemade, and Sujith Ravi. 2020. GoEmotions: A Dataset of Fine-Grained Emotions. Number: arXiv:2005.00547 arXiv:2005.00547 [cs].

Jacob Devlin, Ming-Wei Chang, Kenton Lee, and Kristina Toutanova. 2018. BERT: pre-training of deep bidirectional transformers for language understanding. *CoRR*, abs/1810.04805.

Liviu P. Dinu, Ioan-Bogdan Iordache, Ana Sabina Uban, and Marcos Zampieri. 2021. A Computational Exploration of Pejorative Language in Social Media. In *Findings of the Association for Computational Linguistics: EMNLP 2021*, pages 3493–3498, Punta Cana, Dominican Republic. Association for Computational Linguistics.

Mai ElSherief, Caleb Ziems, David Muchlinski, Vaishnavi Anupindi, Jordyn Seybolt, Munmun De Choudhury, and Diyi Yang. 2021. Latent hatred: A benchmark for understanding implicit hate speech. *CoRR*, abs/2109.05322.

Elizabeth Excell and Noura Al Moubayed. 2021. Towards equal gender representation in the annotations of toxic language detection.

Kathleen C. Fraser, Isar Nejadgholi, and Svetlana Kiritchenko. 2021. Understanding and countering stereotypes: A computational approach to the stereotype content model.

José García-Díaz, Camilo Caparros-Laiz, and Rafael Valencia-García. 2022. UMUTeam@LT-EDI-ACL2022: Detecting homophobic and transphobic comments in Tamil. In *Proceedings of the Second Workshop on Language Technology for Equality, Diversity and Inclusion*, pages 140–144, Dublin, Ireland. Association for Computational Linguistics.

Manuel Gámez-Guadix and Daniel Incera. 2021. Homophobia is online: Sexual victimization and risks on the internet and mental health among bisexual, homosexual, pansexual, asexual, and queer adolescents. *Computers in Human Behavior*, 119:106728.

Mark L Hatzenbuehler, Andrew R Flores, and Gary J Gates. 2017. Social attitudes regarding same-sex marriage and lgbt health disparities: Results from a national probability sample. *Journal of Social Issues*, 73(3):508–528.

Khalid Hudhayri. 2021. Linguistic harassment against arab lgbts on cyberspace. *International Journal of English Linguistics*, 11(4).

Horacio Jarquín-Vásquez, Hugo Jair Escalante, and Manuel Montes. 2021. Self-contextualized attention for abusive language identification. In *Proceedings of the Ninth International Workshop on Natural Language Processing for Social Media*, pages 103–112, Online. Association for Computational Linguistics.

Aparup Khatua, Erik Cambria, Kuntal Ghosh, Nabendu Chaki, and Apalak Khatua. 2019. Tweeting in support of lgbt? a deep learning approach. In *Proceedings of the ACM India Joint International Conference on Data Science and Management of Data*, CoDS-COMAD '19, page 342–345, New York, NY, USA. Association for Computing Machinery.

Rohan Kshirsagar, Tyus Cukuvac, Kathleen R. McKeown, and Susan McGregor. 2018. Predictive embeddings for hate speech detection on twitter. *CoRR*, abs/1809.10644.

Younghun Lee, Seunghyun Yoon, and Kyomin Jung. 2018. Comparative Studies of Detecting Abusive Language on Twitter. In *Proceedings of the 2nd Workshop on Abusive Language Online (ALW2)*, pages 101–106, Brussels, Belgium. Association for Computational Linguistics.

Jairo Antonio López. 2017. Los derechos lgbt en méxico: Acción colectiva a nivel subnacional. *European Review of Latin American and Caribbean Studies/Revista Europea de Estudios Latinoamericanos y del Caribe*, 104:69–88.

Ignacio Lozano-Verduzco, Julián Alfredo Fernández-Niño, and Ricardo Baruch-Domínguez. 2017. Asociación de la homofobia internalizada con indicadores de salud mental en personas lgbt de la ciudad de méxico. *Salud mental*, 40(5):219–226.

Francesca MONGeLLi, Daniela Perrone, Jessica BaLDUcci, Andrea Sacchetti, Silvia Ferrari, Giorgio Mattei, and Gian M Galeazzi. 2019. Minority stress and mental health among lgbt populations: An update on the evidence. *Minerva Psichiatrica*.

Eddy Ng and Nick Rumens. 2017. Diversity and inclusion for lgbt workers: Current issues and new horizons for research. *Canadian Journal of Administrative Sciences*, 34(2):109–120.

Steven Peck. 2022. The criminal justice system and the lgbtq community: An anti-queer regime. *Themis: Research Journal of Justice Studies and Forensic Science*, 10(1):5.

Flor Miriam Plaza-del Arco, Marco Casavantes, Hugo Jair Escalante, M Teresa Martín-Valdivia, Arturo Montejo-Ráez, Manuel Montes, Horacio Jarquín-Vásquez, Luis Villaseñor-Pineda, et al. 2021. Overview of meoffendes at iberlef 2021: Offensive language detection in spanish variants. *Procesamiento del Lenguaje Natural*, 67:183–194.

Fabio Poletto, Valerio Basile, Manuela Sanguinetti, Cristina Bosco, and Viviana Patti. 2021. Resources and benchmark corpora for hate speech detection: a systematic review. *Language Resources and Evaluation*, 55(2):477–523.

Nico Sifra Quintana. 2009. Poverty in the lgbt community. *American Progress*.

Francisco Rangel, Gretel Liz De la Peña Sarracén, BERTa Chulvi, Elisabetta Fersini, and Paolo Rosso. 2021. Profiling hate speech spreaders on twitter task at pan 2021. In *CLEF (Working Notes)*, pages 1772–1789.

Francisco Rodríguez-Sánchez, Jorge Carrillo-de Albornoz, Laura Plaza, Julio Gonzalo, Paolo Rosso, Miriam Comet, and Trinidad Donoso. 2021. Overview of exist 2021: sexism identification in social networks. *Procesamiento del Lenguaje Natural*, 67:195–207.

Paul Röttger, Bertie Vidgen, Dong Nguyen, Zeerak Waseem, Helen Margetts, and Janet Pierrehumbert. 2021. HateCheck: Functional Tests for Hate Speech Detection Models. In *Proceedings of the 59th Annual Meeting of the Association for Computational Linguistics and the 11th International Joint Conference on Natural Language Processing (Volume 1: Long Papers)*, pages 41–58, Online. Association for Computational Linguistics.

Emily Sheng, Kai-Wei Chang, Premkumar Natarajan, and Nanyun Peng. 2021. Societal biases in language generation: Progress and challenges.

Jiao Sun and Nanyun Peng. 2021. Men are elected, women are married: Events gender bias on wikipedia.

Mariona Taulé, Alejandro Ariza, Montserrat Nofre, Enrique Amigó, and Paolo Rosso. 2021. Overview of detoxis at iberlef 2021: Detection of toxicity in comments in spanish. *Procesamiento del Lenguaje Natural*, 67:209–221.

Grigorios Tsoumakas and Ioannis Katakis. 2007. Multi-label classification: An overview. *International Journal of Data Warehousing and Mining (IJDWM)*, 3(3):1–13.

Mark Ungar. 2000. State violence and lesbian, gay, bisexual and transgender (lgbt) rights. *New Political Science*, 22(1):61–75.

Francielle Vargas, Isabelle Carvalho, Fabiana Rodrigues de Góes, Thiago Pardo, and Fabrício Benevenuto. 2022. Hatebr: A large expert annotated corpus of brazilian instagram comments for offensive language and hate speech detection. In *Proceedings of the Thirteenth Language Resources and Evaluation Conference*, pages 7174–7183.

Francielle Vargas, Fabiana Rodrigues de Góes, Isabelle Carvalho, Fabrício Benevenuto, and Thiago Pardo. 2021. Contextual-lexicon approach for abusive language detection. In *Proceedings of the International Conference on Recent Advances in Natural Language Processing (RANLP 2021)*, pages 1438–1447.

Barbara C Wallace and Erik Santacruz. 2017. Addictions and substance abuse in the lgbt community: New approaches. *LGBT psychology and mental health: Emerging research and advances*, pages 153–175.

Thomas Wolf, Lysandre Debut, Victor Sanh, Julien Chaumond, Clement Delangue, Anthony Moi, Pierric Cistac, Tim Rault, Rémi Louf, Morgan Funtowicz, et al. 2019. Huggingface's transformers: State-of-the-art natural language processing. *arXiv preprint arXiv:1910.03771*.

Albert Xu, Eshaan Pathak, Eric Wallace, Suchin Gururangan, Maarten Sap, and Dan Klein. 2021. Detoxifying Language Models Risks Marginalizing Minority Voices. In *Proceedings of the 2021 Conference of the North American Chapter of the Association for Computational Linguistics: Human Language Technologies*, pages 2390–2397, Online. Association for Computational Linguistics.

A Appendix

Data Statement We follow the guidelines specified by (Bender and Friedman, 2018) for creating a Data Statement, which serves to help mitigate bias in data collection.

A. Curation Rationale We collect tweets from popular social media platform Twitter, we use Twitter because it provides a convenient medium to collect short statements from general users on various topics in a digital medium. We use specific search terms that are common nouns to refer the LGBT+ community to help identify hateful speech against the community.

B. Language variety We scrape a set of tweets that contained desired keywords and were in Spanish with the specified region of Mexico to get language of this region. Also, we took in consideration possible inflection of the terms. Since all the data is collected from social media, this means that there could be present hashtags, mentions, gifs, videos, images, and emojis within the tweets, however only the text of the tweet was utilized for annotation.

C. Tweet author demographic The demographics of the authors is not available to us since we compiled the data using Twitter's data collection API. However, due to our sampling methods, we expect the tweets to come from the diverse set of authors of various ages, genders, nationalities, races, ethnicities, native languages, socioeconomic classes and education backgrounds that are to be expected to be found within Mexico.

D. Annotator demographic We selected annotators that self identified as members of the LGBT+ community and non-members. The demographic information is shown in Table 9.

E. Speech Situation Each tweet may be on a different topic. Most of them are related to trends, events or memes from the year of extraction (2022).

F. Text characteristics The tweets collected come from a diverse set of contexts, as they could be published alone by the author, or in response to another user. The tweets are subject to the restrictions of text limit and policies of Twitter. All tweets were posted publicly, and we remove identifying characteristics of the user for anonymity.

G. Recording Quality We extracted the tweets from the Twitter API.

Categories	Data
Age	22-35 years
Gender Identity	1 non-binary 6 women 5 men
Sex	6 female 6 male
Sexual Orientation	6 LGBT+ 6 Cis-Heterosexual
Native Languague	Spanish
Nationality	11 Mexican 1 Colombian
Residence	México City
Education level	University

Table 9: Annotator demographic

H. Ethical Statements All tweets were uploaded only by their ID. The textual content was omitted to assure the privacy of the author and the username of the people that could be mention on the tweet. All scraped tweets were posted publicly and can be collected for academic use according to Twitter's privacy policy.

Also, all the annotators were informed about the task and what type of profile we pursued for the project. In the annotation guidelines, we warned the annotators that the tweets could be offensive and that they could leave the study at any time.

Factoring Hate Speech: A New Annotation Framework to Study Hate Speech in Social Media

Gal Ron[1†], Effi Levi[2†], Odelia Oshri[1], Shaul R. Shenhav[1]

[1]Department of Political Science, The Hebrew University of Jerusalem
[2]Institute of Computer Science, The Hebrew University of Jerusalem
{gal.ron2|odelia.oshri|shaul.shenhav}@mail.huji.ac.il
efle@cs.huji.ac.il

Abstract

In this work we propose a novel annotation scheme which factors hate speech into five separate discursive categories. To evaluate our scheme, we construct a corpus of over 2.9M Twitter posts containing hateful expressions directed at Jews, and annotate a sample dataset of 1,050 tweets. We present a statistical analysis of the annotated dataset as well as discuss annotation examples, and conclude by discussing promising directions for future work.

1 Introduction

Social media has come to constitute a space for the propagation of hostility (see ElSherief et al., 2018, p. 1) and provides fertile grounds for the radicalization of individuals in support of violent extremist groups (Reynolds and Tuck, 2016; Mitts, 2019). Much research has been devoted to automatically identifying hate speech in online forums (Mathew et al., 2021; Kim et al., 2022; Wiegand et al., 2022) along with factors that facilitate its propagation (Scharwächter and Müller, 2020; Newman et al., 2021), and classifying different forms of hateful and abusive content (Davidson et al., 2017; Founta et al., 2018). However, the very concept of "hate" and its presence in written text is somewhat illusive and amorphous (Fortuna et al., 2020); therefore, some efforts have been made to define different typologies of hate speech (Waseem et al., 2017; Founta et al., 2018; Davidson et al., 2017; Mathew et al., 2021).

In this work, we address this important subject through the specific case of hate speech directed towards Jews in Twitter posts. Rather than attempting to classify hate speech into different types, we present a novel annotation scheme which factors hate speech into a comprehensive set of separate discursive aspects that often appear in hate speech, capturing its intricate and diverse nature.

This factorization aims to achieve several goals: first, make the annotation process more focused and accurate, by decomposing the amorphous and ambiguous concept of "hate" into more specific and narrowly defined discourse aspects, rendering the annotation process more objective. Second, it allows exploring and analyzing hate speech across these different aspects, hopefully leading to a deeper understanding of its complexities, variety, and nuance. Furthermore, this set of aspects defines various possible distinct combinations, each of which encodes a different and unique configuration of hate speech. Although this annotation scheme was designed to capture and characterize hate speech directed towards Jews, with the exception of one group-specific aspect, it is general enough to be applied to any other group-directed hate speech.

We constructed a corpus of Twitter conversations in English containing over 2.9M tweets, collected through Twitter API v2. In order to evaluate our annotation scheme on real Twitter posts, we used it to annotate a sample of 1,050 tweets taken from the corpus. We present a quantitative analysis of the annotated dataset, as well as a qualitative one (through the use of some examples). We conclude by discussing several directions to extend and develop our work.

Content Warning: This document contains some examples of hateful content. This is strictly for the purpose of enabling this research. Please be aware that this content could be offensive and cause you distress.

2 Tweets Corpus

The tweets were extracted through the Twitter API v2 using the tweepy python module [1]. We applied

† Both authors contributed equally to this work.

[1] https://github.com/tweepy/tweepy

The 7th Workshop on Online Abuse and Harms (WOAH), pages 215–220

	Single Tweets	Conversations		Total	Conversation Length	
	# Tweets	# Conversations	# Tweets	# Tweets	Mean	STD
Neutral	601,917	109,172	1,005,095	1,607,012	9.21	71.73
Racial	527,541	97,730	788,576	1,316,117	8.07	127.43
Total	1,129,458	206,902	1,793,671	2,923,129		

Table 1: Complete tweet corpus statistics. "Single Tweets": tweets that were posted as new tweets rather than as a reply, and were not replied to.

for, and were granted, an Academic Research Access to the API [2], which offers a full-archive access to public data posted on the platform, going back to April 2006.

To increase the likelihood of retrieving tweets that contain expressions of hate towards Jews, we used two types of keyword-based filters in our queries: *neutral* keywords and *racial* keywords. The neutral stop list – containing 14 words – was compiled from keywords referenced in previous studies (Gunther et al., 2021; Chandra et al., 2021). The racial stop list – containing 28 words and expressions – was compiled using the `Hatebase` database, a multilingual lexicon for racial terms [3], by extracting from the database all the English terms pertaining to Jews and Judaism that had at least one sighting.

Following preliminary experimentation with the API directed at increasing the chances of retrieving a conversation (thread) containing Jew-related hate expressions, we decided to focus on collecting conversations which stemmed from a "source" tweet (a new post rather than a reply to another tweet) adhering to our keyword filters. We devised the following 2-step process. Given a specific date (24-hour interval) and a specific keyword filter:

1. Query the API for English "source" tweets containing any of the keywords in the filter, posted within the specified date.

2. For every tweet extracted in step 1: if the tweet was replied to, query the API for all the available tweets in the resulting conversation (some tweets, such as deleted or private tweets, were not available for extraction).

For each date between July 1st 2018 and June 30th 2022 (defining a period of exactly 4 years), we applied the procedure with the *racial* keywords filter and collected as many tweets as possible. Then, we applied the same procedure with the *neutral* keyword filter to collect a similar number of tweets from the same date [4]. This was done in order to keep the corpus as balanced as possible between the two types of keyword filters.

The result is a large corpus of Twitter conversations started between July 1st 2018 and June 30th 2022, segmented by the type of the filter applied to the conversation's source tweet (*neutral* or *racial* Jews-related keywords). Aside from the text itself, the corpus includes additional meta-data for each tweet: tweet ID, conversation ID, posting date, reply-to ID (if the tweet was written as a reply to another tweet), tweet statistics (retweets, replies, likes, quotes and views), place & country (if available), author ID (a unique identifier for the author of the tweet) and author statistics (followers, verified status). Note that the "conversation ID" and "reply-to ID" fields allow a complete hierarchical reconstruction of a conversation given any tweet from that conversation.

Statistics for the corpus are given in Table 1.

3 Hate Speech Annotation

3.1 Annotation Scheme

As discussed in Section 1, we have devised a novel annotation scheme with the goal of factoring hate speech into several separate aspects. The scheme encodes five different discursive categories, which are designed to capture the main recurring aspects of hate speech as employed and defined in previous studies (Kaid and Holtz-Bacha, 2007; Davidson et al., 2017; Arango et al., 2022; Khurana et al., 2022), as well as the discursive elements of hate speech that are described in the United Nations' "Strategy and Plan of Action on Hate Speech" [5]. An aggregative definition, as suggested here, enables us to identify hate speech towards the target

[2] No longer available, as of May 2023

[3] `https://hatebase.org`

[4] preliminary experiments showed that tweets containing the *neutral* keywords are significantly more abundant compared to the *racial* keywords

[5] `https://www.un.org/en/hate-speech/understanding-hate-speech/what-is-hate-speech`

	Single Tweets	Conversations		Total
	# Tweets	# Conversations	# Tweets	# Tweets
Neutral	263	82	263	526
Racial	262	82	262	524
Total	525	164	525	1,050

Table 2: Statistics for the sample dataset

group in a broad yet nuanced sense, while also differentiating between various forms of expression. Importantly, our annotation scheme aims to capture clear expressions of hate rather than mere hateful terms. As such, tweets containing the racial keywords which were used in our queries to the Twitter API were annotated under the relevant category only when it was plausible to suspect that these words were indeed employed to express hate.

Category	# Tweets
Contempt	5
Abuse	181
Call for Anti-Group Action	31
Prejudice	12
Holocaust Denial	4

Table 3: Annotation statistics for the sample dataset

The five categories are:

1. **Contempt** – speech that conveys a strong disliking of, or negative attitudes towards the targeted group, and does so in a neutral tone or form of expression.

2. **Abuse** – speech that demeans, degrades, vilifies, mocks, humiliates, or conveys general hostility that is expressed using emotionally-charged language.

3. **Call for Anti-Group Action** – an incitement of violence and/or discrimination against the target group.

4. **Prejudice** – the expression of negative thoughts/beliefs regarding the targeted group on the basis of the group's characteristics, and/or (negative) monolithic references to the targeted group.

5. **Holocaust Denial** – the only category specific to our target group (Jews), this includes derecognition of the holocaust, or statements that recognize the fact that the holocaust happened but degrade from its scope, mock it (and/or the people it hurt), and belittle its significance.

These discursive categories not only encompass substantive elements of hate, such as contempt and prejudice, but also address the manner in which negative discourse is conveyed, including abusive language and incitement of violence.

All the categories, except the fifth (`Holocaust Denial`), are general and may naturally be applied to other groups besides our target group (Jews). In addition, while the categories encode separate aspects of hateful discourse, they may conjointly characterize the same expression; for example, a post can be abusive while also expressing prejudice. Consequently, the annotation scheme defines a *multi-label* classification task.

3.2 Annotated Sample Dataset

For the purpose of conducting a preliminary analysis of our annotation scheme over real tweet data, we annotated a sample dataset of 1,050 tweets from the corpus described in Section 2. These tweets were sampled by iterating the dates backwards, starting from June 30th 2022. For each date, one conversation with a length of $2 \leq k \leq 10$ tweets was randomly selected, then k additional single tweets (1-tweet conversations) were randomly selected from the same date. This procedure was performed separately for each of the two keyword filter types (*neutral* and *racial*). The result is a collection of 1,050 tweets from conversations started between June 4th 2022 and June 30th 2022 (statistics are given in Table 2). Each tweet was encoded with a subset of the five possible categories (described in Section 3.1), including the empty set (none of the categories).

Table 3 shows the annotation statistics for the sample dataset. Note that despite the use of keyword filters to retrieve the tweets from the Twitter API, all five categories are generally sparse in the dataset. The most common category is `Abuse`, with 181 instances (out of the 1,050 tweets in the dataset). Given that half of these tweets were col-

	Contempt	Abuse	Call for Anti-Gruop Action	Prejudice
Abuse	-0.0316			
Call for Anti-Gruop Action	-0.0121	0.2332		
Prejudice	0.1227	0.1644	0.0342	
Holocaust Denial	-0.0043	0.0536	-0.0108	0.1388

Table 4: Inter-category Pearson's correlations in the sample dataset

lected using the *racial* keywords filter, this is consistent with previous findings that hate speech is highly likely to contain racial slurs (Davidson et al., 2017); intuitively, it is the most "direct" way to express hate (among the five categories). It is important to note, however, that the mere presence of a racial slur does not automatically merit an `Abuse` annotation, as evident in the following example:

(1) In the span of 5 min I have been both called a "toxic fan" for not liking the Kenobi show and a "Zionazi" by a fan of the show. Maybe you should reconsider who are the "toxic" ones (`None`)

The second most common category is `Call for Anti-Group Action`, followed by `Prejudice` and `Contempt`, with the most uncommon category being `Holocaust Denial`.

Table 4 displays the inter-category correlations (measured in Pearson's r) in the sample dataset. In general, no considerable correlations were found between any two categories. `Abuse` was found to be somewhat correlated with `Call for Anti-Group Action` ($r = 0.2332$), and to a lesser degree with `Prejudice` ($r = 0.1644$). Naturally, calls for violence and prejudiced expressions are often accompanied by abusive language, for example:

(2) Ahhhhhh the good old days , yids were bums then still bums now. (`Abuse`, `Prejudice`)

A minor correlation between `Prejudice` and `Contempt` ($r = 0.1227$) is possibly an indication that prejudiced perspectives serve as a kind of "rationale" for hate that does not always require the more emotional use of abusive language. This is demonstrated in the following example:

(3) Perhaps America is just too fat, spoiled and lazy not to be noosed by the Jews into another low road oblivion that profits the jews. It seems incapable of tweaking itself or nurturing and governing through its' higher itself. Better perhaps to help it rot? (`Prejudice`, `Contempt`)

Another minor correlation between `Prejudice` and `Holocaust Denial` ($r = 0.1388$) may be attributed to the fact that both categories are closely associated with conspiracy theories.

4 Conclusion

In this paper, we address the task of capturing and characterizing hate speech directed towards Jews in Twitter posts. For that purpose, we devised a novel annotation scheme that encodes five different aspects of hate speech, four of which are not specific to our target group (Jews), allowing us to factorize the generally amorphous concept of "hate" into more concretely defined aspects. We utilized the Twitter API v2 to collect and assemble a corpus of Twitter conversations in English containing over 2.9M tweets, using two types of keyword filters (*neutral* and *racial*) to maximize the likelihood of retrieving tweets that contain expressions of hate towards Jews. We then used our annotation scheme to annotate a sample of 1,050 tweets, and demonstrated its potential contribution through select examples. We intend to make all of these resources (tweet corpus, annotation guidelines and sample dataset) available to the research community.

We are currently engaged in an ongoing effort to train additional annotators and use our assembled tweet corpus to produce a large and comprehensive annotated dataset. We are also working – in parallel – on assembling and annotating a similar corpus for Muslim-related hateful expressions.

Another direction we are currently pursuing is taking advantage of the fact that the corpus is comprised of complete Twitter conversations, to annotate expressions of hate in the context of the conversation which the tweet is a part of (rather than just based on the content of the tweet itself).

For example, replying to a hateful post with strong agreement may be considered as hate speech only if the context (preceding posts) is taken into account. Using the hierarchical structure of the conversation will allow not only encoding such cases, but also modelling the dynamics of hate speech as it progresses through the conversation and over time.

In addition, we plan to utilize the tweet corpus to explore *counter-hate* speech (Benesch et al., 2016; Wright et al., 2017; Garland et al., 2020). As these types of expressions are reactive by nature, complete Twitter conversations are instrumental in addressing and analyzing them. Augmenting hate-speech annotated Twitter conversations with counter-hate annotation will allow us to explore the inter-changing dynamics of hate and counter-hate speech, as well as which kinds of counter messages are tailored to the different hate categories. We might find for example that the effective counter messages for abusive speech are those that attack the user, while most effective counter messages for prejudice deliver data and facts to contradict the prejudiced beliefs.

Limitations

There are three main limitations to our work. One limitation results directly from the single target group included in our analysis (Jews). While our annotation scheme was designed to be as general as possible (with the exception of the `Holocaust Denial` category), applying it to a single target group does not allow us to evaluate the extent of its generalizability to other target groups.

A second limitation has to do with messages that support and fuel hate, without containing actual hateful content (expressing agreement with another hateful message). While such messages may spread hate, they would not be encoded in our annotation setup, since the message context (e.g., the surrounding conversation) is not taken into account during the annotation process.

Thirdly, our annotation scheme does not currently account for how the annotated hate is perceived by the message's readers. This information may lie in the reaction incurred by the hateful message – the tweet's replies, as well as the its meta-data (number of likes, quotes, etc.).

By applying the annotation to other target groups, and by annotating complete conversations (thus capturing the context of the tweets), future research could address the three limitations.

5 Acknowledgments

We wish to thank Prof. Peter J. Loewen, Prof. Ron Levi, Prof. Christopher Cochrane, and Mr. Thomas Bergeron for their valuable contribution.

This research was partially funded by the University of Toronto - Hebrew University of Jerusalem Research and Training Alliance, and by the Knapp Family Foundation Doctoral Fellowship at the Vidal Sassoon International Center for the Study of Antisemitism.

References

Aymé Arango, Jorge Pérez, Bárbara Poblete, Valentina Proust, and Magdalena Saldaña. 2022. Multilingual resources for offensive language detection. *WOAH 2022*, page 122.

Susan Benesch, Derek Ruths, Kelly P Dillon, Haji Mohammad Saleem, and Lucas Wright. 2016. Considerations for successful counterspeech. *Dangerous speech project*.

Mohit Chandra, Dheeraj Pailla, Himanshu Bhatia, Aadilmehdi Sanchawala, Manish Gupta, Manish Shrivastava, and Ponnurangam Kumaraguru. 2021. "subverting the jewtocracy": Online antisemitism detection using multimodal deep learning. In *13th ACM Web Science Conference 2021*, pages 148–157.

Thomas Davidson, Dana Warmsley, Michael Macy, and Ingmar Weber. 2017. Automated hate speech detection and the problem of offensive language. In *Proceedings of the international AAAI conference on web and social media*, volume 11, pages 512–515.

Mai ElSherief, Shirin Nilizadeh, Dana Nguyen, Giovanni Vigna, and Elizabeth Belding. 2018. Peer to peer hate: Hate speech instigators and their targets. In *Proceedings of the International AAAI Conference on Web and Social Media*, volume 12.

Paula Fortuna, Juan Soler, and Leo Wanner. 2020. Toxic, hateful, offensive or abusive? what are we really classifying? an empirical analysis of hate speech datasets. In *Proceedings of the Twelfth Language Resources and Evaluation Conference*, pages 6786–6794, Marseille, France. European Language Resources Association.

Antigoni Founta, Constantinos Djouvas, Despoina Chatzakou, Ilias Leontiadis, Jeremy Blackburn, Gianluca Stringhini, Athena Vakali, Michael Sirivianos, and Nicolas Kourtellis. 2018. Large scale crowdsourcing and characterization of twitter abusive behavior. In *Proceedings of the international AAAI conference on web and social media*, volume 12.

Joshua Garland, Keyan Ghazi-Zahedi, Jean-Gabriel Young, Laurent Hébert-Dufresne, and Mirta Galesic. 2020. Countering hate on social media: Large scale classification of hate and counter speech. In *Proceedings of the Fourth Workshop on Online Abuse and Harms*, pages 102–112, Online. Association for Computational Linguistics.

Jikeli Gunther, Deepika Awasthi, David Axelrod, Daniel Miehling, Pauravi Wagh, and Weejoeng Joeng. 2021. Detecting anti-jewish messages on social media. building an annotated corpus that can serve as a preliminary gold standard. In *Workshop Proceedings of the 15th International AAAI Conference on Web and Social Media*.

Lynda Lee Kaid and Christina Holtz-Bacha. 2007. *Encyclopedia of political communication*. SAGE publications.

Urja Khurana, Ivar Vermeulen, Eric Nalisnick, Marloes Van Noorloos, and Antske Fokkens. 2022. Hate speech criteria: A modular approach to task-specific hate speech definitions. In *Proceedings of the Sixth Workshop on Online Abuse and Harms (WOAH)*, pages 176–191, Seattle, Washington (Hybrid). Association for Computational Linguistics.

Youngwook Kim, Shinwoo Park, and Yo-Sub Han. 2022. Generalizable implicit hate speech detection using contrastive learning. In *Proceedings of the 29th International Conference on Computational Linguistics*, pages 6667–6679, Gyeongju, Republic of Korea. International Committee on Computational Linguistics.

Binny Mathew, Punyajoy Saha, Seid Muhie Yimam, Chris Biemann, Pawan Goyal, and Animesh Mukherjee. 2021. Hatexplain: A benchmark dataset for explainable hate speech detection. In *Proceedings of the AAAI Conference on Artificial Intelligence*, volume 35, pages 14867–14875.

Tamar Mitts. 2019. From isolation to radicalization: Anti-muslim hostility and support for isis in the west. *American Political Science Review*, 113(1):173–194.

Benjamin Newman, Jennifer L Merolla, Sono Shah, Danielle Casarez Lemi, Loren Collingwood, and S Karthick Ramakrishnan. 2021. The trump effect: An experimental investigation of the emboldening effect of racially inflammatory elite communication. *British Journal of Political Science*, 51(3):1138–1159.

Louis Reynolds and Henry Tuck. 2016. The counter-narrative monitoring & evaluation handbook. *Institute for Strategic Dialogue*.

Erik Scharwächter and Emmanuel Müller. 2020. Does terrorism trigger online hate speech? on the association of events and time series. *The Annals of Applied Statistics*, 14(3).

Zeerak Waseem, Thomas Davidson, Dana Warmsley, and Ingmar Weber. 2017. Understanding abuse: A typology of abusive language detection subtasks. *arXiv preprint arXiv:1705.09899*.

Michael Wiegand, Elisabeth Eder, and Josef Ruppenhofer. 2022. Identifying implicitly abusive remarks about identity groups using a linguistically informed approach. In *Proceedings of the 2022 Conference of the North American Chapter of the Association for Computational Linguistics: Human Language Technologies*, pages 5600–5612, Seattle, United States. Association for Computational Linguistics.

Lucas Wright, Derek Ruths, Kelly P Dillon, Haji Mohammad Saleem, and Susan Benesch. 2017. Vectors for counterspeech on twitter. In *Proceedings of the first workshop on abusive language online*, pages 57–62.

Harmful Language Datasets: An Assessment of Robustness

Katerina Korre
University of Bologna
aikaterini.korre2@unibo.it

John Pavlopoulos
Athens University of Economics and Business
annis@aueb.gr

Jeffrey Sorensen
Google Jigsaw
sorenj@google.com

Léo Laugier
EPFL
leo.laugier@epfl.ch

Ion Androutsopoulos
Athens University of Economics and Business
ion@aueb.gr

Lucas Dixon
Google Research
ldixon@google.com

Alberto Barrón-Cedeño
University of Bologna
a.barron@unibo.it

Abstract

The automated detection of harmful language has been of great importance for the online world, especially with the growing importance of social media and, consequently, polarisation. There are many open challenges to high quality detection of harmful text, from dataset creation to generalisable application, thus calling for more systematic studies. In this paper, we explore re-annotation as a means of examining the robustness of already existing labelled datasets, showing that, despite using alternative definitions, the inter-annotator agreement remains very inconsistent, highlighting the intrinsically subjective and variable nature of the task. In addition, we build automatic toxicity detectors using the existing datasets, with their original labels, and we evaluate them on our multi-definition and multi-source datasets. Surprisingly, while other studies show that hate speech detection models perform better on data that are derived from the same distribution as the training set, our analysis demonstrates this is not necessarily true.

1 Introduction

Many forms of harmful language impact social media despite efforts —legal and technological— to suppress it.[1] Social media has been under significant scrutiny with regard to the effectiveness of their anti-hate speech policies, which usually involve users manually reporting a potentially malicious post in order to trigger a human review, and platforms adjusting their community guidelines by, for example, banning hateful comments, and employing automated moderation assistants.

A robust and general solution to the problem does not yet exist, and given that there are many factors that influence the phenomenon of online hate speech, we expect this area of research to continue to pose significant challenges. One of the main reasons is that harmful language detection is an inherently subjective task. There have been many attempts to approach harmful language detection by introducing or selecting specific definitions (Fortuna et al., 2020). From blanket terms, such as abusiveness and offensiveness to sub-categories, such as misogyny and cyber-bullying, researchers have explored many variants. However, this begs the question of how to select and compare the possible definitions, especially when some categories are more efficient for cross-dataset training than others (Fortuna et al., 2021). The problem gets more intricate when multiple languages are involved, and when the translation of a term does not necessarily carry the same implications as in the source language. This can have significant implications for the development of cross-lingual systems (Bigoulaeva et al., 2021; Deshpande et al., 2022).

In this study, we attempt to shed light on the effectiveness of different definitions of harmful language both for annotation purposes and model development. We use the term "harmful language" as a wildcard term that can be potentially replaced with terms like toxic, hate speech, and offensiveness, among others. We perform a re-annotation of existing datasets with a range of definitions and replicate the experiments to assess robustness. Then, we perform a qualitative error analysis on the re-annotations, showing that even instances that contain potentially harmful terms might not be perceived as harmful by annotators, underlining the subjectivity of the task. Finally, we analyse the generalisability of the existing datasets across the different definitions by training BERT-based classifiers with the original annotations and with our re-annotations, concluding that evaluating on broader definitions can yield higher accuracy.

The rest of this article is structured as follows. Section 2 overviews existing studies on the issue of the definition of harmful language and its implications, as well as how state-of-the-art (SOTA) sys-

[1] https://edition.cnn.com/2022/06/14/asia/japan-cyberbullying-law-intl-hnk-scli/index.html

The 7th Workshop on Online Abuse and Harms (WOAH), pages 221–230
July 13, 2023 ©2023 Association for Computational Linguistics

tems handle generalisability. Section 3 presents our re-annotation strategy. In Section 4, we describe our experimental setup for training and evaluating with the the original and the re-annotated datasets. Finally, after presenting our results in Section 4.3, we assess our contribution in Section 5, concluding by speculating on limitations and future work.

Disclaimer: This paper contains potentially offensive, toxic, or otherwise harmful language.

2 Related Work

Harmful language is becoming all the more frequent due to the widespread use of social media and the Internet, thus creating a vicious cycle that compromises the civility of the online community and threatens a healthy user experience (Nobata et al., 2016). The need for automatically moderating toxic language has led to the development of a considerable body of related work, proposing solutions and highlighting existing problems.

2.1 Generalisability

One of the most frequently discussed problems is the inability of toxicity detection models to generalise, namely the fact that models underperform when tested on a test set from different source than the training set (Swamy et al., 2019; Karan and Šnajder, 2018; Gröndahl et al., 2018). Yin and Zubiaga (2021) claim that, when models are applied cross-lingually, this performance drop indicates that model performance had been severely over-estimated as testing on the same dataset the training set derived from is not a realistic representation of the distribution of unseen data. Attempts to improve the performance of such models involve merging seen and unseen datasets, using transfer learning, and re-labelling (Talat et al., 2018; Karan and Šnajder, 2018). However, in the majority of cases, instances from the source dataset are needed to achieve high performance (Fortuna et al., 2021). In addition, various characteristics of datasets have been examined as variables for an effective generalisation, including the work of Swamy et al. (2019), who suggested that more balanced datasets are healthier for generalisation, and that datasets need to be as representative as possible of all facets of harmful language, in order for detection models to generalise better.

2.2 The Challenge of Definitions

Properly defining toxic content poses a great challenge, not only in computational linguistics but also in socio-linguistics and discourse studies. Discussing two important terms 'trolling' and 'flaming', KhosraviNik and Esposito (2018) very eloquently suggest that "[d]espite the widespread (and often overlapping) use of these two terms, the utmost complexity of the discursive practices and behaviours of online hostility has somehow managed to hinder the development of principled definitions and univocal terminology". Regarding hate speech, according to Davidson et al. (2017), no formal definition exists yet, while also legislation differs from place to place, rendering the creation of a universal framework very difficult. The NLP community usually deals with this problem by adapting definitions to their specific purposes. However, Fortuna et al. (2020) suggest that this can lead to the use of ambiguous or misleading terms for equivalent categories. The authors come to the conclusion that it is necessary to accurately define 'keyterms' in order to achieve better communication and collaboration in the field.

3 Methodology

Our methodology is divided in two parts. The first part investigates whether closely-related definitions have an effect on inter-annotator agreement while the second part examines the compatibility and versatility of the present datasets by using them to train models.

3.1 Annotation Experiments

In order to study the effect of the definition on inter-annotator agreement, we re-annotated toxicity datasets by using alternating definitions and by repeating the annotation in rounds for robustness.

Datasets For this study we try to use the same data used in Fortuna et al. (2020) in order to produce comparable results. However, not all of the datasets could be used, as the classes used would make it harder for the models to generalise since they were referring to specific target groups. For example, the AMI (Fersini et al., 2018) and HatEval (Basile et al., 2019) datasets referred specifically to women or immigrant minorities. Therefore, the final selection of datasets includes Davidson (2017), TRAC-1 (Kumar et al., 2018b), and Toxkaggle (Jigsaw, 2019). It must also be noted

Term	Definitions of harmful language	Citation
TOXIC	A rude, disrespectful, or unreasonable comment that is likely to make you leave a discussion.	Jigsaw (2019))
ABUSIVE	Hurtful language, including hate speech, derogatory language and also profanity	Founta et al. (2018)
OFFENSIVE	Containing "any form of non-acceptable language (profanity) or a targeted offense, which can be veiled or direct."	Zampieri et al. (2019)
HATE	Expressing hatred towards a targeted group or is intended to be derogatory, to humiliate, or to insult the members of the group. In extreme cases this may also be language that threatens or incites violence.	Davidson et al. (2017)
HOTA	*Any* of the following: Hateful, Offensive, Toxic, Abusive language (HOTA)	Ours

Table 1: The terms and definitions of harmful language that were provided to the annotators during re-annotation.

that, for this research, the Davidson dataset is split into two subsets: DavidsonHS (for hate speech) and DavidsonOFF (for offensiveness), as the two classes correspond to two different definitions.

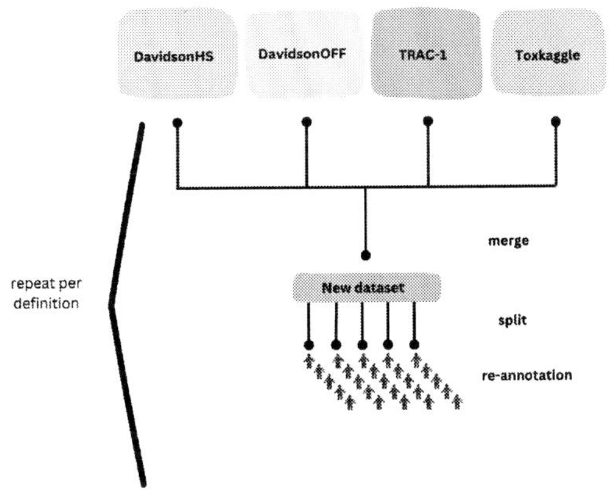

Figure 1: Annotation procedure. Instances from the 4 datasets were used to create a new dataset that would later be divided into 5 annotation batches.

Data Compilation For our annotation purposes, we create 5 different batches of data that contain instances from all aforementioned datasets. Each batch contains an equal number of different instances from each dataset, while the instances are also shuffled. To be able to map the datasets with the corresponding instances later in the analysis, a code is given for each dataset, as well as to anonymise it. The total number of instances of each of the batches was 200 (out of which we randlomly selected 80 as test questions, for quality control). In each batch we keep a balanced distribution between positive and negative instances, while we also keep the balance among the classes derived from each dataset, following the suggestions of Swamy et al. (2019) for better generalisation. Information about class distribution for each batch is presented in brackets in the column Classes in Table 2.

Annotation Procedure The annotation procedure consists of five annotation experiments, each relating to a different definition for potentially harmful content. For the annotation, we used crowdsourcing via the Appen platform.[2] The guidelines for the annotations can be found in the Appendix A. Since this project was carried out in collaboration with Jigsaw, [3] the raters were compensated according to the company's regulations, namely a compensation above minimum wage for the annotator region (USA), based on estimates of time to task completion. Jigsaw's regulations with regard to Appen annotations include reviewing feedback from raters to insure that the task is considered doable and that the raters feel they are compensated fairly. Each annotation experiment was repeated 5 times with different data each time. This variation in the data helps to ensure that the results are not specific to a particular dataset and can be generalized. Regarding the guidelines, annotators were instructed to read carefully the given definition and examples, and decide whether each text was harmful or not according to the definition provided. The same examples were provided to the annotators across all annotation experiments, and the only thing changed was the term and the definition of harmful language, presented in Table 1. Since we used crowdsourcing, each batch is not necessarily annotated by the same annotators. The quality of the annotators was ensured provided they answer correctly the aforementioned test questions. The annotation procedure is also summarised in Figure 1.

3.2 Annotation analysis

An initial exploratory analysis of the results of the annotation not only shows low inter-annotator agreement in general but also inconsistency both across datasets and across repetitions. This is evi-

[2] `https://appen.com/`
[3] `https://jigsaw.google.com/`

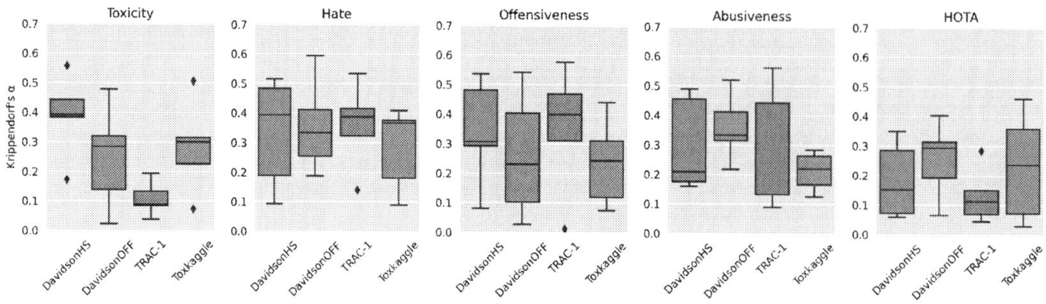

Figure 2: Boxplots showing Krippendorf's alpha inter-annotator agreement. The y axis shows the Krippendorf's alpha values while the x axis shows the different datasets. Each plot refers to a different definition.

dent in Figure 2. Among the 5 definitions, Toxicity and HOTA (see Table 1 for the acronym explanation) show more consistent annotation despite the low inter-annotator agreement, which is under 0.5. This poses the question of whether we should trust high inter-annotator agreement and potential inconsistency among repetitions or accept a lower but more robust inter-annotator agreement. Moreover, looking at the inter-annotator agreement per dataset, we see that instances of datasets that were originally annotated with a given definition present a more consistent annotation when re-annotated with another definition. For example, we would expect DavidsonHS to have a more consistent inter-annotator agreement when annotated for hate speech, but we see that it is when it is annotated for toxicity that the result is more robust. Similarly, DavidsonOFF presents slightly more consistent results when annotated for hate speech and abusiveness rather than offensiveness.

Annotation variance can be used to isolate instances with high disagreement. Table 3 presents a subset out of the 10 instances with the highest variance per definition that were sampled for the analysis. When annotated for toxicity, these posts included forms of irony. For instance, the example of the 1st row is possibly written by a woman, which might mean that the intention is not to be toxic but to cauterize misogynistic behaviours. In addition, many posts contained vocabulary that is associated with negative sentiments, such as "crazy", "cheater", and "hate". With regard to abusive language, annotators disagreed even for instances that present raw profanity ("bitch", "cocksucker"), potential racism as seen in the 2nd example of the table, and ableism as seen in the third. Similarly, when annotating for offensiveness, the raters did not necessarily annotate positively an instance that contained profanity. Also, racist instances that do not contain obscenities might have been trickier to classify. For example, the author of the 4th example resorts to ostensibly logical reasoning that might disguise the racism that pervades the sentence. Compared to the other definitions that were given during the re-annotation, the sampled re-annotations for hate speech did not show any clear pattern possibly because the definition of hate speech is more restricting referring to specific target groups. However, the same holds true for HOTA, which was the broader term during the re-annotation. The sample that we checked during this qualitative analysis included profanity, references to homosexuality or racism and misogyny, as well as instances that did not contain any harmful language. Noteworthy is also the fact that the sentence in Example 5 appeared with high variance in 3 out of 5 definitions, possibly because of the mixed language use and modified words.

4 Experimental setup

4.1 Datasets

We use the same four datasets that were used in annotation (Davidson et al., 2017; Kumar et al., 2018b) to perform toxicity/hate speech/offensiveness/aggressiveness classification. More specifically, we first extracted the 1,000 (200 per definition) instances used for the human annotation from the original datasets. Then, with the remaining instances we created 4 balanced datasets that contained an equal amount of positive and negative instances (2650 in total), with 10% of the data used for development. The evaluation of the model was carried out by calculating the accuracy with respect to the original annotation labels and the ones produced for the new annotation.

Dataset	Annotation Procedure	Classes	Source
DavidsonHS (Davidson et al., 2017)	Begining with the hatebase lexicon then CrowdFlower, users coded each tweet (minimum number of annotations per tweet is 3 , sometimes more users coded a tweet when judgments were determined to be unreliable by CF).	Hate speech (25), Not-Hate Speech (25)	Twitter
DavidsonOFF (Davidson et al., 2017)	>>	Offensiveness (25), Not-offensiveness (25)	Twitter
TRAC-1 (Zampieri et al., 2019; Kumar et al., 2018b,a)	The annotation was done using the Crowdflower platform but by what is known as 'internal' annotators in the Crowdflower lingo. The whole of annotation was done by 4 annotators – all of them were native speakers of Hindi, with a nativelike competence in English and were pursuing a doctoral degree in Linguistics.	Overtly Aggressive (OAG) (13), Covertly Aggressive (CAG) (12), Non-Aggressive (NAG) (25)	Facebook
Toxkaggle (Jigsaw, 2019)	Not provided.	Threat (3), Identity hate (3), Severe Toxic (3), Insult (3), Obscene (4), Toxic (9), NonToxic (25)	Wikipedia

Table 2: Basic description of dataset. This table was inspired by a similar table found in Fortuna et al. (2020). Davidson (2017) dataset was split into two separate datasets as Hate Speech and Offensives are too different as definitions.

4.2 Model training

We fine-tuned BERT with early stopping,[4] using patience of 3 and a max length defined per dataset, i.e., the mean length with one unit of standard deviation: 30 tokens for DavidsonHS, 37 for DavidsonOFF, 70 for Trac-1, and 100 for Toxkaggle. The code is publicly available.[5]

4.3 Results

We assess the classifiers using both the original and the re-annotated ground truth.

Using the source annotations as our evaluation ground truth, the accuracy of the classifiers is presented in Figure 3. We observe that when the model is trained on DavidsonHS datasets, it reaches an accuracy of more than 0.75 in all test sets. As expected the accuracy is higher when the model is also tested on DavidsonHS. When the model is trained on DavidsonOFF the accuracy is high only when tested again on DavidsonOFF. Training on

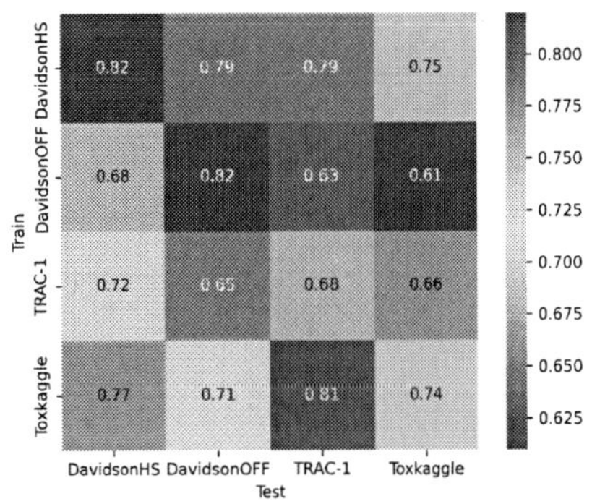

Figure 3: Heatmap showing the accuracy on the different test sets using the original ground truth (horizontally) when the model is trained on each corresponding dataset (vertically).

Toxkaggle results in more than 0.70 accuracy in all test sets, with the the highest accuracy in the TRAC-1 test set (0.81). TRAC-1, on the other hand, shows the lowest accuracy across all test sets (0.65-0.72), with the highest accuracy obtained when tesing on DavidsonHS.

[4]We used the base model and the KTRAIN library.

[5]https://github.com/katkorre/reannotation-robustness.git

	Example	Source
1.	*according to you my place is in kitchen. Excuse me while I take out the trash*	Davidson
2.	*It's because you can't bend me, you can't buy me and you can't make me into your nigger!*	Davidson
3.	*California's biggest retards*	Davidson
4.	*"Just because she has light skin doesn't mean anything... I know some Asian with really dark brown skin but that doesn't make them any less Chinese"*	Toxkaggle
5.	*and we shud also destroy taj mahal... qutub minar ....laal qila aftr that visiters seen only GBRoad vd hvng a fun vd ur neighbours*	TRAC-1

Table 3: Texts from the evaluation sets with the highest variance of inter-annotator agreement.

		Evaluation (re-annotated)			
Training	**Definition**	**DavidsonHS**	**DavidsonOFF**	**TRAC-1**	**Toxkaggle**
DavidsonHS	Toxicity	0.75 (-0.07)	0.69 (-0.10)	0.75 (-0.04)	**0.83** (+0.08)
	Hate Speech	0.64 (-0.18)	0.59 (-0.20)	0.58 (-0.21)	0.59 (-0.16)
	Offensiveness	0.64 (-0.18)	0.64 (-0.15)	0.56 (-0.23)	0.62 (-0.13)
	Abusiveness	0.63 (-0.19)	0.57 (-0.22)	0.62 (-0.17)	0.59 (-0.16)
	HOTA	**0.76** (-0.06)	**0.78** (-0.01)	**0.78** (-0.01)	0.82 (+0.07)
DavidsonOFF	Toxicity	**0.64** (+0.04)	0.72 (-0.10)	0.83 (+0.20)	**0.75** (+0.14)
	Hate Speech	0.58 (-0.10)	0.63 (-0.19)	0.59 (-0.04)	0.59 (-0.02)
	Offensiveness	0.50 (-0.18)	0.66 (-0.16)	0.56 (-0.07)	0.59 (-0.02)
	Abusiveness	0.57 (-0.11)	0.61 (-0.21)	0.62 (-0.01)	0.60 (-0.01)
	HOTA	0.62 (-0.06)	**0.76** (-0.06)	**0.84** (+0.21)	0.74 (+0.13)
TRAC-1	Toxicity	0.67 (-0.05)	0.59 (-0.06)	0.50 (-0.18)	0.53 (-0.13)
	Hate Speech	0.69 (-0.03)	**0.66** (+0.01)	0.53 (-0.15)	0.63 (-0.03)
	Offensiveness	0.69 (-0.03)	0.63 (-0.02)	**0.55** (-0.13)	**0.66** (=)
	Abusiveness	0.70 (-0.02)	0.64 (-0.01)	0.51 (-0.17)	0.65 (+0.01)
	HOTA	**0.71** (-0.01)	**0.66** (+0.01)	0.47 (-0.21)	0.57 (-0.09)
Toxkaggle	Toxicity	0.73 (-0.04)	0.67 (-0.04)	0.77 (-0.04)	**0.85** (+11)
	Hate Speech	0.68 (-0.09)	0.67 (-0.09)	0.63(-0.18)	0.61 (-0.13)
	Offensiveness	0.67(-0.10)	0.69 (-0.02)	0.63(-0.18)	0.68(-0.06)
	Abusiveness	0.71 (-0.06)	0.65 (-0.06)	0.63 (-0.18)	0.61 (-0.13)
	HOTA	**0.79** (+0.02)	**0.77** (+0.06)	**0.81** (=)	0.83 (+0.08)

Table 4: Accuracy of BERT trained per dataset (1st column), using the original annotations, and evaluated on our re-annotations per definition. In parentheses is the accuracy increase (green) or decrease (red) compared to the scores obtained on the evaluation data with the original annotations (Figure 3).

Using our re-annotations as the evaluation ground truth, is shown in Table 4. Models did not manage to generalise across datasets consistently, which is shown by the fact that accuracy decreases, in comparison to the scores obtained when the original annotations were used for testing our models. There are sparse exceptions were the accuracy increases, for example, when training on Toxkaggle and testing on re-annotations of HOTA, where results were equal (TRAC-1) or better (DavidsonHS, DavidsonOFF, Toxkaggle). In general, the highest accuracy, although still low in terms of what current language models can achieve, is achieved when testing either on the toxicity or HOTA re-annotations. Excluding Toxkaggle, however, we observe that accuracy deteriorated in our re-annotations even when evaluating on test sets derived from the same source as the training set, except for TRAC-1 that it presents a slight increase of 0.01 when testing on hate speech and HOTA.

5 Discussion

Taking into account the existing literature (Fortuna et al., 2020; Karan and Šnajder, 2018; Swamy et al., 2019; Yin and Zubiaga, 2021), this study confirms that models face a serious difficulty generalising. Yet, our results show a promising aspect when it comes to model reproducibility for harmful language detection purposes, as well as building robust datasets though a robust annotation procedure.

5.1 Accuracy per definition

Models perform better in the two most general definitions, i.e., Toxicity and HOTA (Table 4). This can be due to pragmatic reasons, namely classifying items using broad definitions can be an easier task for both the annotators and the models. On the other hand, it might be a matter of compatibility between the training data and the testing data. For example, the classes used in the re-annotation procedure were more similar to the ones used in the two Davidson sub-sets and Toxkaggle, while they were more different compared to TRAC-1, where another definition was originally used (aggressiveness), which we did not include in our experiments.

5.2 Robustness and reproducibility

If we consider the evaluation on the original gold labels (Figure 3) as the baseline of the experiment, and compare with the re-annotations (Figure 4, we see that in many cases the performance fluctuates when the models are tested on our re-annotated data. Specifically, the performance drops when the models are tested on the re-annotations of the same source as the training set, while it can occasionally increase when tested on the re-annotations of a different source from that of the training set. This implies that the models' performance is sensitive to the specific data sources used for re-annotation. It suggests that it is possible that the models may struggle to generalise well to new data from the same source, resulting in a drop in performance and contrasting previous studies. On the other hand, there are cases that when presented with re-annotations from a different source and under certain conditions (providing a specific definition), the models might perform better, indicating a potential capability to generalise across different data sources, even when the source of the test set is different from that of the training set.

5.3 Drawing the line

Focusing on such differences among different datasets could enable researchers to outline the DOs and DON'Ts for annotations and dataset creation. Finding the correct combination between the appropriate definition to use and the correct data source can be pivotal for an efficient harmful language detection model. Moreover, we underline the need for parallel annotation (both longitudinal and by increasing the number of annotators) as "collecting the opinions of more users gives a more detailed picture of objective (or intersubjective) hatefulness" (Roß et al., 2016). According to Fortuna et al. (2020), fine-grained toxicity categories are not the optimum option, while more general categories yield better results. Considering that, for the purposes of this experiment, we tried to binarise and simplify the datasets, as much as possible, by separating the Davidson dataset and by merging the subcategories in TRAC-1 and Toxkaggle. However, this did not help the performance when it comes to TRAC-1. One possible reason behind this could be the fact that TRAC-1 contains implicit aggressiveness that is harder to detect, even when the model is trained on the respective dataset. The difficulty to detect implicit aggressiveness or other forms of harmful language is not only true for models, but also for human annotators, as we saw in Section 3.1.

6 Conclusion

In spite of recent advances, model generalisation and method robustness still has a long way to go especially regarding harmful language online. In this study, we attempt to shed some light on the issue, first, by performing a re-annotation experiment with existing datasets employing crowdsourcing annotators and, second, by using the same datasets to train a baseline model as an automatic annotator. The human annotation shows that, although in most cases the annotations were inconsistent, Toxicity and HOTA (any of the following: Hateful, Offensive, Toxic, Abusive language) appear to be the most consistent definitions, indicating that the broader the term used the more robust the annotations The experimental model, on the other hand, showed that, assessing on data from the same source as the training set, when using the original ground truth, can yield higher accuracy compared to assessing data from a different source, confirming previous studies. Yet, this cannot be used as a rule of thumb since testing on the re-annotations showed that the performance can drop when testing on the data from the same source as the training set and it can increase when testing on previously completely unseen data.

Limitations

Our study is limited in three perspectives. First, not all datasets relevant to toxicity have been studied. Also, we only experimented with BERT-based classifiers. We let the study of more datasets and algorithms for future work. Another limitation is that our annotation is only based on crowdsourcing, but the opinion of expert annotators could also be acquired. We note that such an extension would also allow a study of the effect of the quality of the two different approaches (crowdraters vs. experts) on model performance.

Ethical statement

The ethical considerations of this study mainly concern the re-annotation procedure. The original datasets were anonymised before re-annotating. After the re-annotation, and as instructed by the Appen platform, we avoided including any sensitive information of the annotators by only using their IDs for identifying any particular instance.

Acknowledgements

K. Korre's research is carried out under the project "RACHS: Rilevazione e Analisi Computazionale dell'Hate Speech in rete", in the framework of the PON programme FSE REACT-EU, Ref. DOT1303118.

References

Valerio Basile, Cristina Bosco, Elisabetta Fersini, Debora Nozza, Viviana Patti, Francisco Manuel Rangel Pardo, Paolo Rosso, and Manuela Sanguinetti. 2019. SemEval-2019 task 5: Multilingual detection of hate speech against immigrants and women in Twitter. In *Proceedings of the 13th International Workshop on Semantic Evaluation*, pages 54–63, Minneapolis, Minnesota, USA. Association for Computational Linguistics.

Irina Bigoulaeva, Viktor Hangya, and Alexander Fraser. 2021. Cross-lingual transfer learning for hate speech detection. In *Proceedings of the First Workshop on Language Technology for Equality, Diversity and Inclusion*, pages 15–25, Kyiv. Association for Computational Linguistics.

Thomas Davidson, Dana Warmsley, Michael Macy, and Ingmar Weber. 2017. Automated hate speech detection and the problem of offensive language.

Neha Deshpande, Nicholas Farris, and Vidhur Kumar. 2022. Highly generalizable models for multilingual hate speech detection. *ArXiv*, abs/2201.11294.

Elisabetta Fersini, Debora Nozza, and Paolo Rosso. 2018. Overview of the evalita 2018 task on automatic misogyny identification (ami). In *EVALITA@CLiC-it*.

Paula Fortuna, Juan Soler, and Leo Wanner. 2020. Toxic, hateful, offensive or abusive? what are we really classifying? an empirical analysis of hate speech datasets. In *Proceedings of the Twelfth Language Resources and Evaluation Conference*, pages 6786–6794, Marseille, France. European Language Resources Association.

Paula Fortuna, Juan Soler-Company, and Leo Wanner. 2021. How well do hate speech, toxicity, abusive and offensive language classification models generalize across datasets? *Information Processing & Management*, 58(3):102524.

Antigoni Founta, Constantinos Djouvas, Despoina Chatzakou, Ilias Leontiadis, Jeremy Blackburn, Gianluca Stringhini, Athena Vakali, Michael Sirivianos, and Nicolas Kourtellis. 2018. Large scale crowdsourcing and characterization of twitter abusive behavior. In *Proceedings of the international AAAI conference on web and social media*, volume 12.

Tommi Gröndahl, Luca Pajola, Mika Juuti, Mauro Conti, and N. Asokan. 2018. All you need is "love": Evading hate speech detection. In *Proceedings of the 11th ACM Workshop on Artificial Intelligence and Security*, AISec '18, page 2–12, New York, NY, USA. Association for Computing Machinery.

Jigsaw. 2019. Jigsaw toxic comment classification challenge. `https://www.kaggle.com/c/jigsaw-toxic-comment-classification-challenge`. Accessed: [8 May 2023].

Mladen Karan and Jan Šnajder. 2018. Cross-domain detection of abusive language online. In *Proceedings of the 2nd Workshop on Abusive Language Online (ALW2)*, pages 132–137, Brussels, Belgium. Association for Computational Linguistics.

Majid KhosraviNik and Eleonora Esposito. 2018. Online hate, digital discourse and critique: Exploring digitally-mediated discursive practices of gender-based hostility. *Lodz Papers in Pragmatics*, 14(1):45–68.

Ritesh Kumar, Atul Kr. Ojha, Shervin Malmasi, and Marcos Zampieri. 2018a. Benchmarking aggression identification in social media. In *Proceedings of the First Workshop on Trolling, Aggression and Cyberbullying (TRAC-2018)*, pages 1–11, Santa Fe, New Mexico, USA. Association for Computational Linguistics.

Ritesh Kumar, Aishwarya N. Reganti, Akshit Bhatia, and Tushar Maheshwari. 2018b. Aggression-annotated corpus of Hindi-English code-mixed data. In *Proceedings of the Eleventh International Conference on Language Resources and Evaluation (LREC 2018)*, Miyazaki, Japan. European Language Resources Association (ELRA).

Chikashi Nobata, Joel R. Tetreault, Achint Oommen Thomas, Yashar Mehdad, and Yi Chang. 2016. Abusive language detection in online user content. *Proceedings of the 25th International Conference on World Wide Web*.

Björn Roß, Michael Rist, Guillermo Carbonell, Benjamin Cabrera, Nils Kurowsky, and Michael Wojatzki. 2016. Measuring the reliability of hate speech annotations: The case of the european refugee crisis.

Steve Durairaj Swamy, Anupam Jamatia, and Björn Gambäck. 2019. Studying generalisability across abusive language detection datasets. In *Proceedings of the 23rd Conference on Computational Natural Language Learning (CoNLL)*, pages 940–950, Hong Kong, China. Association for Computational Linguistics.

Zeerak Talat, James Thorne, and Joachim Bingel. 2018. *Bridging the Gaps: Multi Task Learning for Domain Transfer of Hate Speech Detection*, pages 29–55.

Wenjie Yin and Arkaitz Zubiaga. 2021. Towards generalisable hate speech detection: a review on obstacles and solutions. *PeerJ Computer Science*, 7.

Marcos Zampieri, Shervin Malmasi, Preslav Nakov, Sara Rosenthal, Noura Farra, and Ritesh Kumar. 2019. SemEval-2019 task 6: Identifying and categorizing offensive language in social media (OffensEval). In *Proceedings of the 13th International Workshop on Semantic Evaluation*, pages 75–86, Minneapolis, Minnesota, USA. Association for Computational Linguistics.

A Annotation instructions and interface

Figures 4 and 5 in the next page of this Appendix present the instructions (only for toxicity shown) and the interface the annotators were provided with during their re-annotation tasks.

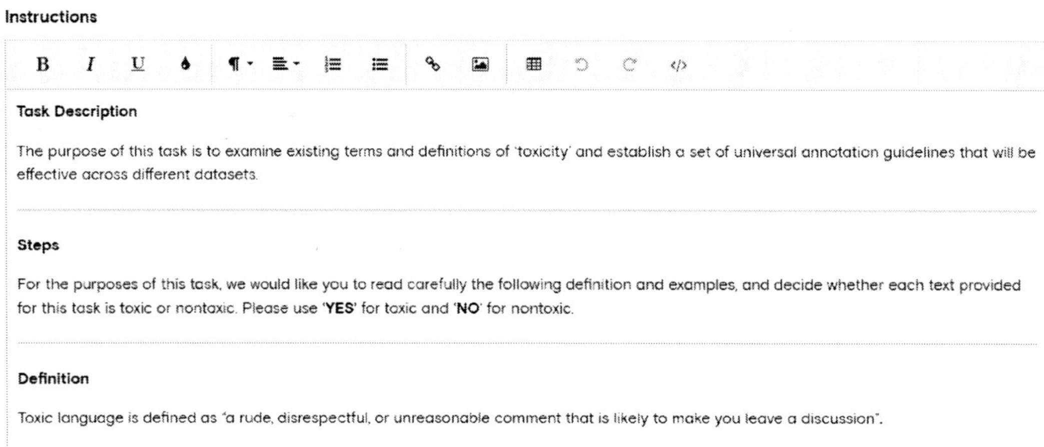

Figure 4: Instructions during re-annotation, using the term and definition of Toxicity.

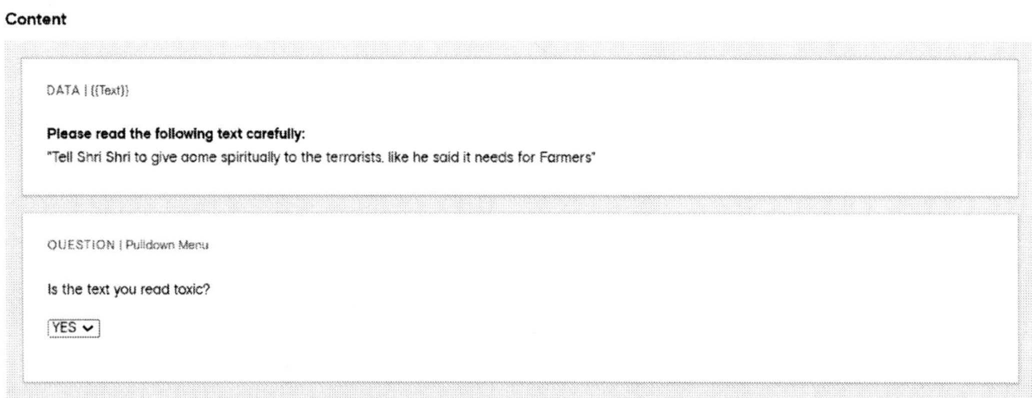

Figure 5: Interface for re-annotation.

Robust Hate Speech Detection in Social Media: A Cross-Dataset Empirical Evaluation

Dimosthenis Antypas and **Jose Camacho-Collados**
Cardiff NLP, School of Computer Science and Informatics
Cardiff University, United Kingdom
{AntypasD,CamachoColladosJ}@cardiff.ac.uk

Abstract

The automatic detection of hate speech online is an active research area in NLP. Most of the studies to date are based on social media datasets that contribute to the creation of hate speech detection models trained on them. However, data creation processes contain their own biases, and models inherently learn from these dataset-specific biases. In this paper, we perform a large-scale cross-dataset comparison where we fine-tune language models on different hate speech detection datasets. This analysis shows how some datasets are more generalizable than others when used as training data. Crucially, our experiments show how combining hate speech detection datasets can contribute to the development of robust hate speech detection models. This robustness holds even when controlling by data size and compared with the best individual datasets.

1 Introduction

Social media has led to a new form of communication that has changed how people interact across the world. With the emergence of this medium, hateful conduct has also found a place to propagate online. From more obscure online communities such as 4chan (Knuttila, 2011) and Telegram rooms (Walther and McCoy, 2021) to mainstream social media platforms such as Facebook (Del Vigna12 et al., 2017) and Twitter (Udanor and Anyanwu, 2019), the spread of hate speech is an on going issue.

Hate speech detection is a complex problem that has received a lot of attention from the Natural Language Processing (NLP) community. It shares a lot of challenges with other social media problems (emotion detection, offensive language detection, etc), such as an increasingly amount of user generated content, unstructured (Elsayed et al., 2019) and constantly evolving text (Ebadi et al., 2021), and the need of efficient large scale solutions. When dealing with hate speech in particular, one has to consider the sensitivity of the topics, their wide range (e.g. sexism, sexual orientation, racism), and their evolution through time and location (Matamoros-Fernández and Farkas, 2021). Understanding the extent of the problem and tracking hate speech online through automatic techniques can therefore be part of the solution of this ongoing challenge. One way to contribute to this goal is to both improve the current hate speech detection models and, crucially, the data used to train them.

The contributions of this paper are twofold. First, we provide a summary and unify existing hate speech detection datasets from social media, in particular Twitter. Second, we analyse the performance of language models trained on all datasets, and highlight deficiencies in generalisation across datasets, including the evaluation in a new independently-constructed dataset. Finally, as a practical added value stemming from this paper, we share all the best models trained on the unification of all datasets, providing a relatively small-size hate speech detection model that is generalisable across datasets.[1]

Content Warning The article contains examples of hateful and abusive language. The first vowel in hateful slurs, vulgar words, and in general profanity language is replaced with an asterisk (*).

2 Related Work

Identifying hate speech in social media is an increasingly important research topic in NLP. It is often framed as a classification task (binary or multiclass) and through the years various machine learning and information sources approaches have been

[1]The best binary hate speech detection model is available at `https://huggingface.co/cardiffnlp/twitter-roberta-base-hate-latest`; the multiclass hate speech detection model identifying target groups is available at `https://huggingface.co/cardiffnlp/twitter-roberta-base-hate-multiclass-latest`. These models have been integrated into the TweetNLP library (Camacho-Collados et al., 2022).

The 7th Workshop on Online Abuse and Harms (WOAH), pages 231–242

utilised (Mullah and Zainon, 2021; Ali et al., 2022; Khanday et al., 2022; del Valle-Cano et al., 2023). A common issue of supervised approaches lies not necessarily with their architecture, but with the existing hate speech datasets that are available to train supervised models. It is often the case that the datasets are focused on specific target groups (Grimminger and Klinger, 2021), constructed using some specific keyword search terms (Waseem and Hovy, 2016; Zampieri et al., 2019), or have particular class distributions (Basile et al., 2019) that leads to a training process that may or may not generalise. For instance, Florio et al. (2020) analysed the temporal aspect of hate speech, and demonstrate how brittle hate speech models are when evaluated on different periods. Recent work has also shown that there is a need to both focus on the resources available and also try to expand them in order to develop robust hate speech classifiers that can be applied in various context and in different time periods (Bourgeade et al., 2023; Bose et al., 2022).

In this paper, we perform a large-scale evaluation to analyse how generalisable supervised models are depending on the underlying training set. Then, we propose to mitigate the relative lack of generalisation by using datasets from various sources and time periods aiming to offer a more robust solution.

3 Data

In this section, we describe the data used in our experiments. First, we describe existing hate speech datasets in Section 3.1. Then, we unify those datasets and provide statistics of the final data in Section 3.2

3.1 Hate Speech datasets

In total, we collected 13 datasets related to hate speech in social media. The datasets selected are diverse both in content, different kind of hate speech, and in a temporal aspect.

Measuring hate speech (MHS) *MHS* (Kennedy et al., 2020; Sachdeva et al., 2022) consists of 39,565 social media (YouTube, Reddit, Twitter) manually annotated comments. The coders were asked to annotate each entry on 10 different attributes such as the presence of sentiment, respect, insults and others; and also indicate the target of the comment (e.g. age, disability). They use Rasch measurment theory (Rasch, 1960) to aggregate the annotators' rating in a continuous value that indicates the hate score of the comment.

Call me sexist, but (CMS) This dataset of 6,325 entries (Samory et al., 2021) focuses on the aspect of sexism and includes social psychology scales and tweets extracted by utilising the "Call me sexist, but" phrase. The authors also include two other sexism datasets (Jha and Mamidi, 2017; Waseem and Hovy, 2016) which they re-annotate. Each entry is annotated by five coders and is labelled based on its content (e.g. sexist, maybe-sexist) and phrasing (e.g. civil, uncivil).

Hate Towards the Political Opponent (HTPO) *HTPO* (Grimminger and Klinger, 2021) is a collection of 3,000 tweets related to the 2020 USA presidential election. The tweets were extracted using a set of keywords linked to the presidential and vice presidential candidates and each tweet is annotated for stance detection (in favor of/against the candidate) and whether it contains hateful language or not.

HateX *HateX* (Mathew et al., 2021) is a collection of 20,148 posts from Twitter and Gab extracted by utilising relevant hate lexicons. For each entry, three annotators are asked to indicate: (1) the existence of hate speech, offensive speech, or neither of them, (2) the target group of the post (e.g. Arab, Homosexual), and (3) the reasons for the label assigned.

Offense The *Offense* dataset (Zampieri et al., 2019) contains 14,100 tweets extracted by utilising a set of keywords and categorises them in three levels: (1) offensive and non-offensive; (2) targeted/untargeted insult; (3) targeted to individual, group, or other.

Automated Hate Speech Detection (AHSD) In this dataset, (Davidson et al., 2017) the authors utilise a set of keywords to extract 24,783 tweets which are manually labelled as either hate speech, offensive but not hate speech, or neither offensive nor hate speech.

Hateful Symbols or Hateful People? (HSHP) This is a collection (Waseem and Hovy, 2016) of 16,000 tweets extracted based on keywords related to sexism and racism. The tweets are annotated as on whether they contain racism, sexism or neither of them by three different annotators.[2]

Are You a Racist or Am I Seeing Things? (AYR) This dataset (Waseem, 2016) is an extension of *Hateful Symbols or Hateful People?* and adds the "both" (sexism and racism) as a potential label. Overlapping tweets were not considered.

Multilingual and Multi-Aspect Hate Speech Analysis (MMHS) MMHS (Ousidhoum et al., 2019) contains hateful tweets in three different languages (English, French, Arabic). Each tweet has been labelled by three annotators on five different levels: (1) directness, (2) hostility (e.g. abusive, hateful), (3) target (e.g. origin, gender), (4) group (e.g. women, individual) and (5) annotator emotion (disgust, shock, etc). A total of 5,647 tweets are included in the dataset.

HatE *HatE* (Basile et al., 2019) consists of English and Spanish tweets (19,600 in total) that are labelled on whether they contain hate speech or not. The tweets in this dataset focus on hate speech towards two groups: (1) immigrants and (2) women.

HASOC This dataset (Mandl et al., 2019) contains 17,657 tweets in Hindi, German and English which are annotated on three levels: (1) whether they contain hate-offensive content or not; (2) in the case of hate-offensive tweets, whether a post contains hate, offensive, or profane content/words; (3) on the nature of the insult (targeted or un-targeted).

Detecting East Asian Prejudice on Social Media (DEAP) This is a collection of 20,000 tweets (Vidgen et al., 2020) focused on East Asian prejudice, e.g. Sinophobia, in relation to the COVID-19 pandemic. The annotators were asked to labelled each entry based on five different categories (hostility, criticism, counter speech, discussion, non-related) and also indicate the target of the entry (e.g. Hong Kongers, China).

Large Scale Crowdsourcing and Characterization of Twitter Abusive Behavior (LSC) The dataset (Founta et al., 2018) consists of 80,000 tweets extracted using a boosted random sample technique. Each tweet is labelled as either offensive, abusive, hateful, aggressive, cyberbullying or normal.

[2]A subset of the dataset is included in the *Call me sexist, but* and is not considered.

3.2 Unification

Even though all of the datasets that were collected revolve around hate speech, there are major differences among them in terms of both format and content. We attempt to unify the datasets by standarizing their format and combining the available content into two settings: (1) binary hate speech classification and (2) a multiclass classification task including the target group. We note that in cases where the original annotation results were provided, we decided to assign a label if at least two of the coders agree on it and not necessarily the majority of them. This approach can lead to a more realistic dataset and contribute in creating more robust systems (Antypas et al., 2022; Mohammad et al., 2018).

3.2.1 Initial preprocessing

For each dataset collected, a simple preprocessing pipeline is applied. Firstly, any non-Twitter content is removed; despite the similarities between the content shared in various social media (e.g. internet slang, emojis), Twitter displays unique characteristics, such as the concept of retweets and shorter texts, which differentiate it from other platforms such as Reddit or Youtube (Smith et al., 2012). Moreover, as our main consideration is hate speech in the English language, we exclude any non-English subset of tweets, and also verify the language by using a fastText based language identifier (Bojanowski et al., 2017). Finally, considering that some datasets in this study utilise similar keywords to extract tweets, we remove near duplicated entries to avoid any overlap between them. This is accomplished by applying a normalisation step where entries that are considered duplicated based on their lemmmatised form are ignored. Also, all URLs and mentions are removed.

As a final note, three of the datasets (*HSHP, AYR, LSC*) were dehydrated using the Twitter API since only their tweet IDs and their labels were publicly available. Unfortunately, a significant number of tweets ($\approx 10,000$) were no longer available from the API.

3.2.2 Binary Setting

The majority of the datasets collected are either set as a binary hate classification task and no further preprocessing is applied (*HTPO*), or offer a more fine-grained classification of hate speech (e.g. *HateX, CMS*) where we consider all "hate" subclasses as one. In general, when a dataset focuses on a specific type of hate speech (e.g. sexism) we map it as hate speech. Notable exceptions are: (1) The *MSH* dataset, where a continues hate score is provided which is transformed into a binary class according to the mapping proposed by the original authors. (2) Datasets that consist of offensive speech but also provide information about the target of the tweet. In these cases, (*Offense*), we consider only entries that are classified as offensive and are targeting a group of people and not individuals. Our assumption is that offensive language towards a group of people is highly likely to target protected characteristics and thus be classified as hate speech. (3) Finally, only entries classified as hate speech were considered in datasets where there is a clear distinction between hate, offensive, or profound speech (*LSC*, *AHSD*, *HASOC*). All data labelled as normal or not-hateful are also included as *not-hate* speech.

3.2.3 Multiclass Setting

Having established our binary setting, we aggregated the available datasets aiming to construct a more detailed hate speech classification task. As an initial step, all available hate speech sub-classes present were considered. However, this led to a very detailed but sparse hate taxonomy, with 44 different hate speech categories, but with only a few entries for some of the classes (e.g. "economic" category with only four tweets present). Aiming to create an easy-to-use and extendable data resource, several categories were grouped together. All classes related to ethnicity (e.g. Arab, Hispanic) or immigration were grouped under *racism*, while religious categories (e.g. Muslim, Christian) were considered separately. Categories related to sexuality and sexual orientation (e.g. heterosexual, homosexual) were also grouped in one class, and tweets with topics regarding gender (men, women) constitute the *sexism* class. Finally, all entries labelled as "not-hate" speech were also included. To keep our dataset relatively balanced we also ignored classes that constitute less than 1% of the total hate speech data. Overall, the multiclass setting proposed consists of 7 classes: *Racism, Sexism, Disability, Sexual orientation, Religion, Other*, and *Not-Hate*. It is worth noting that tweets falling under the *Other* class do not belong to any of the other five hate speech classes.

3.2.4 Statistics and Data Splits

In total, we collected 83,230 tweets, from 13 different datasets (Table 1), of which only 33% are classified as hate speech. This unified dataset may seem imbalanced but it is commonly assumed that only around 1% of the content shared on social media contains hate speech (Pereira-Kohatsu et al., 2019). When considering the multiclass setting, the hate speech percentage decreases even more with only 26% of tweets labelled as a form of hate speech, with the *religion* class being the least popular with only 709 entries.

The data in both settings (binary & multiclass) are divided into train and test sets using a stratified split to ensure class balance between the splits (Table 2). In general, for each dataset present, we allocate 70% as training data, 10% as validation, and 20% as test data. Exceptions to the aforementioned approach are datasets where the authors provide a preexisting data split which we use.

4 Evaluation

We present our main experimental results comparing various language models trained on single datasets and in the unified dataset presented in the previous section.

4.1 Experimental Setting

Models. For our experiments we rely on four language models of a similar size, two of them being general-purposes and the other two specialized on social media: BERT-base (Devlin et al., 2019) and RoBERTa-base (Liu et al., 2019) as general-purpose models; and BERTweet (Nguyen et al., 2020) and TimeLMs-21 (Loureiro et al., 2022) as language models specialized on social media, and particularly Twitter. There is an important difference between BERTweet and TimeLMs-21: since BERTweet was trained from scratch, TimeLMs-21 used the RoBERTa-base checkpoint as initialization and then continued training on a Twitter corpus. An SVM classifier is also utilized as a baseline model.

Settings. Aiming to investigate the effect of a larger and more diverse hate speech training corpus on various types of hate speech, we perform an evaluation on both the binary and multiclass settings described in Section 3.2. Specifically, for the binary setting we fine-tune the models selected first on each individual dataset, and secondly while using the unified dataset created. For the multiclass

<table>
<tr><th rowspan="2">Dataset</th><th colspan="2">Binary</th><th colspan="6">Multiclass</th></tr>
<tr><th>hate</th><th>not-hate</th><th>racism</th><th>sexism</th><th>sexual orientation</th><th>disability</th><th>religion</th><th>other</th></tr>
<tr><td>HatE</td><td>5303</td><td>7364</td><td>2474</td><td>2829</td><td colspan="4">-</td></tr>
<tr><td>MHS</td><td>2485</td><td>5074</td><td>735</td><td>784</td><td>251</td><td>21</td><td>246</td><td>10</td></tr>
<tr><td>DEAP</td><td>3727</td><td>105</td><td>3727</td><td colspan="5">-</td></tr>
<tr><td>CMS</td><td>1237</td><td>10861</td><td>-</td><td>1237</td><td colspan="4">-</td></tr>
<tr><td>Offense</td><td>1142</td><td>12547</td><td colspan="6">-</td></tr>
<tr><td>HateX</td><td>2562</td><td>5678</td><td>757</td><td>492</td><td>407</td><td>30</td><td>239</td><td>143</td></tr>
<tr><td>LSC</td><td>889</td><td>1267</td><td colspan="6">-</td></tr>
<tr><td>MMHS</td><td>5392</td><td>-</td><td>472</td><td>764</td><td>512</td><td>1387</td><td>224</td><td>2033</td></tr>
<tr><td>HASOC</td><td>1237</td><td>4348</td><td colspan="6">-</td></tr>
<tr><td>AYR</td><td>393</td><td>1246</td><td>42</td><td>343</td><td colspan="4">-</td></tr>
<tr><td>AHSD</td><td>1363</td><td>4088</td><td colspan="6">-</td></tr>
<tr><td>HTPO</td><td>351</td><td>2647</td><td colspan="6">-</td></tr>
<tr><td>HSHP</td><td>1498</td><td>426</td><td>9</td><td>1489</td><td colspan="4">-</td></tr>
<tr><td>Total</td><td>27,579</td><td>55,651</td><td>8,216</td><td>7,938</td><td>1,170</td><td>1,438</td><td>709</td><td>2,186</td></tr>
</table>

Table 1: Distribution of tweets gathered across hate speech datasets, including those where the target information is available (multiclass).

Dataset	train		test	
	not-hate	hate	not-hate	hate
AHSD	3270	1090	818	273
AYR	996	314	250	79
CMS	8688	989	2173	248
DEAP	84	2981	21	746
HASOC*	3489	1113	859	124
HSHP	341	1197	85	301
HTPO*	2106	292	541	59
HatE*	5757	4197	1607	1106
HateX	4542	2050	1136	512
LSC	1013	711	254	178
MHS	4058	1988	1016	497
Offense*	10037	913	2510	229
All	**44,381**	**17,835**	**11,270**	**4,352**

Table 2: Binary class distribution in train and test splits of the unified hate speech datasets. * indicates datasets where preexisting train/test splits were available and retrieved.

setting, we considered the unified and the HateX dataset, which includes data for all classes. In total, we fine-tuned 54 different binary[3] and 8 multiclass models.

Training. The implementations provided by Hugging Face (Wolf et al., 2020) are used to train and evaluate all language models, while we utilise Ray Tune (Liaw et al., 2018) along with HyperOpt (Bergstra et al., 2022) and Adaptive Successive Halving (Li et al., 2018) for optimizing the learning rate, warmup steps, number of epochs, and batch size, hyper-parameteres of each model.[4]

Evaluation metrics. The macro-averaged F1 score is reported and used to compare the performance of the different models. Macro-F1 is commonly used in similar tasks (Basile et al., 2019; Zampieri et al., 2020) as it provides a more concrete view on the performance of each model.

4.2 Datasets

For training and evaluation, we use the splits described in Section 3.2.4. As described above, for each language model we trained on each dataset training set independently, and in the combination of all dataset-specific training sets. The results on the combination of all datasets are averaged across each dataset-specific test set (AVG), i.e., each dataset is given the same weight irrespective of its size. In addition to the datasets presented in Section 3.1, we constructed an independent test set (Indep) to test the robustness of models outside existing datasets.

Independent test set (Indep). This dataset was built by utilising a set of keywords related to the *International Women's Day* and *International Day Against Homophobia, Transphobia and Biphobia* and extracting tweets from the respected days of 2022. Then, these tweets were manually annotated

[3]MMHS dataset was used only for the training/evaluation of the unified dataset as it is lacking the *not-hate* class

[4]Optimal hyperparameters can be found in Table 5 in the Appendix

Model	Train Data	Train Size	HatE	MHS	DEAP	CMS	Off.	HateX	LSC	HASOC	AYR	AHSD	HTPO	HSHP	AVG	Indep
BERTweet	All	58213	57.1	87.7	**57.7**	**82.4**	59.4	**75.1**	61.5	59.4	85.5	**90.2**	59.5	**65.4**	**70.1**	61.0
	All*	5290	51.1	80.5	53.7	73.1	**60.8**	67.3	72.1	**63.9**	**85.6**	85.4	67.6	62.1	68.6	**69.2**
	MHS	5291	**65.5**	**89.3**	13.3	50.6	53.2	69.6	58.8	58.0	66.8	78.8	**67.7**	28.6	58.3	58.6
TimeLMs	All	58213	54.2	**86.6**	**68.0**	**79.7**	**56.9**	**74.8**	59.1	63.2	87.2	**89.4**	65.2	**64.5**	**70.7**	63.7
	All*	1146	48.3	74.9	49.3	69.3	54.7	59.7	**63.8**	**63.8**	82.3	79.9	59.6	63.0	64.0	**70.6**
	AYR	1147	**61.0**	71.4	9.8	63.5	52.5	56.3	60.9	63.6	**87.7**	80.7	**66.8**	57.9	61.0	59.3
RoBERTa	All	58213	52.3	**85.9**	**66.6**	**79.9**	**54.7**	**73.8**	59.5	60.8	**87.0**	**89.8**	64.4	61.4	**69.7**	56.2
	All*	1146	**56.0**	73.7	53.2	64.2	53.0	48.9	**70.2**	**65.8**	74.3	74.1	58.9	61.0	62.8	**78.3**
	AYR	1147	54.8	63.8	17.5	69.8	55.2	50.1	57.7	63.4	86.3	81.9	**64.6**	55.6	60.1	53.8
BERT	All	58213	52.3	**84.0**	49.3	79.7	**56.8**	**74.1**	56.9	**60.9**	**85.2**	**89.6**	60.5	**65.5**	**67.9**	50.7
	All*	2098	44.7	75.0	49.2	**66.1**	55.9	59.1	**63.5**	60.5	71.1	74.1	57.0	60.5	61.4	**60.9**
	HTPO	2099	54.9	77.5	19.8	52.1	52.1	58.6	64.8	55.9	61.3	78.1	**73.5**	38.3	57.2	50.7
SVM	All	58213	50.6	77.0	**61.6**	66.1	48.5	71.2	47.8	48.9	**86.9**	**87.3**	47.3	54.9	61.2	46.7
	All*	5290	44.5	76.1	55.7	**68.4**	**50.7**	64.4	**57.0**	**56.2**	81.0	81.9	**52.7**	57.4	**67.2**	**59.3**
	MHS	5291	**57.9**	**80.0**	4.8	48.3	48.4	**67.2**	46.4	46.4	47.8	75.0	50.1	22.7	47.7	51.8
All hate baseline			29.0	25.0	49.0	9.0	8.0	24.0	29.0	11.0	19.0	20.0	9.0	44.0	23.0	10.0

Table 3: Macro-averaged F1 scores across all hate speech test sets and our manually annotated set (Indep). For each model, the table includes: (1) the performance of the model trained on all the datasets (All); (2) the performance of the model when trained on a balanced sample of all datasets of the same size as the best single-dataset baseline (All*); and (3) the best overall performing model trained on a single dataset (BERTweet: *MHS*, TimeLMs: *AYR*, RoBERTa: *AYR*, BERT: *HTPO*, SVM: *MHS*). The best result for each dataset and model is bolded.

model	Train	sexism	racism	disability	sexual orientation	religion	other	not-hate	AVG
TimeLMs	All Datasets	**72.2**	**72.9**	**74.2**	**76.9**	**52.6**	**58.8**	**90.6**	**71.6**
	HateX	52.1	16.5	0	58.8	31.8	5.8	86.0	35.9
BERTweet	All Datasets	**73.1**	**72.5**	**74.1**	**77.6**	**48.6**	**59.3**	**90.9**	**70.9**
	HateX	47.8	6.8	0	43.9	0	0	85.5	26.3
RoBERTa	All Datasets	**70.4**	**72.4**	**73.9**	**76.5**	**47.3**	**55.5**	**90.3**	**69.5**
	HateX	50.5	16.3	0	67.9	29.1	7.7	85.5	36.3
BERT	All	**68.9**	**66.3**	**75.5**	**69.3**	**40.3**	**54.9**	**93.3**	**66.9**
	HateX	40.4	16.0	0	66.2	15.9	0	85.4	32.0
SVM	All	**62.7**	**67.0**	**71.5**	**70.5**	4.1	**49.0**	**59.11**	**81.9**
	HateX	20.1	6.0	0	54.9	**6.8**	0	84.5	24.6
Baseline (most frequent)		0	0	0	0	0	0	84.0	12.0

Table 4: F1 score for each class in the multiclass setting when trained on all the datasets (All) and when trained only with HateX. Macro-average F1 (AVG) is also reported.

by an expert. In total 200 tweets were annotated as hateful, not-hateful, or as "NA" in cases where the annotator was not sure whether a tweet contained hate speech or not. The *Indep* test set consists of 151 non-hate and 20 hate tweets and due to its nature (specific content & expert annotation) can be leveraged to perform a targeted evaluation on models trained on similar and unrelated data. While we acknowledge the limitations of the *Indep* test set (i.e., relative small number of tweets and only one annotator present), our aim is to use these tweets, collected using relatively simple guidelines[5], to test the overall generalisation ability of our models and how it aligns to what people think of hate speech.

[5]Annotator guidelines are available in Appendix A.

4.3 Results

4.3.1 Binary Setting

Table 3 displays the macro-F1 scores achieved by the models across all test sets when fine-tuned: (1) on all available datasets (*All*), (2) on the best overall performing model trained on a single dataset, and (3) on a balanced sample of the unified dataset of the same data size as (2). When looking at the average performance of (1) and (2), it is clear that when utilising the combined data, all models perform considerably better overall. This increased performance may not be achieved across all the datasets tested, but it does provide evidence that the relatively limited scope of the individual datasets hinder the potential capabilities of our models. An even bigger constrast is observed when considering the performance difference on the *DEAP* subset, which deals with a less common type of hate speech (prejudice towards Asian people), where even the best performing single dataset model achieves barely 19.79% F1 compared to the worst combined classifier with 49.27% F1 (BERT All / BERT *HTPO*).

To further explore the importance of the size and diversity of the training data we train and evaluate our models in an additional settings. Considering the sample size of the best performing dataset for each model, an equally sized training set is extracted from all available data while enforcing a balanced distribution between hate and not-hate tweets (*All**). Finally, we make sure to sample proportionally across the available datasets. The results (Table 3) reveal the significance that a diverse dataset has in the models' performance. All models tested perform on average better when trained on the newly created subsets (*All**) when compared to the respective models trained only on the best performing individual dataset. Interestingly, this setting also achieves the best overall scores on the *Indep.* set, which reinforces the importance of balancing the data. Nonetheless, all the transformers models still achieve their best score when trained on all the combined datasets (*All*) which suggests that even for these models, the amount of available training data remains an important factor of their performance.

4.3.2 Multiclass Setting

Similarly to our binary setting, utilising the combined datasets in the multiclass setting enhances the models' performance. As can be observed from Table 4, all the models struggle to function at a satisfactory degree when trained on the *HateX* subset only. In particular, when looking at the "disability" class, none of the models manage to classify any of the entries correctly. This occurs even though "disability" entries exist in the *HateX* training subset, albeit in a limited number (21). This behaviour suggests that even when information about a class is available in the training data, language models may fail to distinguish and utilise it. Imbalanced datasets are a common challenge in machine learning applications. This issue is also present in hate speech, in this case exacerbated given the nature of the problem (including a potential big overlap of features between classes) and the lack of resources available.

5 Analysis

In this section, we dissect the results presented in the previous section by performing a cross-dataset comparison and a qualitative error analysis.

5.1 Cross-dataset Analysis

Figure 1 presents a cross-dataset comparison of the language models used for the evaluation. The heatmap presents the results of the models fine-tuned and tested for all dataset pair combinations. All models evaluated tend to perform better when they are trained and tested on specific subsets (left diagonal line on the heat-maps). Even when we evaluate models on similar subsets, they tend to display a deterioration in performance. For example both *CMS* and *AYR* datasets deal with sexism but the models trained only on *CMS* perform poorly when evaluated on *AYR* (e.g. BERTweet-CSM achieves 87% F1 on *CSM*, but only 52% on *AYR*). Finally, it is observable again that the models trained on the combined datasets (column "all") display the best overall performance and attain consistently high results in each individual test set. When analysing the difficulty of each individual dataset when used as a test set, DEAP is clearly the most challenging one overall. This may be due to the scope of the dataset, dealing with East Asian Prejudice during the COVID-19 pandemic, which is probably not well captured in the rest of the datasets. When used as training sets, none of the individual datasets is widely generalisable, with the results of the model fine-tuned on them being over 10 points lower than when fine-tuned on the unified dataset in all cases.

5.2 Qualitative Error Analysis

Aiming to better understand the models' results we perform a qualitative analysis focusing on entries miss-classified by our best performing model, *TimeLMs-All*.

Multiclass. When considering the multiclass setting, common errors are tweets that have been labelled as hateful, e.g. "U right, probably some old n*gga named Clyde" is labelled as *racism* and "@user @user she not a historian a jihadi is the correct term" as *religion*, but the model classifies them as *not-hate*. However, depending on the context and without having access to additional information (author/target of the tweet) these entries may not actually be hateful.

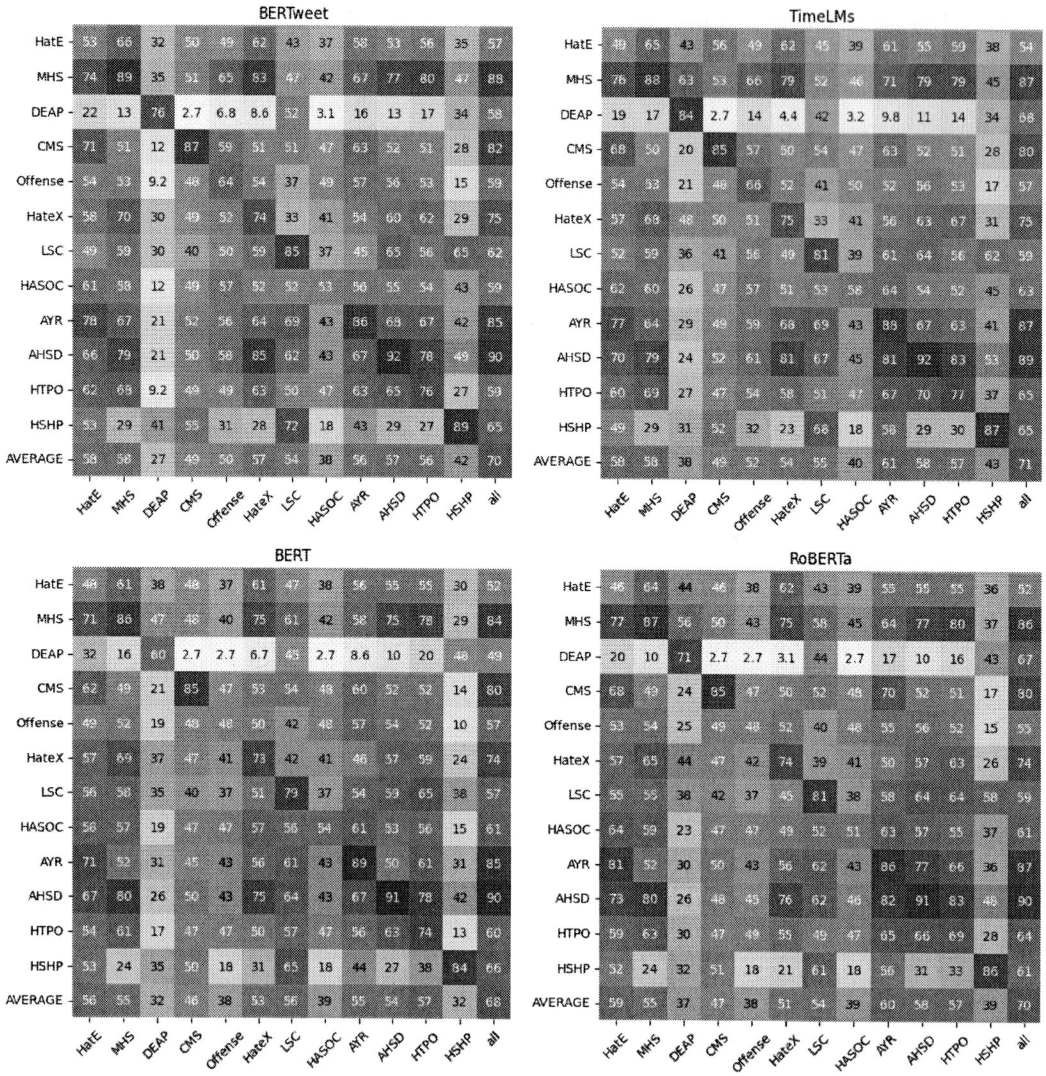

Figure 1: Macro-averaged F1 score for each dataset/model combination. The X axis indicates on which dataset the model was trained while the Y axis indicates the test set used to evaluate it. *AVERAGE* indicates the result by averaging across all datasets, and *all* represents the aggregated training set including all datasets.

It is also interesting to note the limitations that arise when training only on a single dataset, particularly if the data collection is done by utilising specific keywords. For example the tweets "Lana i love you b*tch. Put that flag back up h*e #lustfoflife" and "happy birthday b*tch, hope you have a great one h*e! @user" are correctly classified as *not-hate* by *TimeLMs-All* but are miss-classified as *sexism* by *TimeLMs-HateX*, despite *sexism* being present in the *HateX* dataset.

Binary In the binary setting, the model seems to struggle with entries such as "Meanwhile in Spain..#stopimmigration" and "This is outrageous. Congress should be fired on the spot. #BuildThatWall #stopwastingmytaxdollars" where both entries are classified as *hate* but are labelled as *not-hate*. Similarly to the previous case, the classification of such tweets without additional context is a difficult task. While these tweets have hateful undertones, they may not be necessarily hate speech without considering them in their broader context.

Finally, when looking at the classification errors of *TimeLMs-AYR* (trained only on sexist and racist tweets) the need of diverse training data becomes apparent. For example, *TimeLM-AYR* fails to classify as hate speech the tweets "@user that r*tarded guy should not be a reporter" and "I'm going to sell my iPhone and both my Macs, I don't support f*ggots." as hate speech in contrast to *TimeLMs-All* which classifies the tweets correctly as hateful.

6 Conclusion

In this paper, we presented a large-scale analysis of hate speech detection systems based on language models. In particular, our goal was to show the divergences across datasets and the importance of having access to a diverse and complete training set. Our results show how the combination of datasets make for a robust model performing competitively across all datasets. This is not a surprising finding given the size of the corresponding training sets, but the considerable gap (e.g. 70.7% to 61.0% in Macro-F1 for the best TimeLMs-21 performing model) shows that models trained on single datasets have considerable room for improvement. Moreover, even when controlling for data size, a model trained on a diverse set instead of a single dataset leads to better overall results.

As future work, we are planning to extend this analysis beyond English, in the line of previous multilingual approaches (Ousidhoum et al., 2019; Chiril et al., 2019; Bigoulaeva et al., 2021), and masked language models by including, among others, generative and instruction-tuning language models. In addition to the extensive binary-level evaluation, recognising the target group is a challenging area of research. While in Section 4.3.2, we provided some encouraging results, the results could be expanded with a unified taxonomy.

7 Ethics Statement

Our work aims to contribute and extend research regarding hate speech detection in social media and particular in Twitter. We believe that our efforts to contribute on the ongoing concerns around the status of hate speech on social medial.

We acknowledge the importance of the ACM Code of Ethics, and are committed on following it's guidelines. Our current work, uses either publicly available tweets under open licence and does not infringe any of the rules of Twitter's API. Moreover, given that our task includes user generated content we are committed to respect the privacy of the users, by replacing each user mention in the texts with a placeholder.

8 Limitations

In this paper, we have focused on existing datasets and a unification stemming from their features. The decisions taken to this unification, particularly in the selection of dataset and target groups, may influence the results of the paper.

We have focused on social media (particularly Twitter) and on the English language. While there has been extensive work on this medium and language, the conclusions that we can take from this study can be limiting, as the detection of hate speech involves other areas, domains and languages. In general, we studied a particular aspect of hate speech detection which may or not be generalizable.

Finally, due to computational limitations, all our experiments are based on base-sized language models. It is likely that larger models, while exhibiting similar behaviours, would lead to higher results overall.

9 Acknowledgements

The authors are supported by a UKRI Future Leaders Fellowship. They also acknowledge the collaboration with the Spanish National Office Against Hate Crimes and the support of the EU Citizens, Equality, Rights and Values (CERV) programme. However, the authors have the exclusive responsibility for the contents of this publication.

References

Raza Ali, Umar Farooq, Umair Arshad, Waseem Shahzad, and Mirza Omer Beg. 2022. Hate speech detection on twitter using transfer learning. *Computer Speech & Language*, 74:101365.

Dimosthenis Antypas, Asahi Ushio, Jose Camacho-Collados, Vitor Silva, Leonardo Neves, and Francesco Barbieri. 2022. Twitter topic classification. In *Proceedings of the 29th International Conference on Computational Linguistics*, pages 3386–3400, Gyeongju, Republic of Korea. International Committee on Computational Linguistics.

Valerio Basile, Cristina Bosco, Elisabetta Fersini, Debora Nozza, Viviana Patti, Francisco Manuel Rangel Pardo, Paolo Rosso, and Manuela Sanguinetti. 2019. SemEval-2019 task 5: Multilingual detection of hate speech against immigrants and women in Twitter. In *Proceedings of the 13th International Workshop on Semantic Evaluation*, pages 54–63, Minneapolis, Minnesota, USA. Association for Computational Linguistics.

James Bergstra, Daniel Yamins, and DD Cox. 2022. Hyperopt: Distributed asynchronous hyper-parameter optimization. *Astrophysics Source Code Library*, pages ascl–2205.

Irina Bigoulaeva, Viktor Hangya, and Alexander Fraser. 2021. Cross-lingual transfer learning for hate speech detection. In *Proceedings of the First Workshop on Language Technology for Equality, Diversity and Inclusion*, pages 15–25, Kyiv. Association for Computational Linguistics.

Piotr Bojanowski, Edouard Grave, Armand Joulin, and Tomas Mikolov. 2017. Enriching word vectors with subword information. *Transactions of the Association for Computational Linguistics*, 5:135–146.

Tulika Bose, Nikolaos Aletras, Irina Illina, and Dominique Fohr. 2022. Dynamically refined regularization for improving cross-corpora hate speech detection. In *Findings of the Association for Computational Linguistics: ACL 2022*, pages 372–382, Dublin, Ireland. Association for Computational Linguistics.

Tom Bourgeade, Patricia Chiril, Farah Benamara, and Véronique Moriceau. 2023. What did you learn to hate? a topic-oriented analysis of generalization in hate speech detection. In *Proceedings of the 17th Conference of the European Chapter of the Association for Computational Linguistics*, pages 3495–3508, Dubrovnik, Croatia. Association for Computational Linguistics.

Jose Camacho-Collados, Kiamehr Rezaee, Talayeh Riahi, Asahi Ushio, Daniel Loureiro, Dimosthenis Antypas, Joanne Boisson, Luis Espinosa Anke, Fangyu Liu, and Eugenio Martínez Cámara. 2022. TweetNLP: Cutting-edge natural language processing for social media. In *Proceedings of the 2022 Conference on Empirical Methods in Natural Language Processing: System Demonstrations*, pages 38–49, Abu Dhabi, UAE. Association for Computational Linguistics.

Patricia Chiril, Farah Benamara Zitoune, Véronique Moriceau, Marlène Coulomb-Gully, and Abhishek Kumar. 2019. Multilingual and multitarget hate speech detection in tweets. In *Actes de la Conférence sur le Traitement Automatique des Langues Naturelles (TALN) PFIA 2019. Volume II : Articles courts*, pages 351–360, Toulouse, France. ATALA.

Thomas Davidson, Dana Warmsley, Michael Macy, and Ingmar Weber. 2017. Automated hate speech detection and the problem of offensive language. In *Proceedings of the international AAAI conference on web and social media*, volume 11, pages 512–515.

Gloria del Valle-Cano, Lara Quijano-Sánchez, Federico Liberatore, and Jesús Gómez. 2023. Socialhaterbert: A dichotomous approach for automatically detecting hate speech on twitter through textual analysis and user profiles. *Expert Systems with Applications*, 216:119446.

Fabio Del Vigna12, Andrea Cimino23, Felice Dell'Orletta, Marinella Petrocchi, and Maurizio Tesconi. 2017. Hate me, hate me not: Hate speech detection on facebook. In *Proceedings of the first Italian conference on cybersecurity (ITASEC17)*, pages 86–95.

Jacob Devlin, Ming-Wei Chang, Kenton Lee, and Kristina Toutanova. 2019. BERT: Pre-training of deep bidirectional transformers for language understanding. In *Proceedings of the 2019 Conference of the North American Chapter of the Association for Computational Linguistics: Human Language Technologies, Volume 1 (Long and Short Papers)*, pages 4171–4186, Minneapolis, Minnesota. Association for Computational Linguistics.

Ashkan Ebadi, Pengcheng Xi, Stéphane Tremblay, Bruce Spencer, Raman Pall, and Alexander Wong. 2021. Understanding the temporal evolution of covid-19 research through machine learning and natural language processing. *Scientometrics*, 126:725–739.

Mohamed Elsayed, Amira Abdelwahab, and Hatem Ahdelkader. 2019. A proposed framework for improving analysis of big unstructured data in social media. In *2019 14th International conference on computer engineering and systems (ICCES)*, pages 61–65. IEEE.

Komal Florio, Valerio Basile, Marco Polignano, Pierpaolo Basile, and Viviana Patti. 2020. Time of your hate: The challenge of time in hate speech detection on social media. *Applied Sciences*, 10(12):4180.

Antigoni Founta, Constantinos Djouvas, Despoina Chatzakou, Ilias Leontiadis, Jeremy Blackburn, Gianluca Stringhini, Athena Vakali, Michael Sirivianos, and Nicolas Kourtellis. 2018. Large scale crowdsourcing and characterization of twitter abusive behavior. In *Proceedings of the international AAAI conference on web and social media*, volume 12.

Lara Grimminger and Roman Klinger. 2021. Hate towards the political opponent: A Twitter corpus study of the 2020 US elections on the basis of offensive speech and stance detection. In *Proceedings of the Eleventh Workshop on Computational Approaches to Subjectivity, Sentiment and Social Media Analysis*, pages 171–180, Online. Association for Computational Linguistics.

Akshita Jha and Radhika Mamidi. 2017. When does a compliment become sexist? analysis and classification of ambivalent sexism using twitter data. In *Proceedings of the Second Workshop on NLP and Computational Social Science*, pages 7–16, Vancouver, Canada. Association for Computational Linguistics.

Chris J Kennedy, Geoff Bacon, Alexander Sahn, and Claudia von Vacano. 2020. Constructing interval variables via faceted rasch measurement and multitask deep learning: a hate speech application. *arXiv preprint arXiv:2009.10277*.

Akib Mohi Ud Din Khanday, Syed Tanzeel Rabani, Qamar Rayees Khan, and Showkat Hassan Malik. 2022. Detecting twitter hate speech in covid-19 era using machine learning and ensemble learning techniques. *International Journal of Information Management Data Insights*, 2(2):100120.

Lee Knuttila. 2011. User unknown: 4chan, anonymity and contingency. *First Monday*.

Liam Li, Kevin Jamieson, Afshin Rostamizadeh, Ekaterina Gonina, Moritz Hardt, Benjamin Recht, and Ameet Talwalkar. 2018. Massively parallel hyperparameter tuning. *arXiv preprint arXiv:1810.05934*, 5.

Richard Liaw, Eric Liang, Robert Nishihara, Philipp Moritz, Joseph E Gonzalez, and Ion Stoica. 2018. Tune: A research platform for distributed model selection and training. *arXiv preprint arXiv:1807.05118*.

Yinhan Liu, Myle Ott, Naman Goyal, Jingfei Du, Mandar Joshi, Danqi Chen, Omer Levy, Mike Lewis, Luke Zettlemoyer, and Veselin Stoyanov. 2019. Roberta: A robustly optimized BERT pretraining approach. *CoRR*, abs/1907.11692.

Daniel Loureiro, Francesco Barbieri, Leonardo Neves, Luis Espinosa Anke, and Jose Camacho-collados. 2022. TimeLMs: Diachronic language models from Twitter. In *Proceedings of the 60th Annual Meeting of the Association for Computational Linguistics: System Demonstrations*, pages 251–260, Dublin, Ireland. Association for Computational Linguistics.

Thomas Mandl, Sandip Modha, Prasenjit Majumder, Daksh Patel, Mohana Dave, Chintak Mandlia, and Aditya Patel. 2019. Overview of the hasoc track at fire 2019: Hate speech and offensive content identification in indo-european languages. In *Proceedings of the 11th forum for information retrieval evaluation*, pages 14–17.

Ariadna Matamoros-Fernández and Johan Farkas. 2021. Racism, hate speech, and social media: A systematic review and critique. *Television & New Media*, 22(2):205–224.

Binny Mathew, Punyajoy Saha, Seid Muhie Yimam, Chris Biemann, Pawan Goyal, and Animesh Mukherjee. 2021. Hatexplain: A benchmark dataset for explainable hate speech detection. In *Proceedings of the AAAI Conference on Artificial Intelligence*, volume 35, pages 14867–14875.

Saif Mohammad, Felipe Bravo-Marquez, Mohammad Salameh, and Svetlana Kiritchenko. 2018. Semeval-2018 task 1: Affect in tweets. In *Proceedings of the 12th international workshop on semantic evaluation*, pages 1–17.

Nanlir Sallau Mullah and Wan Mohd Nazmee Wan Zainon. 2021. Advances in machine learning algorithms for hate speech detection in social media: a review. *IEEE Access*, 9:88364–88376.

Dat Quoc Nguyen, Thanh Vu, and Anh Tuan Nguyen. 2020. BERTweet: A pre-trained language model for English tweets. In *Proceedings of the 2020 Conference on Empirical Methods in Natural Language Processing: System Demonstrations*, pages 9–14, Online. Association for Computational Linguistics.

Nedjma Ousidhoum, Zizheng Lin, Hongming Zhang, Yangqiu Song, and Dit-Yan Yeung. 2019. Multilingual and multi-aspect hate speech analysis. In *Proceedings of the 2019 Conference on Empirical Methods in Natural Language Processing and the 9th International Joint Conference on Natural Language Processing (EMNLP-IJCNLP)*, pages 4675–4684, Hong Kong, China. Association for Computational Linguistics.

Juan Carlos Pereira-Kohatsu, Lara Quijano-Sánchez, Federico Liberatore, and Miguel Camacho-Collados. 2019. Detecting and monitoring hate speech in twitter. *Sensors*, 19(21):4654.

Georg Rasch. 1960. Studies in mathematical psychology: I. probabilistic models for some intelligence and attainment tests.

Pratik Sachdeva, Renata Barreto, Geoff Bacon, Alexander Sahn, Claudia von Vacano, and Chris Kennedy. 2022. The measuring hate speech corpus: Leveraging rasch measurement theory for data perspectivism. In *Proceedings of the 1st Workshop on Perspectivist Approaches to NLP @LREC2022*, pages 83–94, Marseille, France. European Language Resources Association.

Mattia Samory, Indira Sen, Julian Kohne, Fabian Flöck, and Claudia Wagner. 2021. "call me sexist, but...": Revisiting sexism detection using psychological scales and adversarial samples. In *Proceedings of the International AAAI Conference on Web and Social Media*, volume 15, pages 573–584.

Andrew N Smith, Eileen Fischer, and Chen Yongjian. 2012. How does brand-related user-generated content differ across youtube, facebook, and twitter? *Journal of interactive marketing*, 26(2):102–113.

Collins Udanor and Chinatu C Anyanwu. 2019. Combating the challenges of social media hate speech in a polarized society: A twitter ego lexalytics approach. *Data Technologies and Applications*.

Bertie Vidgen, Scott Hale, Ella Guest, Helen Margetts, David Broniatowski, Zeerak Waseem, Austin Botelho, Matthew Hall, and Rebekah Tromble. 2020. Detecting East Asian prejudice on social media. In *Proceedings of the Fourth Workshop on Online Abuse and Harms*, pages 162–172, Online. Association for Computational Linguistics.

Samantha Walther and Andrew McCoy. 2021. Us extremism on telegram. *Perspectives on Terrorism*, 15(2):100–124.

Zeerak Waseem. 2016. Are you a racist or am I seeing things? annotator influence on hate speech detection on Twitter. In *Proceedings of the First Workshop on NLP and Computational Social Science*, pages 138–142, Austin, Texas. Association for Computational Linguistics.

Zeerak Waseem and Dirk Hovy. 2016. Hateful symbols or hateful people? predictive features for hate speech detection on Twitter. In *Proceedings of the NAACL Student Research Workshop*, pages 88–93, San Diego, California. Association for Computational Linguistics.

Thomas Wolf, Lysandre Debut, Victor Sanh, Julien Chaumond, Clement Delangue, Anthony Moi, Pierric Cistac, Tim Rault, Remi Louf, Morgan Funtowicz, Joe Davison, Sam Shleifer, Patrick von Platen, Clara Ma, Yacine Jernite, Julien Plu, Canwen Xu, Teven Le Scao, Sylvain Gugger, Mariama Drame, Quentin Lhoest, and Alexander Rush. 2020. Transformers: State-of-the-art natural language processing. In *Proceedings of the 2020 Conference on Empirical Methods in Natural Language Processing: System Demonstrations*, pages 38–45, Online. Association for Computational Linguistics.

Marcos Zampieri, Shervin Malmasi, Preslav Nakov, Sara Rosenthal, Noura Farra, and Ritesh Kumar. 2019. Predicting the type and target of offensive posts in social media. In *Proceedings of the 2019 Conference of the North American Chapter of the Association for Computational Linguistics: Human Language Technologies, Volume 1 (Long and Short Papers)*, pages 1415–1420, Minneapolis, Minnesota. Association for Computational Linguistics.

Marcos Zampieri, Preslav Nakov, Sara Rosenthal, Pepa Atanasova, Georgi Karadzhov, Hamdy Mubarak, Leon Derczynski, Zeses Pitenis, and Çağrı Çöltekin. 2020. SemEval-2020 task 12: Multilingual offensive language identification in social media (OffensEval 2020). In *Proceedings of the Fourteenth Workshop on Semantic Evaluation*, pages 1425–1447, Barcelona (online). International Committee for Computational Linguistics.

A Annotation Guidelines

In the following we present the guidelines provided to the annotator for the independent test set (Section 4.2).

A tweet is:

- labelled as "1" ("hate speech") if it contains any "discriminatory" (biased, bigoted or intolerant) or "pejorative" (prejudiced, contemptuous or demeaning) speech towards individuals or group of people.
- labelled as "0" ("not-hate-speech") if it does not contain hate speech as defined above.
- labelled "NA" if the coder is not sure whether the tweet contains hate speech or not.

The annotation should be based only on the text content of the tweet. This means that the coder should not follow any URL/media links if present.

B Hyperparameter Tuning

Table 5 lists the best hyperparameters for each of the models used in the evaluation.

model	setting	learning rate	epochs	batch size	warm-up steps
TimeLMs	binary	1.5857E-05	2	16	50
BERTweet	binary	1.4608E-05	2	4	100
BERT	binary	1.7882E-05	2	4	10
RoBERTa	binary	1.0377E-05	2	4	50
TimeLMs	multiclass	1.9100E-05	3	16	100
BERTweet	multiclass	9.0295E-06	3	4	10
BERT	multiclass	8.1260E-06	4	8	100
RoBERTa	multiclass	8.1260E-06	4	16	10

Table 5: Best hyper-parameters for models trained on the combined datasets for the binary and multiclass settings.

Author Index

Association for Computational Linguistics
209 N. Eighth Street
Stroudsburg, Pennsylvania 18360

ISBN 978-1-7138-8239-8

CURRAN ASSOCIATES INC.
proceedings.com